INTERNATIONAL CHEMICAL SERIES

JAMES F. NORRIS, Ph.D., Consulting Editor

COLLOID CHEMISTRY

INTERNATIONAL CHEMICAL SERIES

(James F. Norris, Ph.D., Consulting Editor)

Adkins and McElvain—
Elementary Organic Chemistry
Practice of Organic Chemistry

Bancroft—
Applied Colloid Chemistry

Bingham—
Fluidity and Plasticity

Bogue—
The Theory and Application of Colloidal Behavior

Briscoe—
The Structure and Properties of Matter

Burrell—
Chemistry for Students of Agriculture and Home Economics

Cady—
General Chemistry
Inorganic Chemistry

Daniels—
Mathematical Preparation for Physical Chemistry

Daniels, Mathews and Williams—
Experimental Physical Chemistry

Eucken, Jette and LaMer—
Fundamentals of Physical Chemistry

Gillespie—
Physical Chemistry

Griffin—
Technical Methods of Analysis as Employed in the Laboratories of Arthur D. Little, Inc.

Hall and Williams—
Chemical and Metallographic Examination of Iron, Steel and Brass

Hamilton and Simpson—
Calculations of Quantitative Chemical Analysis

Hammett—
Solutions of Electrolytes

Leighou—
Chemistry of Engineering Materials

Lewis—
Fundamentals of Organic Chemistry

Loeb—
Proteins and the Theory of Colloidal Behavior

Long and Anderson—
Chemical Calculations

Lord and Demorest—
Metallurgical Analysis

Mahin—
Introduction to Quantitative Analysis
Quantitative Analysis

Mahin and Carr—
Quantitative Agricultural Analysis

Mellon—
Chemical Publications

Millard—
Physical Chemistry for Colleges

Moore—
History of Chemistry

Norris—
Experimental Organic Chemistry
Inorganic Chemistry for Colleges
The Principles of Organic Chemistry

Norris and Mark—
Laboratory Exercises in Inorganic Chemistry

Parr—
The Analysis of Fuel, Gas, Water and Lubricants

Reedy—
Elementary Qualitative Analysis for College Students

Rice—
Organic Chemistry

Robinson—
The Elements of Fractional Distillation

Schorger—
The Chemistry of Cellulose and Wood

Smith and Miller—
An Introduction to Qualitative Chemical Analysis and the Related Chemical Principles

Stock and Stähler (translated by Patnode and Dennis)—
Quantitative Chemical Analysis

Stone and Dunn—
Experiments in General Chemistry

Thomas—
Colloid Chemistry

Timm—
An Introduction to Chemistry

Timm and Schupp—
Laboratory Exercises in General Chemistry

Underwood—
Problems in Organic Chemistry

Weiser—
The Colloidal Salts
The Hydrous Oxides

White—
Technical Gas and Fuel Analysis

Wilkinson—
Calculations in Quantitative Chemical Analysis

Williams and Homerberg—
Principles of Metallography

Woodman—
Food Analysis

COLLOID CHEMISTRY

BY

ARTHUR W. THOMAS

Professor of Chemistry, Columbia University

FIRST EDITION
SECOND IMPRESSION

McGRAW-HILL BOOK COMPANY, INC.

NEW YORK AND LONDON

1934

THE MAPLE PRESS COMPANY, YORK, PA.

PREFACE

Treatises on colloid chemistry are based generally upon a physical viewpoint, treating the colloidally dispersed particle as a suspended, insoluble unit providing an interface to which noncolloidal substances may be adsorbed in an empirical manner quite devoid of any relationship with the phenomena of classical chemistry.

In this book, the attempt has been made to treat colloidal dispersions from the point of view of crystalloidal chemistry. Here the particle is regarded, partly at least, as in solution, as the polar groups of water-insoluble organic compounds are dissolved in water with the nonpolar parts protruding according to the postulates of Langmuir, and also of Harkins, about 17 years ago. The merit of the application of the classical viewpoint to protein solutions has been proven by the researches of Pauli, Michaelis, Loeb, Cohn and others.

For inorganic dispersions, the viewpoint of this book revives the ideas of Linder, Picton and Duclaux, among others, of 25 to 35 years ago. It is undoubtedly easier to consider inorganic dispersions from a physical angle but the writer feels that such a treatment is inadequate unless supplemented by considerations of the chemical nature of the constituents. The application of the Werner-Pfeiffer concepts of complex compound formation has provided a rational basis for an explanation of the behavior of these dispersions in some specific instances.

This book is the outgrowth of the author's courses on colloid chemistry, the first of which was started in 1915, and has been written for those who are familiar with elementary inorganic, organic and physical chemistry. The fundamental techniques of colloid chemistry are critically discussed with references to the literature for those who desire further details. The writer has endeavored to assemble interesting facts, even where explanation is lacking, with the hope that workers in applied fields as well as pure science investigators may find this book useful and

be informed where the elucidation of colloid problems needs
their assistance.

The author expresses his appreciation to Dr. M. Irene Bailey
and to Dr. M. Mattikow for their suggestions after reading the
manuscript and proofs, to Mr. H. S. Miller and to Mr. H. S.
Owens who assisted in reading the proofs, and to Mr. Benja-
min Cohen for his aid in the preparation of the chapter on
electrokinetics.

The writer is indebted also to Professors V. K. LaMer and
T. C. Taylor for their suggestions concerning certain parts of
the manuscript.

ARTHUR W. THOMAS.

DEPARTMENT OF CHEMISTRY,
 COLUMBIA UNIVERSITY,
  NEW YORK, N. Y.,
   July, 1934.

CONTENTS

COLLOID CHEMISTRY

CHAPTER I

INTRODUCTION

Thomas Graham, Master of the Mint in London, published in 1861 a memoir[1]* upon his investigations of free hydrodiffusion which showed that substances inclined to form gelatinous and amorphous precipitates like alumina, caramel, gum arabic, albumin, and gelatin diffused through water at an exceedingly low rate in comparison with crystalline substances such as sodium chloride, sugar, and glycerol; and further that while the crystalline substances diffused readily through a membrane of parchment paper, this septum was practically impervious to the amorphous bodies.

Since glue belonged to this class of substances of extremely slight diffusibility, he "proposed to designate substances of the class as *colloids* [from the Greek κολλα, glue], "and to speak of their peculiar form of aggregation as the *colloidal condition of matter.*" The crystalline and highly diffusible substances were set in an opposing class with the name of *crystalloids*.

Quoting from Graham's original paper:

The distinction is no doubt one of intimate molecular constitution. . . . Although chemically inert in the ordinary sense, colloids possess a compensating activity of their own arising out of their physical properties. While the rigidity of the crystalline structure shuts out external impressions, the softness of the gelatinous colloid partakes of fluidity, and enables the colloid to become a medium for liquid diffusion, like the water itself. . . . Another and eminently characteristic quality of colloids is their mutability. Their existence is a continued metastasis. A colloid may be compared in this respect to water while existing liquid at a temperature under its usual freezing point, or to a

* Superior numbers refer to items in the bibliography at the end of each chapter.

1

supersaturated saline solution. Fluid colloids appear to have always a *pectous* modification; and they often pass under the slightest influences from the first into the second condition. The solution of hydrated silicic acid, for instance, is easily obtained in a state of purity, but it cannot be preserved. It may remain fluid for days or weeks in a sealed tube, but it is sure to gelatinize and become insoluble at last. Nor does the change of this colloid appear to stop at that point. For the mineral forms of silicic acid, deposited from water, such as flint, are often found to have passed, during the geological ages of their existence, from the vitreous or colloidal into the crystalline condition. The colloidal is, in fact, a dynamical state of matter; the crystalloidal being the statical condition. . . .

The phenomena of the solution of a salt or crystalloid probably all appear in the solution of a colloid, but greatly reduced in degree. The process becomes slow; time, indeed, appearing essential to all colloidal changes. The change of temperature, usually occurring in the act of solution, becomes barely perceptible. The liquid is always sensibly gummy or viscous when concentrated. The colloid, although often dissolved in a large proportion by its solvent, is held in solution by a singularly feeble force. Hence colloids are generally displaced and precipitated by the addition to their solution of any substance from the other class. Of all the properties of liquid colloids, their slow diffusion in water, and their arrest by colloidal septa, are the most serviceable in distinguishing them from crystalloids. . . .

While soluble crystalloids are always highly sapid, soluble colloids are singularly insipid. It may be questioned whether a colloid, when tasted, ever reaches the sentient extremities of the nerves of the palate, as the latter are probably protected by a colloidal membrane, impermeable to soluble substances of the same physical constitution. . . .

The equivalent of a colloid appears to be always high, although the ratio between the elements of the substance may be simple. Gummic acid, for instance, may be represented by $C_{12}H_{11}O_{11}$, but judging from the small proportions of lime and potash which suffice to neutralize this acid, the true numbers of its formula must be several times greater. It is difficult to avoid associating the inertness of colloids with their high equivalents, particularly where the high number appears to be attained by the repetition of a smaller number. The inquiry suggests itself whether the colloid molecule may not be constituted by the grouping together of a number of smaller crystalloid molecules, and whether the basis of colloidality may not really be this composite character of the molecule. . . .

The hardness of the crystalloid, with its crystalline planes and angles, is replaced in the colloid by a degree of softness, with a more or less rounded outline. The water of crystallization is represented by the water of gelatination. The water in gelatinous hydrates is aptly described by M. Chevreul as retained by "capillary affinity," that is, by an attraction partaking both of the physical and chemical character.

The systematic studies made by Graham won for him the title of "father of colloid chemistry," despite the fact that colloidal solutions and suspensions had been described before 1861.

Gold in the colloidal form was utilized in the manufacture of ruby glass in the sixteenth century, although to be sure the nature of its dispersion was not understood. Andreas Libau, in his *Alchemia* (1595), described the use of gold solutions in making red glass, stating that the color permeated the entire mass of the glass[2] analogous to rubies.

Probably T. Bergmann[3] should be credited with the discovery of colloidal silicic acid, in 1779. Bergmann found that the precipitate from sodium silicate solution formed by the addition of acids redispersed upon copious dilution. His explanation was:

The silica particles are widely separated and made finer by the diluting water and scattered throughout the whole mass. By each extension the surface is expanded and likewise the contact with the surrounding fluid. In this state the silica cannot settle out since it cannot overcome the frictional resistance. The silica particles remain therefore floating in the liquid and due to their fineness and transparency are invisible.

Francesco Selmi,[4] after extensive studies, stated that there were two distinct classes of solutions which he called "solutions" and "pseudo-solutions."

Faraday prepared and described colloidal gold at least five years prior to Graham's publication. The following is a quotation from one of his papers:[5]

If a pint or two of the weak solution of gold before described [*i.e.* about 2 grains of gold chloride in two or three pints of water] be put into a *very clean* glass bottle, a drop or two of the solution of phosphorus in sulphide of carbon added, and the whole well shaken together, it immediately changes in appearance, becomes red, and being left for six to twelve hours, forms the ruby fluid required; too much sulphide and phosphorus should not be added, for the reduced gold then tends to clot about the portions which sink to the bottom.

The novice is cautioned against an erroneous impression which the general tendency of using the term *colloid* in the substantive sense may create in his mind. No definite relationship between chemical constitution and colloidal condition exists, nor are there any particular elements or compounds which have the specific nature of being "colloids." Many substances may exist in either a colloidal or a crystalloidal condition. Von Veimarn[6] in fact claims that any common crystalloid under properly arranged conditions can be made to assume the colloidal state.

The state of dispersion of a given substance in solution is influenced by the dielectric constant of the solvent,[7] the degree of dissociation decreasing and the degree of association increasing with decreasing dielectric constant. This is shown in Table 1 for the crystalloid salts tetrapropylammonium iodide and

TABLE 1.—DIFFERENT DEGREES OF DISPERSION ACCORDING TO NATURE OF SOLVENT

Solvent	Dielectric constant	Ratio* of $\frac{M.\ W.\ found}{Formula\ weight}$	
		For $N(C_3H_7)_4I$	For $N(C_5H_{11})_4I$
Nitrobenzene....................	35.7	0.81	0.76
Ethyl alcohol...................	25.7	0.98	
Methylene chloride..............	8.3	>2	
Isoamyl alcohol.................	5.7	2.12	
Acetic acid.....................	6.4	3.6	3.7
Chloroform.....................	5.0	6	>3
Benzene........................	2.3	Insoluble	∞
Carbon tetrachloride............	2.2	Insoluble	∞

* "M. W. found" was determined by freezing-point depression for nitrobenzene and acetic acid, and by boiling-point elevation for the rest.

tetraisoamylammonium iodide. With decreasing dielectric constant of solvent both compounds become more associated in solution, tetraisoamylammonium iodide existing in the colloidal state in benzene and in carbon tetrachloride.

Soaps are nonassociated in alcohol but are crystalloidal to colloidal in water, the latter state being favored by increase in concentration, especially with the soaps of higher molecular weight.[8] Hexadecylamine hydrochloride, $C_{16}H_{33}NH_3Cl$, acts like soaps.

There are other cases of transitions between crystalloidal and colloidal dispersions. The compound bromphenanthrene-3-sulfonic acid[9] is a nonassociated electrolyte in dilute solution but colloidal in concentrated dispersions. The glucoside saponarin[10] acts similarly. Several products of the incomplete hydrolysis of proteins show these transitional properties.

Solutions of salts of weak base cations with stronger acid anions, or *vice versa*, may be completely colloidal in dilute solution owing to hydrolysis, while mainly crystalloidal when the solutions are concentrated. For example, a 0.00025 equivalent normal solution of ferric chloride undergoes complete hydrolysis to colloidal ferric hydroxide and hydrochloric acid in 40 min. at 25°C.[11] Hence solutions of hydrolyzable salts may contain colloidal as well as simple particles, the relative amount of each depending upon the concentration.

The terms *colloid* and *colloids* should then be used in the adjectival sense, just as *amorphous, crystalline, soluble, dense,* etc., since they refer to a *state* or *condition* of aggregation of matter rather than to a kind of matter. Since *colloid* and *colloids* are very convenient terms, they will be freely used in the discussion of the subject instead of the more exact and cumbersome expression *substance in the colloidal condition.*

While there is no definite relation between chemical constitution of a substance and colloidal condition, a useful rule has been given by Wolfgang Ostwald;[12] *viz.*, the more complex a compound is, the greater is the possibility that it will be found in the colloidal condition.

There is a general misconception that Graham regarded all colloids as amorphous substances. He admitted the possibility of crystalline colloids as shown by the following sentences in his 1861 paper:

A similar extreme departure from its normal condition appears to be presented by a colloid holding so high a place in its class as albumen. In the so-called blood crystals of Funke, a soft and gelatinous albuminoid body is seen to assume a crystalline contour. Can any facts more strikingly illustrate the maxim that in nature there are no abrupt transitions, and that distinctions of class are never absolute?

The preparation of many proteins in the crystalline form is now a matter of ordinary biochemical technique. In Fig. 1 are shown some protein crystals.

Crystal structure in the apparently amorphous gels obtained by ultrafiltration of and also by precipitation from various inorganic colloidal solutions, including silver, gold, silica, alumina, ferric oxide, silver halides, and the sulfides of mercury, zinc, and cadmium has been revealed by X-ray examination[13,14]. Crystallization of silver from "Carey Lea's silver" hydrosol has been effected.[15] The gels obtained from hydrosols of zirconium and thorium oxides showed but faint X-ray interference, while

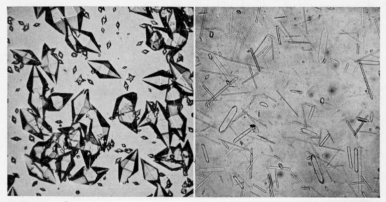

Fig. 1.—Crystals of pepsin (left) and of a cows' milk globulin (right). (*Left from Dr. J. H. Northrop; right from Dr. A. H. Palmer and the Journal of Biological Chemistry.*)

those from arsenious sulfide, sulfur, and selenium hydrosols gave none at all. Haber[15] states that, when the speed of agglomeration of the particles of a sol to form a gel is not too great, the precipitates tend to assume a crystalline structure.

Owing to the impression created by Graham, it is customary to designate all amorphous substances as colloids. As a result, colloid chemistry not only is concerned with dispersions where the dispersed phases have low diffusion constants but embraces also the properties and behavior of substances which have an amorphous appearance. In addition, it deals with the behavior of any systems containing dispersed particles which are so small as to be invisible in a microscope but are larger than atoms and simple molecules.

The following dispersed systems are recognized if one bases a classification upon the states of aggregation.

Medium	Dispersed Phase
1. Solid	Solid
2. Solid	Liquid
3. Solid	Gas
4. Liquid	Solid
5. Liquid	Liquid
6. Liquid	Gas
7. Gas	Solid
8. Gas	Liquid

Examples of these systems which are cited as colloidal are:

1. Colored rock salt, ruby glass, precious stones, and carbon in steel.
2. Minerals with liquid inclusions, jellies, and gels.
3. Minerals with gaseous inclusions, such as pumice stone.
4. Ordinary suspensions and colloidal solutions.
5. Emulsions, such as of oil and water, and colloidal solutions.
6. Foams.
7. Smoke, condensed metallic vapors, ammonium chloride fumes, and cosmic dust.
8. Fogs, mists, and clouds.

The foregoing division gives a survey of the total possible kinds of colloidally dispersed systems and permits a general classification of them provided the state of aggregation of the dispersed phase is known.

Dispersed Systems with Gaseous Dispersion Medium.—The liquid-in-gas systems are of the greatest importance to life on this planet. Clouds and fogs are dispersions of water in air. Common examples of the solid-in-gas system are smoke and volcanic dust. The particles in volcanic-dust dispersions are so small that they may be carried hundreds of miles in the air, causing odd color effects in the sky. These systems will be discussed in Chap. II.

Dispersed Systems with Solid Dispersion Medium.—Ruby glass and certain gems are examples of this class. Beautiful blue-colored crystals of sodium chloride have been found in nature. The blue color has been ascribed to the presence of tiny particles of sodium. Colored rock salt has been artificially made by heating sodium chloride in a vacuum in the presence of sodium vapor.[16]

Gold ruby glass is made by melting lead or barium glass with a very small addition of gold chloride. If cooled quickly, the product is quite colorless. Upon slow cooling, or better, quick cooling with subsequent warming, innumerable tiny particles of gold are formed which color the glass ruby red. According to Zsigmondy 1 cc. of the glass contains several millions of gold particles, the smallest ultramicroscopically visible particles weighing 10^{-15} mg.

A sort of pumice stone has been prepared in the laboratory by heating glass and water under pressure.[17] At about 200°C. glass swells in water, dissolves therein, and sets to a solid mass on cooling. If this mass is warmed at atmospheric pressure, it is transformed to a porous, foamy mass.

Dispersed Systems with Liquid Dispersion Medium.—The best understood dispersions in this class are those with aqueous dispersion medium. Dispersions in media other than water are of great importance, *e.g.*, dispersions of gum resins, rubber, nitrocellulose, etc., in organic solvents.

References

1. THOMAS GRAHAM: *Phil. Trans. Roy. Soc. London,* **151**, 183 (1861).
2. CORNEJO: *Kolloid Z.,* **12**, 1 (1913).
3. Through WALDEN: *Kolloid Z.,* **6**, 233 (1910).
4. SELMI: *Nuovi Ann. Sci. Nat. Bologna* (2), **4**, 146 (1845); **8**, 401 (1847); through HATSCHEK: "The Foundations of Colloid Chemistry; A Selection of Early Papers Bearing on the Subject," The Macmillan Company, New York, 1925.
5. FARADAY: *Phil. Trans. Roy. Soc. London,* **147**, 145 (1857).
6. VON WEIMARN: "Grundzüge der Dispersoidchemie," T. Steinkopf, Leipzig, 1911; "Die Allgemeinheit des Kolloidzustandes," T. Steinkopf, Leipzig, 1925; "Zur Lehre von den Zuständen der Materie," T. Steinkopf, 1914.
7. WALDEN: *Kolloid Z.,* **27**, 97 (1920).
8. KRAFFT and STUTZ: *Ber.,* **29**, 1328 (1896).
9. SANDQVIST: *Kolloid Z.,* **19**, 113 (1916).
10. BARGER and FIELD: *J. Chem. Soc.,* **101**, 1394 (1912).
11. WAGNER: *Kolloid Z.,* **14**, 149 (1914).
12. OSTWALD-FISCHER: "Handbook of Colloid Chemistry," P. Blakiston's Son & Co., Philadelphia, 1912.
13. SHERRER: *Nachr. Kgl. Ges. Wiss. Göttingen,* **96** (1918); through *Chem. Abs.,* **13**, 2624 (1919); *Physik. Z.,* **17**, 277 (1916).
14. HABER: *Ber.,* **55B**, 1717 (1922).
15. KOHLSCHÜTTER and STECK: *Z. Elektrochem.,* **28**, 554 (1922).
16. SIEDENTOPF: *Verh. deutsch. Phys. Ges.,* **7**, 268 (1905).
17. BARUS: *Am. J. Sci.* (4), **9**, 161 (1900).

CHAPTER II

CLOUDS AND SMOKES

Dispersions of liquid or solid particles in gases are called clouds, smokes, dusts, fogs, mists, hazes, and fumes. William E. Gibbs[1] proposes the term *aerosols* for such dispersed systems, denoting as *clouds* or *cloudy aerosols* those systems in which the particles are too large to exhibit Brownian movement at ordinary temperature and pressure, and calling the more highly dispersed systems *smokes* or *smoky aerosols*.

Formation of Aerosols by Dispersion.—Mechanical disintegration of solids may be accomplished by shearing and tensile stresses gradually applied, as in attrition mills, or by a crushing pressure applied by means of rolls or by sudden blows as in the disintegrator type of impact mills; in all of which the substance to be divided is torn to pieces against its force of cohesion. The work performed is directly proportional to the resulting increase in surface area, the energy that is expended appearing as heat. It is said to be impossible to obtain a degree of dispersion higher than 10^{-4} cm. by ordinary grinding processes.[1]

Decrepitation incidental to the heating of certain substances may form aerosols; crystals containing liquid are shattered by the gas pressure generated in them upon heating. A close connection between water content and degree of decrepitation of a crystal has been shown.[2] When barytes crystals containing 0.04 per cent water were decrepitated, only 14 per cent of the powder passed through a 30-mesh sieve, while 94 per cent of the powder from crystals containing 0.45 per cent water passed through the 30-mesh sieve, 30 per cent of which was finer than 120 mesh. This process has been used to separate a decrepitating mineral, such as barytes, from nondecrepitating minerals, such as galena, pyrites, and quartz.

The reduction of solubility of a saturated solution of a gas in a liquid upon sudden release of pressure may cause decrepital

9

disintegration. For example, when molten volcanic magma saturated with steam at a high pressure is suddenly injected into the ordinary atmospheric pressure, the violence of explosive disruption disperses the mineral matter into a volcanic smoke so fine that it may float about in the upper atmosphere for years.

The most complete dispersion of a dry solid in a gas is accomplished by the instantaneous release of an enormous amount of energy, *i.e.*, detonation, which spreads it violently in all directions. Certain toxic smokes were formed in the past war by detonating solids or liquids in shells.

Liquids are easily disintegrated owing to their low cohesive forces. When a liquid is projected rapidly against a surface, it is stretched from the point of contact until the resulting tension exceeds its surface tension. When tiny streams of liquid are forced through a perforated plate, the emerging filaments break up into drops when their length exceeds three times the diameter.

The spray method for disintegration of liquids such as molten metals, water, and aqueous solutions has been extensively developed for the purpose of obtaining fine metallic powders or for removing water, as in the spray process for milk. In these processes the action consists in a violent collision between a jet of the liquid and a solid surface such as a rapidly rotating disk, a second jet of the same liquid, or a jet of compressed gas. The degree of dispersion obtained depends upon (1) the velocity of impact, *i.e.*, the energy of dispersion, (2) the viscosity of the liquid, (3) the surface tension, and (4) the density. Since much more energy is consumed in extending the surface of a very viscous liquid, much greater pressures are required. Sometimes it is more feasible to decrease the viscosity of a viscous solution by dilution than to increase the pressure to a point that will form a spray with the viscous liquid. Decreasing the surface tension by addition of suitable capillary active substances will increase the spray efficiency. It is also apparent that the lower the density of a liquid, the farther it will extend upon impact.

Formation of Aerosols by Condensation.—In disintegration processes, energy is applied to large particles of liquid or solid to increase their specific surface. In condensation processes, molecular particles are condensed to larger ones by abstraction of energy from them. Once such a condensation process sets in, it is difficult to stop it, the particles coalescing owing to surface forces and ultimately falling as rain. Nuclei such as dust or smoke particles or gaseous ions are essential for the production of an aerosol by this method. In the absence of suitable condensation nuclei, a gas may be cooled until it has become a highly supersaturated vapor which will not condense as fine particles. It may condense progressively upon the walls of the containing vessel or condense abruptly throughout forming large drops.

When the pressure upon a volume V_1 of air is decreased, the air expands to the volume V_2. To effect this expansion, which involves the expenditure of energy, a part of the heat energy of the air is utilized; and if the gas is expanded very rapidly or if the containing vessel be thermally insulated (adiabatic expansion), then the expansion will effect a lowering of the temperature of the air proportional to the work done. The degree of cooling $(t_1 - t_2)$ will be directly proportional to the degree of expansion V_2/V_1, and, if air originally saturated with water vapor is taken, the cooling of the air produces supersaturation to an extent which also is proportional to V_2/V_1.

If condensation takes place, it will proceed until so much water is condensed that the heat liberated by this process makes the air just saturated at the temperature attained. In Fig. 2 are shown the maximal cooling t_2, the supersaturation S, and the equilibrium temperature t' plotted against the ratio V_2/V_1, starting with air at 20°C., saturated with water vapor. The degree of supersaturation $S = W_1/W_2$, where W_1 denotes the grams of water per cubic centimeter immediately after expansion, and W_2 at the temperature t_2. The initial pressures are chosen so that after the expansion the pressure in the gas is 760 mm. Figure 2 shows also the mass of water condensed per cubic centimeter (q) and the percentage of the total water condensed $[(q/W_1)100]$.

In a pure mixture of air and water vapor, there is no condensation under supersaturation of about 4.2 $(V_2/V_1 < 1.25)$. If dust particles or products from chemical or photochemical processes be present, however, water is condensed on these nuclei even at low supersaturation. The degree of dispersion of the condensed water depends entirely on the number of such nuclei present. The greater the number of condensation nuclei, the greater will be the number of droplets produced, and, therefore, since the total amount of water formed is fixed for a given expansion, the smaller will be the average size of the droplets.

As previously stated, in a pure air and water-vapor mixture, condensation starts at $S = 4.2$ $(V_2/V_1 = 1.25)$, and, according

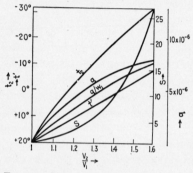

to C. T. R. Wilson,[3] in the region of $S = 4.2$ to 5 $(V_2/V_1 = 1.25$ to 1.28) the negative ions in the air constitute the nuclei whereas from $S = 5.8$ to 6.8 $(V_2/V_1 = 1.31$ to 1.34) the positive ions act as condensation centers. Since the "natural" ionization of air is very small, there are under normal conditions very few condensation nuclei at supersaturations between 4.2 and 6.8. Hence

FIG. 2.—Condensation of water upon adiabatic expansion of saturated air.

the degree of dispersion of the condensed water is very low. The size of the drops usually varies from 0.2-mm. radius at $S = 4.2$ to 0.02 mm. at $S = 6.8$ and the condensate in this range is called "rainlike."

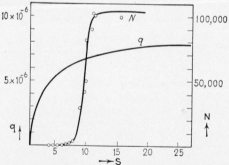

FIG. 3.—Variation of mass of condensate q and of number of drops N per cubic centimeter with saturation S resulting upon adiabatic expansion of air containing water vapor. (*Andrén.*)

A series of measurements of the number of drops of water per cubic centimeter at varying degrees of supersaturation is plotted in Fig. 3.[4] The mass of condensate per cubic centimeter is also plotted. While the values of N refer to different total masses of condensate, the q curve shows that the variation is small within the range $S = 4.2$ to 20.

There is a very rapid increase in the degree of dispersion of the condensate from $S = 8$ ($V_2/V_1 = 1.4$) where it becomes foglike* up to $S = 12$ ($V_2/V_1 = 1.43$), the drops here having a radius of about 0.6 mμ.† Beyond $S = 12$, the degree of dispersion decreases.

If the ionization of the air is increased by exposure to X-rays or radium emanations, for example, the condensation centers are increased in number and consequently the degree of dispersion is increased. By such exposure it is possible to form dense fogs in the range of $S = 4.2$ to 6.8. C. T. R. Wilson[5] utilized this principle to render visible the paths of single α- and β-particles traveling through supersaturated air.

Very little is known concerning the nuclei responsible for the condensation between supersaturations of 8 and 15. It has been suggested that they are probably electrically neutral, consisting of aggregates of water molecules.[6]

The condensation by adiabatic expansion of vapors other than water has been found to be similar to that of water, although the constants of the process are different and characteristic for each substance. Andrén[4] has shown that the values for S where highly dispersed condensates just begin to be formed for methyl alcohol, ethyl alcohol, propyl alcohol, and benzene are 4.0,

---

* In this range startling color effects are obtained,[3] from green at 1.41 through blue green, purple to red at 1.43 to greenish white at 1.46. Wilson estimated the fog to contain 10^8 droplets per cubic centimeter at $S = 1.42$.

† 1 micron (1 μ) = 10^{-3} mm. = 10^{-4} cm.

1 millimicron (1 mμ) = 10^{-6} mm. = 10^{-7} cm.

The abbreviation $\mu\mu$ is frequently used to signify millimicron, which is unfortunate and not in accord with the metric system. μ in this system denotes one-millionth part, *i.e.*, one-millionth of the standard unit of length, the meter. Hence 1 μ = 10^{-6} meter = 10^{-3} mm., or one micrometer. The prefix m denotes the one-thousandth part and consequently the symbol for millimicron becomes mμ. Consistently, then $\mu\mu$ denotes micro-micron, or one-millionth of a micron. The student is cautioned, however, to interpret $\mu\mu$ in papers on colloid chemistry (and when used for light wave lengths) as meaning 10^{-7} cm., and he is referred to the paper by Dorsey, *Science*, **71**, 67 (1930), for an introduction to the discussion of the "Micrometric Muddle."

2.5, 3.5, and 11.0, respectively, while the maximal number of drops per cubic centimeter is 160,000, 340,000, 360,000, and 190,000, respectively.

Experiments with different gases show that, within the region $S = 4.2$ to 6.8, N is to some extent dependent upon the nature of the gas.[7] The extent to which the gas is naturally ionized is different in different gases.

Chlorin, for example, normally contains more ions than many other gases, such as oxygen, nitrogen, carbon dioxide, hydrogen. Consequently between $S = 4.2$ and $S = 8.0$, the condensation in chlorin is more foglike than in these other gases.

When a cloud of any substance is formed, the particles of the cloud may exist either as supercooled liquid or as solid if the temperature is below the freezing point of the dispersed phase. If the concentration of the vapor be sufficiently high for the dew point to be above the freezing point of the liquid, condensation will produce droplets of liquid, which, as the temperature falls below the freezing point, will become supercooled. Water droplets in a cloud may, in the complete absence of the solid phase, be supercooled to temperatures as low as $-30°C$.[1] If, however, the concentration of vapor is so low that the freezing point is passed before the dew point is reached, then, instead of liquid droplets being formed, the molecules of the vapor will condense upon the nuclei that are present to form crystals of the solid phase. Instead of a dew point, a "hoar-frost" point is obtained.

Since, at temperatures below $0°C$. the vapor pressure of ice is lower than that of liquid water, the relative humidity of air in equilibrium with ice at such temperatures is lower than the relative humidity of air that is in equilibrium with supercooled liquid water.

Influence of Nuclei upon Condensation Process.—Variations in the character of the condensation process arise owing to the specific action of different kinds of condensation nuclei. The degree of supersaturation at which vapor will condense upon them will be determined by their shape, electrical charge, and chemical nature.

Lord Kelvin demonstrated that the vapor pressure of a liquid is modified according to the curvature of the surface of the liquid.[8] The vapor pressure at a convex liquid surface of a sufficiently small radius of curvature is greater, while that at a concave surface is less, than that at a plane surface. Consequently, vapor will condense more readily upon a concave surface than upon a convex one. Since liquid nuclei are generally spherical and, therefore, have a convex surface, while solid, crystalline nuclei may present a series of plane surfaces to the vapor or, if irregularly crystalline or amorphous in structure, may at some point be concave, then vapor will condense more readily upon such a particle, *e.g.*, a dust particle.

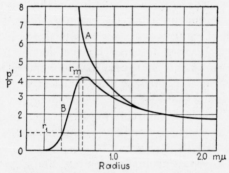

Fig. 4.—Vapor pressure of water droplets.

The vapor pressures p above a plane surface and p' above a curved surface with radius of curvature r are related to each other and to r by the expression[9]

$$RT \ln \frac{p'}{p} = \frac{2\gamma}{r\rho} \qquad (1)$$

where γ = surface tension of the liquid.

ρ = density of the liquid.

R = gas constant.

T = absolute temperature.

The values of p'/p for different values of r are plotted in Fig. 4 (curve A) if it is assumed that the surface is convex, and that p' therefore is greater than p. For a concave surface p'/p would possess values less than 1.

At a plane water surface at 0°C. the vapor pressure p is 6,000 dynes per square centimeter, while for a water droplet of radius 10^{-4} cm., the vapor pressure at 0°C., p', is 6,007.3 dynes per square centimeter, a negligible difference. It is seen from the curve, however, that when the value of r has become 1.6×10^{-7} cm.,

p' is twice as great as p. As the radius is further diminished, p' increases with increasing rapidity. Such small droplets would evaporate, therefore, extremely rapidly at ordinary degrees of supersaturation. Conversely, it is impossible for vapor to condense upon them, unless the degree of supersaturation is very high. In the absence of nuclei, therefore, it is impossible for droplets to form, unless, perhaps, at supersaturation of 8 or more, where molecular aggregates exist of radius of about 0.6 mμ. Very little is known concerning the surface tension of drops as small as these, consisting as they do of only a few molecules. The surface tension probably has a lower value than for large drops and the p' value would therefore be decreased. Thus the increase of vapor pressure may not be very great with such extreme values of the curvature of the surface of the drops, but it is sufficient to prevent condensation at low degrees of supersaturation.

To induce condensation, therefore, it is necessary to introduce suitable nuclei which will reduce the pressure of the vapor at their surfaces. Such nuclei may be placed in four categories:

1. Particles possessing plane surfaces, the vapor pressure at such a surface being equal to p and, therefore, lower than the pressure of supersaturated vapor, induce condensation.

2. Porous particles wherein the radius of curvature of the pores is less than 10^{-4} cm. induce condensation owing to the fact that this is the value of r at which, for a concave surface, the pressure of the vapor begins to be less than at a plane surface.

3. Particles carrying an electrical charge, e.g., ionized gas molecules, induce condensation. The presence of an electrical charge on the surface of a liquid opposes the surface tension and, therefore, diminishes the vapor pressure to an extent that is proportional to the fourth power of the radius of the drop.

For charged liquid surfaces,[9]

$$RT \ ln \ \frac{p'}{p} = \frac{1}{\rho}\left(\frac{2\gamma}{r} - \frac{e^2}{8\pi r^4}\right) \tag{2}$$

where e is the quantity of charge per square centimeter of surface.

The relation between p'/p and r for charged droplets is shown in Fig. 4 by curve B.

For a droplet of radius r_1 carrying unit charge, p'/p is equal to 1, so that the vapor pressure of the charged drop is just equal to that of a plane liquid surface. If more vapor were to condense upon it, r would increase, and its vapor pressure would rapidly increase until, at a radius of 0.63 mμ, the vapor pressure would reach a maximum, p' being 4.2 times as great as p. Condensation is, therefore, impossible upon such charged droplets if the radius is less than 0.63 mμ. It is possible only if the vapor pressure diminishes as r increases, *i.e.*, when r is greater than 0.63 mμ.

The vapor pressure at which condensation to form a charged droplet first becomes possible, therefore, is that corresponding to radius r_m. This pressure is 4.2 times that above a plane surface, a value which corresponds with that obtained experimentally.

4. Substances that have a strong chemical affinity for the vapor induce condensation. With water vapor, for example, substances such as sodium chloride and sulfur trioxide combine with molecules of the vapor to form droplets possessing a lower vapor pressure, upon which more vapor easily condenses, even from unsaturated vapor. Droplets so formed have, to be sure, a permanently lowered vapor pressure, although it increases slightly as the drop becomes diluted by further condensation. Such droplets, therefore, remain stable even when the air has become unsaturated. Atmospheric water vapor condenses to form a mist or cloud because of the presence of hygroscopic nuclei in the atmosphere. The stability of a city fog, often in a highly unsaturated atmosphere, has been attributed to the lowered vapor pressure of the droplets, due to the presence of sulfuric acid dissolved in them.

It is evident that the air of a room contains all sorts of condensation nuclei. Consequently condensation in such air occurs readily at low degrees of supersaturation. Prior to making a study of adiabatic expansion of such air, it is saturated with water vapor and expanded once or twice. The resulting cloud is allowed to settle and the particles which served as condensation nuclei are thus washed out. Such purified air will not give a cloudy condensation at expansions below $V_2/V_1 = 1.25$ (or $S = 4.2$).

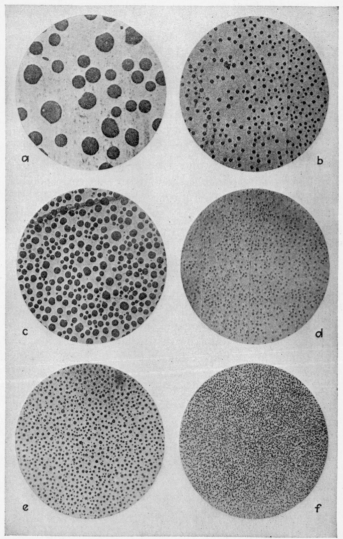

Fig. 5.—Kohlschütter's zinc condensates,[10] *a*, *c*, and *e* in hydrogen at 50, 300, and 700 mm. pressure, respectively, and *b*, *d*, and *f* in nitrogen at 50, 300, and 700 mm. respectively.

Condensation of Vapors to Solids.—The condensation of metals in gases has been investigated by Kohlschütter.[10] He heated metals in various gases and collected the condensates on glass or silica plates enclosed in a tube and also collected condensates arising from the evaporation of metals exposed to an intense beam of positive rays. This was accomplished by making the specimen the cathode in a vacuum tube. The glass plate which collected the condensed metallic particles was situated near the cathode.

As a rule the degree of dispersion of the metallic vapor was found to increase with the molecular weight and pressure of the gas. Figure 5 shows the influence of the gas on the degree of dispersion of zinc condensates in nitrogen and hydrogen at different pressures. It is seen that the size of the particles increases as the pressure decreases and that at equal pressures coarser condensates were obtained in hydrogen than in nitrogen. It was found also that the degree of dispersion was higher in the case of the more refractory metals.

Formation of Aerosols by Chemical Interaction of Gases.— When two gases react to form a product which is solid at ordinary temperatures, the degree of dispersion is high. It is especially so if the gases have been thoroughly mixed before they react. An example is the interaction of hydrogen sulfide and sulfur dioxide. These gases can be mixed without any immediate reaction. The reaction can be catalyzed by light, however, and then the precipitation of sulfur taking place from a homogeneous medium produces a uniform dispersion.

In the case of two gases which react immediately upon mutual contact such as ammonia and hydrogen chloride, the formation of the ammonium chloride occurs at the surface of contact of the two gases and spreads only as the gases mingle. This produces a smoke of a lower and more uneven degree of dispersion.

In both cases the initial degree of dispersion of the smoke is higher the more dilute the reacting gases are. Ammonium chloride smokes can be prepared over a wide range of concentrations, 0.02 to 1.2 mg. per liter.

In many cases, as in combustion processes, a gas reaction proceeds exothermally, and the reaction product, gaseous at the temperature of formation, condenses as it cools. A volatile solid, such as iodin, volatilizes when heated sufficiently and upon contact with cold air the vapor condenses to form a smoke. If a current of air is passed over certain hot solids or liquids which are only slightly volatile, highly dispersed smokes are formed when the air saturated with the vapor passes to a cool region. Such materials are anthracene, acetanilide, diphenyl-amine, orthophthalic acid, and paraffin wax.[1] Other substances such as benzyl benzoate, or clean mercury, produce either a cloud of low degree of dispersion or no detectable smoke. If a hygroscopic substance, or one of its hydrolytic products, possesses a considerable vapor pressure, it will cause fumes to arise in moist air. Such substances are hydrogen chloride, aluminum chloride, and stannic chloride. The fume is produced by the condensation of atmospheric water vapor upon the hygroscopic-vapor molecules. If the vapor pressure is slight at ordinary temperature, no fume is produced, as in the case of calcium chloride or sulfuric acid.

Photophoresis.—Photophoresis is the migration of particles caused by impact of light rays. Fine particles, suspended in a gas, are attracted or repulsed by the light of an electric arc.[11] Tiny particles of gold, silver, and mercury formed in nitrogen and smokes of camphor and turpentine are repelled. Sulfur and selenium particles distilled in argon, nitric acid mist, water mist, cigar and wood smokes are attracted. Water droplets suspended in oxygen or hydrogen are unaffected.

The velocity of displacement is increased by increasing the intensity of the light or by diminishing the pressure of the gas. Whether a particle will be attracted or repelled will depend upon its capacity for absorbing or transmitting radiant energy. The illuminated side of a strongly absorbing particle will be heated more than the other side and consequently, owing to the greater impacts of the gas molecules on the heated side, the particle will be driven away from the source of light. Weakly absorbing particles, owing to the refraction of the light within them, become warmer on the reverse side, thus provoking a tendency to move toward the light.[12]

Electric Charge.—Clouds and smokes usually contain a certain proportion of charged particles, depending upon the age of the aerosol and the manner in which it was produced. The stability of aerosols is greatly influenced by the number of charged particles and the relative proportions of positively and negatively charged particles. The unlike-charged particles attract each other and coalesce as do also uncharged and charged particles. If all the particles are charged and of the same sign, the mutual repulsion results in a more stable dispersion.

With liquid particles, the effect of an electrical charge, opposing the surface tension, is reduction of the vapor pressure of the liquid, as shown previously. For example, when an object such as a charged stick of sealing wax is held near a fine spray of water, the droplets coalesce to a coarse rain. Owing to the lower vapor pressure of charged drops ($r > 0.63$ mμ), uncharged drops tend to evaporate and condense upon the former.

The particles may become charged in one of two general methods: (1) by contact with gaseous ions originally present in the dispersion medium or arising through formation of the aerosol, or (2) by the direct action of an ionizing agent. When dust is blown in air, the particles become electrically charged. The charge of such particles varies according to the chemical composition.[13] In general, the dust of nonmetals and of acidic oxides is positive, while that of metals and basic oxides is negative. The charge of salt dusts appears to depend upon the relative strength of the acid and basic ions.

Studies of the charges of fume particles arising through chemical action have produced the following information[14]: Fumes produced by chemical action without rise in temperature do not contain charged particles, as, for example, by the action of moist air upon hydrochloric acid, phosphorus pentachloride, arsenious chloride, tin chloride, silicon tetrafluoride. Fumes produced by violent chemical action, as, for example, through the action of water upon sulfuric acid, metallic sodium, phosphorus pentoxide, phosphorus pentachloride, contain charged particles of both signs. Likewise fumes arising through flaming combustion, as, for instance, powdered arsenic or antimony projected into chlorin, or the exposure of phosphine to air, contain charged particles.

When a liquid is sprayed in a gas, the droplets become electrified.[15] In waterfalls, the spray becomes positively charged, as do large raindrops broken up by the resistance of the air, the air in the neighborhood becoming negatively charged.[16] Faraday studied the electrification of expanded steam, attributing it to friction of the water droplets against the walls of the orifice. The nature of the charge depends on the nature of the orifice and is markedly influenced by impurities in the dry steam. If turpentine is present in the steam, the particles become negatively charged. A charged cloud is formed when water is vigorously aspirated by the passage of an ionized gas through it. The cloud disappears when passed through sulfuric acid but reappears as the gas hits moist air again.[17] When a gas containing uncharged nuclei is bubbled through ionizing liquids, the nuclei become charged. Water, alcohol, and salt solutions are ionizing liquids, while benzene, ether, and mineral oils are not.

The action of radioactive substances and of ultraviolet light may give rise to charges. Both positive and negative ions are produced when neutral clouds and smokes are exposed to radioactive substances.[18]

In an electrical field, a charged particle will move under the action of the field, the force imparted to the particle being the product of the intensity of the field X and the charge e on the particle. Applying Stokes's law, the velocity of the movement

$$v = \frac{Xe}{6\pi\eta r} \qquad (3)$$

By expressing the field X in volts per centimeter and taking the electronic charge $e = 1.59 \times 10^{-20}$ electromagnetic units, the radius can be measured approximately by

$$r = 4.65 \times 10^{-10} \frac{X}{v}$$

This method has been used by Wells and Gerke[19] for the estimation of the sizes of particles dispersed in a gaseous medium. By reversing the direction of the field with a rotating commutator, the particle is made to describe a definite stroke many times in succession. The convection due to the source of the light is perpendicular to this motion so that a zigzag line is obtained. The amplitude of this oscillation is an accurate measure of the distance traversed by the particle under the electrical force for a definite small interval of time. Photographic records of these oscillations have been obtained, giving simultaneously the sizes of a large number of particles and thus making possible a study of the size distribution of the particles.

Ultramicrographs of tobacco smoke, in which the oscillation time was varied, gave the results shown in Table 2. The mean

TABLE 2.—MOTION OF CHARGED PARTICLES IN AN ELECTRIC FIELD[19]

Time of one-half oscillation, sec.	Field strength, volts per cm.	Velocity, cm. per sec. $\times 10^2$	Average diameter of particles, d, cm. $\times 10^5$
0.25	587	1.97	2.76
0.25	590	2.07	2.65
0.545	587	2.03	2.70
0.545	585	1.87	2.80

of these four determinations of d is 2.73×10^{-5} cm. with an average deviation from the mean of 1.8 per cent and a maximum difference between two determinations of 5.4 per cent.

At sufficiently high voltages, particles which were originally uncharged acquire a mobility[20] due to contact with streams of rapidly moving gas ions. The velocity acquired between two successive collisions by an ion of mass m and charge e, moving under the action of a field of intensity X, is

$$v = \frac{Xe\lambda}{mV} \tag{4}$$

where λ is the mean free path length of the ion and V its mean velocity of "thermal agitation."[21]

When the field is sufficiently intense, ionization by collision with the molecules of the gas or electrode is produced. The negative ions thus produced will move away from the negative electrode where the charging took place and move with a high velocity to the opposite electrode, driving by impact the suspended particles in their path.

Settling and Flocculation.—Since a particle suspended in a gas is subjected to bombardment by the molecules of the gas, and if the particle is larger than the mean free path of the gaseous molecules (mean free path = 10^{-5} cm. at ordinary temperature and pressure), the general effect is that of a uniform continuous pressure over the entire surface of the particle. If the particle is falling through the gas under the influence of gravity, the force of the molecular impacts will be greater from below than from above and consequently the particle will encounter a continuous uniform resistance to its fall, increasing as the velocity of falling increases. A constant limiting velocity is reached when $F = F'$, where F = force of gravity, F' = force of frictional resistance.

The velocity of fall of a spherical body under the influence of gravity was studied by Sir G. G. Stokes,[22] who demonstrated that $F' = 6\pi\eta rv$, where η = viscosity of the medium, r = the radius of particle, and v = velocity of particle. It is seen that the resistance increases as the particle becomes larger and moves more rapidly.

The force F by which the spherical particle is pulled downward is equal to mg where m = its mass and g is the acceleration due to gravity. Now for a spherical particle $m = \frac{4}{3}\pi r^3(\rho_1 - \rho_2)$, where ρ_1 and ρ_2 are the densities of the particle substance and of the medium, respectively. Hence, when $F = F'$,

$$6\pi\eta rv = \frac{4}{3}\pi r^3(\rho_1 - \rho_2)g$$

from which the constant velocity of the particle

$$v = \frac{2r^2(\rho_1 - \rho_2)g}{9\eta} \tag{5}$$

Stokes used this formula to calculate the rate of fall of water droplets in air. Here $\rho_1 = 1$, ρ_2 is small enough to be neglected, $\eta = 1.8 \times 10^{-4}$ c.g.s. units, and therefore $v = 12 \times 10^5 \times r^2$ cm. per second. Consequently a water drop of radius equal to 10^{-2} cm. will fall at the rate of 120 cm. per second. Lord Rayleigh has shown that Stokes's law does not apply to water drops larger than 10^{-2} cm. Such drops fall as rain.

When the particle is smaller than the mean free path of the molecules of the medium, it will tend to slip between the molecules, the pressure will no longer be uniform, and it will be knocked about by the irregular impacts of the molecules. It will also rotate and its fall will be along a zigzag path. If the gas is under reduced pressure, a larger particle will, of course, fall in the same manner. In such cases the particle will encounter less resistance and will fall more rapidly than predicted by Stokes's law.

It has been shown by Cunningham[23] and by Millikan[24] that

$$v = v'\left(1 + K\frac{l}{r}\right) \tag{6}$$

where v = actual velocity.

v' = velocity predicted by Stokes's law.

l = length of mean free path of gas molecules.

r = radius of particles.

K = constant equal to 0.82.

The following tabulation[19] gives the diameters of particles computed from observed velocities using Millikan's data for oil drops.

From Stokes's Law	By Applying Cunningham's Correction
1×10^{-4} cm.	1.14×10^{-4} cm.
1×10^{-5} cm.	2.57×10^{-5} cm.
1×10^{-6} cm.	4.5×10^{-6} cm.
1×10^{-7} cm.	17.0×10^{-7} cm.

Stokes's law is valid then for aerosol particles in the approximate range of diameter 10^{-4} to 10^{-2} cm. in a gas under standard conditions of pressure and temperature. When more than one particle is settling, the degree of dispersion must be uniform for quantitative validity since the larger particles of a nonuniform dispersion would collide with the smaller ones. If the particles deviate from spherical shape, the law likewise cannot be applied in a rigid, quantitative manner. Nonspherical particles fall in the position which causes the greatest frictional resistance; a disk falls with its plane surface at right angles to the path of fall, a cube with a point downward.

When the particles of an aerosol come in contact with a solid surface, they tend to adhere to it and to each other. Consequently, the stability of an aerosol may be decreased by agitation because the frequency with which the particles strike the solid surface[25] is thereby increased.

When an aerosol is first formed, the smallest particles, owing to their high diffusion velocity and corresponding frequency of contact, rapidly coalesce, decreasing the degree of dispersion. The stability of the system then increases as a result of the more sluggish movement of the enlarged particles. The life history of smokes of ammonium chloride, cadmium oxide, cupric oxide, and zinc oxide has been found to be separable into three periods[26]:

1. An unstable period, lasting about 5 hr., in which the decrease in number of particles due to mutual coalescence is very rapid.
2. A stable period, of about 24 hr., in which the number of particles decreases slowly due to sedimentation.
3. These two stages overlap, producing an intermediate stage of coalescence and sedimentation.

The curves in Fig. 6 show the distribution of the particles of a smoke, obtained by detonating oil in air, according to their size at different time intervals.

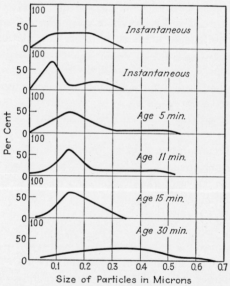

Fig. 6.—Frequency distribution of mineral-oil smoke particles.[19]

The particles of an aerosol may adsorb gas films and become stabilized thereby. The stability of the blue zinc oxide smoke from a brass foundry may be so explained. When this zinc oxide is collected in woolen filters, it is light and mobile. It flows and surges like a liquid and has an apparent density of 0.1.[27]

When gas-enveloped particles come in contact with each other, strong forces of cohesion will cause them to adhere to each other, especially since the surface molecules, owing to the high degree of curvature of the particles, exercise a stronger attractive force than the molecules of a plane surface. While the particles adhere, they do not coalesce, owing to the intervention of the gaseous envelopes, and so may form loose flocks. In some cases, the particles may be electrically polarized owing to their chemical nature. Such particles become attached to each other by their oppositely charged poles, tending to form threadlike aggregates. Smokes of the oxides of zinc, cadmium, magnesium, aluminum, and antimony readily form such strings.

The electric charge of like sign confers stability not only through the electric repulsive forces but also because a charge acts to oppose the effect of surface tension.[28] However, in the case of the protective envelopes of gas, this opposition to the effect of surface tension tends to promote flocculation by diminishing the force of attraction between the adsorbed gas and the particle. When water particles collide in air, they may rebound from one another probably owing to their gaseous envelopes, but if the air near the drops is charged, the particles coalesce upon collision owing to the adsorbed ions overcoming the effect of the gas films.

An aerosol containing neutral particles may be flocculated by the introduction of a charged aerosol because the charged particles induce an opposite charge upon the neutral ones.

The most satisfactory method of precipitating smoke particles is electrostatic precipitation. Alternating or direct current can be used. Since in commercial work the smoke must be removed from moving volumes of gas, the direct-current method is employed where the charged smoke particles are attracted to oppositely charged plates. This is used in the Cottrell process of fume and smoke precipitation. The principle involved was suggested by Hohlfeld in 1824 and by Guitard in 1850 and was applied by Lodge in 1886.

A thermal gradient will decrease the stability of an aerosol. The introduction of a heated rod in an aerosol results in driving the suspended particles away from the rod. This is due to the increase in energy of the gas molecules near the rod thus moving more energetically than the colder remote gas molecules. The hot rod thus becomes surrounded by a region of warm dust-free air moving upward.

A rod colder than the aerosol becomes surrounded by a down-streaming current of dust-free air, but in this case the particles are deposited on the surface. Suspended particles are attracted by a solid surface which is colder than the aerosol. For this reason the walls and ceilings of rooms heated by steam or hot-water radiator systems become blackened by the dust and smoke in the room; the walls are colder than the air. Tobacco smoke passed between two concentric tubes maintained at a temperature difference of from 50 to 80° is quantitatively deposited on the colder tube.[29] An automatic smoke recorder based on this principle has been described by Thomson.[30] Paper mounted on a water-cooled drum moves at a constant rate across a slit exposed to smoke. The density of the deposit is a record of the smoke at a given time.

The removal of smoke and cloud particles by filtration through fabrics such as cotton or wool or through granular particles such as charcoal presents interesting problems. The dispersed particles obviously must come in contact with the solid structure in order to be adsorbed. The efficiency of a filter depends therefore upon the rate at which the particles diffuse toward the filtering surface as the aerosol passes through. It will also depend upon the eddy currents produced, which by centrifugal action throw the suspended particles against the filtering surface. Diffusion effects apply to the smaller particles, while centrifugal action is important in the case of large particles. The relationship between the efficiency of filtration through paper felt and particle size is shown in Table 3, which gives the results obtained

TABLE 3.—FILTRATION OF A FOG AS A FUNCTION OF PARTICLE SIZE

Radius of Particles, $m\mu$	Percentage Which Passed through Filter
Under 50	52.4
50 to 100	87.6
100 to 200	93.9
200 to 400	30.4
400 to 800	4.2
Over 800	0

by filtering a fog of diphenylchlorarsine, obtained by detonation.[31] It is seen that the efficiency of the filter was least for particles 100 to 200 $m\mu$ in radius.

Freundlich states that during the war it was found that gas mask filters made of felt or paper afforded much better protection than charcoal against chemical-warfare fogs and smokes. A paper filter made of a felted mass of loosely packed long fibers was more efficient than tightly packed short fibers, probably owing to the greater centrifugal action of the whirling motion imparted to the aerosol as it passed through the ramifications of the loosely packed long fibers. This would apply to coarse aerosols rather than to highly dispersed ones.

Smokes will become less stable in humid air owing to the condensation of moisture upon the particles, which thus become larger and heavier.

Various commercial methods of removing the dispersed phase from aerosols, using settling by gravity, centrifugal action, loading the particles with water, contact with solid surfaces, flocculation by electrical wind, electrostatic precipitation, filtration, and gas washing have been devised.

Thermal Effects of Aerosols.—The presence of dust or smoke in the atmosphere increases its capacity for absorbing heat. This affects atmospheric temperature in three ways:[1]

1. The heat rays are partly absorbed by the particles which then warm the surrounding air by conduction.

2. The diurnal temperature range is decreased because the temperature rise at the ground level during the day is checked by virtue of the diminution in the intensity of the heat rays that pass through.

3. Conversely, radiation of heat from the ground to the upper cooler air is checked by the dust particles. This last principle has long been applied in orchards when a frost is feared. Smudge pots are burned under the trees not merely to produce heat but to provide soot that will retain the heat and inhibit ground radiation of heat.

Many of the brickworks in northern Sweden produce smoke in the drying houses by burning peat with insufficient access of air on cold nights in the spring and autumn in order to protect the raw bricks against low temperature.

Owing to their heat-absorbing capacity, dusts and smokes striking warm air may give rise to fogs and mists.

Dust Explosions.—The reactivity of a substance increases with its degree of dispersion. Consequently the rate of oxidation of highly dispersed particles is very much greater than that of massive particles. The best possible contact between oxygen and a combustible substance is attained when the combustible is a gas. When a portion of such a mixture is heated to its ignition temperature, the heat from the resulting combustion at that point is communicated to the adjacent gas molecules, raising them to the ignition temperature. Hence a wave of ignition spreads through the gas-air mixture, followed by a flame, or wave of combustion. If the gas and oxygen of the air are mixed in approximately their combining proportions, combustion spreads through the mixture with explosive velocity. Flame velocities of 9,000 ft. per second are reported to have been observed with mixtures of hydrogen and oxygen. Mixtures of gases become less explosive as the proportion of either gas is increased beyond that of the combining proportion.

When combustion occurs in a portion of a gas mixture, the adjacent gas becomes expanded owing to the rise in temperature, so that a wave of pressure arises. This has the effect of compressing the gas immediately in front of it and so raising its temperature. If this is sufficient to reach the ignition temperature, combustion occurs with much greater velocity, producing detonation.

The inflammability of a gas mixture is lowered by reduction of pressure or by dilution with anything that is incombustible and which will absorb heat, thus inhibiting the ignition wave. Such a substance may be an inert gas, an excess of either of the reacting gases, water vapor, fog, or an aerosol of inert particles. A metallic screen may absorb the heat of combustion, preventing the spread of ignition, as in the Davy safety lamp used by miners.

Oxidizable solids or liquids in the form of smokes or clouds in air may be ignited and caused to burst into flame. Since there cannot be as intimate contact between the particles of an aerosol and oxygen as between gas molecules, the facility of flame propagation is less. The inflammability of an oxidizable dust or fog in air depends upon:

1. The size and concentration of the dispersed particles. The greater the specific surface, the more rapid is the combustion. Also with increasing fineness the more active Brownian movement helps to bring the particles in more frequent contact.

2. The ease of oxidation of the particles controlling the propagation of the ignition wave which depends upon their chemical nature.

3. The partial pressure of oxygen and the presence of adsorbed films of oxygen or of inert gas or water vapor.

4. The specific heat and the thermal conductivity of the dust or cloud.

5. The presence of water on the particles or of mineral matter in them.

A study of the inflammability of 66 different samples of dust collected from factories in Great Britain has been made by

TABLE 4.—IGNITION AND PROPAGATION TEMPERATURES OF DUSTS IN AIR
(In degrees centigrade)

Dust	Ignition temperature	Propagation temperature
Sugar........................	540	805
Dextrin......................	540	940
Starch.......................	640	1035
Cocoa........................	620	970
Flour........................	630	{ 995 (1265)*
Cork.........................	630	1000
Rice.........................	630	970
Mustard......................	680	1050
Wheat elevator...............	...	(1295)
Oat and corn elevator........	...	(995)
Oat hull.....................	...	(1020)

* Values in parentheses taken from Price.[33]

Wheeler.[32] Some of Wheeler's results are given in Table 4. The "propagation temperatures" at which the various dusts could be ignited freely were determined by passing the dust over elec-

TABLE 5.—LOWER EXPLOSIVE LIMITS[34]
(In milligrams per liter of air)

Dust	Glowing platinum wire	Arc	Induction spark
Starch........................	7.0	10.3	13.7
Corn elevator.................	10.3	10.3	13.7
Wheat elevator................	10.3	10.3	
Sulfur........................	7.0	13.7	13.7
Sugar.........................	10.3	17.2	34.4
Aluminum......................	7.0	7.0	13.7
Coal..........................	17.2	24.1	No ignition

trically heated platinum and noting the temperature at which combustion occurred. The lowest temperatures at which ignition occurred were determined by passing the dusts through a small glass tube containing an electrically heated copper spiral. The nature of the source of heat has an influence on the tendency to explode, particularly on the lower concentration limit of the dust.[34] This is illustrated by Table 5.

The relative inflammability of dusts as indicated by the pressure generated during combustion is given in Table 6.[35]

TABLE 6.—SOME MEASUREMENTS OF EXPLOSION PRESSURES[35]

Dust	Pressure Generated, lb. per sq. in.
Lycopodium	17.5
Dextrin	14.6
Wheat starch	14.0
Tanbark dust	13.3
Wood dust	12.8
Cornstarch	12.7
Wheat elevator	12.5
Sugar	12.2
Linseed meal	11.7
Pittsburgh coal	10.1
Cocoa	9.9
Sulfur flour	8.8
Rice-bran dust	8.7
Ground-cork dust	7.4

A dusty atmosphere such as prevails in certain industrial operations is exceedingly perilous. A number of conditions must be satisfied before an explosion can take place and, owing to the rarity of the fulfillment of all optimum conditions, the danger is apt to be overlooked. Once the conditions have been fulfilled, however, the result may be frightful. In large-scale experiments with coal dust, pressures as high as 270 lb. per square inch have been recorded and flame velocities of 3,000 to 6,000 ft. per second have been observed.[33,35] Starch, flour, sugar, and other factory dusts which are more inflammable than coal dust have been found capable of producing many times the pressure of a coal-dust explosion. As an example of the disastrous results obtainable from the explosion of starch dust, the description of the accident at Pekin, Illinois, in which 30 persons were killed is impressive.[36]

References

1. GIBBS: "Clouds and Smokes," J. and A. Churchill, London, 1924.

2. LOWRY and McHATTON: *Trans. Faraday Soc.*, **18**, 82 (1922–1923).

3. WILSON: *Phil. Trans. Roy. Soc. London*, **A189**, 265 (1897); **A192**, 403 (1899); **193**, 289 (1899); ANDERSON and FROEMKE: *Z. physik. Chem.*, **142A**, 321 (1929).

4. ANDRÉN: Dissertation, Upsala, 1918; through SVEDBERG: "The Formation of Colloids," D. Van Nostrand Company, New York, 1921.

5. WILSON: *Proc. Roy. Soc. (London)*, **A85**, 285 (1911); **A87**, 277 (1912).

6. SVEDBERG: "Colloid Chemistry," A.C.S. Monograph, p. 32, Chemical Catalog Company, New York, 1924.

7. BECKER: *Z. physik. Chem.*, **78**, 39 (1911–1912); BESSON: *Compt. rend.*, **154**, 342 (1912); M. S. CURIE: *Compt. rend.*, **147**, 379 (1908); OWEN and HUGHES: *Phil. Mag.*, (6) **15**, 746 (1908).

8. W. THOMSON: *Phil. Mag.*, (4) **42**, 448 (1871).

9. POYNTING and THOMSON: "The Properties of Matter," p. 166, Chas. Griffen & Co., Ltd., London, 1903; J. J. THOMSON: "Conduction of Electricity through Gases," p. 149, University Press, Cambridge, 1903; J. J. THOMSON: "Applications of Dynamics to Physics and Chemistry," p. 163, Macmillan & Co., Ltd., London, 1888.

10. KOHLSCHÜTTER and EHLERS: *Z. Elektrochem.*, **18**, 373 (1912); KOHLSCHÜTTER and NOLL: *ibid.*, **18**, 419 (1912).

11. EHRENHAFT: *Ann. Physik*, (4) **56**, 81 (1918).

12. LASKI and ZERNER: *Z. Physik*, **3**, 224 (1920).

13. RUDGE: *Phil. Mag.*, (6) **25**, 481 (1913).

14. DEBROGLIE and BRIZARD: *Compt. rend.*, **148**, 1457 (1909); **149**, 923 (1910).

15. DEBROGLIE: *Compt. rend.*, **150**, 1115 (1910); VON BRUNOLAK: *Ann. Physik*, **39**, 497 (1912); SEELIGER: *Ann. Physik*, **31**, 500 (1910).

16. SIMPSON: *Phil. Mag.*, (6) **30**, 1 (1915).

17. TOWNSEND: *Proc. Cambridge Phil. Soc.*, **9**, 244 (1897).

18. DEBROGLIE: *Ann. chim. phys.*, (8) **16**, 5 (1909).

19. WELLS and GERKE: *J. Am. Chem. Soc.*, **41**, 312 (1919).

20. STRONG: *Trans. Am. Electrochem. Soc.*, **31**, 415 (1917).

21. LANGEVIN: *Ann. chim. phys.*, (7) **28**, 289 (1903).

22. STOKES: *Trans. Cambridge Phil. Soc.*, **9**, 8 (1851).

23. CUNNINGHAM: *Proc. Roy. Soc. (London)*, **83A**, 357 (1910).

24. MILLIKAN: *Physik. Z.*, **11**, 1097 (1910); *Phys. Rev.*, **32**, 349 (1911).

25. TOLMAN et al.: *J. Am. Chem. Soc.*, **41**, 304 (1919).

26. WHYTLAW-GRAY, SPEAKMAN, and CAMPBELL: *Proc. Roy. Soc. (London)*, **102A**, 600 (1923).

27. GIBBS: Ref. 1, p. 76.

28. BURTON and WIEGAND: *Phil. Mag.*, (6) **23**, 148 (1912).

29. BANCROFT: *J. Phys. Chem.*, **24**, 421 (1920).

30. WILLIAM THOMSON: *J. Soc. Chem. Ind.*, **11**, 12 (1892); also EDDY: U. S. Patent No. 971,670 (1910).

31. FREUNDLICH: "Kapillarchemie," p. 1085, Akademische Verlagsgesellschaft m.b.H., Leipzig, 1922.
32. WHEELER: *Report to Home Office*, Cd 6662 (March, 1913); through GIBBS: "Clouds and Smokes," p. 166.
33. PRICE: *Chem. Met. Eng.*, **24**, 29 (1921).
34. TROSTEL and FREVERT: *Chem. Met. Eng.*, **30**, 141 (1924). This paper describes experimental apparatus.
35. BROWN: *J. Ind. Eng. Chem.*, **9**, 269 (1917).
36. PRICE, BROWN, and EDWARDS: *Chem. Met. Eng.*, **30**, 579 (1924).

CHAPTER III

OPTICS—BROWNIAN MOVEMENT

The path of a beam of light projected through a medium is visible or invisible to the eye depending upon the presence of dispersed particles which scatter the light, upon certain properties of the particles, and upon the intensity of the projected light. This phenomenon of light scattering is called the *Tyndall effect* in honor of the English physicist who was the first to use and study it intensively, although by no means the discoverer of the phenomenon.

Particles that are large in comparison with the wave length of light reflect and refract the light in a regular manner, while particles that are small in comparison with light waves scatter the incident light in all directions. The scattered light is plane polarized, each particle becoming the source of a new wave front.[1]

Tyndall found that very fine smoke particles scatter blue light and transmit orange-red. This can be observed in producer gas or freshly formed cigar smoke which appears blue against a dark background and orange-red against the light. As the particles increase in size, the blue color disappears and the scattered light finally appears white.

The scattering of light by colloidal solutions was reported by Faraday[2] in 1856, who stated his belief of the heterogeneous nature of a colloidal gold solution which was based on the scattering of light by the hydrosol.

The first attempt to give a mathematical formulation to the scattering of light by turbid media is that of Lord Rayleigh. The Rayleigh formula relating intensity of light scattering with the number and size of uniform suspended spherical particles and the wave length of light is:

$$I_s \propto I_i \left(\frac{n_1^2}{n^2} - 1 \right)^2 (1 + \cos^2 \beta) \frac{mv^2}{a^2 \lambda^4} \qquad (1)$$

35

where I_s = intensity of scattered light.

I_i = intensity of incident light.

n_1 = index of refraction of dispersed phase.

n = index of refraction of dispersion medium.

β = angle between line of sight and the incident direction.

m = number of particles per unit volume.

v = average volume of particles.

λ = wave length of the scattered light.

a = distance from the particle to point of observation.

The particles are supposed to be contained in such a small volume that the distance a and the angle β are the same for all the particles. For particles of different size, all small in respect to the wave length, a summation must be made requiring the size distribution of the particles. Furthermore, all of the light scattered by the particles in the direction β is assumed to reach the eye. When the medium is densely packed with particles, however, secondary scattering cannot be ignored. The fractional decrease of the intensity I in traversing a thickness dx of the system is

$$\frac{dI}{dx} = -\frac{hI}{\lambda^4}$$

where h is a constant independent of λ. Integrating, we get

$$I_x = I_0 e^{\frac{-hx}{\lambda^4}} \tag{2}$$

where I_0 is the intensity of the light when $x = 0$ and I_x is the intensity after traversing the thickness x.

A striking characteristic of these equations is the inverse proportion of the fourth power of the wave length to the intensity of scattering. The scattered light is therefore much bluer than the incident light, while the blue is correspondingly absent from the transmitted light. This was used by Rayleigh to account for the blue color of the sky[3] and for the red colors of the sunset. The blue color of tobacco smoke observed at an angle to the source of white light is likewise explained.

An observation of the traffic lights along an avenue in a foggy or smoky atmosphere will serve as an illustration. The red lights are visible to a greater distance than the green lights.

Rayleigh's equation requires that the particles be dielectrics; hence it is not valid for metallic particles. The colors of metallic dispersions are so characteristic that no simple theory can apply.[4]

A "Tyndallmeter" for measuring the intensity of the Tyndall beam has been devised by Tolman and Vliet.[5] It is shown in

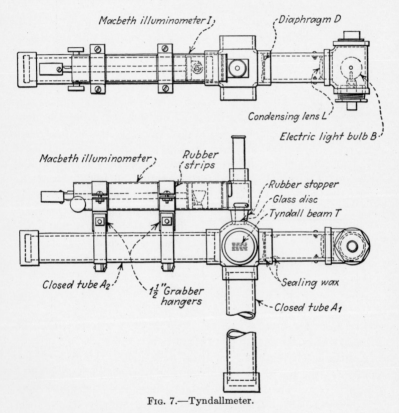

Fig. 7.—Tyndallmeter.

Fig. 7. This instrument was used during the war to determine the concentrations of obscuring and toxic smokes or clouds and to study their change in concentration with time.

The apparatus consists essentially of an electric-light bulb B, a condensing lens L, giving a beam of parallel light which passes through the diaphragm D, and a Macbeth illuminometer I for measuring the strength of the Tyndall beam T. In case the material to be examined is a liquid suspension or solution, it is introduced at T in a cylindrical glass tube, while smokes and clouds are pumped directly through the apparatus. The long closed tubes A_1 and A_2 are provided, respectively, for absorbing

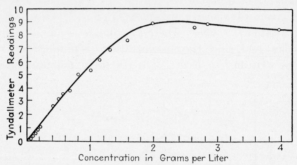

FIG. 8.—Relation of Tyndallmeter reading to concentration of silica suspensions.

the beam after it has passed through the dispersed system and for giving a dark background for observing the Tyndall beam.

The instrument was standardized by means of silica suspensions prepared from ground silica that passed a 200-mesh sieve. The readings obtained from a series of silica suspensions of varying concentrations are shown in Fig. 8. It is seen that the intensity of the Tyndall beam is directly proportional to the concentration up to about 1.4 g. silicon dioxide per liter, beyond which it is no longer proportional owing to the fact that an appreciable part of the light is absorbed [Eq. (2)]. The direct proportionality between the concentration of an ammonium chloride smoke and Tyndall-beam intensity is shown in Fig. 9.

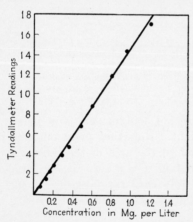

FIG. 9.—Relation of concentration of ammonium chloride smoke to Tyndallmeter reading.

The measurements by Tolman and associates show that the intensity of the Tyndall beam that is produced when cloud or smoke is illuminated by a light of given intensity will be proportional to the concentration of the dispersed phase, provided that (1) the concentration is not high enough for the opacity of the cloud or smoke to affect the result, and (2) the degree of dispersion at the different concentrations remains constant.

For a given wave length of light the intensity of scattered light may be written $I = kmd^6$ (where d = diameter and m = number of particles) and, since the concentration c is proportional to md^3, it may be written $I = Kcd^3$. The results of Tolman and associ-

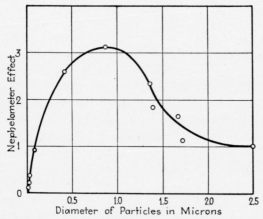

Fɪɢ. 10.—Nephelometer effect with barium sulfate suspensions of identical concentration, 3.5×10^{-3} mole per liter, but of different particle size.

ates showed that this relation does not hold for very large particles which reflect the incident light. Here they point out that $I = k_1 md^2$; *i.e.*, I is proportional to the area of the reflecting surface, or, in terms of concentration, $I = k_1 c/d$; *i.e.*, for large particles (probably larger than 10^{-4} cm.) the intensity of the scattered light as a function of concentration is inversely proportional to the diameter.

Figure 10 shows the results obtained by Bechhold and Hebler[6] with suspensions of barium sulfate in water of equal concentration but of different particle size, thus involving variation in the number as well as the volumes of the particles. It is seen that the maximum Tyndall effect was found at a particle size of about $0.88\ \mu$ diameter.

Equation (1) may be written

$$I_s = kI_i \frac{mv^2}{\lambda^4} \qquad (3)$$

if we ignore the refractive indices. Then for a given wave length of light, the intensities of light scattered by two dispersions of the same substance* would be proportional to the numbers of particles if the particle sizes are identical, or to the squares of the particle volumes if the number of particles is identical in the two hydrosols. Since concentration $(c) = mv\rho$ where m = number, v = volume, and ρ = density of particles, then

$$I_s = kI_i \frac{cv}{\rho\lambda^4} \qquad (4)$$

and the scattered light intensities are proportional to the concentrations provided all other factors are constant. This is fundamental to nephelometry. For a more detailed discussion the reader is referred to the article by P. V. Wells.[7]

Microscopic Observation.—The application of a microscope to the examination of a Tyndall beam is termed *ultramicroscopy*.

The limit of resolution (ϵ) of a microscope objective is expressed by the equation

$$\epsilon = \frac{\lambda}{2n \sin \alpha} = \frac{\lambda}{2 \text{ N.A.}} \qquad (5)$$

where ϵ = distance by which two points must be separated in order to be distinguished as two points.

n = index of refraction of the medium between the objective lens and the object.

α = half the angle of aperture of the objective lens.

λ = wave length of light employed.

N.A. = "numerical aperture" of lens, *i.e.*, = $n \sin \alpha$.

It is apparent that the resolving power of a microscope can be increased either by decreasing λ or by increasing the numerical aperture or both. The limit for $\sin \alpha = 1$, ($\alpha = 90°$) and the maximum for n is 1.66—that of α-monobromnaphthalene. With $\lambda = 5607$ Å. as a mean value for white light, the limit value of $\epsilon = 0.17 \times 10^{-4}$ cm. for white light. This has not been realized experimentally.

* In this case the refractive indices are alike in both cases.

Stoney[8] showed by use of an immersion objective of N.A. 1.35 and an immersion condenser of N.A. 1.30 with blue light (λ = about 4500 Å.) that the limit of resolution was about 0.19 to 0.20 μ. Actually he determined the displacement at which two particles would still appear as two and not as one. This may also be taken to represent the limit of smallness of particles at which it is possible to detect detail by microscopic vision. Light of this wave length is about the limit of visual range. Of course, by use of rays in the ultraviolet region, with quartz lenses,

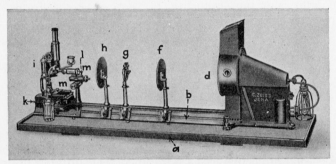

Fig. 11.—Slit ultramicroscope.

and a photographic camera, images of smaller particles may be obtained. The greatest resolving power[9] reported by such means is 0.075 μ.

The limit of visibility may be set then at 0.1 to 0.2×10^{-4} cm. For the investigation of particles smaller* than this, the ultramicroscope was devised. The ultramicroscope actually is an ordinary microscope provided with illumination that reveals the particles as spots of light against a dark background.

Slit Ultramicroscope.—The slit ultramicroscope devised by Siedentopf and Zsigmondy[10] is shown in Fig. 11. The optical bench *b* is screwed on the base board *a*, at the right end of which is an electric arc lamp *d* placed in such a position that the axis of the narrow pencil of light which passes through the diaphragm set up in front may be parallel to the optical bench. Next to the arc lamp is a small projection lens *f* having a focal length of about 120 mm. The lens is surrounded by a screen to block out stray light. The rays from *f* impinge upon a movable slit *g* which is

---

* Such particles are called *ultramicroscopic particles*.[10]

accurately controlled by knife edges and can be rotated through an angle of 90°.

The slit furnishes a means of obtaining a definitely measurable volume of liquid within the preparation, the depth of which may thereby be very exactly adjusted to conform to the penetration of the microscope objective employed for observation. For, obviously, in the absence of a slit the illumination would extend to so many ill-defined strata above and below the stratum in the focal plane that the circles of confusion arising from them would inevitably blur the entire field of view. The sharply defined diffraction disks would then cease to be perceptible.

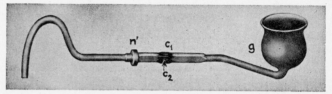

Fig. 12.—Cell with quartz windows.

A second projection lens h is set up at some distance from the slit. It forms a real image of the slit, reduced in size, $1\frac{1}{2}$ to 5 times according to its position. This image is projected into the objective lens fitted in a tube fixed upon the compound slides l, which can be moved in two directions horizontally by the screws m to center the beam of light. This objective reduces the image of the slit g about ten times. It forms then in the focal plane of the viewing objective of the microscope i an image which is fifteen to fifty times smaller than the slit. Consequently the illuminated stratum of the observed preparation is in most cases only a few microns thick.

The solution under examination is in a cell (Fig. 12) which is clamped to the viewing objective, optical contact being effected by a drop of water. The cell is rectangular in cross section to insure a well-defined position in the clamp. At one end it carries a funnel g, while the other open end is fitted with a piece of rubber tubing and a pinch cock. The observation chamber of the cell is the black portion which is provided with the quartz* (or glass) windows c_1 and c_2. The beam of light from the conden-

---

* Quartz is preferable to glass because the latter is slightly fluorescent.

ser objective enters c_2 and is viewed at right angles by means of the viewing objective through c_1.

The only light visible to the observer is that diffracted by the particles. By means of this type of ultramicroscope it is said that the light diffracted from particles as small as about 5 mμ can be seen and the particles thereby counted.

That the light scattered by the particles is polarized can be proved by viewing through a Nicol prism superimposed on the microscope ocular. As the prism is turned, the light of the cone changes sensibly in brilliance. If attention is focused on one particle, the speck of light may disappear at a certain position of the Nicol. Fluorescent light does not change in intensity when thus viewed. The appearance of the individual spots of light gives an indication of the shape of the particles.[11] Spherical particles scatter light with uniform intensity, while nonspherical ones such as rod-shaped and leaf-shaped particles produce a twinkling or scintillation because the scattered light is most intense when such a particle, in the course of the Brownian movement, lies with its long axis in the plane of the line of observation and with its side of greatest area perpendicular to the illuminating light. As it turns, the scattered light diminishes in intensity, owing to the orientation of its smaller side (rod) or edge (leaf) perpendicular to the incident illumination.

An advanced type of instrument is the immersion ultramicroscope of Zsigmondy[12] which eliminates the observation cell. Both the illuminating and the viewing objectives are beveled at the ends so as to allow their front lenses to be brought very close together with their axes at right angles. The drop of liquid under examination clings by capillarity between the front lenses of the objectives. It is claimed that particles as small as 3 mμ can be counted in this instrument.[13]

Dark-ground Illuminators.—Substage illumination by means of the paraboloid and cardioid illuminators gives very brilliant results with certain colloidal solutions. A cross section of a paraboloid illuminator is shown diagrammatically in Fig. 13. A drop of the observed solution is placed on a slide (s) and covered with a cover glass. The slide is in cedar-oil contact with the top of the illuminator. With the illumination and the objective lens properly adjusted, the particles of a suspension appear as bright spots against a dark background. Only the light scattered by the particles travels up the microscope tube. A more powerful type of dark-ground illuminator is the cardioid condenser shown in Fig. 14.

Recently, a dark-ground condenser and lens system developed by Spierer[14] surpasses in illuminating power, especially for thin sheets of organized structures, those illuminators mentioned above. The Spierer lens system provides illumination not only

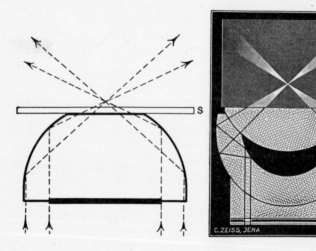

FIG. 13.—Diagram of a paraboloid condenser.

FIG. 14.—Course of the rays through a cardioid condenser and a plate of uranium glass placed upon it.

from the sides but also at nearly a zero angle to the source of the light. The expression $(1 + \cos^2 \beta)$ in Eq. (1) states that the intensity of the scattered light is greatest when the angle $\beta = 0$. The Spierer system (Fig. 15) consists of two parts:

A. A special immersion objective with a central mirror.
B. A special dark-field condenser.

In the center of the front lens (1) of the immersion objective there is a tiny concave mirror (2) consisting of deposited platinum. The illuminating beam of small aperture (3), which has passed up from below through the object, is thrown back on to the object by the reflector so that both principal surfaces of the preparation are intensively illuminated. The observed rays consist of the light which had been scattered and diffracted in the object.

The special condenser consists of two concentric systems. First, as in the case of the common dark-field condensers, there are the reflecting surfaces (4, 5) which illuminate the specimen with rays of large aperture (6, 7) at an oblique angle. Second, by means of a lens (8) in the center of the condenser, a light beam of small aperture (3) is directed to the specimen. By means of three movable stops the illumination is regulated so that light beams of very large or very small aperture may be readily produced.

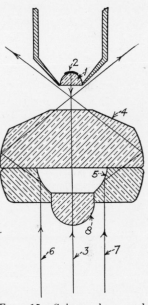

Particles which are below the limit of resolution are called ultramicroscopic particles. Ultramicroscopic particles which show as points of light in an ultramicroscope or dark-field condenser are termed *submicroscopic particles*, while those which are not detectable by ultramicroscopic methods are *amicroscopic particles*.

The reader is reminded that size alone does not control "visibility" in an ultramicroscope. From Eq. (1) it is to be noted that

Fig. 15.—Spierer lens and illuminator.

$$I_s = kI_i\left(\frac{n_1^2}{n^2} - 1\right)^2 \tag{6}$$

Curiously, this function is frequently ignored in discussions of size of particles as revealed by ultramicroscopy although the originators were well aware of it, Siedentopf[15] pointing out that the particles in hydrosols of alumina, silica, and albumin were invisible "doubtless because the refractive indices of these bodies do not differ sufficiently from those of the medium in which they are contained." Consequently, dispersions which contain large amicroscopic particles may exist.

The Tyndall cone popularly associated with colloidal dispersions may be exceedingly faint and in fact nondistinguishable in the electric-arc illuminated ultramicroscope if the refractive indices of the phases are nearly alike. On the other hand, by means of a heliostat, light scattering by chemically homogeneous liquids is discernible.[16]

Certain solutions undergo photochemical changes in the brilliant light used in ultramicroscopic observation. Sometimes these changes produce suspended particles.[17] Such solutions may be examined without interference of decomposition by means of longer wave lengths.

Counting of Particles. Estimation of Size.—If m = the mass of particles dispersed in unit volume, n the total number, and ρ the density of particle substance, then the average particle volume v would be

$$v = \frac{m}{\rho n}$$

or, assuming cubical shape the length of side of particle,

$$l = \sqrt[3]{\frac{m}{\rho n}} \tag{7}$$

The number of particles in a given volume of a colloidal dispersion may be counted in the ultramicroscope provided they are not amicroscopic. The volume of dispersion observed may be measured by means of an ocular micrometer. Figure 16 shows how the dimensions are obtained. The Tyndall beam D from the condenser objective AA passing through the cell B is measured at its brightest width ab by means of the ocular scale C. When the slit (g, Fig. 11) is rotated through 90°, the former depth of the observed portion is revealed as a width which can be measured. Thus from these dimensions and the third dimension of the length observed, the volume is obtained. The spots of light in this volume are counted. Then on the assumption that (1) all particles present are revealed as spots of light, (2) the density for macroscopic particle substance is the same as for the particles in state of fine subdivision, (3) the particles are cubical in shape, the average size of the particles may be calculated.

The most serious limitation of this method of estimating the size of colloidal particles is the fact that no amicroscopic particles are permissible. As a consequence an error of unknown magnitude is present which quite overshadows the others, such as the error in measuring the volume of the part of Tyndall cone observed, the error in count (where a cluster of particles might be taken for one particle), the possible density difference as a

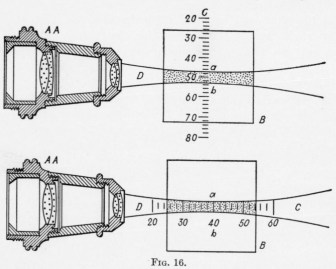

Fig. 16.

result of fineness of substance, and the assumption of cubical shape.

When a colloidal dispersion is too concentrated for accurate counting, it is diluted to such an extent that the number of particles can be counted at a glance. This may introduce another error as shown by the following experiment made by Zsigmondy: A silver hydrosol containing 0.0037 g. of Ag per 100 cc., and 3.5 particles per 440 cu. μ, yielded the following results:

Dilution	Number of particles found	Number of particles expected from original count
1 volume of sol + 1 volume of water...............	2.28	1.75
1 volume of sol + 7 volumes of water...............	1.62	0.45

An increase in number of particles upon dilution is shown in this experiment. This may mean that clusters disaggregated on dilution and thus another appreciable error may be introduced if a sol is diluted prior to counting.

A quicker and less accurate method of estimating the size of particles is through determination of their average displacement and use of the formula

$$l = D\sqrt[3]{\frac{m}{\rho}} \qquad (8)$$

where l = length of side of particle.

D = mean displacement of particles.

m = mass of particle substance per unit volume.

ρ = density of particle substance.

When this method is used, the depth of focus of the microscope must be about the same as the displacement of the particles; if it is larger, the observed displacement will be too small, and *vice versa*.

Brownian Movement.—The ultramicroscope reveals the particles trembling and swarming, making very little progress in motion despite their ceaseless activity. This is called the *Brownian movement* after the botanist Robert Brown who, in 1827, showed that the motions of particles suspended in water are not limited to living matter.[18] Up to this time such motions of suspended particles were believed to be due to life forces. Brown's experiments with powders of lifeless substances disproved this notion. He was led to examine such substances since spore dusts of mosses which had been dry about one hundred years showed to his surprise a lively motion when suspended in water.

After Brown, the motion was studied notably by Wiener (1863), Exner (1867), Jevons (1870), and Gouy (1888), who demonstrated that the motion was not caused by living matter or by external influences such as vibration of the apparatus or incident light or heat. Then the questions of the influence of gravitational, electrical, magnetic, and surface-tension forces between the particles were argued by Gouy, Jevons, Ramsay (1892), Bliss (1894), Maltézos (1894), Bache (1894), and Spring (1900) with the result that these influences were eliminated as possible causes.

A molecular kinetic theory for the motion was suggested by Wiener, Exner, Gouy, and Maltézos. The mathematical development of a molecular kinetic explanation was published by Einstein[19] (1905–1906), Smoluchowski[20] (1906), and Langevin[21] (1908), all of whom arrived at the same equation by different modes of attack.

For the present purpose a simplified derivation will suffice and such a one by Einstein,[22] taken almost verbatim from his article, follows.

We shall consider how diffusion of a solute in a dilute solution depends upon the osmotic pressure in the solution and upon the

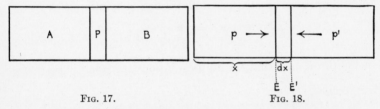

Fig. 17.   Fig. 18.

motion of the solute particles in tne solvent. It will be assumed that the molecules of the solute are large in comparison with those of the solvent and obtain an equation for the diffusion constant which depends only on the size of the dissolved molecules and the viscosity of the solvent. From this it will be shown how the mean magnitude of the disorganized motion of the particles, whether dissolved or suspended, can be calculated involving merely the two factors above mentioned, *viz.*, size of particle and viscosity of the medium.

Diffusion and Osmotic Pressure.—Consider the cylindrical vessel in Fig. 17 filled with a dilute solution. The interior of the cylinder is divided into two compartments, A and B, by the movable piston P which is freely permeable to the solvent molecules but impermeable to the molecules of solute. If the concentration in A is greater than in B, the piston P will move from left to right until equilibrium is attained. The force causing the movement of the piston is the difference in osmotic pressure (K) between A and B, which the dissolved substance exerts from left to right, and becomes zero when the concentrations in the two compartments are equal. It is evident then that the osmotic forces are responsible for the equalization of concentration brought about by diffusion since this can be prevented by the exertion of an external force on the piston which just balances the osmotic force K.

Consider a similar cylindrical vessel (Fig. 18) of unit cross section in which there is no piston but as above the concentration on left-hand side is greater than on the right-hand side. From the left, the osmotic pressure p acts upon the plane E and from the right the osmotic pressure p' is exerted upon E', the distance between E and E' being dx. Since E is located at the distance x from the end, E' will be $x + dx$ distant.

Since $p - p'$ is the difference in osmotic pressure, then the osmotic pressure exerted per unit volume of solution is

$$K = \frac{p - p'}{dx} = -\frac{p' - p}{dx} = -\frac{dp}{dx}$$

Owing to the fact that for dilute solutions the osmotic pressure

$$p = RTn$$

where n = number of gram molecules of solute per unit volume of solution, we obtain for the effective osmotic force K, acting in the dissolved substance per unit volume,

$$K = -RT\frac{dn}{dx} \tag{9}$$

Now the velocity v of the motion of a molecule under the influence of the force k is

$$v = \frac{k}{f} \tag{10}$$

where f is the frictional resistance opposed to its motion. If the moving molecule is taken to be spherical and large in respect to the molecules of the solvent, we may set

$$f = 6\pi\eta r \tag{11}$$

where η = viscosity of the solvent.

r = radius of the spherical particle.

Since in the unit volume under consideration there are n gram molecules of solute, then there are nN actual molecules. Since the force K is distributed over these nN molecules, the velocity imparted to each is $1/nN$ of that which would have resulted if the force were acting on one molecule only. From Eqs. (9) and (10) we have for the velocity of motion resulting from the driving force:

$$v = \frac{1}{nN} \frac{K}{6\pi\eta r}$$

Since K is the osmotic force, we have from Eq. (9)

$$vn = -\frac{RT}{N} \cdot \frac{1}{6\pi\eta r} \frac{dn}{dx} \tag{12}$$

dividing both sides by $-dn/dx$,

$$-\frac{vn}{dn/dx} = \frac{RT}{N} \cdot \frac{1}{6\pi\eta r} \tag{13}$$

According to Fick's law, the amount of solute which will diffuse across unit area under a concentration gradient of unity, in unit time, at constant rate, is the specific diffusion rate, or the diffusion constant D.

Therefore

$$-D\frac{dn}{dx} = nv \tag{14}$$

The minus sign denotes that the solute diffuses in the direction of decreasing concentration.

Combining Eqs. (13) and (14) we get

$$D = \frac{RT}{N} \frac{1}{6\pi\eta r} \tag{15}$$

an expression for the diffusion constant in terms of the viscosity of the medium and the radius of the dispersed molecules. Its validity, it will be recalled, depends upon the assumptions that the diffusing molecules are spherical and are large in comparison with those of the dispersion medium [Eq. (11)].

The Relationship between Diffusion and the Irregular Motion of the Molecules.—A second point of view of the process of diffusion is opened up by the molecular theory of heat. Owing to the thermal energy, a single molecule of a liquid moves about in an entirely irregular manner with the end result that any original inequality in concentration of the dissolved substance will disappear.

Restricting the argument to the assumptions involved previously, let us consider the case of diffusion solely along the x-axis of the cylinder indicated in Fig. 19. Imagine that the position along the x-axis of all molecules is known at the given time t and likewise at the time $t + \tau$ where τ is an exceedingly short interval in which there are but very slight changes in the distribution of the molecules in the solution. During the time τ the x coordinate of a given molecule will have shifted the

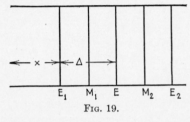

FIG. 19.

magnitude Δ_1, of another Δ_2, etc., owing to the irregular motion. These displacements Δ_1, Δ_2, Δ_3, etc., will be in part negative (to the left) and in part positive (to the right). Furthermore the magnitudes of these displacements for a single molecule will differ. Since a dilute solution was postulated, the displacement is due to the solvent molecules alone because the solute molecules are too widely scattered to influence each other appreciably, and therefore the mean displacement Δ will be the same in various parts of the solution where the concentrations may vary somewhat and will be as often positive as negative. We may now see how large the mean diffusion of the dissolved molecules is in the time τ through unit cross-sectional area of the cylinder along the x-axis, if the extent Δ of the displacements is known. In order to simplify this task it will be assumed that all molecules undergo the same displacement Δ (*i.e.*, substitute the mean value for the individual displacements Δ_1, Δ_2, Δ_3, etc.) and that as many move to the right $(+\Delta)$ as to the left $(-\Delta)$. According to the simplifying assumptions, there will pass from left to right through the plane E in the time τ only those molecules which are less than Δ distant to the left of E. These molecules are all located between the planes E_1 and E. But since only half of these molecules have positive displacement, only half of them will pass through E. The half of the dissolved molecules located between E_1 and E expressed in gram molecules is

$$\tfrac{1}{2} n_1 \Delta$$

where n_1 is the mean concentration in the volume E_1E, or the concentration in the mean plane M_1. Consequently when the concentration n_1 is multiplied by Δ, the result is the number of gram molecules in the volume between E_1 and E because the cross section is unity.

In an analogous manner it is found that the amount of solute which passes through E from right to left in the time τ is

$$\tfrac{1}{2}n_2\Delta$$

where n_2 is the concentration in the mean plane M_2. The difference between these two values

$$\tfrac{1}{2}\Delta(n_1 - n_2) \tag{16}$$

obviously is the net quantity of solute which diffuses across the plane E in the time τ. Since the coordinate of E is x and expressing in terms of a differential quotient

$$n_1 - n_2 = -\Delta\frac{dn}{dx} \tag{17}$$

From (16) and (17) we have

$$-\frac{\Delta^2}{2}\frac{dn}{dx} \tag{18}$$

Then the quantity in gram molecules which diffuses through the unit area E per second under the concentration gradient dn/dx is

$$-\frac{\Delta^2}{2\tau}\frac{dn}{dx} \tag{19}$$

Hence the quantity which would diffuse under unit concentration gradient is [Eq. (19)] divided by dn/dx which is equal to $-\tfrac{1}{2}(\Delta^2/\tau)$. This is the diffusion constant D; hence

$$D = \frac{\Delta^2}{2\tau} \tag{20}$$

Combining this equation with Eq. (15) we have

$$\Delta^2 = \frac{RT}{N}\frac{\tau}{3\pi\eta r} \tag{21}$$

the general formula for the Brownian movement where Δ is the average displacement* of a spherical particle of the radius r along the x-axis in the time τ in a liquid of viscosity η.

Perrin[23] and his collaborators Chaudesaigues and Dabrowski traced the motion of a given particle by marking its position at intervals of 30 sec. on cross-sectional paper. A typical tracing is shown in Fig. 20. They used suspensions of gamboge in water. Intermittent photographic exposures of rubber latex were taken by Henri[24] and of vermilion particles by Seddig.[25]

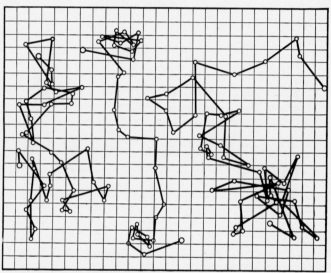

Fig. 20.—Perrin's tracings of the Brownian motion of particles.

Another method for measuring the displacement of the particles consists in allowing a dispersion to flow slowly through an ultra-microscope cell. This method, devised by Svedberg,[26] showed the particles as wavy lines (Fig. 21). If the time t required for the velocity of flow to carry a particle the distance x is known, then the mean absolute velocity of the particle would be $4A/t$.

Experimental Verification of the Brownian-movement Equation.— The experimental methods just mentioned were devised to

---

* More exactly, Δ is the root-mean-square of the single displacements Δ_1^2, Δ_2^2, etc.

test the validity of the Brownian-movement equation. By combining the constants, this equation may be written

$$\Delta^2 = k\frac{Tt}{\eta r} \tag{22}$$

i.e., the square of the displacement of a particle in the time t is directly proportional to the absolute temperature of the system and inversely proportional to the viscosity of the medium and the radius of the particle.

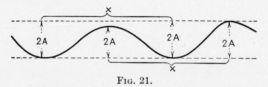

Fig. 21.

The first quantitative confirmation of the kinetic theory of Brownian motion was given in 1906 by Svedberg,[26] who studied platinum dispersions by means of his flowing method. Table 7

TABLE 7.—BROWNIAN MOVEMENTS OF PLATINUM PARTICLES

Dispersion medium	$\eta \cdot 10^3$	$2A, \mu$	t, sec.	$2A/t \cdot 10^{-2}$	$2A\eta \cdot 10^2$
Acetone	3.2	6.2	0.016	3.9	2.0
Ethyl acetate	4.6	3.9	0.014	2.8	1.8
Amyl acetate	5.9	2.9	0.013	2.2	1.7
Water	10.2	2.1	0.0065	3.2	2.1
Normal propyl alcohol	22.6	1.3	0.0045	2.9	2.9

gives his results. The platinum particles were about 25 mμ in radius and the temperature was 19°C.

From the values in Table 7, Svedberg came to the conclusion that $2A/t$ and $2A\eta$ were constant. Since in the experiments both of these factors were interdependent,

$$4A^2 = k\frac{t}{\eta}$$

which is the Einstein formula in qualitative form for the displacement of a particle at constant temperature.

Seddig's photographs of vermilion particles taken at time intervals of 0.1 sec. gave quantitative verification of the relationship between displacement, temperature, and viscosity. For the mean displacement of particles of equal size at two different temperatures we have

$$\frac{\Delta_1}{\Delta_2} = \sqrt{\frac{T_1\eta_2}{T_2\eta_1}}$$

The experimental values for Δ obtained by Seddig were 6 per cent higher than those demanded by this formula. This discrepancy was ascribed to error in the measurement of the temperature of the thin layers of dispersion photographed.

Chaudesaigues varied the viscosity of an aqueous gamboge suspension by addition of sugar. In this way, using two dispersions of viscosity ratio 1:4, he found that the motion was twice as fast in the less viscous as it was in the dispersion of higher viscosity.

This experimenter also measured the displacements of gamboge particles (one of 0.450 μ and another of 0.213 μ radius) at various time intervals and found, for the times 30, 60, 90, 120 sec., the displacements 6.7, 9.3, 11.8, 13.95 μ. The square roots of the times are proportional to the numbers 6.7, 9.46, 11.6, 13.4, giving an ideal confirmation of the theoretical $\Delta = k\sqrt{t}$. He also found that the velocities for the two sizes of particles varied inversely as the square of the radii, thus proving $\Delta = k/\sqrt{r}$.

Brownian Movement of Rotation.—The molecular shocks received by a suspended particle confer upon it a rotational as well as a translatory motion. Einstein obtained the following equation for the mean square of the angle of rotation d, in a time t, relative to an arbitrary axis:

$$d^2 = \frac{RT}{N} \frac{t}{4\pi\eta r^3} \tag{23}$$

By observation of the time of rotation of rather large particles of mastic ($r = 6.5 \times 10^{-4}$ cm.), Perrin[27] obtained most satisfactory quantitative confirmation.

Brownian Movement in Gases.—Smoluchowski,[20] recalling an observation of dancing movements in fumes made by Bodaszewski in 1881, pointed out that small particles suspended in gases ought to show Brownian movement and calculated the magnitudes of the same. He noted that the formula for motion in liquids applies to gases when the radius of the particles is large in comparison with the mean free path of the gaseous molecules.

Ehrenhaft[28] was the first to make measurements on the Brownian movement of particles in gases and found, as the theory predicts, a much livelier motion. Confirmatory quantitative data were supplied by deBroglie.[29]

References

1. LORD RAYLEIGH (J. W. STRUTT): *Phil. Mag.*, (4) **41**, 107, 274, 447 (1871); (5) **12**, 81 (1881); (5) **47**, 375 (1899).
2. FARADAY: *Phil. Mag.*, (4) **14**, 402 (1857).
3. See also STRUTT: *Proc. Roy. Soc. (London)*, **94A**, 453 (1918).
4. The interested reader is referred to the following papers: MAXWELL-GARNETT: *Phil. Trans. Roy. Soc. London*, **203**, 385 (1904); **205**, 237 (1906); MIE: *Ann. Physik*, **25**, 377 (1908); PIHLBLAD: *Z. physik. Chem.*, **92**, 471 (1917); GANS: *Ann. Physik*, **37**, 881 (1912).
5. TOLMAN et al.: *J. Am. Chem. Soc.*, **41**, 297, 575 (1919).
6. BECHHOLD and HEBLER: *Kolloid-Z.*, **31**, 70 (1922).
7. WELLS: *Chem. Rev.*, **3**, 331 (1927).
8. STONEY: *J. Roy. Micro. Soc.*, **1903**, 564; see also JENTSCH: *Z. wiss. Mikrosk.*, **47**, 145 (1930).
9. BARNARD: *Lancet*, **209**, 117 (1925).
10. SIEDENTOPF and ZSIGMONDY: *Ann. Physik*, (4) **10**, 1 (1903); see also COTTON and MOUTON: *Ann. chim. phys.*, **11**, 145, 289 (1907).
11. DIESELHORST and FREUNDLICH: *Physik. Z.*, **17**, 117 (1916); FREUNDLICH: "Second Colloid Symposium Monograph," p. 46, Chemical Catalog Co., New York, 1925; *Trans. Faraday Soc.*, **23**, 614 (1927); *Ber.*, **61B**, 2219 (1928).
12. ZSIGMONDY: *Physik. Z.*, **14**, 975 (1913); R. ZSIGMONDY and BACHMANN: *Kolloid-Z.*, **14**, 281 (1914).
13. KING: *J. Soc. Chem. Ind.*, **38**, 4 (1919).
14. SPIERER: *Kolloid-Z.*, **51**, 162; **53**, 88 (1930).
15. SIEDENTOPF: *J. Roy. Micro. Soc.*, **1903**, 573; see also ZSIGMONDY and CARIUS: *Ber.*, **60B**, 1047 (1927).
16. MARTIN and LEHRMAN: *J. Phys. Chem.*, **26**, 75, 471 (1922); **27**, 558 (1923); KENRICK: *ibid.*, **26**, 72 (1922).
17. SIEDENTOPF: *Kolloid-Z.*, **6**, 3 (1910); BILTZ: *Kolloid-Z.*, **12**, 296 (1913).
18. BROWN: *Phil. Mag.*, (2) **4**, 161 (1828).
19. EINSTEIN: *Ann. Physik*, **17**, 549 (1905); **19**, 371 (1906).
20. SMOLUCHOWSKI: *Ann. Physik*, (4) **21**, 756 (1906).
21. LANGEVIN: *Compt. rend.*, **146**, 530 (1908).
22. EINSTEIN: *Z. Elektrochem.*, **14**, 235 (1908).
23. PERRIN: *Bull. soc. franç. phys.*, **3**, 170 (1909); CHAUDESAIGUES: *Compt. rend.*, **147**, 1044 (1908); DABROWSKI: *Compt. rend.*, **149**, 477 (1909).

24. HENRI: *Bull. soc. franç. phys.*, **4**, 45, 61 (1908); *Compt. rend.*, **146**, 1024; **147**, 62 (1908).
25. SEDDIG: *Physik. Z.*, **9**, 465 (1908).
26. SVEDBERG: *Z. Elektrochem.*, **12**, 853, 909 (1906); *Z. physik. Chem.*, **71**, 571 (1910).
27. PERRIN: *Compt. rend.*, **149**, 549 (1909).
28. EHRENHAFT: *Wien. Sitz. Ber. Natur-Wiss.*, **116**, Pt. 2A, 1139 (1907).
29. DEBROGLIE: *Compt. rend.*, **146**, 624, 1010 (1908); **148**, 1163, 1315 (1909).

CHAPTER IV

LIQUID DISPERSED SYSTEMS

There are three commonly recognized classes of liquid dispersed systems:

1. Crystalloidal or true solutions or molecular dispersions.*
2. Colloidal solutions or colloidal dispersions.
3. Emulsions and suspensions or coarse dispersions.

Distinction between Colloidal and Crystalloidal Solutions.—
Fluorescence excepted, crystalloidal solutions are clear in appearance and are optically void when viewed in the ordinary electric-arc ultramicroscope. Colloidal solutions may be clear or turbid in appearance and may or may not show the Tyndall effect in the same type of ultramicroscope.

Returning to the property by means of which Graham originated the recognition of colloidal solutions, the dispersed phase in a crystalloidal solution diffuses readily through a superimposed layer of the dispersion medium, whereas the dispersed phase of a colloidal dispersion manifests but slight diffusibility† through the medium. As a consequence, the osmotic pressure of a crystalloidal solution is great in contrast to that of a colloidal solution.

Since tests of the rate of diffusion through the dispersion medium are not convenient to make, and while osmotic pressure measurements require apparatus which is not simple in preparation, the measurements of the colligative properties of freezing-point depression, boiling-point elevation, or vapor-pressure depression may be employed. If a liquid containing an appreciable amount of dispersed phase has a freezing point or vapor

---

* Some writers prefer the general term *dispersion*. The dissolved or suspended particles are called the *dispersed phase* and the solvent or suspending medium is the *dispersion medium*.

† There are recorded instances, however, of fast-diffusing colloidal particles due to the influence of accompanying oppositely charged ions. [See McBain, Dawson, and Barker: *J. Am. Chem. Soc.*, **56**, 1021 (1934).]

pressure appreciably lower than that of the pure solvent, or boiling point appreciably higher than that of the solvent, it may be judged to be a crystalloidal solution. No appreciable or measurable difference in these properties characterizes the dispersion as colloidal.*

For the purpose of qualitative differentiation, convenient diffusion tests are available by the use of jellies and of certain types of membranes. As shown by Graham, colloidally dispersed particles do not diffuse through jellies or dialyzing membranes, while the solute in a crystalloidal solution readily permeates such media. Convenient jellies are prepared with agar-agar or gelatin. A hot 2 per cent aqueous solution of agar-agar, or a hot 5 per cent solution of gelatin, is poured into a test tube. Upon cooling to room temperature a firm jelly forms. Then a portion of the dispersion to be tested is placed on top of the jelly in the tube and permitted to stand for several hours; then it is examined to determine whether diffusion through the jelly has taken place. For comparison, two jelly tubes may be prepared and one may be used to note the rate of diffusion of the solute in a colored crystalloidal dispersion. The observation should be made with care for the reason that the jelly occasionally pulls away from the wall of the tube and thus allows the solution under test to run down between the jelly and the glass wall. Twenty-four hours is usually sufficient time to elapse before examination.

The dialyzing membrane test should be interpreted with caution because the membranes vary widely in permeability. This will be discussed in detail in Chap. V. The author would point out that there is a fairly widespread erroneous impression concerning the use of these membranes in establishing the nature of a dispersion.

Inasmuch as there is no abrupt transition between crystalloidal and colloidal solutions, and since no arbitrary definition concerning any line of demarcation has been announced or agreed upon, a general statement concerning a differentiation between crystalloidal and colloidal dispersions must of necessity be vague. In 1892, Picton[1] said:

---

* Thus a molecular dispersion of a high molecular weight substance is also a colloidal dispersion. Aqueous solutions of proteins are examples (see Chap. XII).

Arsenic sulfide is capable of existing in a state of suspension so perfect as to simulate the phenomena of liquid diffusion, but yet revealing solid particles by Tyndall's experiment. It is easy to conceive of a case in which the process of subdivision has gone still further, and Tyndall's experiment is no longer adequate to discover the suspended particles. Passing on from this, there seems no satisfactory reason for imagining the existence of any sharp boundary between solution and pseudo-solution. It is quite possible that the one merges by imperceptible gradations into the other.

Distinction between Colloidal and Coarse Dispersions.— It is generally agreed that if the dispersed particles can be optically resolved, *i.e.*, seen in their true shape, the dispersion is coarse and not colloidal. Consequently, by means of this arbitrary definition, these dispersions are sharply differentiated from colloidal dispersions at a particle size of about 0.2 μ. The best test in this instance is made therefore by use of a microscope of highest power, illuminated by light of short wave length.

Comparing coarse dispersions of particle size appreciably greater than 0.2 μ with colloidal solutions containing much smaller particles, certain differences in properties are noted. Coarse dispersions are always turbid. A clear coarse dispersion is possible only when the dispersed phase possesses the same refractive index as the dispersion medium. While it is possible to prepare such a dispersed system especially if monochromatic light be used for the illumination, the chance of meeting one accidentally is slight.

In the ultramicroscope, coarse dispersions display a brilliant Tyndall effect provided they are not too concentrated. Any coarse dispersion, except for the rare case noted in the paragraph above, will show a Tyndall cone either in its original condition or when diluted.

Coarse dispersion particles, as expected, are less diffusible than colloidal particles and the diffusibility is so slight as to be called zero for most theoretical as well as for all practical purposes. The particles do not pass through dialyzing membranes or jellies. In fact many coarse dispersion particles can be separated from the dispersion medium by ordinary filters, provided *protective colloids* such as, for example, gelatin, gum arabic, or soap are not present.

An idea of the porosity of some common filters is given in Table 8.[2] By application of a series of such filters, a rough

TABLE 8.—POROSITY OF CERTAIN FILTERS[2]

Filters	Approximate Diameter of Pores, Microns
Common thick filter paper	3.3
Schleicher and Schüll filter paper 556	1.7
Schleicher and Schüll filter paper 602 (hard)	0.9 to 1.5
Chamberland filter (earthenware)	0.2 to 0.4
Reichel filter (earthenware)	0.17

idea of the size of suspension particles may be obtained. A protective colloid is likely to cause the dispersed phase of a coarse dispersion to run through ordinary filters. The reason for this is that the particles of such coarse dispersions consist of loosely bound aggregates of small particles which are disintegrated into their individual parts by the surface active films of protective colloid. Furthermore, while pure coarse dispersion particles may be adsorbed by the fibers and walls of the pores of a filter, thus making the pores smaller in size, the presence of a protective colloid may prevent such adsorption because it is adsorbed instead.

In the absence of a protective colloid, the dispersed phase of a coarse dispersion settles rather rapidly either upward or downward according to the density. The more viscous the medium is, the less rapid is the settling. A protective colloid tends to hold the particles in suspension not only owing to the disintegration of large aggregates into smaller particles but also on account of the surface layer of attached protective colloid particles. This film tends to hold the central core of inert matter in suspension by virtue of the forces which hold the protective colloid itself in dispersion.

The sedimentation of a coarse dispersion may be accelerated by centrifugal force. The ordinary laboratory centrifuges in short times of action exert no grossly apparent action upon either colloidal or crystalloidal solutions, while coarse dispersion particles may be readily thrown out thereby,[3] if the medium is not too viscous and in the absence of protective colloids. An equation for the effect of centrifugal force upon a particle may be derived by means of Stokes's law.

If x is the distance through which a spherical particle of radius r moves from the center of rotation in the time t, then the equality between the viscous resistance $6\pi\eta r(dx/dt)$ and the centrifugal force $\tfrac{4}{3}\pi r^3(\rho_1 - \rho_2)\omega^2 x$

where $\omega =$ the angular velocity of rotation,

$\eta =$ the viscosity of the medium,

$\rho_1 =$ the density of the particle substance,

$\rho_2 =$ the density of the dispersion medium,

gives

$$\frac{dx}{dt} = \frac{2r^2(\rho_1 - \rho_2)\omega^2 x}{9\eta}. \tag{1}$$

Integrating between the settling distances x_1 and x_2,

$$\int_{x_1}^{x_2}\frac{dx}{x} = \frac{2}{9}r^2(\rho_1 - \rho_2)\frac{\omega^2}{\eta}\int_0^t dt \tag{2}$$

or

$$ln\,\frac{x_2}{x_1} = \frac{2r^2(\rho_1 - \rho_2)\omega^2 t}{9\eta} \tag{3}$$

Nomenclature.—Graham[4] named aqueous colloidal dispersions *hydrosols*, alcoholic dispersions *alcosols*, and, in general, dispersions in organic liquids *organosols*. Colloidal dispersions are now frequently called *sols*.

Certain sols change to semisolid jelly-like masses upon partial evaporation of the dispersion medium or by decrease in temperature. Such jellies are now commonly called *hydrogels* or *gels*, although Graham applied this term to the *precipitated* or *coagulated* gelatinous residue from a sol.

Upon complete desiccation of a sol or of a jelly, a solid residue is obtained which may be transparent and glassy in appearance or porous and spongelike or an amorphous powder. In the case of many of the inorganic and some of the organic colloids, this dry matter will not redisperse upon addition of some of its former dispersing liquid. These residues also are termed *gels*. Dried colloids such as gelatin, gums, dextrins, which will redisperse in water or in general in any pure liquid in which they are soluble, are also very commonly referred to as *gels*. Freundlich has proposed the term *xerogel* (from ξηρος, dry) for such dry substances.

In his discussion of colloidal tungstic acid, Graham stated:

"It is remarkable that the purified acid is not pectized by acids or salts even at boiling temperature. Evaporated to dryness, it forms vitreous scales, like gum or gelatine." It is to be noted that he described the dry residue as "scales, like gum or gelatine" and not as gel. Further, in his paper of 1861, in explanation of the word *pectous* (πηκτος, curdled) he stated: "as fibrin, casein, albumen. But certain liquid colloid substances are capable of forming a jelly and yet still remain liquefiable by heat and soluble in water. Such is gelatine itself, which is not pectous in the condition of animal jelly. . . . "

The indiscriminate use of the term *gel* in colloid literature produces confusion. It has been suggested by Weissenberger[5] that the word gel be restricted to jellies and that coagula and precipitates be called *coagel*. Thus another term is coined and an old one is changed in meaning.

Coagulation or transformation of sols into gels was termed *pectinization* (now shortened to *pectization*) by Graham. This term is becoming obsolete since the words *precipitation, coagulation,* and *flocculation* adequately describe all such cases.

When gels are converted to sols by the influence of added foreign substances, a reaction takes place which resembles in appearance the peptonizing of proteins in animal digestion and consequently was named *peptinization* (now shortened to *peptization*) by Graham. Bancroft[6] has stated his preference for a more general use of this term and he has applied it whenever a substance is dispersed to a sol, thus avoiding the words *solution* or *dissolve*. Accordingly when a piece of dry gelatin is dissolved in warm water, following this usage, the process would be referred to as the peptization of the gelatin by water.

Types of Hydrosols.—Two main types of colloidal dispersions have been recognized. These have been diversely named:

Reversible colloids	Irreversible colloids
Stable colloids	Unstable colloids
Hydrophilic colloids	Hydrophobic colloids
Emulsoids	Suspensoids

According to the difference in behavior toward electrolytes, the *stable* and *unstable* distinctions were made. Upon evaporation to dryness, the difference in behavior upon attempts to redisperse the material by addition of the dispersion liquid gave rise to the terms *reversible* and *irreversible*. Both these classifications are practically the same. Since the stable or reversible dispersions seemed to resemble emulsions, they were also called *emulsoid*, while the unstable and irreversible dispersions were termed *suspensoid* owing to their resemblance to suspensions.

Lyophobic and *lyophilic* or the analogous terms, which are generally restricted to hydrosols, *hydrophilic* and *hydrophobic* are probably the most expressive.*

The classification of colloidal solutions in two groups is inadequate. Graham's ferric oxide hydrosol is fairly stable in the presence of neutral electrolyte (more so than gold or platinum hydrosols, for example) while it is irreversible when evaporated to dryness and thoroughly desiccated, although frequently reversible if not completely dried. Most writers classify Graham's ferric oxide hydrosol as a suspensoid, while some others call it emulsoid. Actually, its properties place it between the suspensoid and emulsoid classes and this is so for many of the hydrosols of the weakly basic or acidic oxides. It is better, therefore, to classify hydrosols in three groups. Those whose properties locate them intermediate between the two extremes of hydrophobic and hydrophilic may be called the *intermediate* type of dispersion. These have also been called *inorganic hydrophilic* colloids.

The properties of the three main types of dispersions may be expressed briefly, as follows.

Hydrophobic Dispersions

1. Dispersed phase is precipitated by very small amounts of electrolyte.
2. Coagulate upon prolonged dialysis. Presence of small amount and kind of electrolyte is essential.

* *Hydrophobic* and *hydrophilic* come from Greek roots which signify *water fearing* and *water loving*, respectively. *Lyophobic* and *lyophilic* are made up of Greek roots meaning *fear to loosen* and *love to loosen*, respectively. Hence a hydrophobic substance is lyophilic while a hydrophilic substance is lyophobic. However, confusion has arisen in the use of the terms with the *lyo-* prefix and the reader is warned to suspect that a stable, reversible, emulsoid sol is meant when he sees the word *lyophilic*, and the reverse type when he finds the word *lyophobic*, used in colloid literature. Owing to the confusion, the lyo- terms are avoided in this book. There is no objection to the use of hydrophilic or hydrophobic in describing systems containing liquids other than water, when it is understood that the *hydro-* prefixes are used to denote liquids in general.

3. Migrate in an electrical field according to the sign of charge.

4. Irreversibly coagulate upon desiccation.

5. Surface tension is not very different from that of the dispersion medium.

6. Viscosity is not very different from that of the dispersion medium.

7. Viewed in ultramicroscope, show decided optical heterogeneity.

Some examples of this class are the hydrosols of gold, silver, platinum, certain sulfides, and the silver halides.

INTERMEDIATE DISPERSIONS

1. Tolerate the presence of more electrolyte than hydrophobic dispersions do but are more sensitive to electrolyte precipitation than hydrophilic dispersions.

2. Coagulate upon prolonged dialysis. Presence of certain amount and kind of electrolyte is essential.

3. Migrate in an electrical field according to the sign of charge.

4. Upon evaporation to dryness, residue is reversible if sol was not too "pure" and if not thoroughly desiccated; is irreversible if sol was very pure or thoroughly desiccated.

5. Surface tension is not very different from that of the dispersion medium.

6. Viscosity is higher than that of the dispersion medium.

7. Show a faint Tyndall effect.

Some examples of this class of dispersion are certain hydrosols of the oxides of iron, chromium, silicon, vanadium, etc.

HYDROPHILIC DISPERSIONS

1. With the exception of the formation of insoluble complexes in some cases, they tolerate the presence of considerable amounts of electrolyte.

2. Upon prolonged dialysis there is no change (a few cases, such as globulins excepted).

3. May or may not migrate in an electrical field.

4. Residue obtained upon evaporation to dryness is reversible (with exception of "heat-coagulated" proteins).

5. Surface tension is generally lower than that of the dispersion medium. Show tendency to form persistent foams when shaken.

6. Viscosity is greater than that of the dispersion medium. The viscosity rises markedly with temperature decrease or with increase in concentration.

7. Frequently there is no striking optical heterogeneity in ultramicroscope.

Some examples of this class are hydrosols of gums, starches, proteins, and alkali soaps.

It should be noted that the properties listed refer to kinds of dispersions rather than to kinds of colloids. Once more the criterion of state, not of kind, is involved. Gelatin is frequently termed a hydrophilic or emulsoid colloid because its aqueous dispersions are of that class. It is true that it is hydrophilic toward water, but it is hydrophobic when dispersed in a medium consisting of a mixture of alcohol and water. Addition of alcohol to an aqueous solution of gelatin or of gum arabic produces a turbid dispersion with certain of the properties of hydrophobic dispersions. For example, the presence of a trace of an electrolyte will precipitate the dispersed phase. The explanation for this behavior is that the dispersed phase in the hydrophilic dispersion is highly hydrated. Since these particles do not imbibe alcohol; *i.e.*, they are insoluble in alcohol, which dehydrates them.

Some dyes are hydrophilic in water but hydrophobic in alcohol.[8] Sulfur hydrosol prepared by Odén's method belongs to the intermediate class, while von Veimarn's sulfur hydrosol is hydrophobic. Some of the sulfide hydrosols have properties which place them between the intermediate and the hydrophobic dispersions. Iron oxide hydrosol made by Graham's method is intermediate while the iron oxide hydrosol of Péan de St. Gilles is rather hydrophobic.

Pyrosols.—Colloidal dispersions of metals in molten mineral media are called *pyrosols.*[9] Pyrosols may be prepared by the solution of certain metals in their salts, the metallic particles giving off a colored mist in a lively fashion. Upon cooling, the dispersed particles separate in the metallic form. The metal is claimed to be present in the colloidal form owing to the intense color of the molten mass, to the homogeneous appearance to the naked eye, and to the fact that addition of alkali salts destroys the color.

References

1. PICTON: *J. Chem. Soc.*, **61**, 137 (1892).
2. BECHHOLD: *Z. physik. Chem.*, **64**, 328 (1908).
3. For a discussion of centrifugal sedimentation see AYRES: *Chem. Met. Eng.*, **16**, 190 (1917).
4. GRAHAM: *Proc. Roy. Soc. (London)*, **13**, 335 (1864).
5. WEISSENBERGER: *Kolloid-Z.*, **25**, 230 (1919).
6. BANCROFT: *J. Phys. Chem.*, **20**, 85 (1916).
7. SCARPA: *Kolloid-Z.*, **15**, 8 (1914).
8. FREUNDLICH and NEUMANN: *Kolloid-Z.*, **3**, 80 (1908).
9. LORENZ: *Z. anorg. Chem.*, **10**, 78 (1895); *Kolloid-Z.*, **18**, 177 (1916); LORENZ and EITEL: "Pyrosole," Akademische Verlagsgesellschaft m.b.H., Leipzig, 1926.

CHAPTER V

DIALYSIS AND ULTRAFILTRATION

Since membranes of parchment paper, nitrocellulose, cellulose acetate, "Cellophane,"* and animal gut are generally quite permeable to crystalloids while rather impervious to colloids, dialysis by means of these membranes is extensively used for the purification of colloidal solutions. Although the first application of dialytic purification of colloids is attributed to Graham, dialyzing membranes† were generally known before Graham's work. Dutrochet (1826) noted the osmosis of solutes from a solution through animal-gut membranes to an outer water phase and of water into the solution phase. He named the former *exosmosis* and the latter *endosmosis*. Liebig (1849), L'Hermite (1854), Fick (1855), Dubrunfaut (1855), and Naegeli (1858) are others who used dialyzing membranes. Fick made flat pyroxylin membranes. Dubrunfaut pointed to the cell walls in sugar beets as the separating septa which allowed the sugar to diffuse from the cosettes whilst holding the colloidal matter back.

When a dialyzing membrane is used for the filtration of dispersions to remove the dispersed phase from the liquid medium, the process is called *ultrafiltration*, the name having been suggested by Bechhold.[1] Apparently ultrafiltration was first performed by Martin[2] (1896), who used unglazed porcelain filter "candles" impregnated with gelatin or with silicic acid gel.

---

* "Cellophane," manufactured by the E. I. du Pont de Nemours Co., is a transparent film composed of regenerated cellulose. It contains glycerol. "Moisture Proof Cellophane" has a lacquer coating containing wax.

† Since the name "semipermeable membrane" is generally taken to mean a membrane which is permeable to a solvent while impermeable to a crystalloid solute, such as the copper ferrocyanide membrane which is pervious to the water of a sugar solution but not to the dissolved sugar, the term "dialyzing membrane" will be used here to denote membranes which show selective degrees of permeability toward dissolved or dispersed substances.

Nitrocellulose films seem to have been first employed in 1904 by Borrel and Manea in the purification of bacteriological sera and by Malfitano in the filtration of ferric oxide hydrosols.[3]

Walpole[4] has combined dialysis and ultrafiltration in a process which he termed *pressure dialysis* and has applied the method to the commercial purification of diphtheria toxin and tuberculin. In this process the "filtrate" side of the membrane in the ultra-filter was bathed by a constantly flowing stream of water, thus purifying the crude toxin by dialysis while it was being concentrated by ultrafiltration.

The removal of electrolyte in dialysis and in ultrafiltration is accelerated by the application of an electric current. When an e.m.f. is applied, the processes are called *electrodialysis* and *electroultrafiltration*. Electrodialysis was first applied to the purification of inorganic hydrosols[5] and is now widely used, particularly for removal of electrolyte from solutions of biocolloids.

Dialysis and Ultrafiltration Apparatus.—An early form of dialyzer consisted of a sheet of parchment paper affixed to a cylindrical or conical vessel, open at both bases. Figure 22 illustrates this type of apparatus. An improvement for providing greater dialyzing surface consists in folding a pleated sheet of parchment paper over a cylindrical frame.[6]

Nitrocellulose is very convenient inasmuch as collodion (a solution of nitrocellulose in a mixture of ether and alcohol) may be flowed on the outside of test tubes or on the inside of any vessel such as a test tube, a volumetric cylinder, Kjeldahl flask, and later a nitrocellulose model of the vessel obtained.[7] A

Fig. 22.—Thomas Graham's bulb dialyzer.

flask, free from sharp points or rough areas on the inside, is thoroughly cleaned, rinsed with alcohol, and drained. About 25 to 50 cc.of collodion is poured in and the flask rotated slowly while inverted to secure a uniform coating and to remove the excess of the collodion. The flask is inverted on a ring in order to drain and to allow most of the ether to evaporate. This may be hastened by introducing a glass tube connected to a pump. When most of the ether has evaporated, the flask is filled with water and allowed to stand about 10 min. or longer. The adhering nitrocellulose is cut loose from the outer edge of the mouth of the flask and the water poured out. Then water is introduced between the nitrocellulose and the flask and by gentle pulling the nitrocellulose sack is removed from the mold. It is then filled with water and examined for perforations before using in dialysis.

The solution to be dialyzed is poured into the sack to about a third of its volume, a bent glass tube is tied in the neck, and the bag is then hung in distilled water. Owing to the occasional high rate of osmosis of water into the bag, the contents become diluted. This dilution is avoided by using a round flask to cast the bag, and tying the open end, or by insertion of a long vertical glass tube through a stopper on to which the bag is tied, i.e., pressure dialysis. One objection to this is that the contents of the bag cannot be conveniently stirred.

The speed of dialysis is, of course, increased by stirring[6] the contents of the dialyzer and of the outer liquid.

Parchment paper or regenerated cellulose tubing* is frequently employed instead of nitrocellulose bags. The colloidal solution may be placed in a U-shaped loop and suspended in water, or the water may flow through the tube which reposes in a receptacle holding the colloidal solution. The advantage of this procedure is the facility of stirring the colloidal solution. The disadvantage is the possible dilution of the latter. Tubes of nitrocellulose may readily be made in the laboratory, to be sure, but they are not so tough as the regenerated cellulose tubing which is made for use as sausage casing.

A very serviceable dialyzer for use especially where the diffusate† is wanted for subsequent tests is illustrated by Fig. 23.[8]

* "Visking" sausage casings, sold in 30-ft. lengths, are convenient.

† Diffusate is the term which Graham applied to the material which diffused through the membrane. One often hears the term dialysate applied to Graham's diffusate. According to Webster's International Dictionary (1927) dialysate is defined as: "That part of material subjected to dialysis which fails to pass through the membrane: opposed to diffusate." The Oxford New English Dictionary concurs in this definition. In this book these terms are used according to these authorities.

A flat dialyzing membrane is clamped between two glass bells and then put in a rotating machine. In the author's laboratory two vacuum desiccator lids are used. Parchment paper or Cellophane may be used, or a flat sheet of nitrocellulose may be made by pouring collodion on to a glass plate or a dish of mercury.

For general dialysis purposes, unglazed porcelain vessels are frequently very convenient. The fact that some grades of porcelain act "osmotically" was shown by Graham.[9] Pipe clay was used by Dutrochet.[10] The application of unglazed porcelain as a dialyzing septum for the purification of a colloidal solution seems to have been overlooked until it was used again in the purification of iron oxide

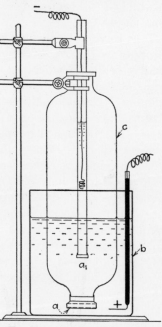

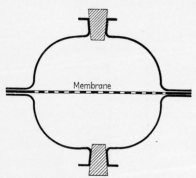

FIG. 23.—Thoms's dialyzer.

FIG. 24.—Apparatus for electrodialysis.[14] a and a_1 are nitrocellulose membranes, b is a battery jar, and c is a cylindrical vessel.

hydrosols.[11] Unglazed porcelain pots are convenient since they are rigid, permitting the convenient use of mechanical stirring devices. Iron oxide sols deposit a coating of hydrous ferric oxide gel in the porcelain and the latter serves as a support for a dialyzing septum of the gel. The gel is impervious to ferric ion.[47]

Unglazed porcelain in which barium sulfate has been precipitated is proposed as a "mechanical colloid sieve."[12]

A simple type of electrodialyzer consists of a three-compartment vessel, the compartments separated from each other by dialyzing membranes.[13] The central compartment contains the solution to be purified and the end compartments the electrodes.* An electrodialyzer[14] used in the separation of the amy-

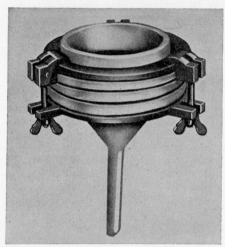

Fig. 25.—Zsigmondy's suction ultrafiltration apparatus.

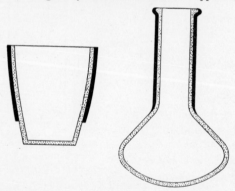

Fig. 26.—Bechhold's porcelain suction filters.

loses of starch is shown in Fig. 24. The electrodes are connected to a 110-volt or higher direct current.

* Frequently in this horizontal type of electrodialyzer, the dialysate separates in layers (see Blank and Valko[13]), the colloidal solution on the bottom and crystalloidal solution on top. The upper layer can be siphoned off. This process has been called *electrodecantation* by Professor Pauli of the University of Vienna.

There are three main kinds of ultrafilters: the sack or "spontaneous," the suction or low-pressure, and the high-pressure type.

The spontaneous ultrafilter[15] consists of a bag made of a suitable dialyzing membrane filled with solution which is allowed to hang free, the solvent and permeable solute slowly filtering under the pressure of the weight of the contents.

The suction ultrafilter consists of a modified type of Buchner funnel which has been developed by Zsigmondy,[16] who has suggested useful applications for it in analytical operations. It is shown in Fig. 25.

Bechhold's[17] suction ultrafilters consist of partially glazed porcelain containers as shown in Fig. 26. The heavy black markings indicate the glazed portion. The unglazed part of the device is coated with acetic acid collodion.

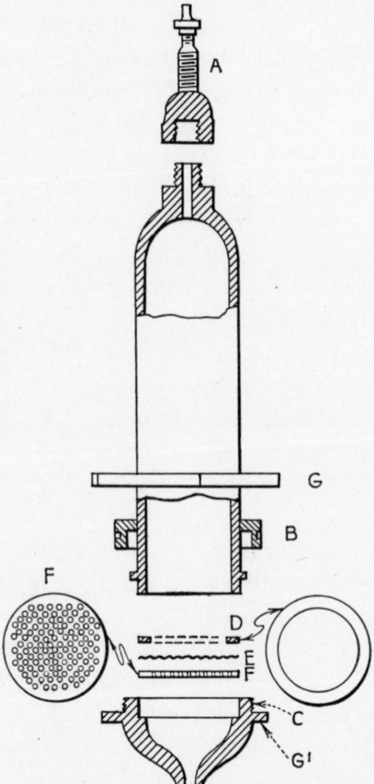

When it is desired to ultrafilter at pressures higher than atmospheric, the pressure type originated by Bechhold[18] is employed. A simple pressure ultrafilter designed in the chemical laboratory of Columbia University* is illustrated in Fig. 27. The Columbia

Fig. 27.—Columbia pressure ultrafiltration apparatus. *A*, automobile tire valve; *B*, collar which takes up on funnel at *C*; *D*, rubber gasket; *E*, wire gauze on which membrane rests; *F*, perforated heavy plate; *G* and *G'*, hexagonal forms for holding in vise.

ultrafilter is easily manipulated since the pressure may be applied by an ordinary tire pump, the inlet on the top being an automobile tire valve. If air is objectionable, the

* Improved upon and manufactured by Hayes & Whitmore, Urbana, Ill.

pressure may be furnished by connection with a cylinder of compressed nitrogen.[19]

Since the slime of colloidal matter collecting on the ultrafiltration membrane tends to retard the process, Bechhold has fitted his ultrafilter with a scraping device. The advantage of this is doubtful since a very thin deposit is about as effective in retarding ultrafiltration as a thick one and the scraper or stirrer cannot effectually remove it. Ultrafiltration is an exceedingly slow and tedious operation and at present is restricted to the laboratory. It has been found very useful in the study of bacterial toxins.[20]

An approach to a commercial scale ultrafilter is the "streamline" filter in which many sheets of water-and-oil-proof paper are pressed tightly together.[21] The liquid to be filtered is forced between the sheets.

Electroultrafilters are now available, also.[22]

The membranes used in ultrafiltration may be any suitable dialyzing membrane. Cellophane has been recommended[23] because it resists compression. An unusual ultrafilter septum is 200-mesh nickel or phosphor bronze gauze which is nickel plated to such an extent that only submicroscopic openings are left.[24]

Preparation of Membranes of Graded Permeability.—The permeability of a given membrane substance may vary greatly. With nitrocellulose taken as an example, it has been found that the permeability of its membranes is influenced by (1) the kind of nitrocellulose employed,[25] (2) the nature of the solvent and, when it is a mixture such as alcohol and ether, the relative proportions,[26,27,28] (3) the time of drying[4] and the amount of swelling of the film,[29] (4) the concentration of the nitrocellulose in the collodion used,[1] and (5) the presence of nonsolvent agents such as glycerol[30] and ethylene glycol.[31] Pyroxylin membranes can be prepared for the purpose of separating two crystalloids or two colloids or colloids and crystalloids from each other if care is exercised in the preparation of the membranes according to a standard technique; i.e., it is possible to make pyroxylin membranes of a wide range of graded permeability.

Bechhold[1] was the first to devise a practical method of making a graded series of membranes. He discovered that the permeability of the ultrafilters depended on the concentration of the jellies used in preparing them. Filter papers were impregnated with glacial acetic acid collodions of various strengths, drained, and immersed in water to gel the collodion and wash it free from the acid, or the papers were soaked in warm gelatin solutions of different strengths, drained, and cooled to jellify the gelatin which was subsequently tanned by formaldehyde.

An excellent method of grading has been devised by Brown.[29] Since the permeability is affected by the thickness of the membrane, the simple manner of casting in a flask as described previously for ordinary work cannot be employed because the rate of evaporation of ether from the film cannot be controlled. Consequently the thickness of the film will vary. Brown overcame this difficulty by dipping a closed tube in collodion, allowing it to drain in the atmosphere of the collodion, thus permitting drainage without evaporation of ether. His technique briefly is as follows.

An 8 per cent solution of pyroxylin* in a mixture of equal volumes of absolute ethyl alcohol and ethyl ether is prepared. A closed glass tube is dipped in a flask of the collodion and allowed to drain for 5 min. (hanging in the flask over the collodion solution) in order to obtain regularity in thickness. Then the tube is exposed to the air for 1 min., following which it is plunged in water for 1 min., then it is removed from the tube. The temperature of operation is 20°C. or lower.

The concentration of 8 per cent nitrocellulose was found best; over 8 per cent gave tendency to uneven drainage; under 5 per cent resulted in delicate membranes which tore easily and shrank excessively.

The proportion of equal volumes of alcohol and ether was arrived at after trial of various mixtures. Membranes made from collodion containing much ether and little alcohol are highly impermeable, white, and have a low water content after soaking. They show very small shrinkage on drying, however. Membranes made from pyroxylin in absolute alcohol alone† are clear,

---

* Brown used Schering's "Celloidin."

† Certain kinds of pyroxylin are soluble in absolute ethyl alcohol. Others are insoluble in alcohol and require esters, ketones, or a mixture of alcohol and ether for solution.

highly permeable and have a high water content after soaking. They shrink to a large extent on drying.

Since the permeability of the membrane is a function of the alcohol held in it previous to removal from the tube, it is now thoroughly dried out by exposure to air overnight and then graded by alcohol-water solutions. The air-dry membrane is soaked in the alcohol-water grading solution for 24 hr. at 20°C. Then it is thoroughly washed in distilled water for 24 hr., after which it is ready for use. When such uniform air-dried membranes are used, the permeability may be specified in terms of the alcohol percentage of the grading solution; *i.e.*, a "75-index" membrane is a previously air-dried membrane that has been soaked in 75 per cent alcohol for 24 hr. at 20°C. and washed in water. By 75 per cent alcohol is meant an alcohol-water mixture made up of 75 cc. of absolute alcohol plus 25 cc. water.

The degree of swelling as a function of the alcohol content of the grading solution is shown in Table 9. The wet weights

TABLE 9.—SWELLING OF PYROXYLIN MEMBRANES IN ALCOHOL-WATER MIXTURES[29]

Alcohol index of membrane	Wet weight after washing	Weight on drying again
0	106	100
50	111	99.3
70	116	98.6
80	122	98.2
90	142	97.0
92	161	93.8
94	209	89.1
96	388	74.8

given in the table are the weights of sheets of membrane after washing in distilled water given in terms of an original dry weight of 100. (The air-dried membranes contained 3 per cent moisture.)

It will be noticed that the degree of swelling is gradual at first but increases abruptly above 92-index alcohol and also that the membrane undergoes partial solution which, while slight up to 90 per cent, is considerable in 96-index alcohol. The swelling is anisotropic. For example, in 94 per cent alcohol the longitudinal extension is 12 per cent, while the increase in thickness is 180 per cent.

TABLE 10.—INCREASE OF PERMEABILITY WITH SWELLING[29]

Potassium permanganate		Methylene blue	
Index	Time of penetration	Index	Time of penetration
70	1 min.	95	12 min.
60	5 min.	90	70 min.
50	25 min.	85	4 hr.
40	120 min.	80	10 hr.
30	None in 24 hr.	75	24 hr.
		70	6 days

The increase in permeability with swelling is shown in Table 10 where the times of appearance of color in the diffusates from 0.1 per cent solution of methylene blue and in another case from 0.5 per cent solution of potassium permanganate are tabulated. Brown's membranes of index zero (dry membranes) were impermeable to crystalloids such as sodium sulfate, barium chloride, and glucose, although water, sodium chloride, and ammonium chloride passed through them. On the other hand, membranes of index 96 and higher permitted the colloids starch, Congo red, and night blue to dialyze through them. Thus it is seen that by means of these graded membranes it is possible to separate two crystalloids or two colloids from each other.

An example of the application of the graded membrane is shown in Table 11 where a mixed solution of sodium chloride,

TABLE 11.—EXAMPLE OF GRADED PERMEABILITY OF MEMBRANES[29]

Solute	Test for solute in diffusate through membranes of index		
	50	85	92
NaCl............................	+	+	+
Glucose..........................	0	+	+
Dextrin..........................	0	0	+
Starch...........................	0	0	0

glucose, dextrin, and starch were dialyzed against different membranes for 24 hr.

The sensitivity of the grading is parallel to the degree of swelling. In the range of 40 to 70 per cent alcohol, variations of 10 per cent alcohol strength produce continuous gradation, while in the range of 70 to 80 per cent an alcohol treatment which varies by 2.5 per cent definitely produces continuous gradation in an average set of membranes. From 85 per cent upward, 1 per cent increments in alcohol strength are significant until in the region of 96 to 98 per cent where the imbibition changes so profoundly with slight increase in alcohol as to render fine grading impracticable.

If a liquid in which the membrane swells is called the *swelling liquid* and one for which the membrane has no affinity is called the *restraining liquid* and provided that a given *restraining* liquid and a *swelling* liquid are miscible, a general principle of membrane grading may be stated: Membranes of graded permeability for use in dialysis of solutes in the restraining liquid can be prepared by soaking the membranes in a series of mixtures of the swelling and restraining liquids followed by washing in the restraining liquid, the permeability increasing with increasing degree of swelling, *i.e.*, with increasing proportion of swelling liquid to restraining liquid.

It ought to be possible then to make graded membranes of gelatin for dialysis of alcoholic solutions by soaking gelatin films in mixtures of alcohol (restraining) and water (swelling). Such have been prepared by Brown. A 2 per cent aqueous solution of gelatin at 40 to 50°C. was poured on a clean mercury surface and allowed to dry completely. The dry sheets were then soaked in alcohol-water mixtures for 24 hr. at 20°C. and then were washed in absolute alcohol (two days with three changes of alcohol). An example of the grading as revealed by swelling is given in Table 12. The graded permeabilities were retained for six weeks.

As an example of the gradation of gelatin membranes an experiment with an alcoholic solution of night blue is pertinent. No trace of dye passed through 0- and 20-index membranes in 24 hr., a 40-index membrane permitted slight diffusion, while an appreciable amount of the dye passed through a 60-index membrane in 5 min.

TABLE 12.—GRADING OF GELATIN MEMBRANES[29]

Percentage Water in Grading Solution	Wet Weight*
100	505
60	204
40	151
20	133
0	117

* Wet weight referred to a dry weight of 100. It is to be noted that here the membrane is wet with alcohol.

Just as the imbibed water may be displaced from a graded gelatin membrane by alcohol, so may the alcohol be displaced by a liquid miscible with it and in which gelatin is insoluble such as acetone, benzene, toluene. It may then be used for dialysis of solutes in these solvents. Furthermore, if one wished to dialyze a petroleum ether solution, he would first displace the imbibed water by alcohol, the latter by, say, benzene and this in turn by petroleum ether.

Attempts made by Brown to grade rubber membranes by means of benzene-alcohol solutions for dialysis of alcohol solutions were unsuccessful, the differential grading becoming obliterated when the membranes were washed in alcohol. He attributed this to the elastic nature of rubber.

Graded membranes may be used in dialysis of solutions in the swelling liquid if they can be treated after the grading so as to suppress the capacity for imbibition of the swelling liquid. This can be accomplished in the case of gelatin membranes by tanning them with formaldehyde. Films of air-dried gelatin were soaked in alcohol-water mixtures for 24 hr. at 20°C., when formaldehyde was added, 1 cc. of 40 per cent formalin to each 10 cc. of the grading solution. After an additional soaking for 24 hr., the membranes were washed thoroughly in water. A typical series is given in Table 13.

TABLE 13.—GRADING OF FORMALIZED GELATIN MEMBRANES[29]

Percentage Water in Grading Solution	Wet Weight*
100	1,360
80	730
60	410
40	270
20	218
0	209

* Referred to a dry weight of 100. Note that here the membrane is wet with water.

While a pronounced differential effect is produced, it is obvious, upon comparison with Table 12, that the formaldehyde does not entirely prevent the subsequent swelling in water. The swelling in water is merely inhibited. Such membranes might occasionally be used advantageously, however. For example, while pyroxylin membranes can be prepared which definitely allow starch to pass through and hold back night blue, the reverse is true with formaldehyde-tanned gelatin membranes. Brown noted also that dialytic separation of dextrin from starch can be effected with greater rapidity with formaldehyde-tanned gelatin than with pyroxylin membranes.

Pyroxylin membranes of greater permeability than those of Brown have been prepared by Eggerth,[27] the degree of permeability being obtained by variation of the relative proportions of absolute alcohol and anhydrous ether used as solvent for the pyroxylin. Six grams of pyroxylin* are dissolved in 100 g. of alcohol-ether solvent. The parts of alcohol and of ether in the solvent are measured by weight, and the membranes are defined by the weight percentage of alcohol in the solvent; e.g., a "70-index" membrane is one prepared from pyroxylin dissolved in a solvent consisting of 70 per cent alcohol and 30 per cent ether.

A glass tube, melted down at one end to leave a small hole, is the mold. A small fragment of cigarette paper is slightly moistened and placed over the hole, where it dries quickly; a layer of collodion is painted over the paper and the end of the tube; this is allowed to dry for 20 to 30 sec. A few cubic centimeters of collodion solution are poured into a test tube; this is held nearly horizontal while the end of the mold tube is immersed in the collodion. The mold tube is rotated slowly and slowly withdrawn; then it, with its covering of collodion, is thrust horizontally into a large test tube, rotated therein for 1 min., and then immersed in water. Rotating the membrane within the large test tube in the manner described makes the drying slower and more uniform and cuts off air currents.

By filling the mold tube with water and applying air pressure to the open end, water is forced between the glass and the membrane, thus dislodging the latter. The tube and the membrane should be immersed during this process.

* Eggerth used "Parlodion" manufactured by the DuPont Company.

The degree of swelling of membranes made in this manner is shown in Table 14. The relative degrees of permeability are

TABLE 14.—GRADING OF PYROXYLIN MEMBRANES BY VARIATION OF ALCOHOL
AND ETHER IN COLLODION SOLUTION[27]

Alcohol Index of Membrane	Ratio $\dfrac{\text{Wet Weight}}{\text{Dry Weight}}$
10	1.9
15	2.2
20	2.6
30	3.2
40	4.0
50	5.0
60	6.4
70	7.7
80	8.5
85	9.1
90	9.2

given in Fig. 28. The influence of temperature is plotted in Fig. 29. The data from the work of Brown and of Eggerth show how

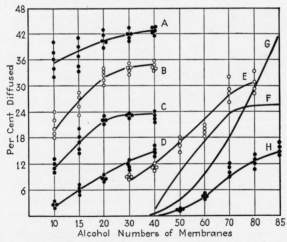

FIG. 28.—Permeability of membranes. *A*, sodium chloride, 10 min.; *B*, potassium dihydrogen phosphate, 10 min.; *C*, sucrose, 30 min.; *D*, indigo carmine, 20 min.; and *E*, primary proteose, 2.5 hr., all at 20°. *F*, methemoglobin; *G*, Congo red; and *H*, dialyzed serum, all 3 hr. at 35°.

widely the permeability of nitrocellulose membranes may be varied. For the purpose of exact reproduction of a definite permeability, however, the tube or bag membranes of these inves-

tigators are surpassed by flat membranes. Walpole[4] developed
a technique for making this type of membrane, the solvent-
nitrocellulose ratio being determined by the length of the drying
time prior to immersion in water.

An improvement in this technique was developed by Nelson
and Morgan,[28] who established the grade of the flat membrane
by its evaporation to a definite weight before soaking in water.

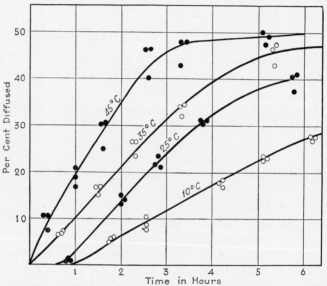

FIG. 29.—Diffusion of methemoglobin through 70-index membranes at different
temperatures.

Five cubic centimeters of a 2 per cent solution of nitrocellulose
(in alcohol ether, 75:25 by weight) is pipetted on to a carefully
leveled, clean 4-in. circular glass plate which was previously
moistened by blowing the breath upon it. A cylindrical glass
shield protects it from draughts while evaporating. As soon as
the jelly stage is reached, the plate is placed on a balance and
allowed to evaporate to a weight which was previously found by
trial to give the permeability required. The plate is then placed
in water to remove the membrane which is allowed to soak
overnight. Highly permeable membranes of this type were found
successful in the purification of crude invertase solutions—

permeable to invertase while impermeable to certain colored colloidal impurities.

Pierce[31] has devised a method of making flat graded membranes of a high degree of reproducibility, based on the principle that the permeability depends upon the ratio between the amounts of nitrocellulose and swelling agent in the membrane at the moment when it is immersed in water. A solution of nitrocellulose is prepared according to the formula:

Nitrocellulose,* dried.....................	1 g.
Ethyl alcohol, absolute...................	25 cc.
Ethylene glycol, anhydrous...............	0.5 to 15 cc.
Ether to make...........................	100 cc.

* Pierce, like Nelson and Morgan, used Du Pont's Parlodion.

Ethylene glycol is a swelling agent for nitrocellulose.

A dish of mercury is placed in a container fitted with an airtight cover, a ground and polished glass plate 7.5 cm. in diameter is floated upon the mercury in the dish, and 4 cc. of the nitrocellulose solution are pipetted on to the plate. The cover is closed, and by means of pipe connections a slow current of dried air is passed through the container for 24 hr. in order to evaporate off the alcohol and ether, leaving upon the plate only the nitrocellulose swollen with the ethylene glycol. The plate is then immersed in water and the membrane floats free within a few minutes. After being washed in running water for 24 hr. the membrane is ready for use.

The higher the ratio of glycol to nitrocellulose in the film, the higher is the permeability. Field[32] has shown that the volatility of the glycol is appreciable and that alcohol is partially retained in Pierce's membranes. However, she points out that, if a definite measured volume of air is passed over the membrane at constant temperature, the method affords satisfactory reproducibility. Snell,[33] in applying Field's improvements, prepared membranes which she applied to the purification of malt amylase.

The writer, having had the opportunity of following the researches of Nelson and Morgan, Pierce, Field, and Snell from the start of each, is inclined to doubt the value of the tremendous effort required in order to make these membranes of precise permeability. They can be exactly duplicated only when of small area; for each usable membrane, another has to be made for the purpose of analysis to determine the grade; and as soon as the ultrafiltration starts, the permeability is altered owing to sorption of dispersed phase. Inasmuch as nitrocellulose is not a definite chemical compound, one can duplicate exactly another investigator's results only provided a specimen of the same batch of nitrocellulose is used. Unless one has a room of constant temperature and constant humidity and his problem is worth spending a great amount of time and energy to obtain a small volume of filtered material, he is advised to be content with the less exact types of membrane proposed by Brown and by Eggerth.

If Cellophane is soaked in water, its permeability is increased, and different degrees of permeability are obtainable by soaking in mixtures of alcohol and water, the latter being the swelling liquid. Its ability to swell diminishes with age, a year-old specimen swelling to only 70 per cent as much as a new one.[23] It has been recommended for ultrafiltration work.

Kahlenberg[34] found that the permeability of pyroxylin membranes for aqueous dialysis is curiously altered by treating collodion films with a chloroform solution of lanolin previous to removing from the glass mold. Such lanolin-treated membranes afforded practically complete aqueous dialytic separation of urea from mannose and sodium chloride, boric acid from sucrose, sodium chloride from nickel chloride (the first-named substance of each pair being the one which diffuses through the membrane more readily). These membranes were found to be practically impervious to Rochelle salt, sodium sulfate, potassium nitrate, copper sulfate, nickel chloride, sodium acetate, silver nitrate, magnesium sulfate, lithium chloride, ferric chloride, alum, sugars, amino acids, and ethyl alcohol. They were very slightly permeable to acids such as citric, tannic, and oxalic; somewhat more permeable to acetic, hydrochloric, and sulfuric acids; and readily permeable to urea, boric acid, borax, and sodium chloride.

There seems to be no end to the possibility of dialytic separation when the difference of behavior of substances in various solvents and toward sundry membranes has been learned. A study of the application of rubber membranes to the dialysis of ethereal solutions by Gies[35] has shown among other things that fats, fatty acids, heavy metal soaps, cholesterol and its esters, and lipochromes will dialyze in ethereal solution through rubber while lecithins, kephalin, and cuorin will not.

Copper oleate, sulfur, naphthalene, and camphor in pyridine solution dialyze through rubber into pyridine, while lithium chloride, silver nitrate, and sucrose do not.[36]

Graded membranes useful for all types of laboratory work are now supplied by chemical-apparatus dealers.

Nature of Membrane Permeability.—Membranes may be regarded as porous structures, through the capillary spaces of which liquids and the solutes pass mechanically, or the diffusing substances pass through as a result of solution in the membrane substance.

If a membrane consists of bundles of capillaries, then the passage of a liquid through it would be expected to follow the law of Poiseuille:

$$Q = \frac{p\pi r^4 t}{8l\eta} \tag{1}$$

where Q = the quantity of liquid of viscosity η passing in the time t through a capillary tube of radius r and length l under the pressure p. Thus the quantity of liquid passing through the membrane in a given time should be a straight-line function of the pressure. This has been found true for the passage of water through pyroxylin, parchment paper, gold beater's skin, and porcelain membranes.[37] It should likewise be proportional to the fluidity which has been demonstrated for diverse liquids and membranes of cellulose, nitrocellulose, and cellulose acetate.[38]

The increase in permeability of a membrane concomitant with increase in swelling would suggest a sievelike action, while several other experimental facts indicate that it is not so simple. For example, copper oleate dissolved in pyridine will not traverse a membrane of parchment paper while it will pass through a rubber membrane. Parchment paper is pervious to larger molecules when in aqueous solution. Rubber is not permeated by certain smaller molecules in aqueous solution. Parchment paper imbibes water but not pyridine, while the reverse is true for rubber. Hence it is evident in this case that the membrane must have an affinity for the solvent in order to be permeable to the solute. Further, a rubber membrane is porous to camphor and copper oleate in pyridine solution but acts like a solid wall toward smaller molecules like lithium chloride and silver nitrate in pyridine. It has been mentioned earlier that a nitrocellulose membrane can be made permeable to starch while impermeable to night blue in aqueous solution while the reverse is true when formaldehyde-tanned gelatin membranes are used. In these instances it would appear that there is some interaction between the membrane and the solute.

A chemical mechanism for membrane permeability was announced by L'Hermite[39] in 1854, who showed that, if water is covered by a thin layer of castor oil on top of which is a layer of alcohol, the alcohol passes through the castor oil and enters the water layer. He repeated this experiment with other combinations of liquids and ascribed osmosis through a membrane to solution therein. L'Hermite's view was soon abandoned but later was readopted.[40] The problem is not yet solved, however, and it seems that membrane permeability may be entirely mechanical, profoundly chemical, or a combination of both, depending upon the nature of the membrane and of the system with which it is in contact.

Michaelis,[41] having found that a potential difference arises when a dried nitrocellulose membrane separates aqueous solutions of electrolytes, states that the negatively charged nitrocellulose prevents the passage of negative ions, thus setting up a diffusion potential. He retains the idea of pores in these very impermeable membranes, the pores being too small for the passage of large molecules. Michaelis's suggestion that the potential arises through differential ionic mobility in the pores of an inert membrane has been questioned by Beutner,[42] who has shown that sodium chloride reacts with a nitrocellulose producing hydrochloric acid.

A comprehensive series of experiments by Northrop[43] has proved that dry nitrocellulose membranes are not porous and that the diffusion of molecules through them is the result of solution in the membrane. The relative rates of penetration of the gases hydrogen, nitrogen, oxygen, hydrogen chloride, and carbon dioxide through them bore no relationship to the densities of these gases. The rate of penetration of hydrogen and carbon dioxide was the same whether the membrane and gas were dry or the membrane was immersed in water. Phenol passed through many times more rapidly than acetic acid, and aminoacetic acid did not pass through at all. Solubility measurements showed that those substances which pass through at higher rates were more soluble in nitrocellulose than those passing through less readily.

Northrop found that nitrocellulose reversibly holds about 5 per cent water in solution at 22 mm. aqueous tension, amounts in excess of this, such as are effected when collodion films containing solvent are perfused with water, being held in capillaries.

Thus it is seen that dry nitrocellulose is permeable to substances soluble in it, while in swollen nitrocellulose membranes the presence also of pores must be considered.[44]

The following is a method for testing the nature of dialysis.[45]

If an aqueous solution of a substance is separated by a thin porous membrane from pure water (or a dilute solution of the same substance) and if the liquids on both sides of the membrane are well stirred, then a diffusion experiment is instituted in which the length of the space in which the process of diffusion takes place is exceedingly small. The equalization of the differences in concentration will then be proportional to the diffusion coefficient of free hydrodiffusion provided that no disturbing influences are set up in the capillary spaces of the membrane.

Under these suppositions the driving force will be proportional to the difference of the concentrations on both sides of the membrane. Then

$$dc_2 = k(c_1 - c_2)dt \qquad (2)$$

where the concentration c_1 is greater than c_2 and t represents time.

Upon integration for the case where the volume of the concentrated solution (outer) is selected as much greater than that of the dilute solution (inner), and hence where c_1 is regarded as constant:

$$\frac{c_2}{c_1} = 1 - \frac{1}{e^{k \cdot t}} \qquad (3)$$

This condition may seldom be realized, however.

With C representing the initial concentration of the outside solution, V its volume, v the volume of the water in the thimble, then the outside concentration is, if the inner concentration rose from zero to c_2,

$$c_1 = C - \frac{vc_2}{V}$$

Then Eq. (2) becomes

$$dc_2 = k\left(C - c_2\frac{v + V}{V}\right)dt \tag{4}$$

which upon integration gives

$$\frac{c_2}{C\dfrac{V}{v + V}} = 1 - \frac{1}{e^{k\frac{v+V}{V}t}} \tag{5}$$

The expression $C\dfrac{V}{v + V}$ is the final concentration at equilibrium. Letting $V/(v + V) = m$, then Eq. (5) may be written

$$0.43k = K = m\frac{-\log\left(1 - \dfrac{c_2}{Cm}\right)}{t} \tag{6}$$

Experiments with glucose, sucrose, and urea against parchment paper verified Eq. (6), showing that the dialysis of these non-electrolytes was a simple hydrodiffusion through the capillaries of the parchment-paper membrane. While sodium chloride gave results predicted by the equation, hydrochloric acid and sodium hydroxide as well as other electrolytes (not neutral in reaction) did not. This shows that in general the dialysis of many electrolytes through parchment paper is not a simple diffusion but is complicated by other forces arising in the membrane.

The complication of chemical forces arising in the membrane is demonstrated very strikingly by precipitate membranes. Precipitate membranes are made by the interaction of two substances which form an insoluble compound. These membranes are impermeable to ions which form a part of the membrane substance[46] or which would form an insoluble compound with one of the ions of the precipitate membrane. For example, a copper ferrocyanide membrane is impermeable to copper salts and to ferrocyanides; when barium sulfate is deposited in a gelatin-tannate membrane it becomes impermeable to sulfates and to barium salts, while silver chloride renders it impervious to chlorides. The results of extensive experimentation upon permeability of "precipitate membranes" published by Walden[47] show that ions common to ions forming part of a precipitate membrane, or which enter into a double decomposition reaction producing a less soluble membrane substance, cannot penetrate the membrane.

When the precipitated particles in such membranes, as, for example, in copper ferrocyanide and Prussian blue membranes, are small enough, the membranes are *semipermeable, i.e.,* permeable to solvent and not to solute.

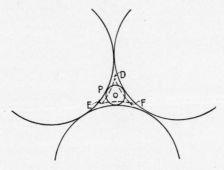

Fig. 30.

Tinker,[48] working with precipitate membranes, has proposed a theory of permeability which involves surface-bound solvent. Assuming that the precipitated particles are spherical, the radius of the largest particle which could penetrate between them would be the perpendicular distance *OP* in Fig. 30. If the solution bathing the membrane, however, is one in which the solute is negatively sorbed by the membrane substance (it raises the interfacial tension), then there will be a film of surface-bound solvent indicated by the dotted lines *DEF*, thus leaving a canal of free water with a radius less than *OP*. Thus a solute molecule smaller than *OP* but larger than the canal of free solvent cannot penetrate the membrane if it raises the interfacial tension, while one which may be larger (provided its radius is less than *OP*) will penetrate if it lowers the interfacial tension. Tinker, from his estimates of the size of the particles in some precipitate membranes based on microscope examination, and the fact that surface-bound films of water are supposed to be as thick as 140 mμ,[49] assumes that the water between the particles in semipermeable membranes is entirely surface bound or in the sorbed state, whereas in swollen membranes of parchment paper, nitrocellulose, etc., the maximal pore radii are very much larger providing space for unsorbed water.

Tinker's hypothesis is serviceable in considering the following strange behavior: A pyroxylin membrane impermeable to hemoglobin in aqueous solution becomes permeable to it when sodium oleate, linoleate, glycocholate, peptone, digitonin, atropine, pilocarpine, caffein, strychnine, quinine or morphine is added to the solution.[50] Codeine, cocaine, and novocaine do not produce this effect. That the increase in permeability is not due to enlargement of the pores of the membrane was proved by the fact that the catalysts did not affect the rate of passage of water through the membrane. Furthermore, the action was reversible since prolonged washing of the membrane rendered it impermeable to hemoglobin again. Unfortunately, the effect upon the pyroxylin-water interfacial tension is not known. An analogy might throw light on the question, however. Cocaine does not lower the interfacial tension between petroleum ether and water, while atropine, strychnine, morphine, caffein, and pilocarpine do lower it just as they lower the air-water surface tension. Consequently, they might also lower the pyroxylin-water interfacial tension, thus decreasing the thickness of surface-force bound water on the walls of the pores, enlarging the free-water canal in the pores so that the hemoglobin particles could freely pass through.

Speed of Dialysis and of Ultrafiltration.—From what has been said about membranes, it would be expected that the rate of diffusion through them would be increased by elevation in temperature. A few hours hot dialysis of the chlorides of iron, chromium, and aluminum equals many days operation at room temperature.[51]

The rate of dialysis of a strong acid or base such as hydrochloric acid or sodium hydroxide is increased by the presence of a salt such as sodium chloride,[52] while the dialytic speed of weak acids is decreased by the presence of a salt.[53] These facts correspond with the fact that strong acids and bases diffuse more rapidly through a salt solution than through pure water, while in the free hydrodiffusion of nonelectrolytes and weak electrolytes, the rate of diffusion is lowered by the presence of a salt.[54]

The colloid on the inside of a dialyzing or ultrafiltration membrane may decrease the speed of dialysis owing to its sorption by the membrane.[55] Loeb[55] found that the mere dipping of a pyroxylin membrane into a solution of a protein resulted in such a tenacious sorption that repeated washing failed to remove the

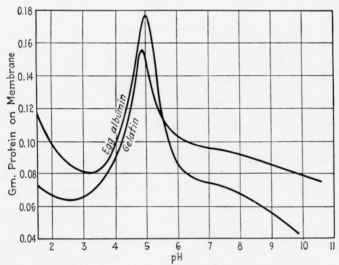

Fig. 31.—Sorption of gelatin and albumin from 2 per cent solutions by nitrocellulose membranes (0.2 g. nitrocellulose in 10-cm. diameter sheet).

last traces of the protein from the membrane. A quantitative study of the sorption of proteins by pyroxylin membranes[56] has shown that the pore cross section may be diminished by over 50 per cent. The sorption of protein is greatest at the isoelectric point as shown in Fig. 31.

The Donnan Equilibrium.—If an electrolyte, NaR, dissolved in water (solution 1) is separated from an aqueous solution of NaCl (solution 2) by a membrane *impermeable to* R^- *but permeable to the other ions present*, it is obvious that Na^+ ions cannot diffuse from solution 1 to solution 2 on account of the electrostatic force of attraction of the R^- ions. On the other hand, there is nothing to prevent the diffusion of Na^+ and Cl^- ions from solution 2 to solution 1. The presence of NaR in solution 1, however, influences the amount of NaCl transferred by diffusion across the membrane; and inasmuch as its presence results in an unequal concentration of oppositely charged, diffusible ions, *i.e.*, $[Na^+]$ will be greater than $[Cl^-]$ in solution 1, a potential difference will be set up across the membrane. This was pointed out by Donnan[57] in 1911, who derived equations for the quantitative distribution of the ions and the calculation of the difference in electrical potential.

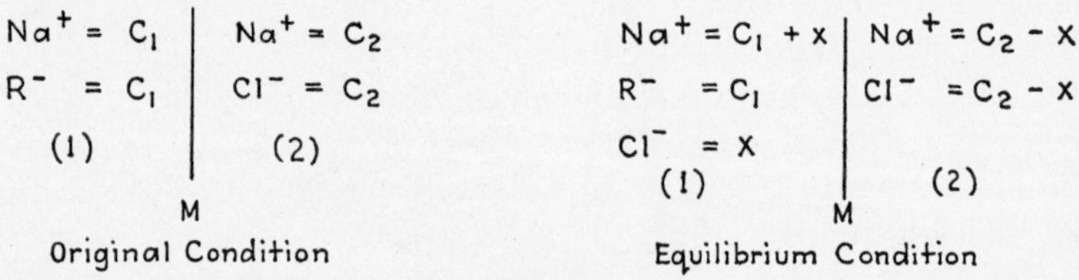

$$
\begin{array}{c|c}
Na^+ = C_1 & Na^+ = C_2 \\
R^- = C_1 & Cl^- = C_2 \\
(1) & (2)
\end{array}
\qquad
\begin{array}{c|c}
Na^+ = C_1 + x & Na^+ = C_2 - x \\
R^- = C_1 & Cl^- = C_2 - x \\
Cl^- = x & \\
(1) & (2)
\end{array}
$$

M   M

Original Condition   Equilibrium Condition

FIG. 32.

Following Donnan's terminology, the initial and equilibrium states are pictured in Fig. 32 where equal initial volumes of solutions 1 and 2 are separated by the membrane M,

$$C_1 = [Na^+] = [R^-]$$

in 1 and $C_2 = [Na^+] = [Cl^-]$ in 2 initially, while x = the concentration of Na^+ and of Cl^- which diffused from solution 2 to solution 1 to the establishment of equilibrium. At equilibrium, let us consider the reversible transport, isothermally and at constant volume of δn moles of Na^+ and of Cl^- from solution 2 to solution 1. The free energy of the system is not changed, *i.e.*, no work is done; hence,

$$\delta n RT \ln \frac{[Na^+]_2}{[Na^+]_1} + \delta n RT \ln \frac{[Cl^-]_2}{[Cl^-]_1} = 0 \tag{7}$$

whence

$$[Na^+]_1 \cdot [Cl^-]_1 = [Na^+]_2 \cdot [Cl^-]_2 \tag{8}$$

or at equilibrium the product of the concentrations of a pair of oppositely charged, diffusible ions on one side of the membrane is equal to the product of the concentrations of the same pair of oppositely charged, diffusible ions on the other side of the membrane.

Equation (8) may be arrived at in a pictorial manner. In passing from one solution across the membrane to the other solution, it is obvious that positively and negatively charged ions must move in electrical balance, owing to the electrostatic forces of attraction between them. Consequently, a cation or an anion striking the membrane alone could not pass through. However, if a diffusible cation and a diffusible anion strike it together, there is nothing to prevent their passage through it. The rate of their transfer through the membrane depends then upon the frequency with which they strike the membrane in pairs, which is equal to the product of their concentrations. Since, at equilibrium, the amount of Na^+ and Cl^- ions diffusing from solution 2 to solution 1 is equal to the amount diffusing from 1 to 2, obviously the product of the concentrations on one side of the membrane is equal to the product of the concentrations on the other side as shown in Eq. (8).*

Substituting the values for the concentrations in Eq. (8), we have

$$x(C_1 + x) = (C_2 - x)^2 \tag{9}$$

or

$$x = \frac{C_2^2}{C_1 + 2C_2} \tag{10}$$

from which it is seen that $x = \frac{1}{2}$ when $C_1 = 0$. With different ratios of C_1 to C_2 considered, the percentage of the NaCl which diffuses from solution 2 to solution 1, $100x/C_2$, is as follows:

C_1	C_2	$100x/C_2$
0.01	1	49.7
0.1	1	47.6
1	1	33.3
1	0.1	8.3
1	0.01	1

With the system taken at equilibrium and concentrations assigned as done in Fig. 33, Eq. (8) becomes

$$x^2 = y(y + z) \tag{11}$$

* For the salt $K_n A_m$ consisting of the polyvalent ions K^{m+} and A^{n-}, the equation would be $[K^{m+}]_1^n \cdot [A^{n-}]_1^m = [K^{m+}]_2^n \cdot [A^{n-}]_2^m$.

Since, in Eq. (11), the product of equals is equated to the product of unequals, then the sum of the equal parameters is less than the sum of the unequal parameters, or

$$2x < 2y + z$$

thus showing that the sum of the concentrations of the diffusible ions is greater in solution 2 than in solution 1. Further, from Eq. (11),

$$x = y\sqrt{1 + \frac{z}{y}}$$

and, since z and y are both greater than zero, then $x > y$ and in consequence $(y + z)$ must be greater than x. Thus $[Cl^-]_2 > [Cl^-]_1$ and $[Na^+]_1 > [Na^+]_2$ and a difference of potential thus arises.

Letting π_1, and π_2 represent the positive electric potentials of solutions 1 and 2, respectively, at equilibrium and isothermally and reversibly transporting $\delta n F$ coulombs of positive electricity from solution 2 to solution 1, the electrical work $\delta n F (\pi_1 - \pi_2)$ will be performed, but it will be exactly balanced by the work of transferring $p\delta n$ moles of Na^+ from solution 2 to solution 1 and

$R^- = z$	$Na^+ = x$
$Na^+ = y + z$	$Cl^- = x$
$Cl^- = y$	
(1)	**(2)**

M

FIG. 33.

$q\delta n$ moles of Cl^- from 1 to 2, where p and q are the respective transport numbers. The osmotic work thus gained is

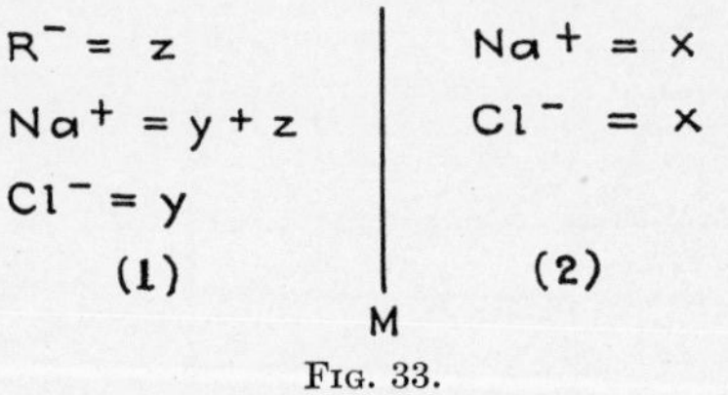

$$p\delta n R T \; ln \; \frac{[Na^+]_2}{[Na^+]_1} + q\delta n R T \; ln \; \frac{[Cl^-]_1}{[Cl^-]_2}$$

and, since $p + q = 1$ and $[Na^+]_2/[Na^+]_1 = [Cl^-]_1/[Cl^-]_2$

$$\pi_1 - \pi_2 = \frac{RT}{F} \; ln \; \frac{x}{y + z} = \frac{RT}{F} \; ln \; \frac{y}{x}$$

or $$\pi_2 - \pi_1 = \frac{RT}{F} \; ln \; \frac{y + z}{x} = \frac{RT}{F} \; ln \; \frac{x}{y} \tag{12}$$

In the general case, where the ions concerned in the ratio x/y, etc., have the valence n, and E represents the potential difference

$$E = \frac{RT}{nF} \; ln \; \frac{x}{y} \tag{13}$$

Eliminating x by substitution of its value $\sqrt{y^2 + yz}$ [from Eq. (11)], we have

$$E = \frac{RT}{2nF} \ln \left(1 + \frac{z}{y} \right) \tag{14}$$

Thus the potential difference is large when z is large with respect to y and decreases with increasing values of y.

In Fig. 34 are plotted the experimental values[58] obtained upon the addition of potassium chloride, sodium chloride, and

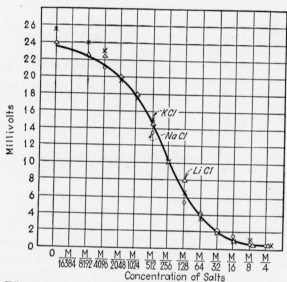

FIG. 34.—Effect of salts on the membrane potentials of a 1 per cent solution of gelatin at pH 11.

lithium chloride to a system where R^- was the negatively charged gelatin micelle.

The consequences of the Donnan distribution of ions will be considered in subsequent chapters. For a more rigorous development of the equilibria the reader is referred to later papers by Donnan[59] and by Hückel.[60]

References

1. BECHHOLD: *Chem. Ztg.*, **30**, 921 (1906); *Z. physik. Chem.*, **60**, 257 (1907); **64**, 328 (1908); *Biochem. Z.*, **6**, 379 (1908); *Kolloid-Z.*, **1**, 107 (1906); **2**, 3, 33 (1907).

2. MARTIN: *J. Physiol.*, **20**, 364 (1896); *Proc. Roy. Soc. (London)*, **63**, 420 (1898).

3. BORREL and MANEA: *Compt. rend. soc. biol.*, **2**, 317 (1904); MALFITANO: *Compt. rend.*, **139**, 1221 (1904); through DUCLAUX: *Kolloid-Z.*, **3**, 126 (1908).

4. WALPOLE: *Biochem. J.*, **9**, 284, 298 (1915).

5. WHITNEY and BLAKE: *J. Am. Chem. Soc.*, **26**, 1339 (1904); TRIBOT and CHRETIEN: *Compt. rend.*, **140**, 144 (1905); for a historical review and bibliography see DHÉRÉ: *Bull. soc. chim. biol.*, **8**, 144 (1926).

6. GUTBIER et al.: *Ber.*, (*B*) **55**, 1518 (1922); *Chem. Ztg.*, **47**, 109 (1923).

7. This method was used first by SCHUMACHER: *Ann. Phys. Chem.*, **110**, 337 (1860).

8. THOMS: *Ber.*, **50**, 1235 (1917).

9. GRAHAM: *Phil. Trans. Roy. Soc. London*, **144**, 177 (1854).

10. DUTROCHET: *Ann. chim. phys.*, **49**, 411 (1832).

11. THOMAS and FRIEDEN: *J. Am. Chem. Soc.*, **45**, 2522 (1923).

12. ZAKARIAS: *Kolloid-Z.*, **37**, 54 (1925).

13. FOSTER and SCHMIDT: *J. Biol. Chem.*, **56**, 545 (1923); HOFFMAN and GORTNER: *ibid.*, **65**, 373 (1925); BLANK and VALKO: *Biochem. Z.*, **195**, 220 (1928).

14. TAYLOR and IDDLES: *Ind. Eng. Chem.*, **18**, 713 (1926).

15. WOLFGANG OSTWALD: *Kolloid-Z.*, **22**, 143 (1918).

16. ZSIGMONDY: *Z. angew. Chem.*, **26**, Aufsatz 447 (1913); ZSIGMONDY and BACHMANN: *Z. anorg. allgem. Chem.*, **103**, 119 (1918); JANDER: *Z. anal. Chem.*, **63**, 273 (1923).

17. BECHHOLD and GUTLOHN: *Z. angew. Chem.*, **37**, 494 (1924).

18. BECHHOLD: *Kolloid-Z.*, **2**, 3 (1907); **3**, 226 (1908); see also FOUARD: *Bull. soc. chim.*, **37**, 471 (1925).

19. THOMAS and KELLY: *Ind. Eng. Chem.*, **18**, 136 (1926).

20. For reviews on dialyzers and ultrafilters see GENIN: *Rev. prod. chim.*, **30**, 641, 681 (1927); KRATZ: *Chem. Ztg.*, **55**, 257 (1931); RHEINBOLDT: *Kolloid-Z.*, **37**, 387 (1925); ZSIGMONDY: *Z. angew. Chem.*, **39**, 398 (1926); *Biochem. Z.*, **171**, 198 (1926). For a microultrafilter see THIESSEN: *Biochem. Z.*, **140**, 457 (1923).

21. HELE-SHAW: *Proc. Roy. Soc. (London)*, **103A**, 556 (1923); *J. Soc. Chem. Ind.*, **42T**, 353 (1923); for application see PICKARD: *J. Oil Colour Chem. Assoc.*, **7**, 110 (1924); **8**, 36 (1925); *J. Soc. Chem. Ind.*, **49**, 259T (1930).

22. BECHHOLD: *Z. Elektrochem.*, **31**, 496 (1925); BRONFENBRENNER:. *J. Gen. Physiol.*, **10**, 23 (1926).

23. McBAIN and KISTLER: *Trans. Faraday Soc.*, **26**, 157 (1930); *J. Phys. Chem.*, **35**, 130 (1931).

24. MANNING: *J. Chem. Soc.*, **1926**, 1127.

25. BIGELOW and GEMBERLING: *J. Am. Chem. Soc.*, **29**, 1576 (1907).

26. BARANETZKY: *Ann. Phys. Chem.*, **147**, 195 (1872); MALFITANO: *Revue gen. sci.*, **19**, 617 (1908); *Z. physik. Chem.*, **68**, 243 (1910).

27. EGGERTH: *J. Biol. Chem.*, **48**, 203 (1921).

28. NELSON and MORGAN: *J. Biol. Chem.*, **58**, 305 (1923).
29. BROWN: *Biochem. J.*, **9**, 591 (1915); **11**, 40 (1917).
30. SCHOEP: *Kolloid-Z.*, **8**, 80 (1911).
31. PIERCE: *J. Biol. Chem.*, **75**, 795 (1927).
32. FIELD: Dissertation, Columbia University, 1928.
33. SNELL: Dissertation, Columbia University, 1930; *J. Biol. Chem.*, **104**, 43 (1934).
34. KAHLENBERG: *Phil. Mag.*, (7) **1**, 385 (1926).
35. GIES et al.: *Biochem. Bull.*, **2**, 55 (1912).
36. KAHLENBERG: *J. Phys. Chem.*, **10**, 141 (1910).
37. BIGELOW: *J. Am. Chem. Soc.*, **29**, 1675 (1907).
38. DUCLAUX and ERRERA: *Rev. gén. colloides*, **2**, 130 (1924); **3**, 97 (1925); *Kolloid-Z.*, **38**, 54 (1926).
39. L'HERMITE: *Ann. chim. phys.*, **43**, 420 (1854).
40. NERNST: *Z. physik. Chem.*, **6**, 1 (1890); TAMMANN: *Z. physik. Chem.*, **22**, 481 (1897); FLUSIN: *Compt. rend.*, **126**, 1997 (1898); **131**, 1308 (1900); KAHLENBERG: *J. Phys. Chem.*, **10**, 141 (1906).
41. MICHAELIS: *Kolloid-Z.*, **62**, 2 (1933); *J. Gen. Physiol.* (1927–1929).
42. BEUTNER, CAPLAN, and LOEHR: *J. Biol. Chem.*, **101**, 391 (1933).
43. NORTHROP: *J. Gen. Physiol.*, **11**, 233 (1928); **12**, 435 (1929).
44. For a discussion of the physics of membranes see MANEGOLD: *Kolloid-Z.*, **61**, 140 (1932).
45. BETHE and TERADA: *Z. physik. Chem.*, **112**, 250 (1924).
46. TRAUBE: *Arch. Anat. Physiol. Wiss. Med.* (1867), 87 through Ref. 48.
47. WALDEN: *Z. physik. Chem.*, **10**, 699 (1892).
48. TINKER: *Proc. Roy. Soc. (London)*, **92A**, 357 (1915–1916); **93A**, 268 (1916–1917).
49. PARKS: *Phil. Mag.*, (6) **5**, 517 (1903); LEWIS: *ibid.*, **17**, 428 (1909).
50. BRINKMAN and SZENT-GYORGYI: *Biochem. Z.*, **139**, 261, 270 (1923).
51. NEIDLE and BARAB: *J. Am. Chem. Soc.*, **39**, 71 (1917).
52. LOEB: *J. Gen. Physiol.*, **5**, 255 (1922).
53. TERADA: *Z. physik. Chem.*, **109**, 199 (1924).
54. ARRHENIUS: *Z. physik. Chem.*, **10**, 51 (1892).
55. DUCLAUX: *Rev. gén. colloides*, **4**, 137 (1926); LOEB: *J. Gen. Physiol.*, **2**, 255, 577 (1919–1920).
56. HITCHCOCK: *J. Gen. Physiol.*, **8**, 61 (1925); PALMER: *ibid.*, **15**, 551 (1932).
57. DONNAN: *Z. Elektrochem.*, **17**, 572 (1911); *Chem. Rev.*, **1**, 73 (1924); see also HITCHCOCK: *J. Gen. Physiol.*, **9**, 97 (1925).
58. LOEB: *J. Gen. Physiol.*, **6**, 307 (1924).
59. DONNAN: *Kolloid-Z.*, **61**, 160 (1932); DONNAN and GUGGENHEIM: *Z. physik. Chem.*, **162A**, 346 (1932).
60. HÜCKEL: *Kolloid-Z.*, **36**, 204 (1925).

CHAPTER VI

PREPARATION OF COLLOIDAL SOLUTIONS

The fundamental processes available for the preparation of colloidal (and coarse) dispersions are:

1. {
    Dissolution.
    Mechanical.
    Electrical and thermal.

2. {
    Oxidation-reduction.
    Double decomposition.
    Simple precipitation.

The first three mentioned are called *dispersion* methods while the others are termed *condensation* methods.

Dissolution Process.—Colloidal dispersions of certain substances arise merely by contact with a suitable solvent, as, for example, albumin, gelatin, gum arabic, agar-agar, dextrins, starch, soap, and Bentonite in water. Some disperse readily in the cold while others require heating of the liquid or, better, preliminary soaking in the cold liquid followed by heating.

Mechanical Processes. *The Colloid Mill.*—By mechanical processes large particles of solids and liquids may be shattered or torn into small ones, thus forming dispersions of fine particles. Since dispersions of liquids in liquids are discussed in detail in the chapter on Emulsions, only dispersion of solids in liquids will be considered here.

The dispersion of substances by grinding either dry or in the presence of water has been studied by Wegelin,[1] who prepared dispersions from silicon, antimony, tungstic acid, titanic acid, molybdic acid, and vanadium trioxide by this method. He had no success with ductile metals, such as copper and bismuth, or with selenium, tellurium, graphite, sulfur, violet chromium chloride, calcium fluoride, copper oxide, iron oxide, cobalt oxide, lead dioxide, and zinc oxide. One-half to three-quarters of an hour grinding of 0.3 to 0.5 g. of substance in an agate mortar

98

sufficed to produce an appreciable amount of highly dispersed particles. The dispersed phase was readily precipitated by sodium chloride and migrated to the anode.

Grinding in admixture with water-soluble substances such as lactose,[2] glucose,[3] and urea[4] has been found helpful to the formation of dispersions of indigo, aniline blue, sepia, sulfur, selenium, etc.

Kuzel[5] prepared dispersions of tungsten, molybdenum, silicon, zirconium, and titanium by fine grinding followed by alternate treatment with acid and alkali. Washing with water between each treatment produced the dispersions. In all probability, the chemical interaction is the prime factor in this method.

Ordinary ball mill grinding of certain dry hydrophilic colloids promotes their dispersion in water.[6] Dry-milled raw starch is readily dispersed in cold water.[6]

While the idea of preparing dispersions by mechanical grinding or shearing stresses is said to have been originated by von Veimarn in 1906,[7] the first industrial apparatus was built by Plauson (1920).[8] The advent of the so-called *colloid mill* caused considerable excitement in the industries because it was originally believed that colloidal dispersions of a wide variety of materials could be made by the simple process of milling. This excitement has abated for the reason that hard solids cannot be ground to a high degree of dispersion except at prohibitive cost in power[9] and destruction of the apparatus. Such mills are valuable, however, for the disintegration of soft solids or the "deflocculation" of aggregates of particles of harder solids (to a size of 0.5 μ) and the formation of emulsions.

The Plauson mill was the beater type. In this type of mill, now obsolete, lugs on a beater drum revolving at high speed passed grooves notched in stationary baffles, the particles in suspension being mechanically broken to smaller size. The colloid mills on the market in the United States at present (Charlotte, Hurrell, Premier, United States, and Eppenbach) employ smooth surfaces which may or may not have grooves cut in them. Smooth disks may revolve close to each other in opposite directions; a smooth cylinder may revolve in a slightly tapered stator; a truncated cone, smooth or grooved, may rotate in a smooth or grooved conical stator.

The Eppenbach mill (Fig. 35) differs from the others named in that it operates at a very low final clearance (0.5 μ) and at low peripheral speed (1,750 r.p.m. for 6-in. base to 3,500 r.p.m.

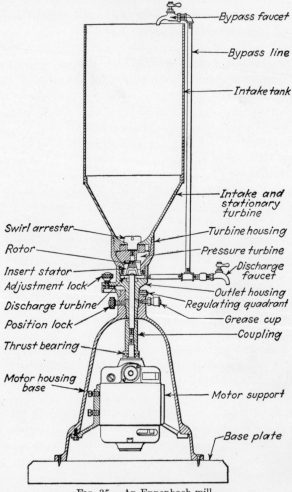

FIG. 35.—An Eppenbach mill.

for a 1-in. base). The material is fed in under high pressure. The others operate at higher peripheral speeds at wider clearance (>50 μ) and low-pressure feed. The speed of these mills varies from 2,000 to 10,000 r.p.m. The high-speed smooth-surfaced mills depend upon hydraulic shearing forces for their effects, while the grooved surfaces add to the hydraulic shearing action an intense turbulence and beating produced by eddy currents in the liquid between the irregular surfaces. The high-speed mills entrap and disperse air in the milled liquid, while the low-speed mill does not.

An example of a smooth-surface high-speed type with truncated-cone working surfaces is shown in Fig. 36. One with counter-revolving smooth disks is illustrated by Fig. 37.

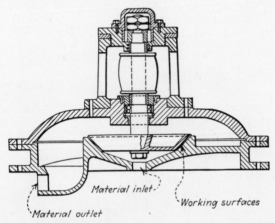

Material inlet

Material outlet

Working surfaces

FIG. 36.—A smooth surface type of mill with truncated-cone working surfaces.

The low-speed mill shown in Fig. 35 has a conical rotor grooved at the top and smooth at the bottom. It relies on positive grinding action for its effect and in view of its low clearance requires a high-pressure feed.

The materials to be dispersed are first mixed with the dispersing medium before being fed into the mill. Generally, a "dispersing agent," such as one of the emulsifying agents mentioned in Chap. XVI, is added. Thus the dispersed particles are not pure dispersions of the solid or liquid phase which is disintegrated but carry the dispersing agent on their surface.

The reader interested in details on colloid mills will find several articles in the literature.[8,10]

Electrical and Thermal Processes.—The first use of the method of forming colloidal dispersions by striking an electric arc between two metallic wires under a liquid is attributed to Bredig[11] and is generally called the *Bredig method.*

The dispersion of gold *in vacuo* by an electrical discharge was reported by Guyton-Morveau[12] in 1809, and its dispersion in air was studied by Faraday.[13]

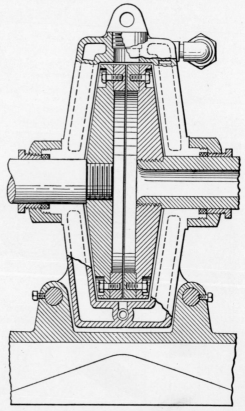

Fig. 37.—A mill with counter-revolving smooth disks.

The apparatus used by Bredig is shown schematically in Fig. 38. His apparatus requires constant manual operation and is suitable merely for the preparation of very small volumes of dilute sols. The most satisfactory apparatus known to the writer is one developed by Beans and Young[14] and illustrated in Fig. 39. The Beans and Young arcing device provides for stirring, cooling, and semi-automatic arcing in one adjustable, compact mechanism producing a hydrosol substantially free from contamination, because hydrolysis of the solution due to breaking of the arc is

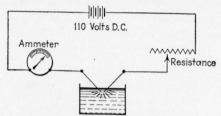

FIG. 38.—Scheme for Bredig arc process.

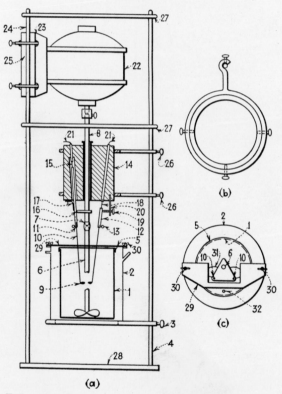

FIG. 39.—Arcing apparatus devised by Beans and Young.

reduced to a minimum. The arcing apparatus was connected to a 60-cycle 110-volt alternating current through a resistance of

16 to 40 ohms, with a 1-microfarad condenser in parallel. Alternating current is preferable to direct because with the former the erosion of the arcing electrodes is equalized.

In Fig. 39a which shows the apparatus in elevation, beaker 1 contains the pure water (plus its trace of suitable electrolyte, if gold is to be arced) and rests in the water jacket 2 which is adjustably attached by ring 3 to the upright rod 4. The glass stirrer 6 extends from the solution through a hole in the cover to the chuck 7 on the end of the drive shaft 8. Pieces of gold 9 form the arcing surface. These are fused at right angles to platinum wires 10 which extend from the solution through the cover to drilled brass rods 11 and 12 into which the wires are inserted and held in place by set screws 13. The brass rods are embedded and insulated from one another in the hard-rubber cylinder 14. The middle of rod 11 contains the steel spring 15 and the cylinder 14 is hollowed out from the spring downward which permits the lower part of 11 to move outward when actuated by the fibrous eccentric 16 which is attached to drive shaft 8. A spring 17 presses rod 11 back into place as the eccentric pressure is released. The gold at the solution terminus of 11 thus moves into contact with and away from the gold at the end of 12 with each revolution of the drive shaft 8. Rod 12 also contains a flat spring junction at 18. A set screw 19, through the brass rod 20, embedded in the rubber cylinder 14, acts against the lower part of rod 12 and the gold terminating 12 should be laterally adjusted to contact with the gold terminating 11 when the eccentric is exerting a minimum push on 11. The upper ends of rods 11 and 12 are soldered to clips 21 through which the electrical connection is made.

Drive shaft 8 is attached to motor 22 which in turn is bolted to a brass plate 23 grooved to fit against upright rods 24 and bolted to a smaller brass plate 25 on the opposite side of rods 24. This permits vertical adjustment of the motor at will.

The rubber cylinder 14 is attached by iron rings 26 to upright rod 4. The rings are larger than the cylinder and are pierced by three set screws acting around the periphery of cylinder 14, as shown in Fig. 39b. A vertical and horizontal adjustment of cylinder 14 is thus possible. Water jacket 2 is similarly adjustable. The rods 24 and 4 are cross-braced at 27 and the iron base 28 securely bolted down to reduce vibration.

Figure 39c shows the beaker 1, glass cover 5, and water jacket 2 in plan. The glass cover and beaker are held firmly within the water jacket by the aluminum piece 29 clamped to the water jacket by bolts and lugs 30. To protect further the solution in 1 from contamination, a cloth 31 is clamped on top of glass cover 5 and under aluminum piece 29 so as completely to cover the hole where stirrer 6 and wires 10 enter the solution. The glass cover is provided with a hole 32 fitted with a removable glass stopper. A thermometer may be inserted or the solution may be withdrawn through this hole without disturbing the set-up.

The arc method of electrical colloid synthesis has been applied to many metals, the most interesting, however, being platinum, gold, and silver arced in water. The base metals yield coarse dispersions mainly of the oxides or hydroxides as might be expected. A large proportion of the dispersed phase of "silver" hydrosol prepared in this manner consists of the oxide or hydroxide[15] and, in fact, when freshly prepared may be alkaline to phenolphthalein.[16]

Gold and Platinum Hydrosols.—It was generally thought that the noble metals formed stable dispersions when electrically dispersed under pure water until proof to the contrary was afforded by the experiments of Beans and Eastlack.[17] Prior to their work it was known that traces of sodium hydroxide or of hydrochloric acid were helpful in the synthesis but were not regarded as essential.

In the case of gold, Beans and Eastlack found that a blue dispersion of momentary stability was formed when gold wires were arced under highly purified water (specific conductivity of 0.6 to 1.2×10^{-6} mho at 25°). Upon the addition of an alkali chloride, bromide, iodide, or hydroxide, or of hydrochloric acid in concentrations ranging from 0.00005 to 0.005 N prior to the arcing of the gold, stable red-gold hydrosols could be formed. Barium chloride also was effective, but not at the higher concentration range. On the other hand, only unstable blue-gold hydrosols resulted when potassium fluoride, nitrate, sulfate, chlorate, or sulfuric acid were added to the pure water prior to the arcing. Furthermore, the addition of the traces of any electrolyte to a blue dispersion in pure water after the arcing process failed to convert the dispersion to the stable red variety.

These experiments proved that the presence of a certain kind and amount of ions in the water is essential for the preparation of a gold sol by the electric-arc process. The electrolyte must be one with which gold reacts to form a stable gold compound and the amount must be below that range which would precipitate red-gold sol. Thus there was established a direct chemical relationship between the metal and the crystalloid ions in the production of a colloidal solution of the metal.

All of the colloidal gold particles upon electrophoresis migrated to the anode whether prepared by arcing in sodium hydroxide, neutral halide, or in hydrochloric acid solution.

With platinum, Beans and Eastlack obtained a result which differed from gold in that stable hydrosols of this metal were formed by striking an arc between platinum electrodes in pure water. This behavior is due to the fact that platinum oxidizes in the arcing process to an extent sufficient to form stabilizing electrolyte. By conductivity measurements it was found that the electrolyte so formed corresponded to a concentration of 0.0001 to 0.0003 N.

By the direct-current arc method a clear red-gold hydrosol has been prepared containing 5 g. of gold per liter.[18] The aqueous solution used was 0.0013 M sodium chloride and the gold content of the hydrosol was measured after coarsely dispersed gold had been removed by centrifuging at a force of twelve hundred times gravity for 1 hr. By direct-current arcing of platinum wires under pure water as much as 1.6 g. of dispersed platinum per liter has been obtained in a sol (after 15 min. centrifuging at twelve hundred times gravity) and 0.9 g. after the sol was centrifuged at this force for 6 hr.[19]

The electrical dispersion of metals has been extensively studied by Svedberg[20] with respect to the influence of the electrical current, the type of arc, dispersion medium, etc. For the purpose of preparing dispersions of metals in organic liquids he developed an arc enclosed in a quartz tube in order to eliminate decomposition of the liquid. Nitrogen or hydrogen is led in at the top and bottom of the tube, emerging at a hole in the center opposite the arc with the particles of metallic solid and vapor thrown off by the arc. The metallic vapor condenses as it strikes the liquid surrounding the tube. In this manner Svedberg prepared a reddish-yellow alcosol of silver. Without a gas-encased arc, the silver alcosols obtained were greenish black in color and more dilute. An objection to the gas-encased arc, however, is that the quartz vaporizes from the tube in the vicinity of the arc forming colloidal silica, and in the case of a low melting-point metal the electrodes fuse together.

Comparing alternating[21] with direct current, Svedberg states that the high-frequency alternating arc produces more highly dispersed colloids than a direct-current or low-frequency alternating arc. At 50 to 500 cycles, a colloid of almost the same properties as one prepared by direct current is obtained. At

1,000 cycles the colloidal particles are slightly more highly dispersed, while the amount of coarse particles is greater. By using alternating currents of extremely high frequencies (10^5 to 10^7 cycles) the dispersions were composed of much finer particles than those produced by low frequency or by direct current and the decomposition of the medium was much reduced. The latter was shown by the fact that the conductivities of sols prepared by the high-frequency arcs were lower than those prepared by the direct-current arcs. Low self-induction, high capacity, and short arc length favored the formation of purer dispersions.

By means of the electrical-dispersion method, hydrosols of platinum, palladium, iridium, gold, and silver have been prepared. As previously stated the silver sols frequently contain a considerable proportion of oxide. Bredig claimed to have prepared a dispersion of the metal cadmium. In the case of more positive metals, however, electric-arc dispersions in water contain more or less oxide.

By a simple thermal process consisting of the condensation of sulfur vapor in water, white, opaque hydrosols of sulfur have been prepared.[22] Polythionic acids and hydrogen sulfide are formed in small amounts by the interaction of the hot sulfur vapor and the water. In the same manner selenium hydrosols have been prepared.[23]

Oxidation-reduction Processes.—The formation of sols by the action of reducing agents has been applied most extensively to the preparation of gold sols and to a certain extent to silver sols.

Gold Hydrosols.—In the preparation of gold sols a wide variety of reducing agents have been employed, such as carbon monoxide, acetylene, nitric oxide, hydrogen sulfide, aldehydes, alcohols, glycerol, acrolein, sugars, organic acids, phenolic compounds, hydrazines, hydroxylamines, hydrogen peroxide, tannin, ferrous salts, stannous salts, sulfites, phosphorus, etc.

The reduction of solutions of gold salts to hydrosols of gold was known long before colloids were recognized. It is discussed in Johann Juncher's "Conspectus Chemiae" (1749) and in Macquer's "Dictionnaire de Chymie" (1774).[24] Mrs. Fulhame (1794) described the coloration of fabrics by dipping them in gold solution followed by treatment with an ether solution of phosphorus or by hydrogen.[25]   She found that hydrogen reduced platinum and silver salts also.   In 1811, Oberkampf[26] prepared a wine-colored solution by reduction of a gold solution with hydrogen.   Faraday's study[13] was the first important contribution to our knowledge of gold hydrosols.   He used various reducing agents, the most successful being phosphorus.

For the preparation of gold hydrosols the most important reducing agents from the point of view of careful study and practical application are formaldehyde, hydrogen peroxide, phosphorus, and perhaps hydrazine and tannin.   The general method of preparation consists of the addition of a small quantity of the reducing agent to a very dilute solution* of chlorauric acid, frequently containing sufficient alkali to neutralize the latter. The addition of a small amount of gold hydrosol facilitates the operation.

The formaldehyde method was developed and extensively studied by Zsigmondy,[28,29] who prescribes reagents of the highest purity and the utmost cleanliness of apparatus for the successful preparation of "formol" gold hydrosols.   He recommends that the water be redistilled preferably through a silver or gold condenser, the first and last third of the distillate being rejected, and that all the glassware be of the Jena variety and steamed thoroughly but not wiped.   The recipe for the preparation is as follows:

One hundred twenty cubic centimeters of the purified water is heated to boiling in a beaker of 300 to 500 cc. capacity.   The beaker is placed preferably on a plain wire gauze over a very hot flame.   While the solution is warming, there is added to it 2.5 cc. of chlorauric acid solution (6 g. of $HAuCl_4.4H_2O$ crystals per liter of distilled water) and 3 cc. of a 0.18 N solution of purest potassium carbonate.   When the solution boils, the beaker is rotated or stirred (stirring rod should not be soft glass) vigorously while 3 to 5 cc. of a dilute solution of formaldehyde (0.3 cc. of formalin solution in 100 cc. water) is quickly added.   Generally after a few seconds, and always in less than a minute, an intense red color develops.   The mixture is stirred until a deep red color develops when the sol is boiled for a few minutes until the odor of formaldehyde is absent.   The color should remain deep red.

* The higher the concentration of the gold compound, the coarser are the reduced particles according to Weiser and Milligan.[27]

The sol is prepared more easily if a small amount of a suitable gold hydrosol is mixed with the dilute formaldehyde solution. This is called the *nucleus method* and will be discussed below.

Some operators do not believe Zsigmondy's extreme precautions are at all necessary and find it possible to prepare larger volumes of the sol at a time, using water redistilled over permanganate through a tin condenser. It has been pointed out that the purity of the formaldehyde is the most important factor. It should be freshly redistilled.[30]

The formol gold hydrosol is used in hospital laboratories for the Lange* test of spinal fluid. At Bellevue Hospital in New York City the technique given below has been found successful.[31] An ordinary glass Florence flask of 1.5 liter capacity cleaned with *aqua regia* and distilled water serves as reaction vessel. The water is prepared by redistilling 10 liters of water to which a few crystals of potassium permanganate have been added in a large copper still, rejecting the first 300 cc. of distillate. The reagents used are the ordinary chemically pure substances. It is stated that the temperature may be raised either slowly or rapidly by means of a gas burner and that it matters little in what sequence or at what temperature the reagents are added. A departure in the method consists in the use of oxalic acid. The recipe in detail taken verbatim from the original paper is as follows:

Into a clean 1.5 liter Florence flask place 1 liter of water, distilled as outlined in the foregoing. To this add 10 cc. of 1 per cent gold chlorid solution, 7 cc. of 2 per cent potassium carbonate and 0.5 cc. of 1 per cent oxalic acid. Heat this mixture to the boiling point, and at this temperature remove the flask from the flame, holding it by means of a towel and shake vigorously. While the solution is still in motion, add quickly from 0.2 to 0.3 cc. of ordinary concentrated 40 per cent chemically pure formaldehyde and at once shake thoroughly for from one-half to one minute. After from three to four minutes the color usually commences to develop. If, however, there should be no indication of color, the solution must again be shaken well and, while still in motion, an additional 0.1 to 0.2 cc. of formaldehyde quickly added; this addition almost invariably produces the desired change. At no time during this process should the shaking be stopped. The color should develop

* See Chap. XVII.

rapidly to a deep red. If, however, there is a delay in the appearance of color, the mixture should be allowed to stand, and in a minute or two the color will start to develop; at this instant the solution should again be thoroughly shaken until the color reaches a deep red shade. The entire process, from the moment the solution reaches the boiling point until the color is fully developed, requires at the most about three minutes.

The sol made according to Zsigmondy's recipe contains particles of about 15 to 30 mμ[32] and is stable for a year or so if kept in stoppered resistance-glass containers. Upon dialysis and evaporation at a temperature of 40 to 50°, it has been concentrated to a gold content of 0.12 per cent without decomposition.[33] Sols containing 0.27 per cent gold have been made by centrifugal sedimentation (3,000 r.p.m., 15 cm. radius) followed by taking up the deposit in water.[34]

Formation of gold hydrosols by reduction with phosphorus is of interest because a very high degree of dispersion is obtained.

A saturated solution of phosphorus in very pure ether diluted with 4 volumes of pure ether is prepared. To 120 cc. of distilled water at room temperature is added 2.5 cc. of the chlorauric acid solution described above, followed by 3 cc. of 0.18 N potassium carbonate and the whole well mixed. Then 1 cc. of the ether solution of phosphorus is stirred into the solution. After standing a few hours at room temperature the solution turns brown and within 24 hr. is deep red in color. If an insufficient amount of reducing agent is added, the solution may undergo a change to blue, violet, or black before it becomes red. This is due to the formation of aurous oxide.[35] The development of the red color can be hastened by boiling the solution about 15 min. after the reducing agent has been added. After the red color has developed in a phosphorus gold sol, it may be boiled to remove ether without suffering decomposition and any excess of phosphorus may be oxidized by aeration.

The particles in sols thus prepared are amicroscopic. If too little or no alkali carbonate is present, turbid dispersions result.[36] Impure phosphorus and, particularly, impure ether give poor results, the impurities preventing complete reduction of the gold. Actually under the best of conditions, all the gold is not reduced, as demonstrated by Thiessen,[37] who devised the following test. A few drops of concentrated ammonium hydroxide is stratified on a few cubic centimeters of the gold sol in a test tube. The formation of a blue ring reveals the presence of traces of unreduced gold compounds, and if more than traces are present, the blue color gradually permeates the whole hydrosol which finally coagulates. Thiessen attributes this reaction to the formation of fulminating gold due to the reaction between ammonia and gold salts or gold oxides. This test can also be applied to formol gold sols.

The reduction of gold solutions by hydrogen peroxide is accomplished[38] by the addition of a few drops of 3 per cent hydrogen peroxide solution to 100 cc. of a solution of chlorauric acid containing 0.006 g. gold. After 1 to 3 min. a wine-red sol is formed.

A method involving heating is described by Beaver and Müller.[39]

A solution of chlorauric acid containing 0.05 g. gold per liter is neutralized to litmus with a 0.1 N solution of potassium carbonate. One liter of this neutral solution is placed in a clean (steamed) resistance-glass beaker on a hot plate, the temperature of the solution being raised to 85°. Then with rapid stirring, 1 cc. of a 0.5 per cent aqueous solution of hydrogen peroxide is added and the sol cooled.

Another method used by the same workers and by Nordenson[40] consists in reducing unneutralized chlorauric acid solutions by hydrogen peroxide under exposure to ultraviolet radiation. If neutralized chlorauric acid is used, the reduction proceeds too fast under the radiation producing coarsely dispersed gold. Exposures of the unneutralized solution varying from 1 to 60 sec. make progressively redder sols.

Beaver and Müller found that red hydrogen peroxide gold sols made under ordinary laboratory illumination turned blue when exposed to ultraviolet light up to two days and then after continued exposure (up to eight days) they regained their red color and underwent no further change on further exposure. This was true also for gold sols prepared by reduction with tannin, quinol, catechol, resorcinol, and pyrogallol, while no change was observed under similar exposure of gold sols made by reduction with hydrazine, phosphorus, formaldehyde, and acetylene, and those prepared by the Bredig-arc method.

When hydrazine hydrate is selected as reducing agent, blue or red sols may be obtained, depending upon whether or not the solution is heated. Reduction in the cold produces blue sols, while at boiling temperature they are red. It has been shown

that the blue sols contain unreduced gold compounds[41] and it
has been stated that the blue color is due to colloidal oxide.[37]
The hydrazine method was invented by Gutbier.[42]   A good recipe
is the following:

A dilute, unneutralized solution of chlorauric acid (as that described under
the formol method) is treated with a few drops of a dilute (0.1 per cent)
solution of hydrazine hydrate in the cold.   A blue sol is thus obtained.   If
the chlorauric acid solution is brought to boiling before the addition of the
hydrazine hydrate, a red sol is obtained.

In all of the preparations of gold sols by reducing agents, the
process is facilitated by the presence of added gold nuclei and,
in fact, the degree of dispersion obtainable can be controlled.
The gold particles formed under the action of the reductant
deposit upon solid nuclei originally present or upon nuclei formed
spontaneously and, as a consequence, without the addition of
some finely dispersed gold particles, the sols obtained with a given
reducing agent may contain larger or smaller particles depending
upon the adventitious presence of less or more nuclei and whether
the reducing action is rapid or slow.[43]   The rate of spontaneous
nucleus formation is diminished by any process which promotes
hydrolysis of the chlorauric acid.   It has been discovered also
that as little as 4×10^{-3} milliequivalent per liter of potassium
ferrocyanide or ferricyanide greatly inhibits spontaneous formation of nuclei.[44]

The nucleus method was invented by Zsigmondy,[45] who
selected the phosphorus gold sol as source of nuclei on account of
the high degree of dispersion of this sol.   The nucleus method
merely consists in the addition of some phosphorus gold hydrosol
to the dilute chlorauric acid solution before the addition of the
reducing agent, or the nucleus sol may be mixed with the reducing
agent.   The amount of nucleus sol to be used is determined by
a series of trials in which from 0.1 to 3 cc. of nucleus sol are
added.   Then that amount is selected which gives the degree of
dispersion desired; the more nuclei present, the higher is the
degree of dispersion.

The influence of nuclei can be strikingly demonstrated according to Zsigmondy and Thiessen[46] in the following manner in
which hydroxylamine is used as reducing agent.   Three reagents
are prepared:

Solution A: 12.5 cc. of a solution of chlorauric acid containing 3 g. Au per liter are mixed with 400 cc. of purest water, 5 cc. of 0.18 N potassium carbonate are added and the mixture is diluted to 500 cc.

Solution B: 0.27 g. of hydroxylamine hydrochloride is dissolved in 1 liter of purest water.

Solution C: 120 cc. of phosphorus gold hydrosol are diluted to 200 cc. with purest water yielding a solution containing 0.038 mg. of Au per cubic centimeter.

A series of sols is then made according to the proportions prescribed in Table 15 by mixing A and C in a large beaker followed by dropwise addition of B while stirring. This is done at room temperature and resistance glass is used.

TABLE 15.—INFLUENCE OF NUCLEI

Number of sol	Amounts of reagents			Relation between size of particle in the resulting sols and in the nucleus sol
	A	B	C	
1	87.5	87.5	25	2:1
2	98.4	98.4	3.12	4:1
3	99.8	99.8	0.39	8:1
4	100	100	0.049	16:1
5	100	100	0.006	32:1

Number 5 was a very turbid blue hydrosol. Number 4 was turbid and reddish. The turbidity decreased and the red color became more brilliant. Number 1 was a clear red sol. This series was used by Professor Zsigmondy as a lecture demonstration.

The influence of nuclei upon the velocity of the reaction can be conveniently studied by conductivity measurements in the case of hydrogen peroxide gold sol formation due to the seeming simplicity of the reaction

$$2HAuCl_4 + 3H_2O_2 = 2Au + 8HCl + 3O_2$$

where only the $HAuCl_4$ and the HCl conduct the electric current appreciably and the latter more than the former. Experiments carried out by Nordenson[47] are shown in Fig. 40. When no nuclei were added, there was a sudden increase in conductivity (A to B) when the peroxide was added and, at the same time, the yellow color of the solution faded. Then there was a very slow rise in conductivity (B to C) with no perceptible color change, followed by the rapid rise (C to D) when the color of the liquid suddenly became red. The course of the reaction BC shows how long it takes for the spontaneous formation of nuclei. When nuclei were added at the beginning, upon the addition of the peroxide the conductivity and the color intensity increased in proportion to time (A to D'). The curve $ABC''D''$ shows the

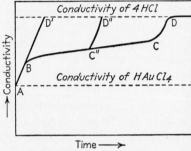

Fig. 40.—Influence of nuclei upon the formation of gold sols.

effect of adding some nuclei when the reaction is in the stage BC.

During the period AB, Svedberg[48] states that about one-third of the gold chloride is reduced, producing an enormously supersaturated solution of metallic gold (10^7) which according to the law of mass action would stop the reaction. Then along BC, the primary particles of gold slowly aggregate to form particles which, when finally large enough, serve as nuclei for molecular gold resulting in the rise CD.

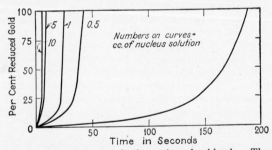

Fig. 41.—Influence of nuclei upon the formation of gold sols. The right-hand curve represents the course of the reduction in the absence of added nuclei.

On the other hand, Zsigmondy[49] thinks it more probable that in the range AB principally di- or monovalent gold is formed, with perhaps some metallic gold, thus rendering the assumption of a supersaturation to the degree of 10,000,000 unnecessary.

In Fig. 41 is shown the influence of added gold nuclei upon the rate of reduction of gold chloride by formaldehyde.[50] Again it is seen that an addition of nuclei greatly accelerates the process. The nucleus sol was mixed with the formaldehyde and the temperature was 70°. At boiling temperature the reaction is too rapid for measurement.

The use of gold nuclei is not restricted to the formation of gold sols. They have been used in the formation of silver sols.[51] Likewise substances other than gold may serve as nuclei in gold sol formation.[52]

Silver Hydrosols.—Silver hydrosols have been prepared by use of a variety of reducing agents such as phosphine,[53] hydrogen,[54] formaldehyde,[55] hydrazine,[56] hydrogen peroxide,[57] acrolein,[58] phosphorus,[51] ferrous citrate mixtures,[59] and hydroquinone.[60] The influence of added nuclei has also been studied.[61]

Kohlschütter's method[54] of reducing an aqueous suspension of silver oxide with hydrogen is interesting because the nature of the walls of the container is of such significance. Hydrosols prepared in quartz or in ordinary soft-glass vessels are yellow to brown to transmitted light and gray to black in reflected light, while those made in Jena-glass vessels are red to brownish red by transmitted light and grayish green by reflected light. In a platinum dish coated with platinum black no hydrosol is formed at all, the reduced silver depositing in crystals on the dish.

About 0.5 g. of freshly precipitated and thoroughly washed silver oxide is suspended in a liter of distilled water in an inclined round flask. With the mixture at 50 to 60° pure hydrogen is bubbled through for 8 to 10 hr. The temperature above which stable sols are not obtained has been given as 70 and 80°.[62] At lower temperatures the rate of reaction diminishes rapidly. The pH of the sols is about 8 depending on the concentration and temperature of reduction. In order to remove silver hydroxide from the solution, it is put in a platinized platinum dish and pure hydrogen is bubbled through a platinum nozzle, air being excluded. The silver oxide is reduced to silver which settles out as glistening crystals.

Silver sols ranging in color from yellow→red→violet→blue→ green can be prepared by the use of hydrogen peroxide.[57]

Silver hydrosols which display a wide color change upon addition of precipitating electrolyte; orange yellow→reddish yellow→ruby red→greenish yellow→green→bluish green→blue →bluish lavender→purple→purple gray→gray are formed by reducing silver bromide or silver iodide with formaldehyde according to the following recipe:[63]

Ten cubic centimeters of 0.1 M silver nitrate is diluted to 250 cc. and 250 cc. of 0.04 M potassium bromide (or iodide) are added slowly while stirring vigorously. Then 10 cc. of 2 per cent formaldehyde solution is added to the mixture, followed by rapid addition with vigorous stirring of 100 cc. of 0.03 M sodium hydroxide. Reduction takes place immediately after the addition of the alkali, the sol changing from brownish yellow by reflected light to a straw yellow in about 1 hr. It then has a clear reddish-yellow color by transmitted light. Similar sols prepared by use of potassium chloride are unstable.

Dilute solutions of silver salts or oxide are readily converted to silver sols upon exposure to ultraviolet light and X-rays. Svedberg[64] observed that a silver plate immersed in water or alcohol produced a silver sol when the whole system was subjected to ultraviolet light or X-rays. He also found that alcohol which had been in contact with silver in the dark gave rise to colloidal silver when illuminated with ultraviolet light. It has been shown that the silver is first oxidized in contact with water (or alcohol) and the dissolved silver compounds so produced are reduced by the subsequent radiation.[65]

The examples of reduction methods given are those which have been subjected to the most study. Other sols formed by the types of reducing agents mentioned are metals of the platinum group, selenium, and tellurium where hydrazine hydrate, hydrazine hydrochloride, phenylhydrazine hydrochloride, and hydroxylamine hydrochloride have been found effective.[66] Paal[67] and coworkers have prepared many of these sols containing the sodium salts of alkaline degradation products of albumin ("lysalbinic" and "protalbinic" acids). Such protected sols of platinum and palladium absorb large quantities of hydrogen, thereupon serving as effective reducing agents useful in organic chemistry. In many cases where such a colloid-hydrogen complex is desired, it is merely necessary to add some platinum or palladium salt to the organic system to be reduced and then to pass hydrogen through it.[68]

Purple of Cassius.—Metallic salts have been used to reduce other metallic ions to the colloidal state, producing complicated mixed dispersions. The oldest example is the purple of Cassius discovered by Andreas Cassius in 1663. A recipe for its formation taken from Zsigmondy[69] is the following:

Two hundred cubic centimeters of chlorauric acid solution (3 g. Au per liter) and 250 cc. of stannous chloride solution (3 g. Sn per liter plus a slight excess of hydrochloric acid) are brought together in 4 l. of water with violent agitation.   After three days the purple of Cassius will have settled out in the form of a dark-purple powder, the supernatant liquid being colorless and free from gold or tin.   The precipitate is washed free from chloride by decantation, followed by suction on a filter paper.   When this precipitate is suspended in water, it can be peptized to a sol by the addition of a little ammonium hydroxide followed by boiling.   While this sol has the color of colloidal gold, its properties are predominantly those of colloidal stannic acid.

An analogous silver precipitate was made by Frick,[70] in 1828, and a method for preparing the sol has been devised by Voigt.[71] Platinum[72] and palladium[73] stannic oxide purple have also been prepared.

Various metal salts have been converted to mixed sols by reduction with titanium trichloride.[74]

Sulfur Hydrosols.—Aqueous dispersions of highly dispersed sulfur received the attention of Stahl (1747), Scheele (1770), Bergmann (1782), Fourcroy (1788), Berthollet (1798), Berzelius (1808), and others who were interested in its formation and presence in natural waters.   From the point of view of modern colloid chemistry, the most important older contributions were made by Döbereiner,[75] Wackenroder,[76] Selmi and Sobrero,[77] and Debus.[78]

Berthollet prepared sulfur hydrosols by the oxidation of hydrogen sulfide, sulfur dioxide being one of the oxidation agents which he employed.   Wackenroder studied extensively the formation of sulfur sols by the interaction of hydrogen sulfide and sulfur dioxide.   Sulfur sols prepared in this manner are frequently called "Wackenroder's sulfur sol."

The sol is readily prepared by passing hydrogen sulfide through a cool solution of sulfurous acid.   Odén[79] has shown that the highest degree of dispersion is obtained when hydrogen sulfide is bubbled through as concentrated a solution of sulfurous acid as possible, stopping when sulfur is seen to separate out.   He used a 1.8 N solution at 10°.   For the highest yield of colloidal sulfur he recommends a less concentrated solution of sulfurous acid, about 1 N.

The colloidal sulfur seems to arise from decomposition of intermediate products resulting from a rather complicated reaction. Wackenroder demonstrated the presence of pentathionic acid and, since his time, sulfuric, hexathionic, tetrathionic, trithionic, and thiosulfuric acids have been reported present. A high initial concentration of sulfur dioxide favors the formation of penta- and hexathionic acids.

The fungicidal action of sulfur itself has been shown to be due to pentathionic acid, resulting from the action of water and air upon sulfur.[80]

Engel[81] showed that sulfur hydrosols can be prepared by the addition of concentrated hydrochloric acid to a cold concentrated solution of sodium thiosulfate. Raffo[82] used sulfuric acid instead of hydrochloric and Odén's very complete study of this method and of the properties of the resulting sols account for the custom of calling such sols "Odén's colloidal sulfur."

From Odén's study of the method one can give the following recipe for the preparation.

Thirty cubic centimeters of a 3 M solution of sodium thiosulfate is added dropwise to 10 cc. of 18 M sulfuric acid which is continuously stirred. The dropping should be at the rate of 2 cc. of thiosulfate solution per minute. The temperature of the reaction mixture should be originally at about 25° and not allowed to exceed 50°. Slower addition of the thiosulfate gives a lower yield of colloidal sulfur; and while a higher temperature produces a greater proportion of highly dispersed sulfur, the reaction becomes rather explosive. Temperatures lower than the range given produce a somewhat lower yield and a lower ratio of amicroscopic to submicroscopic particles. Odén recommends that small proportions be made at a time (never over 100 cc.) and that the reaction vessel be a centrifuge tube.

When the addition of the 30 cc. of thiosulfate solution has been completed, the mixture is immediately cooled and sufficient sodium chloride is added to precipitate the sulfur. The mixture is centrifuged and the supernatant liquid is removed. Then the residue is treated with water at about 80° which effects redispersion of part of the sulfur. This mixture is centrifuged to throw out the irreversibly coagulated sulfur and the supernatant sulfur hydrosol is then removed by decantation.

Sols containing as high as 50 per cent sulfur have been made by this process. The sol so obtained contains particles ranging from amicroscopic to coarse dispersion size. Odén has shown that it may be fractionated by means of sodium chloride precipitation. A small amount of sodium chloride is added to the sol and after 15 min. standing it is centrifuged and the supernatant liquid removed (*A*). The coagulum (*A'*) is then redispersed by treatment with warm water producing a sol (*A''*) containing large particles. The supernatant liquid (*A*) is then treated with a little more sodium chloride, the coagulum (*B'*) centrifuged out

TABLE 16.—PROPERTIES OF SULFUR HYDROSOLS OF DIFFERENT PARTICLE SIZE

Number of fraction	Concentration of NaCl producing this fraction	Macroscopic characteristics	Ultramicroscopic characteristics
1	0.07 *N*	Turbid even at 0.02 per cent concentration. Particles settle out after a few days	No amicroscopic light cone. Large particles of about 210 mμ size
2	0.07 to 0.10 *N*	Milky in appearance up to dilutions to 0.2 per cent. Upon dilution to 0.05 per cent reddish brown color and weakly translucent. Only slight tendency to settle out	No amicroscopic light cone. Particles about 140 mμ in size
3	0.10 to 0.13 *N*	A 1 per cent solution is milky in appearance. When diluted to 0.3 per cent is reddish yellow and turbid to transmitted light and turbid to reflected light	No amicroscopic light cone. Particles about 90 mμ in size and in lively Brownian movement
4	0.13 to 0.16 *N*	A 1 per cent solution is slightly turbid, yellow in color with trace of red. Concentrated solutions are opaque and white	A 0.5 per cent sol shows a brilliant cone of bluish tinge which is visible even at a concentration of 0.001. Particles almost at the limit of ultramicroscope visibility
5	0.16 to 0.20 *N*	1 per cent solution is yellow and nearly clear in transmitted light while turbid to reflected light. A 10 per cent solution is turbid with a reddish color in transmitted light	0.5 per cent sol shows pronounced amicroscopic light cone which disappears at a concentration of 0.008
6	0.20 to 0.25 *N*	Concentrated solution somewhat turbid, at 1 per cent concentration yellow and clear in transmitted light and faintly turbid in reflected light	1 per cent sol shows faint amicroscopic light cone which disappears at 0.02 concentration. No submicrons
7	0.25 *N*–	Concentrated solution (25 per cent S) bright yellow and faintly turbid in transmitted light; greenish to reflected light	1 per cent sol shows a faint amicroscopic light cone which disappears at 0.05 concentration. No submicrons

after 15 min., the supernatant liquid (*B*) removed, and the coagulum (*B'*) redispersed in warm water producing a sol (*B''*) which contains smaller particles than *A''*. Solution *B* is then treated in the same manner, and so on, producing as many sols of as uniform and different degrees of dispersion as one desires. Table 16 gives a description of a typical series of fractions prepared by Odén.

As the temperature is lowered, less sodium chloride is required to precipitate the sulfur. Consequently, purification of sulfur is effected by dispersing the salted out coagulum in as little warm water as possible and then cooling the resulting dispersion to, say, 10°. A new coagulum forms which is centrifuged out and redispersed in warm water. Odén was able to prepare dispersions in this manner containing 50 per cent sulfur and about 5 per cent sodium chloride. He remarks that further elimination of electrolyte may be accomplished by electrodialysis.

The Odén type of sulfur hydrosol can be prepared by the interaction of sulfur monochloride and water. A recipe has been proposed[83] as follows:

Seventy cubic centimeters of water at 35° is added to 10 cc. of sulfur monochloride and shaken. An exothermic reaction soon takes place accompanied by evolution of sulfur dioxide. The system is cooled in an ice bath in order to retard the reaction. After 5 to 10 min., when the evolution of sulfur dioxide ceases, the mixture is treated with a saturated solution of sodium chloride and centrifuged. The precipitated sulfur is peptized upon addition of water after decantation of the supernatant liquid. The precipitation and repeptization may be continued until the desired degree of purification is obtained.

The ease with which Odén's sulfur sols may be prepared at different dispersities makes them especially interesting for certain types of colloid study. Wackenroder's sulfur sols also have been fractionated in the same manner.[84]

Iodin.—Unstable blue hydrosols of iodin arise through the interaction of hydriodic and iodic acids.[85] These quickly turn gray and precipitate. Chandler and Miller[86] have utilized the reaction

$$HI + HIO \rightarrow I_2 + H_2O$$

in the presence of gum arabic to prepare a stable brick-red dispersion which might properly be called an emulsion inasmuch as the dispersed iodin particles appear to be globules of liquid coated with films of the gum. A solution of sodium iodohypoiodite is prepared by rapidly treating a 1 to 2 per cent solution of sodium hydroxide with iodin until the straw-colored liquid, which forms immediately, just begins to turn red and then decanting this solution from the remaining iodin crystals. A solution containing gum arabic is added followed by rapid acidification with hydrochloric acid at 0°.

If this dispersion is converted to a thick syrup by the addition of dextrose or of gum arabic, it may be evaporated without appreciable loss of iodin to a hard brittle mass. This mass readily disperses in water, the dispersion medium consisting of a saturated aqueous solution (0.034 per cent) of iodin. This aqueous dispersion is said to be much less corrosive to animal tissue than the U.S.P. tincture of iodin.[87]

Double Decomposition.—By means of double decomposition reactions a wide variety of sols have been obtained. These are generally divided into "oxide" sols, sulfide sols, and salt sols.

The best known oxide sols are those of iron, aluminum, chromium, molybdenum, vanadium, silicon, and tin. They are prepared by hydrolysis of the salts or by peptization of the hydrous oxides with acids or bases or with salts which readily hydrolyze. The hydrolysis method consists in the dropwise addition of a solution of the salt to an excess of boiling water. The peptization method may be carried out in one of two ways. The hydrous oxide (preferably freshly precipitated) is treated with a small amount of acid or base or of a solution of a salt which is acidic or alkaline, the choice of acid or base depending upon the chemical nature of the substance to be dispersed and the kind of dispersion wanted. The other peptization method consists in the dropwise addition of an acid or base as the case may demand to a stirred solution of the salt of the element. The oxide so precipitated is at first readily peptized by the excess of salt present, the ease of peptization diminishing upon increased additions of the acid or base. When the stage of very slow peptization is reached, the additions are stopped and the mixture is dialyzed.

Ferric Oxide Hydrosols.—Ferric oxide hydrosols were first prepared by Péan de St. Gilles[88] and by Thomas Graham.[89]

The former hydrolyzed a ferric acetate solution by boiling and the latter peptized hydrous ferric oxide by ferric chloride. Péan de St. Gilles iron oxide sols are turbid and somewhat hydrophobic, while Graham iron oxide sols are clear and intermediate in properties.

A simple and quick method of preparing a dilute ferric oxide sol is to add a small quantity of ferric chloride to a large volume of boiling water. The rate of formation of the colloid diminishes as the temperature is lowered.[90,91] At room temperature there is a delay (increasingly large as the concentration of ferric chloride

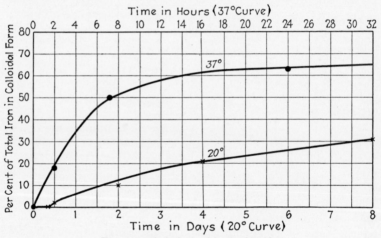

Fig. 42.—Hydrolysis of ferric chloride.

is increased) in the start of the hydrolysis[92] and the rate of colloid formation is increased by the addition of some colloidal ferric oxide.[90,93]

In Fig. 42 are shown the rates of colloidal iron oxide formation at 20 and 37° as found by Heymann[91,94] for solutions containing about 15 milliequivalents of ferric chloride per liter. The autocatalytic nature of the process is seen very markedly in the 20° curve. Heymann showed that the colloid formation is practically complete in 20 min. at 80°. At the concentration of 0.015 N ferric chloride and at 37° he found equilibrium to be reached when 87 per cent of the total iron present was colloidal. Twenty days were required. This equilibrium was also reached from the other direction when a sol prepared at 80° was aged at 37° for about one month.   At 20°, only 64 per cent of the total iron was colloidal in one year.   Sols prepared at low temperatures were found to be less highly dispersed than those formed at higher temperatures.

Heymann showed also that, as the concentration of ferric chloride is raised, the percentage of iron in the colloidal form diminishes.[94]   His results obtained at 37° are given in Table 17.

TABLE 17.—EQUILIBRIUM POINT IN COLLOIDAL IRON OXIDE FORMATION BY HYDROLYSIS OF $FeCl_3$ AT 37°

Concentration of solution, milliequivalents per liter	Percentage of the total iron in colloidal form	Appearance of solution
3.43	100	Yellow-brown
6.89	96.5	Yellow-brown
15.32	87.5	Brown
24.51	79.3	Red-brown to transmitted light. Turbid brown to reflected light
50.10	60.5	Red-brown to transmitted light. Turbid brown to reflected light

While the degree of hydrolysis at boiling temperature is greater than at lower temperatures, it slowly reverses, as shown by Krecke[95] and by Heymann, when the dispersion is cooled.

The formation of a ferric oxide sol free from chloride by the hydrolysis of ferric chloride has been reported by Sorum.[96]

Four hundred cubic centimeters of a molar solution of ferric chloride was allowed to fall at the rate of 2 drops per second, into 5 liters of vigorously boiling distilled water contained in a 6-liter Pyrex flask.   The mixture was then dialyzed at 90 to 97° in 250 cc. capacity nitrocellulose bags against distilled water flowing at the rate of about 3 liters per hour.

In from 7 to 12 days dialysis, "deeply wine-colored" sols, clear to transmitted light, and free from chloride were obtained. The iron content varied from 2 to 3.6 g. per liter.   The sols gave a strong Tyndall cone.   Continuous hot dialysis for as long as five weeks did not induce coagulation.

Ayres and Sorum[97] have prepared similar ferric oxide sols by hydrolysis of ferric chloride (0.0125 to 0.1 M) at temperatures higher than 100° (up to 145°) followed by dialysis at 90 to 97°. They reported that the particle size (52 to 76 mμ) is not a function of the temperature of hydrolysis or of the concentration of the ferric chloride.   More or less ferric oxide sediment was present, however, in the hydrolysis vessels.

Using the method originated by Grimaux,[98] Thiessen[99] has prepared a sol by the hydrolysis of ferric ethylate which is claimed to be free from electrolytic impurities.   The dispersions so formed are very hydrophobic and, unlike the ferric oxide thus far discussed in this chapter, have negatively charged micelles.

When ferric oxide sols of low concentration are desired, the hydrolysis method is a convenient one.   More concentrated dispersions are prepared by the peptization method first used by Ordway[100] and Graham.[101]

Freshly precipitated hydrous ferric oxide is treated with an aqueous solution of ferric chloride.   Hydrochloric acid may be used also, but obviously the amount must be considerably below chemical equivalence to the iron oxide.   When the gel has been peptized, the mixture is dialyzed.   Clear reddish-brown sols are obtained by this method.

A convenient method (likewise used by Graham) consists in precipitating the ferric oxide in the presence of ferric chloride. A recipe which the author uses is as follows:

Prepare an approximately 2 M solution of ferric chloride and approximately 3.7 M ammonium hydroxide solution.   Then at the rate of about 2 drops per second allow the ammonium hydroxide solution to fall into 100 cc. of the ferric chloride solution which is being stirred vigorously.   The precipitated hydrous oxide rapidly peptizes in the presence of the excess of ferric chloride, the rate of peptization decreasing as more ammonia is added. When about 100 cc. of the ammonium hydroxide is added, it is wise to stop and subject the mixture immediately to dialysis against running cold water. Failure to start dialysis immediately may produce a turbid dispersion due to the presence of the crystalloidal electrolyte.   After cold dialysis overnight, the sol may be subjected to dialysis at about 80° if speed in purification is desired.[102]   Hot dialysis must be preceded by cold dialysis, however, since immediate application of hot dialysis produces a turbid dispersion.[102]

The end point in the dialysis depends upon the degree of "purity" desired. There is no simple test. Some workers dialyze to absence of ferric ion, some until the diffusate gives a "faint" test for chloride, and others quantitatively measure the iron, chloride, and ammonium present, terminating when NH_4^+ is absent or at a desired ratio of iron to chlorin. Sols made in this manner have never been prepared free from chloride; the dispersed phase precipitates out before that stage of purity is reached. Thomas and Frieden[103] found that the dialysis may be carried out in large unglazed-porcelain jars. These are convenient dialyzers because mechanical stirring of the contents may be applied which is not so easily accomplished with nitrocellulose membranes.

An interesting iron oxide sol is prepared by the oxidation of iron carbonyl, $Fe(CO)_5$, in aqueous solution by hydrogen peroxide. A clear red-brown sol is obtained, which flocculates upon boiling owing to the expulsion of carbon dioxide.[104]

With the exception of Thiessen's ferric oxide dispersion made by hydrolysis of ferric ethylate, all of the iron oxide sols mentioned above contain positively charged micelles. Sols with negatively charged micelles have been prepared by addition of sodium hydroxide to ferric chloride solutions containing glycerol,[105] sugars,[106] and organic oxy acids.[107] Such sols are doubtless much more complicated than the name "negative iron oxide" implies. Negative colloidal ferric oxide has also been prepared by the hydrolysis of Prussian blue[108] and by the addition of dilute ferric chloride to dilute sodium hydroxide solution.[109] The dispersion prepared in the last-named manner is not stable, precipitating out in a day or so.

Chromic Oxide Hydrosols.—Graham[101] prepared chromic oxide hydrosol by peptization of the hydrous oxide with chromic chloride in the same manner as he made the ferric oxide sol. The sol thus prepared is dark green in color. Neidle and Barab found that in the hydrolysis of pure chromic chloride the particles diffused through a parchment-paper membrane readily when prepared and dialyzed at room temperature, yielding almost no colloid; but that if commercial chromic chloride were similarly treated at room temperature, a fair yield of colloid was obtained. Hot hydrolysis and dialysis of pure chromic chloride likewise gave a good yield of colloid. They prepared a chromic oxide sol containing 59 per cent of the original chromium and a ratio of equivalents Cr:Cl = 65 in the following manner. Forty-nine cubic centimeters of normal ammonium ·hydroxide were added to 162 cc. of normal chromic chloride with vigorous shaking. After standing 20 min., the precipitate entirely dissolved, when the clear green solution was diluted to 400 cc. and dialyzed for 34 hr. against running distilled water at 80°.

The above-mentioned chromic oxide sols contain positively charged micelles. A negative chromic oxide sol can be made by the addition of alkali to a chromic chloride solution, just a little in excess of the amount of alkali required to precipitate the chromic oxide.

A positive chromic oxide sol claimed to be free from electrolyte has been prepared by hydrolyzing chromic ethylate.[110] This sol is quite hydrophobic.

Aluminum Oxide Hydrosols.—Aluminum oxide sols were prepared by Crum[111] who boiled aluminum acetate solution and by Graham who peptized hydrous alumina with aluminum chloride. Neidle and Barab found that aluminum oxide sols showed a tendency to pass through parchment paper on dialysis.

A method for forming hydrous aluminum oxide sols free from other metallic contaminants consists in the amalgamation of pure aluminum with mercury, the amalgam then being subjected to the action of water containing a trace of an acid such as hydrochloric,[112] hydrobromic, or hydriodic.[113] As the hydrous alumina is formed, it is peptized by the acid present. The alumina sols prepared in acidic solutions contain positively charged micelles. Negatively charged colloidal alumina arises when alumina gel is peptized by sodium hydroxide or by ammonia.[114] Such alumina sols are not stable, however.

Hydrous Silica Hydrosols.—Hydrosols of hydrous silica, or "silicic acid" hydrosols, may be prepared by Graham's method[115] of mixing water glass and hydrochloric acid, by the hydrolysis of the methyl ester of silicic acid,[98] or by hydrolysis of silicon tetrafluoride or tetrachloride.[116,117] It seems difficult to prepare stable sols containing over 10 per cent SiO_2.

The simplest method of preparing silica sols consists in mixing hydrochloric acid and water glass, by stirring the acid into the water-glass solution, or *vice versa*, using a water-glass solution containing about 1 to 2 per cent SiO_2 and 2 N, or more, hydrochloric acid. Clear, stable sols result if there is an excess of acid or of alkali. If subjected to dialysis immediately after the interaction of the acid and water glass, an appreciable amount of silica passes through the membrane.[118] This tendency diminishes if dialysis is delayed for a few days. The usual directions are to dialyze to the absence of chloride in the diffusate, which is indeed unsatisfactory. In this case as in most others, there is no convenient and precise end point in dialysis other than that afforded by a quantitative analysis of the dialysate. Even when dialysis of these silica sols is carried to the absence of a chloride test (with Ag^+) in the dialysate, the latter still contains chlorin.[119] Sodium also is tenaciously held in the micelle.

Illustration of some of the points just mentioned is given by one of the experiments made by Brintzinger.[120] He mixed water glass containing 11.68 per cent Na_2O, 26.05 per cent SiO_2 and 0.03 per cent $Al_2O_3 + Fe_2O_3$ with 2 N HCl at 18°. The mixture contained 0.829 g. SiO_2, 0.2758 g. Na, and 0.4539 g. Cl in 100 cc. The ratio of SiO_2:Na:Cl was therefore 1000:870:930. Part of this solution was subjected immediately to rapid dialysis against parchment paper at 18°. After 50 hr., 18 per cent of the SiO_2 had diffused through the membrane. No more diffused upon continued dialysis. After 70 hr. dialysis the test for chloride in the dialysate was negative, although chlorin could be recovered upon distillation after acidification with sulfuric acid. At the end of 70 hr. rapid dialysis the composition was 0.680 g. SiO_2, 0.0013 g. Na, and 0.02 mg. Cl; or SiO_2:Na:Cl was 1,000:5:0.05. Three days after the original mixture was made, the remaining portion was submitted to rapid dialysis. Only 7 per cent of the SiO_2 diffused through the membrane (after 50 hr. and no further loss upon continued dialysis). At the end of 70 hr. dialysis 100 cc. of dialysate contained 0.7711 g. SiO_2, 0.0016 g. Na, and 0.04 mg. Cl; or SiO_2:Na:Cl was 1,000:5.5:0.9.

Silica hydrosols prepared as above described have pH values of 4.5[121] to 4.6.[120]

If insufficient hydrochloric acid is mixed with water glass, alkaline silica hydrosols result. Such sols are most sensitive to electrolyte salting-out in the pH range of 9.5 to 11, beyond 11 becoming more stable and also showing the presence of increasing amounts of fine particles which diffuse through dialyzing membranes.[122] Alkaline silica hydrosols may be made by digesting hydrous silica gel with ammonium hydroxide.[123] They are clear up to 0.4 per cent concentration of SiO_2 but become turbid at 0.5 per cent and begin to flocculate at 0.75 per cent.

A method for preparing reproducible silica sols up to 10.8 per cent SiO_2 is described by Grundmann.[124] These hydrosols are clear, showing practically no Tyndall cone. The micelles are always negatively charged unless an excess of hydrochloric acid is added. The positive sol is unstable.

Stannic Oxide Hydrosols.—Stannic oxide hydrosols were prepared by Graham. Hydrous stannic oxide may be peptized by hydrochloric acid[125] or by alkalies,[126] potassium hydroxide being a better peptizing agent than sodium hydroxide.[127] This is probably due to the fact that sodium stannate is less soluble than the potassium salt.

The commonly used methods for preparation of the hydrous stannic oxide are hydrolysis of tin tetrachloride in water and dissolution of tin in nitric acid or in mixtures of nitric and hydrochloric acids. A tin tetrachloride solution may be made by the action of concentrated hydrochloric acid with platinum-gauze catalyzer on pure tin followed by oxidation with air. The nitric acid method produces β- or meta-stannic acid which is not so readily peptized as the so-called α-stannic acid. The greater the proportion of hydrochloric to nitric acids, the more readily peptizable is the gel formed.[128] It is said that the greater the proportion of nitric acid used, the greater is the ratio of the β- to the α-stannic acid formed. The proportion of β- to α-stannic acid also increases with the temperature used in the hydrolysis of tin chloride and the temperature of the water used to wash the resulting gel.

Sols with positively charged micelles arise when stannic acid is peptized with hydrochloric acid. The peptization is carried out in a few minutes by treatment of the gel with concentrated hydrochloric acid at room temperature after which the solution may be diluted with water. Dilute hydrochloric acid may be used but the time of peptization is prolonged to many days. In any case, when sols of reasonable stability are desired, the hydrochloric acid must be at least 0.4 N.[125]

Sols of a concentration of $SnO_2 = 0.1$ M and $HCl = 0.8$ M have been described as turbid, the turbidity decreasing upon

dilution with 0.8 M HCl to a SnO_2 concentration of 0.001 M
when the sol was clear with a bluish fluorescence.[128] Sols made
by peptization of α-stannic acid have been described as yellowish
orange to transmitted light and faintly green to reflected light,
while the β-stannic acid ones were bluish white to reflected light,
and like the α-variety in transmitted light.[129]

Hydrous stannic oxide has been peptized by tartaric acid.
A sol containing 7.35 g. per liter of SnO_2 and of the composition
243 moles SnO_2 to 1 mole tartaric acid has been described as
neutral, unaffected by boiling but irreversibly coagulated upon
freezing.[130]

Sols prepared by peptization of stannic acid by potassium,
sodium, or ammonium hydroxide possess negatively charged
micelles. Zsigmondy[131] describes a series prepared by peptization with potassium hydroxide. His results are summarized in
Table 18. In the ultramicroscope sol 1 showed a brilliant

TABLE 18.—STANNIC ACID SOLS PEPTIZED BY POTASSIUM HYDROXIDE

Number	Moles SnO_2 to 1 mole K_2O	Peptization	Appearance* to eye	Reaction to* litmus	Ultrafiltrate* through nitro-cellulose contained
1	200	5 hr. heating	Very opalescent	Slightly acid	Water
2	100	1 hr. heating	Less opalescent	Slightly acid	Water
3	50	Readily in cold	Less opalescent	Alkaline	Contaminated water
4	25	Readily in cold	Less opalescent	Alkaline	Appreciable amounts of tin and alkali
5	10	Readily in cold	Clear	Alkaline	All the tin and alkali passed through
6	2	Readily in cold	Clear	Alkaline	

* Diluted to 0.5 per cent SnO_2 content.

Tyndall cone, which disappeared upon dilution. The brilliance
of the Tyndall effect diminished as the ratio $SnO_2 : K_2O$ decreased
and sol 6 was in fact optically void.

The gelatinous mass on the ultrafilter membrane obtained from sols 1 and 2 redispersed in water but did not do so if dried first.

The order of viscosity was $1 > 2 > 3 > 4 > 5 > 6$. The surface tension of all was the same as that of water. One can safely say that 5 and 6 were not colloidal.

A method involving the use of a centrifuge has been proposed for the preparation of oxide sols.[132] Solutions of ferric chloride and of aluminum chloride were precipitated by ammonium hydroxide and washed repeatedly by decantation, followed by centrifuging in a Sharples centrifuge. The deposited solid was removed, redispersed in water, and reprecipitated in the centrifuge. The deposit was then rubbed up with water until it dispersed colloidally. Silica sols were prepared in the same way after precipitation of silica from water glass by means of hydrochloric acid. The resulting sols are claimed to be nearly free from chloride.

Sulfide Hydrosols.—Hydrosols of the insoluble metallic sulfides may be prepared generally by one of the following methods.

1. A solution of the metallic salt is added to H_2S water, or *vice versa*, with or without concomitant bubbling of hydrogen sulfide.
2. A solution or suspension of the metallic oxide has hydrogen sulfide bubbled through it.
3. A suspension of freshly precipitated and thoroughly washed metallic sulfide has hydrogen sulfide bubbled through it.
4. By hydrolysis of a suitable complex salt certain sulfide sols arise.

In 1834, Berzelius remarked about the yellow solution arising upon treatment of arsenious acid solution with hydrogen sulfide and concluded that it was a suspension of transparent particles of arsenious sulfide.

Schulze[133] prepared arsenious sulfide hydrosol by passing hydrogen sulfide through a solution containing 10 g. per liter of arsenious oxide. He also made antimony sulfide sol in the same manner, using a solution of potassium antimonyl tartrate not stronger than 5 g. per liter.[134] In the first instance no coagulating salt is present and in the second the tartrate is without much influence on the stability of the resulting sol. Tartrate ion is not a powerful coagulant for sulfide sols. The method of passing hydrogen sulfide through solutions of metallic salts will produce stable sols only in the absence of electrolytes which would precipitate the dispersed phase. Lottermoser,[135] in recognition of this fact, showed that treatment of mercuric cyanide and of copper glycine solutions with hydrogen sulfide produced stable sols owing to the low degree of ionization of these salts and to the inertness of the products of the reaction.

In some cases, where the metallic sulfide precipitates during the passage of hydrogen sulfide through the salt solution, the sol may be formed by washing the precipitate with H_2S water. Copper sulfide[136,137] and mercuric sulfide[138] sols readily form in this manner as soon as the greater proportion of the active electrolyte is washed away. Zinc sulfide is very prone to act in this way. This is well known in analytical technique where zinc sulfide is always washed with H_2S water containing ammonium chloride to prevent its tendency to run through the filter.

The formation of sulfide sols by the action of hydrogen sulfide upon suspensions of freshly precipitated and washed metallic oxides and sulfides has been reported for a wide variety of metals.[138,139] The physical state of the oxide seems to be significant at times. For example, Linder and Picton[139] found that zinc sulfide sols would not form unless the hydrous zinc oxide was in a gelatinous and translucent form. This was accomplished by surrounding the containing vessels with ice. If the sulfides are dried at 100°, they are unlikely to peptize upon subsequent treatment with hydrogen sulfide.

The method of preparing a sulfide hydrosol by hydrolysis of a complex salt has been reported for one case by Hahn.[140] Sodium, potassium, and lithium stibiothiosulfates at 0.001 M concentration are dialyzed, whereupon antimony sulfide sol is formed (and coagulates if the dialysis is prolonged). The reaction is supposed to be the following:

$$2Na_3Sb(S_2O_3)_3 = Sb_2S_5 + 3Na_2SO_4 + 3SO_2 + S$$

The corresponding arsenic complex salts did not give rise to sols.[140]

A simple recipe for the preparation of arsenious sulfide sol is to pass hydrogen sulfide to saturation through a saturated solution of arsenious acid. A bright-yellow sol is thus formed. The excess hydrogen sulfide may be removed by boiling or by a stream of hydrogen. The temperature of the reaction mixture is of very little importance, but the size of the particles in the resulting sol increases with increased concentration of the arsenious acid and decreases with increased speed of hydrogen sulfide addition.[141]

Concentrated arsenious sulfide hydrosols may be prepared by alternate dissolutions of arsenious oxide and gassings with hydrogen sulfide followed by evaporation under reduced pressure. Sols as concentrated as 200 g. As_2S_3 per liter and extremely viscous pastes of 300 g. per liter have been prepared in this fashion.[142]

A recipe for the preparation of a hydrosol of high degree of dispersion is the following:[143]

Forty to one hundred cubic centimeters of a cold saturated solution of arsenious oxide are diluted to 200 cc. and treated with a solution consisting of 1 cc. saturated H_2S water diluted with 100 cc. water. A very faint yellow color develops. Then it is diluted to 1 liter with a hydrogen sulfide solution ten times as concentrated as the former one, following which hydrogen sulfide gas is passed through the solution to saturation. The excess hydrogen sulfide is blown out by means of hydrogen gas. The resulting sol shows a very faint Tyndall cone with no submicroscopic particles. This method is similar to the Zsigmondy nuclear method for the preparation of gold sols.

A recipe for antimony sulfide sol formation is to pass hydrogen sulfide through an aqueous solution of 5 g. potassium antimonyl tartrate (tartar emetic) per liter followed by dialysis. A deep orange-red sol is thus formed.

To prepare copper sulfide hydrosol:

Dissolve 5 to 10 g. of cupric sulfate in a liter of water and precipitate the hydroxide, carbonate, or sulfide. Wash the precipitate by decantation until a sulfate test is very faint. Then suspend the precipitate in about 1 liter of water and pass in hydrogen sulfide until the precipitate peptizes. If the peptization is slow, it is well to let the closed system stand quietly overnight and repeat the gassing with hydrogen sulfide the next day. The excess hydrogen sulfide may be removed by dialysis or by a current of hydrogen, less stable sols thus resulting.

Cupric sulfide sols containing about 5 g. CuS per liter are very stable but dispersions four times as concentrated precipitate within a few hours.[144] These sols are black in color.

Mercuric sulfide sol may be prepared easily in the following manner:[145]

One gram of mercuric chloride is dissolved in 50 cc. water slightly acidulated with hydrochloric acid. The sulfide is precipitated by means of hydrogen sulfide, filtered, and washed to absence of test for chloride ion.

Then it is suspended in 250 cc. of water and hydrogen sulfide passed through until the precipitate is peptized.

This should occur in 1 to 2 hr., producing a black and opaque sol. When dilute, the sol is brown to transmitted light with a greenish cast in reflected light. It has been stated that sols containing 10 g. per liter of HgS can easily be prepared.[146] The excess hydrogen sulfide may be removed by hydrogen gas with attendant decrease in stability.

An interesting behavior of the sulfides of cadmium, zinc, mercury, and lead reported by Young and Goddard[139] is that, when these sols are repeatedly dialyzed to precipitation and repeptized by hydrogen sulfide, the flocculation becomes increasingly difficult upon dialysis and the repeptization by hydrogen sulfide becomes more rapid as the process is repeated.

Other Colloidal Salts.—Without doubt, it would be possible to prepare a wide variety of hydrosols of water-insoluble salts. With the exception of the sulfides, silver halides, Prussian blue, and copper ferrocyanide one finds very little discussion of colloidal salts in the literature.

Silver halide hydrosols and especially silver iodide with the colloidal micelle as anion or as cation have been investigated by Lottermoser,[147] who showed that such hydrosols may be readily prepared by mixing a solution of a potassium halide with one of silver nitrate provided the concentrations are less than 0.1 N. When the halide is in excess, the silver halide micelle is negatively charged. Excess of silver ion produces a positive micelle. The negative sols are more stable than the positive, the latter flocculating immediately if dialysis is attempted. Silver iodide sol with excess Cl^- ion may be prepared at 0.125 N concentration, while silver iodide sols with excess Ag^+ ion may not be made more concentrated than 0.05 N. Freshly precipitated silver iodide is peptizable by potassium iodide but not by silver nitrate. Less excess of iodide is required to stabilize silver iodide particles than in the case of excess silver ion. The latest description of the preparation of a silver halide sol given by Lottermoser (in 1925) is the following one.

Twenty cubic centimeters of a 0.1 N potassium iodide solution is diluted to 500 cc. and is vigorously agitated while 0.1 N silver nitrate solution is added dropwise (to make the negative sol, and *vice versa* to make the positive sol). As the first few drops of silver nitrate are added, a yellow-green solution arises and upon further addition of silver nitrate becomes increasingly opalescent. When near the equivalence point it suddenly becomes turbid, whereupon one more drop of silver nitrate brings about precipitation.

If the reverse process is carried out, *i.e.*, if the potassium iodide is dropped into the silver nitrate, the appearance is in general the same except that the turbidity increases faster. When silver nitrate is titrated into potassium iodide, complete precipitation of silver iodide occurs at exact equivalence but when potassium iodide is titrated into silver nitrate, complete flocculation occurs when the ratio $KI:AgNO_3$ = about 0.996:1. The silver halide sols are not very stable.

Prussian blue hydrosols may be prepared by addition of 0.1 N potassium ferrocyanide solution to 1 cc. of 0.1 N ferric chloride solution in 199 cc. of water.[148] The color and degree of dispersion of the sol are affected by the ratio of ferrocyanide to iron as shown in Table 19. In the ultramicroscope the Tyndall cone intensity

TABLE 19.—INFLUENCE OF FERROCYANIDE: IRON RATIO

Ratio of equivalents of $K_4Fe(CN)_6$ to $FeCl_3$	Color of sol	Color of ultrafiltrate
1	Blue	Colorless
2	Blue	Green
10	Brighter blue	Blue (with greenish tinge)
20	Blue-green	Blue-green
30	Light green	Light green

of the sols decreased from 1 to 30. Addition of an excessive amount of potassium ferrocyanide always produced a blue precipitate.

The sols so prepared are very stable and possess negatively charged micelles. In presence of a slight excess of ferric chloride the micelles are positively charged but such sols are not very stable. They spontaneously flocculate. Upon shaking, an almost clear blue liquid is obtained which starts to settle out when quiet.

Prussian blue precipitate peptizes in solutions of alkali oxalates, forming green solutions.[149] Rochelle salt also peptizes Prussian blue to a green solution which is said to be ferric tartrate and alkali ferrocyanide.[150] Prussian blue can be reprecipitated from the latter solution by the addition of hydrochloric or acetic acid.

Cupric ferrocyanide hydrosol, containing negatively charged micelles, is prepared by mixing dilute solutions of cupric chloride and potassium ferrocyanide, the latter being in excess. This hydrosol is described by Duclaux.[151]

Simple Precipitation.—When a solution of substance A in liquid B is poured into liquid C, a sol generally arises if A is insoluble in C and provided liquids B and C are miscible. For example, sulfur dissolves in hydrazine hydrate forming a deep-red, stable solution. When this solution is poured into water, a clear bright-yellow dispersion is obtained.[152] If insufficient hydrazine is present, the clear dispersion changes in a few minutes to an opaque dispersion. Added ammonia or hydrazine hydrate prevents this. The dispersion must be protected against the carbon dioxide of the air.

Colloidal selenium can be prepared by means of hydrazine also.[153]

If an alcoholic solution of sulfur prepared by the action of hot alcohol upon sulfur is poured into water a white suspensoid sol of sulfur is obtained. This is called "von Veimarn's sulfur sol."

Alcoholic solutions of gum resins, such as shellac, rosin, and mastic, form suspensoid sols when poured into water.

References

1. WEGELIN: *Kolloid-Z.*, **14**, 65 (1914).
2. NEUGEBAUER: *Kolloid-Z.*, **43**, 65 (1927).
3. PIHLBLAD: *Z. physik. Chem.*, **81**, 420 (1912).
4. VON VEIMARN and UTSINO: *Kolloid-Z.*, **32**, 149 (1923).
5. KUZEL: Austrian Patent, Kl. 12 *b*, No. A2573 (1906); through Lotter-moser: *Kolloid-Z.*, **2**, 347 (1908).
6. ALSBERG and GRIFFING: *Proc. Soc. Exptl. Biol. Med.*, **23**, 142 (1925); ALSBERG: *Ind. Eng. Chem.*, **18**, 190 (1926); ALSBERG, GRIFFING, and FIELD: *J. Am. Chem. Soc.*, **48**, 1299 (1926).
7. TRAVIS: *Ind. Eng. Chem.*, **21**, 421 (1929).
8. PLAUSON: *Chem. Ztg.*, **44**, 553, 565 (1920); *Z. angew. Chem.*, **34**, Aufsatzteil, 469 (1921).
9. PODSZUS: *Kolloid-Z.*, **64**, 129 (1933).
10. AUSPITZER: *Z. angew. Chem.*, **40**, 1337 (1927); *Ind. Eng. Chem.*, **20**, 413 (1928); SARROT DU BELLAY: *Rev. prod. chim.*, **28**, 41, 78 (1925); BLOCK: *Chem. App.*, **14**, 145, 158 (1927); FOSTER and REILLY: *J.*

Soc. Chem. Ind., **41**, 435R (1922); KELLY: *Ind. Eng. Chem.*, **15**, 926 (1923); McLEAN: *Chem. Met. Eng.*, **30**, 675 (1924); SCHOTZ: *Chem. Age (London)*, **6**, 790; **7**, 493 (1922); **14**, 99 (1926).

11. BREDIG: *Z. angew. Chem.*, **11**, 951 (1898); *Z. physik. Chem.*, **32**, 127 (1900); *Z. Elektrochem.*, **4**, 514 (1898).

12. GUYTON-MORVEAU: *Ann. chim.*, **69**, 261 (1809).

13. FARADAY: *Phil. Trans. Roy. Soc. London*, **147**, 145 (1857).

14. YOUNG: Dissertation, Columbia University, 1932.

15. McINTOSH: *J. Phys. Chem.*, **6**, 15 (1902); KOHLSCHÜTTER: *Z. Elektrochem.*, **14**, 49 (1908); REBIÈRE: *Compt. rend.*, **148**, 354 (1909); **154**, 1540 (1912); BEST and COX: *J. Chem. Soc.*, **1929**, 2727; WOODARD: *J. Phys. Chem.*, **35**, 425 (1931).

16. BLAKE: *Am. J. Sci.*, (4) **16**, 431 (1903).

17. BEANS and EASTLACK: *J. Am. Chem. Soc.*, **37**, 2668 (1915).

18. MILLER: Dissertation, Columbia University, 1922.

19. BAEYERTZ: Dissertation, Columbia University, 1924.

20. SVEDBERG: "The Formation of Colloids," D. Van Nostrand Company, New York, 1921; "Colloid Chemistry," A.C.S. Monograph, Chemical Catalog Co., New York, 1924.

21. BÖRJESON and SVEDBERG: *Kolloid-Z.*, **25**, 154 (1919); SVEDBERG: *Physik. Z.*, **15**, 361 (1914).

22. GUTBIER: *Z. anorg. allgem. Chem.*, **152**, 163 (1926).

23. GUTBIER: *Z. anorg. allgem. Chem.*, **155**, 199 (1926).

24. SVEDBERG: "The Formation of Colloids," p. 75, D. Van Nostrand Company, New York, 1921.

25. FULHAME: An Essay on Combustion with Views on a New Method of Coloring in Which the Phlogiston and Antiphlogiston Hypotheses Are Proven Erroneous, London, 1794; through *Ann. chim.*, **26**, 58 (1798).

26. OBERKAMPF: *Ann. chim.*, **80**, 140 (1811).

27. WEISER and MILLIGAN: *J. Phys. Chem.*, **36**, 1950 (1932).

28. ZSIGMONDY: *Ann. Chem.*, **301**, 29 (1898).

29. ZSIGMONDY and THIESSEN: "Das Kolloide Gold," Akademische Verlagsgesellschaft m.b.H., Leipzig, 1925.

30. VON VEIMARN: *Kolloid-Z.*, **53**, 352 (1930).

31. GETTLER and JACKSON: *Arch. Neurol. Psychiatry*, **6**, 70 (1921).

32. Ref. 29 (p. 43).

33. Ref. 29 (p. 47).

34. WINTGEN and HACKER: *Kolloid-Z.*, **61**, 335 (1932).

35. Ref. 29 (p. 52).

36. GALECKI: *Kolloid-Z.*, **11**, 105 (1912).

37. THIESSEN: *Z. anorg. allgem. Chem.*, **134**, 357 (1924).

38. DOERINCKLE: *Z. anorg. allgem. Chem.*, **63**, 344 (1909).

39. BEAVER and MÜLLER: *J. Am. Chem. Soc.*, **50**, 304 (1928).

40. NORDENSON: *Z. physik. Chem.*, **90**, 603 (1915).

41. STEUBING: *Ann. Physik*, (4) **26**, 335 (1908).

42. GUTBIER: *Z. anorg. allgem. Chem.*, **31**, 448 (1902); **32**, 347 (1902).

43. THIESSEN: *Kolloidchem. Beihefte*, **29**, 122 (1929).
44. HIEGE: *Z. anorg. Chem.*, **91**, 145 (1915).
45. ZSIGMONDY: *Z. physik. Chem.*, **56**, 65 (1906).
46. Ref. 29 (p. 65).
47. NORDENSON: Dissertation, Upsala, 1914; through SVEDBERG: Ref. 24 (p. 61).
48. Ref. 24 (p. 61).
49. Ref. 29 (p. 73).
50. Experiments of Reittstötter through Ref. 29 (p. 90).
51. GALECKI: *Z. anorg. Chem.*, **170**, 45 (1928); VOIGT and HEUMANN: *ibid.*, **164**, 409 (1927); **169**, 140 (1928); **173**, 27 (1928).
52. BÖRJESON: *Kolloid-Z.*, **27**, 18 (1920).
53. ROSE: *Ann. Phys. Chem.*, **14**, 183 (1828).
54. KOHLSCHÜTTER: *Z. Elektrochem.*, **14**, 49 (1908); *Kolloid-Z.*, **12**, 285 (1912).
55. VANINO and HARTL: *Kolloid-Z.*, **1**, 272 (1907); VON VEIMARN: *Kolloid-Z.*, **33**, 82 (1923); **36**, 55 (1924).
56. GUTBIER: *Kolloid-Z.*, **4**, 358 (1908); PAULI and NEUREITER: *Kolloid-Z.*, **33**, 68 (1923).
57. WIEGEL: *Kolloid-Z.*, **51**, 112; **53**, 96 (1930).
58. CASTORO: *Kolloid-Z.*, **6**, 287 (1909).
59. CAREY LEA: *Am. J. Sci. Arts*, **37**, 476 (1889); **42**, 312 (1891); *Phil. Mag.*, (5) **31**, 497; **32**, 337 (1891); *Z. anorg. Chem.*, **7**, 341 (1894).
60. LÜPPO-CRAMER: *Kolloid-Z.*, **7**, 99 (1910).
61. VOIGT and HEUMANN: Ref. 51.
62. MATHUR and DHAR: *Z. anorg. allgem. Chem.*, **199**, 392 (1931).
63. TAYLOR and CONE: *J. Am. Chem. Soc.*, **55**, 3512 (1933).
64. SVEDBERG: *Kolloid-Z.*, **6**, 129 (1910).
65. NORDENSON: *Kolloidchem. Beihefte*, **7**, 91 (1915).
66. GUTBIER: *Z. anorg. Chem.*, **32**, 51, 91, 106, 347 (1902); **42**, 177 (1904); GUTBIER and HOFMEIER: *J. prakt. Chem.*, (2) **71**, 358, 452 (1905).
67. PAAL: *Ber.*, **35**, 2195, 2224, 2236 (1902); **37**, 124 (1904); **38**, 526, 534, 1398 (1905); **39**, 1550 (1906); **40**, 1392 (1907); **47**, 2202 (1914); **50**, 722 (1917); **60B**, 1648 (1927); **46**, 1297 (1913); **48**, 220, 994 (1915); **51**, 894, 1743 (1918).
68. SKITA: *Ber.*, **41**, 2938 (1908); **42**, 1627 (1909); **43**, 3393 (1910); **44**, 2826 (1911); **45**, 3312, 3579, 3589 (1912); BOURGUEL: *Bull. soc. chim.*, **41**, 1443 (1927); CAROTHERS and ADAMS: *J. Am. Chem. Soc.*, **46**, 1675 (1924); GULEVICH: *Ber.*, **57B**, 1645 (1924); KAUFMANN and ADAMS: *J. Am. Chem. Soc.*, **45**, 3029 (1923); LOCHTE and BAILEY: *Ber.*, **56B**, 1799 (1923); RIDEAL: *J. Am. Chem. Soc.*, **42**, 749 (1920); SHRINER and ADAMS: *J. Am. Chem. Soc.*, **46**, 1683 (1924); VOORHEES and ADAMS: *J. Am. Chem. Soc.*, **44**, 1397 (1922).
69. Ref. 29 (p. 211).
70. FRICK: *Ann. Phys. Chem.*, **12**, 285 (1828).
71. VOIGT: "Das Kolloide Silber," p. 61, Akademische Verlagsgesellschaft m.b.H., Leipzig, 1929.

72. Wöhler: *Kolloid-Z.*, **2**, Suppl. Heft. 1, III (1907).
73. Gutbier and Ottenstein: *Z. anorg. allgem. Chem.*, **160**, 27 (1927).
74. Gutbier and coworkers: *Z. anorg. allgem. Chem.*, **162**, 87 (1927); **164**, 274, 281, 287 (1927); **169**, 264 (1928).
75. Döbereiner: *Schweigger's J. Chem. u. Phys.*, **8**, 400 (1813).
76. Wackenroder: *Arch. Pharm.*, **47**, 272 (1846); *Ann. chim. phys.*, (3) **20**, 144 (1847).
77. Selmi and Sobrero: *Mem. R. Accad. Torino*, (2) **11**, 407 (1849); *J. prakt. Chem.*, **49**, 417 (1850); *Ann.*, **76**, 237 (1850).
78. Debus: *J. Chem. Soc.*, **53**, 278 (1888); *Ann.*, **244**, 76 (1888).
79. Odén: Der Kolloide Schwefel, *Nova Acta Regiae Soc. Sci. Upsala*, Ser. 4, Vol. **3**, No. (4) 1–193 (1913).
80. Young and Williams: *Science*, **67**, 19 (1928).
81. Engel: *Compt. rend.*, **112**, 866 (1891).
82. Raffo: *Kolloid-Z.*, **2**, 358 (1908).
83. Freundlich and Scholz: *Kolloidchem. Beihefte*, **16**, 234 (1922).
84. Odén: *Kolloid-Z.*, **8**, 186 (1911).
85. Harrison: *Kolloid-Z.*, **9**, 5 (1911).
86. Chandler and Miller: *J. Phys. Chem.*, **31**, 1091 (1927).
87. Nyiri and Dubois: *J. Am. Pharm. Assoc.*, **20**, 546 (1931).
88. Péan de St. Gilles: *Compt. rend.*, **40**, 568, 1243 (1855).
89. Graham: *Phil. Trans. Roy. Soc. London*, **151**, 183 (1861).
90. Goodwin and Grover: *Phys. Rev.*, **11**, 193 (1900).
91. Heymann: *Z. anorg. allgem. Chem.*, **171**, 18 (1928).
92. Puxeddu: *Gazz. chim. ital.*, **53**, 210 (1923); through *Chem. Abs.*, **17**, 2808 (1923).
93. Heymann: *Kolloid-Z.*, **48**, 25 (1929).
94. Heymann: *Kolloid-Z.*, **47**, 325 (1929).
95. Krecke: *J. prakt. Chem.*, (2) **3**, 286 (1871).
96. Sorum: *J. Am. Chem. Soc.*, **50**, 1263 (1928).
97. Ayres and Sorum: *J. Phys. Chem.*, **34**, 875 (1930).
98. Grimaux: *Compt. rend.*, **98**, 105, 1434 (1884).
99. Thiessen and Koerner: *Z. anorg. allgem. Chem.*, **180**, 115 (1929).
100. Ordway: *Am. J. Sci.*, (2) **76**, 197 (1858).
101. Graham: *Phil. Mag.*, (4) **23**, 204, 290, 368 (1862).
102. Neidle and Barab: *J. Am. Chem. Soc.*, **39**, 71 (1917).
103. Thomas and Frieden: *J. Am. Chem. Soc.*, **45**, 2522 (1923).
104. Freundlich and Wosnessensky: *Kolloid-Z.*, **33**, 222 (1923).
105. Fischer: *Biochem. Z.*, **27**, 223 (1910).
106. Dumanski et al.: *Kolloid-Z.*, **51**, 210 (1930); **54**, 73 (1931).
107. Dumanski and Yakovlev: *Bull. soc. chim.*, (4) **47**, 1211 (1930); Dumanski: *Kolloidchem. Beihefte*, **31**, 418 (1930).
108. Hazel and Sorum: *J. Am. Chem. Soc.*, **52**, 1337 (1930).
109. Powis: *J. Chem. Soc.*, **107**, 817 (1916).
110. Thiessen: *Z. anorg. allgem. Chem.*, **182**, 425 (1929).
111. Crum: *Ann. chim. phys.*, (3) **41**, 185 (1854); *Ann. Chem.*, **89**, 156 (1854).
112. Weiser: *J. Phys. Chem.*, **35**, 1368 (1901).

113. THOMAS and TAI: *J. Am. Chem. Soc.*, **54**, 841 (1932).

114. KOLSCHÜTTER and NEUENCHWANDER: *Z. Elektrochem.*, **29**, 246 (1923); LOTTERMOSER and FRIEDRICH: *Ber.*, **57B**, 808 (1924).

115. GRAHAM: *Proc. Roy. Soc. (London)*, **13**, 335 (1864).

116. EBLER and FELLNER: *Ber.*, **44**, 1915 (1911).

117. KONRAD, BÄCHLE, and SIGNER: *Ann.*, **474**, 276 (1929).

118. MYLIUS and GROSCHUFF: *Ber.*, **39**, 116 (1906); JORDIS and KANTER: *Z. anorg. Chem.*, **35**, 16 (1903); WILLSTÄTTER, KRAUT, and LOBINGER: *Ber.*, **58B**, 2426 (1925); BRINTZINGER: *Z. anorg. allgem. Chem.*, **159**, 256 (1927); **181**, 237 (1929).

119. JORDIS and KANTER: Ref. 118; LOTTERMOSER and KIEHN: *Kolloidchem. Beihefte*, **35**, 123 (1932).

120. BRINTZINGER: Ref. 118.

121. KRUYT and POSTMA: *Rec. trav. chim.*, **44**, 765 (1925).

122. FREUNDLICH and COHN: *Kolloid-Z.*, **39**, 28 (1926).

123. SCHWARZ: *Kolloid-Z.*, **34**, 23 (1924).

124. GRUNDMANN: *Kolloid-Z.*, **36**, 328 (1925).

125. COLLINS and WOOD: *J. Chem. Soc.*, **121**, 1122 (1922); MECKLENBURG: *Z. anorg. Chem.*, **74**, 207 (1912); **84**, 121 (1914).

126. SCHNEIDER: *Z. anorg. Chem.*, **5**, 82 (1914); ZSIGMONDY: *Ann. Chem.*, **301**, 361 (1898); *Z. anorg. Chem.*, **89**, 210 (1914); STIEGLER: *Kolloid-Z.*, **29**, 65 (1921); COLLINS and WOOD: *J. Chem. Soc.*, **121**, 2760 (1922); WINTGEN and KEILHOLZ: *Kolloid-Z.*, **55**, 323 (1931).

127. STIEGLER: Ref. 126.

128. MECKLENBURG: Ref. 125.

129. COLLINS and WOOD: Ref. 125.

130. DUMANSKII and KNIGA: *J. Russ. Phys.-Chem. Soc.*, **60**, 229 (1928); through *Chem. Abs.*, **22**, 4028.

131. ZSIGMONDY (1914): Ref. 126.

132. BRADFIELD: *J. Am. Chem. Soc.*, **44**, 965 (1922).

133. SCHULZE: *J. prakt. Chem.*, **25**, 431 (1882).

134. SCHULZE: *J. prakt. Chem.*, **27**, 320 (1883).

135. LOTTERMOSER: *J. prakt. Chem.*, **183**, 293 (1907).

136. WRIGHT: *J. Chem. Soc.*, **43**, 156 (1883).

137. SPRING: *Ber.*, **16**, 1142 (1883).

138. WINSSINGER: *Bull. soc. chim.*, **49**, 452 (1888).

139. LINDER and PICTON: *J. Chem. Soc.*, **61**, 114 (1892); PICTON: *J. Chem. Soc.*, **61**, 137 (1892); YOUNG and NEAL: *J. Phys. Chem.*, **21**, 14 (1917); YOUNG and GODDARD: *J. Phys. Chem.*, **21**, 1 (1917).

140. VON HAHN: *Kolloid-Z.*, **31**, 200 (1922).

141. BOUTARIC and VUILLAUME: *Compt. rend.*, **178**, 938 (1924).

142. BOUTARIC and SIMONET: *Bull. sci. acad. roy. Belg.*, (5) **10**, 150 (1924).

143. FREUNDLICH and NATHANSOHN: *Kolloid-Z.*, **28**, 258 (1921).

144. SPRING and DE BOECK: *Bull. soc. chim.*, **48**, 165 (1887).

145. LINDER and PICTON: Ref. 139.

146. PICTON: Ref. 139.

147. LOTTERMOSER et al.: *J. prakt. Chem.*, **68,** 341 (1903); **72,** 39 (1905); **73,** 374 (1906); *Z. physik. Chem.*, **62,** 359 (1908); **70,** 239 (1910); *Kolloid-Z.*, Zsigmondy Festschrift, 230 (1925).

148. BACHMANN: *Z. anorg. allgem. Chem.*, **100,** 77 (1917).

149. KOHN: *Monatsh.*, **43,** 373 (1923).

150. KOHN: *Z. anorg. allgem. Chem.*, **197,** 289 (1931).

151. DUCLAUX: *J. chim. phys.*, **5,** 29 (1907).

152. OSTWALD and EGGER: *Kolloid-Z.*, **43,** 353 (1927).

153. GUTBIER and EMSLANDER: *Ber.*, **54B,** 1974 (1921).

CHAPTER VII

THE NATURE OF MICELLES

After Thomas Graham had peptized hydrous ferric oxide by ferric chloride, he attempted to remove the chloride impurity by dialysis only to find that the dispersed phase precipitated before all of the chloride had been removed. This led him to believe that a hydrosol of pure hydrous ferric oxide could not be prepared. Graham's experience has been repeatedly confirmed by many investigators who have worked with sols of the hydrophobic and intermediate classes. One investigator, however, claims to have prepared sols of pure hydrous ferric oxide.[1]

Linder and Picton (1892) showed that hydrosols of the insoluble sulfides could be had only in the presence of some hydrogen sulfide. Jordis and Kanter (1903) noted that some added acid or alkali was essential to the formation of a sol of hydrous silica. Duclaux (1907) demonstrated that a slight excess of potassium ferrocyanide was required in the formation of copper ferrocyanide hydrosol. In the same year, Svedberg[2] found that he could obtain more stable platinum sols by arcing platinum electrodes in ether containing impurities than in pure ether. Then, in 1915, Beans and Eastlack demonstrated the necessity for presence of traces of certain kinds of electrolyte for the preparation of gold hydrosols by the Bredig-arc method.

Thus it has been shown that colloidal dispersions of insoluble substances require the presence of some other substance, usually a particular ion, and in this way the "complex theory of colloids" developed. The presence of electrolytes is not essential to the stability of hydrophilic dispersions, however. A wide variety of the latter can be dialyzed free from all electrolyte without precipitation taking place and certain pure solids which give rise to hydrophilic dispersions will disperse in pure water without the assistance of added electrolyte.

Obviously, when we use the terms "colloidal ferric oxide," "antimony sulfide," "copper ferrocyanide," etc., we are naming only a part which is the more inert chemically. Duclaux (1907) called the extra potassium ferrocyanide in the copper ferrocyanide sols the "active part." Malfitano[3] designated ferric oxide sols prepared by ferric chloride peptization the *chloroferric colloids* and the *ferrichydroxychloride colloids*.

At the present time, the writers who use names such as proposed by Malfitano are in the minority. The majority name the insoluble part, such as *ferric oxide* sol, and then refer to ferric chloride, hydrochloric acid, etc., as the peptizing agent because hydrous ferric oxide gel peptizes under treatment with these electrolytes to form a sol. Then since these micelles are positively charged, ferric or hydrogen ions are called the *stabilizing* or *peptizing ions*.

While it is now generally recognized that insoluble substances cannot exist in a form of reasonably lasting dispersion without the presence of certain crystalloidal ions, the nature of the particles and of the stabilizing forces is under debate. There are two distinct schools: the one maintaining that a hydrosol of, for instance, ferric oxide consists of ferric oxide particles with adsorbed H^+ or Fe^{+++} ions on their surfaces, while the other school prefers to look upon such hydrosol particles as more complicated chemical agglomerates. The prime reason for assuming that the above-named cations are adsorbed on the particle surface is that the micelle migrates to the negative pole in an electrical field.

If water of hydration is ignored, a simple picture of such a colloidal particle is

$$x Fe_2O_3.H^+ \ Cl^- \quad \text{or} \quad x Fe_2O_3.Fe^{+++} \ 3Cl^-$$

and ferric oxide is said to adsorb preferentially H^+ ion or Fe^{+++} ion. By virtue of the fact that the colloidal particles are all charged alike, the stability of the dispersion is said to reside in the electrical repulsive forces which are in opposition to the gravitational force of attraction and the surface forces of agglomeration.

Based on the X-ray revelations of the nature of crystal structure by the Braggs, Langmuir,[4] apart from any thought of colloidally dispersed particles, showed why the surface of a crystal has attractive forces for certain ions. Since, he pointed out, the body of a crystal consists of its component atoms spaced in an orderly arrangement about each other and held to each other by secondary-valence attractive forces, the surface of the crystal must contain atoms part of whose secondary

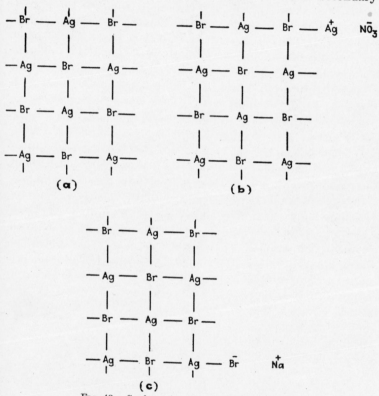

Fig. 43.—Surface of a silver bromide particle.

valences is unsatisfied. Thus he described the surface of a crystal as a sort of checkerboard of inactive and active areas, the latter by virtue of their secondary valences having the property to attract and to hold suitable substances.

An application of Langmuir's idea to silver halide sols is given in Fig. 43. Figure 43a shows the nature of a part of the surface of a particle of silver bromide. Such a particle was shown by

Lottermoser to be unstable, whereas when he mixed together solutions of silver nitrate and sodium bromide in proportions which were not equivalent he obtained stable dispersions. Figure 43*b* indicates the nature of the sol particle when silver nitrate was in excess, and Fig. 43*c* for excess of sodium bromide. The excess silver ion is shown in Fig. 43*b* as satisfying one of the secondary valences of one of the bromin atoms of the particle surface, thus conferring upon the particle a positive charge. Similarly, in Fig. 43*c* the particle becomes negatively charged. As a result of the double-decomposition reaction, Na^+ and NO_3^- are present in abundance in all three cases but, however, in view of the nature of the dispersions mentioned above, these ions evidently are not significant.

The picture just described affords an understanding of positively and negatively charged silver halide sol particles. While such a simple picture may be adequate for these particles and for some other hydrophobic colloids, there is evidence which shows certain kinds of dispersed particles to be more complex in nature.

Oxide Hydrosols.—In keeping with the ideas of Duclaux, Malfitano, and Dumanski[5] concerning the nature of iron oxide hydrosols, Zsigmondy[6] postulated that the peptization of stannic oxide gel by potassium hydroxide produces particles which (water of hydration ignored) could be represented qualitatively as

$$xSnO_2.SnO_3^-\ 2K^+$$

thus describing the colloidal particle as an aggregate of stannic oxide with adsorbed stannate ions, the charge of the latter being balanced by potassium ions.*

As a result of conductivity studies, Varga[7] concluded that the negatively charged ionic micelle of such stannic oxide sols is more complicated, some of the potassium being bound in it. Wintgen[8] confirmed this conclusion by electrical transport as well as by conductivity measurements and gave the qualitative formulation of the dispersed phase as

$$\boxed{SnO_2.K_2O.H_2O}\ SnO_3H^-\ K^+$$

He showed later that part of the chlorin in a sol of ferric oxide peptized by ferric chloride migrated with the iron oxide to the

---

* Such balancing crystalloidal ions are now called "contra-ions."

cathode[9] and likewise in the case of a chromic oxide sol.[10] In his investigation of the iron oxide sols he made calomel-electrode potential measurements which showed that only a fraction of the total chlorin present was in the form of free chloride ion.

Thomas and Frieden[11] noted that ferric oxide sols in which the particles contained an appreciable amount of chlorin had a conductivity lower than that of distilled water used for dialysis. The fact that most of the chlorin in an iron oxide sol could be in an un-ionized form was indicated qualitatively in 1902[12] by Hantzch and Desch, who, upon dialyzing a ferric oxide sol until its composition upon analysis showed a Fe:Cl equivalent ratio of 19, found, that no precipitate was obtained upon addition of silver nitrate.

Linder and Picton[13] obtained results which agreed with those of Hantzch and Desch and concluded that the sol particle "substance present here is a hydroxychloride and not a hydrate associated with ferric chloride or free hydrochloric acid." Neidle[14] claimed the sol to consist of a series of oxychlorides.

In view of the evidence, the qualitative formulation of the dispersed phase in such iron oxide hydrosols (ignoring water) is

$$\boxed{\text{Fe, O, Cl}}^{\,n+} \; n\text{Cl}^-.$$

Apparently a better name for such a sol would be *ferricoxychloride hydrosol*. An objection to such a name would be that it connotes a definite chemical compound. No such connotation is intended by the writer; the dispersed phase undoubtedly consists of an agglomerate of various chemical compounds.

Recently the author and his students[15,16,17] have attempted to elaborate the micellar constitution of such hydrosols, particularly aluminum "oxide" and chromic "oxide" sols,[18] basing their argument upon the Werner theory of complex salts and extensions of this theory to basic salts.

The hydrolysis of chromium or aluminum* salts according to

---

* The citation of aluminum as a complex former surprises some chemists who may not realize that coordinative compounds of this element have been described.[19]

Pfeiffer[20] is, in contradistinction to Arrhenius's theory of hydrolysis, as follows:

$$\begin{bmatrix} H_2O & & OH_2 \\ & \diagdown & \diagup \\ H_2O-Me-OH_2 \\ & \diagup & \diagdown \\ H_2O & & OH_2 \end{bmatrix}^{+++} \rightleftharpoons \begin{bmatrix} H_2O & & OH \\ & \diagdown & \diagup \\ H_2O-Me-OH_2 \\ & \diagup & \diagdown \\ H_2O & & OH_2 \end{bmatrix}^{++} + H^+ \quad (1)$$

The extent of this dissociation depends on the nature of the anion[21] which is associated with it, besides concentration, temperature,[22] and basicity of the solution. Of all these factors, basicity of the solution has the greatest influence on the degree of dissociation because the combination of the base with the hydrogen ion removes one of the products and thus promotes further hydrolysis. Upon addition of sufficient base the dissociation goes so far as to produce a negative ion such as

$$\begin{bmatrix} H_2O & & OH \\ & \diagdown & \diagup \\ H_2O-Me-OH \\ & \diagup & \diagdown \\ HO & & OH \end{bmatrix}^{-} \quad (2)$$

but before this stage of dissociation is reached, polymerization reactions take place.

In 1902, Pfeiffer[23] suggested the possibility of one coordinative bond of each of two metal atoms being shared by one hydroxyl (or rather *hydroxo*) group. To such compounds Werner[24] gave the name *ol compounds* and described the preparation of octamminodioldicobalti sulfate from hydroxoaquotetramminocobalti sulfate. Then Pfeiffer,[25] observing that the red colored diethylenediaminehydroxoaquochromi salts were converted to crystalline blue-violet salts with the loss of 1 molecule of water per atom of chromium upon heating to 100 to 120°, proposed the formation of the diol compound as the most satisfactory explanation, according to the scheme*

$$X_2 \begin{bmatrix} en & OH\ H_2O & en \\ \diagdown\diagdown & \diagup\quad\diagdown & \diagup\diagup \\ & Cr & Cr \\ \diagup\diagup & \diagdown\quad\diagup & \diagdown\diagdown \\ en & OH_2\ HO & en \end{bmatrix} X_2 \rightarrow X_4 \begin{bmatrix} en & \overset{H}{O} & en \\ \diagdown\diagdown & \diagup\cdots\diagdown & \diagup\diagup \\ & Cr \quad Cr \\ \diagup\diagup & \diagdown\cdots\diagup & \diagdown\diagdown \\ en & \underset{H}{O} & en \end{bmatrix} X_4 + 2H_2O \quad (3)$$

2 molecules of the red salt   1 molecule of the blue-violet diol compound

* *en* = ethylenediamine; X = a monovalent anion.

and he pointed out, "dass dieser Vorgang manche analogie mit der Polymerisation organischer Verbindungen, z.B. der der Aldehyde zeigt, ist ohne weiteres ersichtlich." Since the flesh-colored diethylenediaminehydroxoaquo salts did not undergo this change upon heating, he ascribed to them the *trans* configuration,

$$\left[\begin{array}{c} en \qquad OH \\ \diagdown \diagup \\ Cr \\ \diagup \diagdown \\ H_2O \qquad en \end{array}\right] X_2 \tag{4}$$

and to the red salts, the *cis* structure.

At this time Bjerrum[26] found polymerization of basic chromic salts to occur upon heating their aqueous solutions. Bjerrum called these "latent basic" compounds. A few years prior to Bjerrum's publication, Richards and Bonnet[27] also reported the formation of high molecular-weight particles in basic chromic sulfate solutions.

Returning now to a simple basic chromic ion, the schematic representation of the polymerization would be

$$2\left[\begin{array}{c} H_2O \qquad OH \\ \diagdown \diagup \\ H_2O-Cr-OH_2 \\ \diagup \diagdown \\ H_2O \qquad OH_2 \end{array}\right]^{++} \rightleftharpoons \left[(H_2O)_4Cr \begin{array}{c} H \\ O \\ \diagdown \diagup \\ \diagup \diagdown \\ O \\ H \end{array} Cr(H_2O)_4\right]^{++++} + 2H_2O \tag{5}$$

pentaaquohydroxochromi   octaaquodioldichromi ion
ion

The *olation* pictured above is favored by elevation in temperature and increase in concentration. It reverses very slowly upon cooling or upon dilution and also, inasmuch as *ol* compounds react less rapidly than hydroxo compounds upon addition of hydrogen ion, the name *latent basic* applied by Bjerrum is understandable. From what has been said, it is likewise evident that olation, by virtue of removal of one of the products, favors the course of reaction (1) to the right.

The addition of an alkali to a solution of an aluminum or chromic salt, which results in the formation of more hydroxo groups in the complex around the metallic atom, greatly accelerates the process of olation. The change in hydrogen ion concentration accompanying this process becomes noticeable even in a short time during titration. Moreover, as the acidity of the solution is neutralized, especially if the temperature of the solution is raised, not only is the rate of formation of ol compounds increased but also the reaction will involve more nuclei to form polynuclear compounds. That is, dissociation of aquo groups to hydroxo groups in the diol compound [Eq. (5)] renders possible further olation to tetraol compounds, and so on.

Stiasny,[28] in 1926, revived interest in the process of olation and, in 1927, suggested the possibility of the existence, among other complexes, of dodecaoldodecaaquohexachromi chloride (molecular weight = 732) in Bjerrum's "latent basic" chromic chloride solution. Stiasny, owing to his interest in the basic chromium solutions used in chrome leather tanning, has made extensive and illuminating studies of the nature of basic chromic solutions. Finding that solutions of ol compounds of chromium become very acid and produce rather refractory chromic complexes upon heating, he proposed the following mechanism as an explanation:

$$\left[(H_2O)_4Cr \begin{array}{c} \overset{H}{\underset{}{O}} \\ O \\ \overset{}{\underset{H}{O}} \end{array} Cr(H_2O)_4\right]^{++++} \rightleftharpoons \left[(H_2O)_4Cr \begin{array}{c} O \\ O \end{array} Cr(H_2O)_4\right]^{++} + 2H^+ \quad (6)$$

(diol compound)   (dioxo compound)

the hydrogen ions coming from the conversion of the *ol bridges* to *oxygen bridges,* producing *oxo* compounds. This process is called *oxolation* and for convenience a possible intermediate product containing one —O— and one —OH— bridge has been omitted from Eq. (6). Oxo compounds are very resistant to the action of hydrogen ion. Thus once the reaction to the right in Eq. (6) has been effected, its reversal is exceedingly slow.

Olation and oxolation, therefore, explain why freshly precipitated aluminum or chromium hydroxide which is readily soluble in dilute acid becomes more resistant on heating and standing.

On complete oxolation of a polyolated structure such as hydrous alumina, the very inert substance, Al_2O_3, is formed. When the structure of the oxide is represented by a spacial picture with each aluminum atom united with its neighboring aluminum atoms through two adjacent oxygen bridges which are arranged around it at the corners of an octahedron, there will be four aluminum atoms surrounding each oxygen atom. This picture of the structure of aluminum oxide agrees with that which has been revealed by X-ray studies on corundum crystals.[29]

Olation of hydroxo groups provides a theoretical mechanism for the gradual increase in size of hydrous oxide aggregates in solution. An olated nucleus containing six aluminum atoms is shown in Fig. 44. Upon hydrolysis of any of the water molecules shown in this hypothetical complex, it is seen how olation with other similar nuclei may result through the hydroxo groups thus formed, producing larger complexes. Also it is seen how, by dissociation of an aquo group, a hydrogen ion moves from the

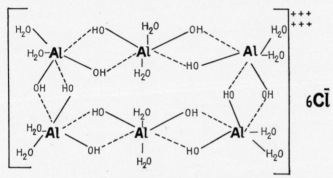

FIG. 44.—Dodecaoldodecaaquohexaalumini hexachloride.

"internal sphere" to the "outer solution," thus leaving the nucleus with a hydroxo group and with one less positive charge. If, then, six aquo groups in the sort of nucleus shown in Fig. 44 were to dissociate, the charge would be reduced to zero. Such dissociation, accompanied by oxolation, would take place upon heating or upon addition of alkali to the solution, or both. When the charge of such nuclei is reduced, so is the stability in solution. It is well-known that addition of alkali or prolonged boiling causes precipitation of the dispersed phase of "hydroxide" sols.

The dissociation of a hexaaquo aluminum or chromic ion in water, resulting in the formation of hydroxo groups bound to the nucleus, may also be regarded as a migration or penetration of hydroxyl ions into the internal sphere. Although the hydroxyl ion concentration in pure water is exceedingly small, yet owing to its high penetrating power, a hydroxyl ion makes its way into the internal sphere and replaces a water molecule. As the concentration of hydroxyl ion in the solution increases, more of it will penetrate into the internal sphere and become bound in the nucleus. However, other anions as well as hydroxyl ion are able to penetrate into the complex to greater or less degree, depending upon the nature and concentration of the anion added to the solution. For example, Feigl and Kraus[30] found that a solution of basic aluminum acetate is rendered alkaline when potassium oxalate is added to it. They accounted for this by the reaction

$$Al(OH)(C_2H_3O_2)_2 + 3K_2C_2O_4 \rightarrow K_3[Al(C_2O_4)_3] + 2KC_2H_3O_2 + KOH \quad (7)$$

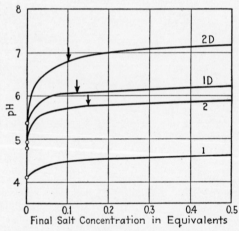

Fig. 45.—Effect of potassium chloride upon the pH values of aluminumoxyiodide sols.

and utilized it for the analysis of solutions of basic aluminum salts. In passing now from such a simple crystalloid solution to a gel, it may be pointed out that, when freshly precipitated alumina hydrate is treated with a neutral salt such as potassium sulfate, citrate, or phosphate, the solution becomes alkaline to phenolphthalein.[31] Since, then, a crystalloid basic aluminum salt and hydrous alumina gel become alkaline upon treatment with certain neutral salts, it would seem logical to assume that dispersions intermediate between the basic crystalloid salts and the gel would act in the same manner. This has actually been found to be the case for aluminum oxysalt hydrosols[15,16,17] and also for chromic oxysalt hydrosols.[18]

In Fig. 45[16] is shown the effect of added potassium chloride upon four aluminum oxyiodide sols. It is seen that all became less acid, two of them actually becoming alkaline in reaction. While the salt is shown to exert the same general effect upon all four sols, it is obvious that the sols react to different degrees, showing that even a more comprehensive name, such as "aluminum oxyiodide" sol, does not in any way refer to one simple system.

The sols used in Fig. 45 were made by the action of a dilute solution of hydriodic acid upon aluminum amalgam.[16] The details of the preparation and the composition are given in Table 20.

TABLE 20.—PREPARATION AND COMPOSITION OF THE SOLS DESCRIBED IN FIGS. 45 AND 51

	Sol				
	1	1D	2	2D	3
Amount of 0.5 N HI added, cc...................	20	......	100	......	50
Total volume, liters.......	3	......	4	......	3
Temperature of reaction...	Room	......	Boiling	......	Boiling
Time of reaction..........	2 days	......	8 hr.	......	8 hr.
Dialysis.................	None	Sol 1 dialyzed for 10 days	......	Sol 2 dialyzed for 4 days	14 days
Aluminum content, m.e.* per liter...............	23.0	8.77	425.6	386.9	143.4
Iodide content..........	2.961	0.363	11.25	4.511	1.291
Ratio Al:I..............	7.8	24	38	86	111
Viscosity, time of outflow in seconds (H_2O = 82.0).	82.4	82.6	92.3	109.4	95.6
pH value................	4.17	5.35	4.88	4.94	5.63

* m.e. = milliequivalents.

Sol 2, which was prepared by the action of a boiling solution of dilute hydriodic acid upon aluminum amalgam instead of at room temperature, liberated more hydroxyl ion as a result of the addition of sodium chloride than sol 1 did.   It is also to be noticed that sol 2 was much more concentrated than sol 1.   When these sols were dialyzed, however, their reactivity increased as shown for the curves 1D and 2D.

In Fig. 46 are shown the effects of the addition of potassium chloride to two aluminum oxychloride sols.[15]   These sols were prepared by peptization of freshly precipitated hydrous aluminum

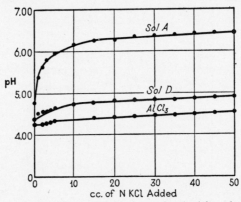

FIG. 46.—Increased effect is noted with increasing basicity of the aluminum complex.

oxide with hydrochloric acid under approximately the same temperature conditions.   The composition of these sols is given in Table 21.

TABLE 21.—COMPOSITION OF ALUMINUM OXYCHLORIDE SOLS SHOWN IN FIG. 46

	Total Al, m.e. per liter	Total Cl, m.e. per liter	Al/Cl	pH
A..........................	44	1.2	37	4.75
D..........................	62	13.4	4.6	4.39
AlCl₃......................	62	62	1	4.36

Thus Fig. 46 shows that the sol A, containing 37 equivalents of Al to each equivalent of Cl, suffered a greater increase in pH than sol D which contained 4.6 equivalents of Al to Cl.   It is noted also that the aluminum chloride solution underwent a slight increase in pH as a result of the added salt.

Salts affect the pH values of an "aluminum oxide" sol to different degrees depending upon the nature of the anion as shown in Fig. 47, where the -oxyiodide sol 2D was used. In Fig. 48,

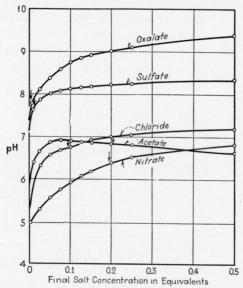

Fig. 47.—Influence of nature of anion of added neutral salt upon pH values of aluminumoxyiodide sol, *2D*.

the pH changes produced by the addition of neutral salts to a chromic oxychloride sol are plotted.

TABLE 22.—DESCRIPTION OF CHROMICOXYCHLORIDE HYDROSOLS*

Sol number	8	12	13
Normality CrCl₃ used......................	1.0	0.5	0.5
Dialysis hours.............................	120	120	192
Cr, m.e. per liter.........................	156.0	144.9	75.88
Cl, m.e. per liter.........................	17.93	15.74	5.14
Ratio Cr:Cl...............................	8.7	9.2	14.8
pH at end of dialysis (25°).................	3.88	3.75	4.30

Normality written as $CrCl_3$.

* Discussed on pages 154, 157 and 160.

It may be well to refer to crystalloidal chromic salt solutions in this connection. First, it is known that oxalate, acetate, tartrate, and sulfate ions readily react with chromic chloride, displacing coordinatively bound aquo groups or chlorido groups and, if at a sufficient concentration, actually convert the chromium cation to an anion resulting in the formation of chromiates.[32] Nitrate and chloride are much less powerful in this respect and do not produce chlorido or nitrato chromiates although the triaquotrichlorido chromium has been recognized. Second, it has been shown that low concentrations of sodium

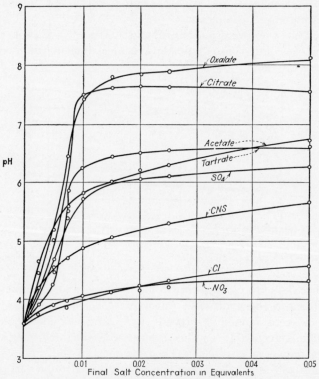

Fig. 48.—Influence of nature of anion of added neutral salt upon pH values of chromicoxychloride sol, 12.

chloride decrease the hydrogen ion activity of chromic chloride solutions[33] and it is known that sodium sulfate is more potent in this respect.[32] Although it has been denied[34] that hydroxo groups can be replaced by neutral salt anions from crystalloid and semicolloid complex ions, the curves in Figs. 47 and 48 give strong indication that either hydroxo or ol (or both) groups have been replaced from the chromic micelles by the added neutral salt anions. Below about 0.005 N concentration of added powerfully acting anion (Fig. 48) the pH curves rise gradually and then ascend steeply. At very low concentrations of added anion, aquo and chlorido groups are presumed to be displaced from the micelle to a greater extent then hydroxo groups. This is reasonable in view of the fact that hydroxo groups are known to be about the most strongly coordinatively bound groups in low molecular-weight chromium complexes.[35]

Thus far, the discussion has involved "oxide" hydrosols containing the contra-ions chloride and iodide. The question arises

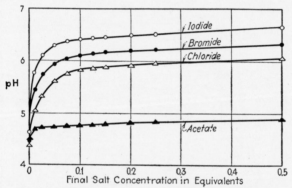

Fig. 49.—Effect of potassium sulfate upon pH values of aluminumoxyiodide, bromide, chloride, and acetate sols.

whether the nature of the contra-ion has any influence upon the properties of the hydrosols. In order to answer this question, four different aluminum oxysalt hydrosols: -oxyiodide, -oxybromide, -oxychloride, and -oxyacetate were prepared in as identical a manner as possible.[16] Then the effect of added potassium chloride and of potassium sulfate upon the pH values of these sols was measured. Figure 49 shows the results obtained for potassium sulfate (potassium chloride gave the same order of curves but, of course, at lower pH values). They are all different! The order of reactivity, -oxyiodide sol > -oxybromide > -oxychloride > -oxyacetate is the reverse of the effect obtained when the corresponding potassium salts are added to an aluminum oxychloride sol. This is to be expected. If acetate is more potent than iodide in entering the internal sphere of an aluminum oxychloride sol and displacing therefrom hydroxo groups, then an aluminum oxyacetate sol should be less affected in this respect than an aluminum oxyiodide sol by the addition of a neutral salt.

When aluminum or chromic oxysalt hydrosols are heated, they become more acid. This may be explained on the basis of two mechanisms. First olation increases, thus removing a reaction product which would favor hydrolysis of aquo groups. Also ol compounds would oxolate, thus contributing further to the hydrogen ion activity of the solution. Since ol groups are less

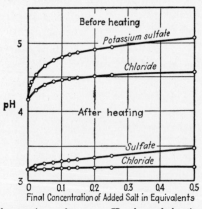

Fig. 50.—Effect of potassium salts upon pH values of aluminumoxyiodide sol, 1.

reactive toward neutral salts than hydroxo groups, and oxo groups are inert, it would be expected that heat-treated sols would be less reactive toward neutral salts. The result of an experiment in which an aluminum oxyiodide sol was heated at 90° for 10 days, cooled at room temperature, and then treated with neutral salts is plotted in Fig. 50.[16] It is seen that the sol became more acid as a result of the heating and that the added neutral salts had very little effect upon the pH of the heat-treated sol. It is also evident that here we have two aluminum oxyiodide sols of identical total aluminum and total iodide content but possessing different properties! Chromic oxychloride sols act similarly.[18]

While the heat treatment would produce oxolation of ol groups, it is to be remembered that olation of hydroxo groups would also occur, thus giving an additional reason for the greater inertness of the heated sol toward neutral salts.

When heat-treated sols are allowed to stand at room temperature, the reaction reverses slowly. For example, aluminum oxyiodide sol 1, with a pH value of 4.20, was at pH = 3.15 immediately following the above-mentioned heating. In 20 days at room temperature the pH rose to 3.31. The unheated sol became more acid on standing at room temperature. In 90 days its pH was 3.87. Chromic oxychloride sol 8 (pH 3.88) was at pH = 2.71 immediately after the same heat treatment and in 28 days at room temperature its pH rose to 2.83, while in the same time the unheated sol showed a pH value of 3.73. Thus one may have two sols containing identical amounts of aluminum (or chromium) and of iodide (or chloride) which are different in properties owing to different degrees of olation and oxolation.

The extent to which an anion becomes coordinatively bound in the positively charged micelle would likewise be expected to influence the properties of such hydrosols.

The internal sphere binding of anionic radicals in crystalloid compounds is well-known, particularly in the case of chromium compounds which have been studied extensively. For example, the following solutions of chlorides of chromium are recognized:

$$\begin{bmatrix} H_2O & & H_2O \\ H_2O & Cr & H_2O \\ H_2O & & H_2O \end{bmatrix}^{+++} 3Cl^-$$

Hexaaquochromichloride. Violet-colored solution. All chloride precipitable by silver nitrate in the cold.

$$\begin{bmatrix} H_2O & & Cl \\ H_2O & Cr & H_2O \\ H_2O & & H_2O \end{bmatrix}^{++} 2Cl^-$$

Pentaaquomonochloridochromichloride. Bright-green solution. Two-thirds of the chloride precipible by silver nitrate in the cold.

$$\begin{bmatrix} H_2O & & Cl \\ H_2O & Cr & Cl \\ H_2O & & H_2O \end{bmatrix}^{+} Cl^-$$

Tetraaquodichloridochromichloride. Dark-green solution. One-third of the chloride precipitable by silver nitrate in the cold.

When any of these salts is dissolved in water, an equilibrium is finally established where certain amounts of all three cations are present. In cold dilute solutions, the hexaaquo ion predominates, while increase in concentration and temperature produces more of the pentaaquomonochlorido and tetraaquo-dichlorido ions. These facts were demonstrated by Bjerrum.

The formation of the green salts is also favored by the addition of chloride ion to solutions of the violet salt. This is readily shown by a simple experiment. Prepare two identical solutions of the violet chromic chloride. To one add some sodium chloride. Warm both solutions and cool them. The one containing sodium chloride will be green, while the other will be violet.

It is seen that in the coordinative binding of an anionic radical at the expense of a neutral group (H_2O in these cases), the positive charge of the complex cation is reduced.

Sulfate, having a greater tendency than chloride to be coordinatively bound, gives rise to some interesting compounds. For instance, there is the compound $Cr_2(SO_4)_3.6H_2O$ which in cold aqueous solution does not react with barium chloride and is not a conductor of electricity. The following formula is ascribed to it

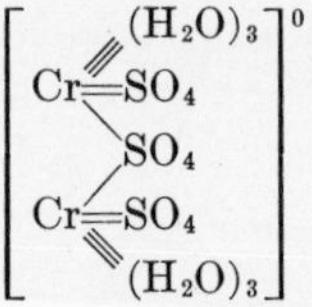

$$\begin{bmatrix} \qquad (H_2O)_3 \\ Cr{=}\!\!\!=\!SO_4 \\ \qquad \diagdown SO_4 \\ Cr{=}\!\!\!=\!SO_4 \\ \qquad (H_2O)_3 \end{bmatrix}^0$$

Hexaaquotrisulfatodichromium

Since, then, anionic radicals are known to exist in a coordinatively bound state in crystalloidal salts, it seems reasonable to assume that they may also so exist in colloidal micelles. Thus one has an explanation for the migration of chlorin to the cathode in certain chromium and iron oxychloride hydrosols and the failure for the detection of the chlorin by the silver nitrate test.

Evidence for the binding of anionic radicals in a cationic micelle has been offered by conductivity titrations of aluminum oxyiodide and of chromic oxychloride hydrosols, the results of two experiments being plotted in Figs. 51 and 52. One hundred cubic centimeters of hydrosol was titrated in a conductivity cell with the silver salts noted on the curves. The dotted vertical line in the figures locates the total available halide content of the sols. It is noted that the steepness of the slopes in Fig. 51 is in the order tartrate > sulfate > acetate > nitrate, while the mobilities of the ions involved in the experiment are sulfate > iodide >

nitrate > acetate > tartrate. Obviously, the drop in conductivity cannot be ascribed alone to the replacement of iodide ions by the added anion. Despite the fact that sulfate ion has a higher mobility than iodide, before the equivalent point was reached the conductivity of the sol was very markedly diminished

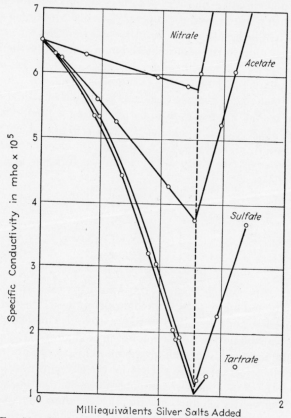

FIG. 51.—Conductance titrations of aluminumoxyiodide sol, 3.

by the silver sulfate. Therefore, it must be admitted that the fast-moving sulfate ions were removed from the solution. This removal is also true for the tartrate ions and to some extent for the acetate ions. The tendency for acetate ions to become coordinatively bound in the aluminum micelle is less than that for sulfate and tartrate, and nitrate has practically no such tendency.   Since in this experiment the concentrations of added anions (with the exception of the highest concentration of silver tartrate) were too low to effect displacement of hydroxo groups, they could displace only aquo and possibly iodo groups.   The replacement of aquo by anionic groups would lower the charge on the ionic micelle and thus further contribute to a drop in conductivity.   The upward slope of the nitrate curve in Fig. 52 is evidence for the failure of nitrate to become attached to the chromium atoms.   Whether the differences in the slopes of the

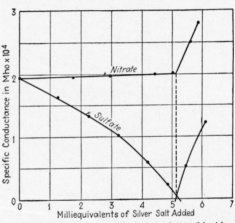

FIG. 52.—Conductance titrations of chromicoxychloride sol, 13.

nitrate curves in Figs. 51 and 52 may be cited as differences between aluminum oxy- and chromium oxysalt hydrosols is, of course, questionable.

The fact that silver nitrate precipitated all of the halide in the hydrosols does not preclude the possibility of the existence of some of the halide as coordinatively bound in the original sols. As soon as the halide ions in the solution were removed by precipitation as silver halide, then iodo or chlorido groups would migrate out from the micelle to restore the equilibrium, and so on, until all had been removed by the silver present.

When the various factors involved in the nature of a given metal oxysalt hydrosol are reviewed, the futility of attempting to define a sol by a few ultimate analytical values is obvious.   It is likewise apparent that there are innumerable hydrosols of the "oxide" of a given element.

The writer has confined his discussion to crystalloidal chromium salts, aluminum oxy-, and chromic oxysalt hydrosols in order to base the argument upon systems which have been studied experimentally.

It is not at all illogical to assume that ferric oxysalt sols are analogous to those discussed and, inasmuch as potassium has been shown to be bound in the stannic "oxide" micelle[8] and chlorin in the "silica" micelle,[36,37] then these also may be similarly complex. The well-known fact that vanadium, tungsten,

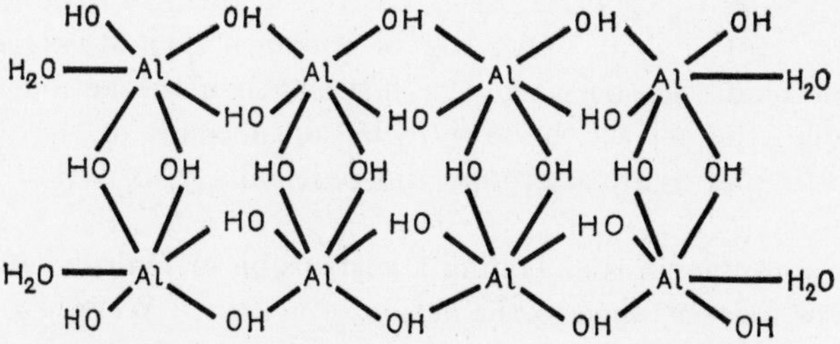

Fig. 53.—A two-dimensional picture for $Al_2O_3.4H_2O$.

and molybdenum form many complex salts would lead one to suppose that their oxide hydrosols are likewise subject to a similar point of view. There is a great opportunity for research in this particular field of colloid chemistry.

Hydrous oxide hydrosols may be formed by the peptization of the hydrous oxide as well as by hydrolysis of the crystalloidal salts. In fact they are generally prepared by the acid peptization of the hydrous oxide. The mechanism may be conceived as follows, taking alumina as typical:

An oxide of aluminum having the definite composition of $Al_2O_3.4H_2O$[38] has been identified. The simplest two-dimensional structure of this compound* would be as depicted in Fig. 53.[39] When acid is added, two possible reactions are expected to take place with a complex of this nature. Hydrogen ions will react with the hydroxo groups (shown at the four corners in the figure), forming aquo groups and conferring one positive charge for each hydroxo group thus converted. Deolation may also take place

---

* This picture is purely hypothetical and is given to simplify the discussion. Pieces of hydrous alumina undoubtedly contain many more atoms per particle.

to some extent. A certain number of anions may also enter the complex, displacing an equivalent number of aquo groups or hydroxo groups or both. As deolation takes place, ol groups become free hydroxo groups and these in turn are converted to aquo groups. Finally aluminum ionic micelles are formed in the solution when the ratio of charge to mass becomes sufficiently great and, naturally, provided the number of equivalents of acid is much less than the number of equivalents of aluminum present. If the solution is warmed during the action of the acid upon the gel, the peptization is facilitated owing to the greater activity of the acid upon the ol linkages. However, if the hydrous oxide has been aged or heated, then the action of the acid upon the gel will be very feeble on account of the olation of the original hydroxo groups and particularly oxolation of the ol groups.

It is well-known that boiling a suspension of hydrous alumina increases its resistance to the action of acids.[40] When oxolation and dehydration are complete, resulting in the formation of

$$Al \begin{matrix} O \\ \diagdown \\ O \end{matrix} \begin{matrix} \diagup \\ O \\ \diagdown \end{matrix} Al$$

which is effected by ignition of hydrous alumina at high temperature, it is impossible to attack it even by strong acid solutions.

Mention has been made of the possibility of anions entering the complex and displacing aquo groups therefrom. The nature of these anions thus coordinatively bound greatly influences the stability of the ol linkage. Stiasny[41] states that the order of resistance of ol compounds of chromium to the action of acids is oxalic < formic < sulfuric < hydrochloric < nitric. This is the reverse order for the tenacity of coordinate binding of the anions of these acids to the central atom. Stiasny accounts for this in the following manner, considering the ol compound:

$$\begin{bmatrix} X & H & X \\ & O & \\ Cr & & Cr \\ & O & \\ (H_2O)_3 & H & (H_2O)_3 \end{bmatrix}^{++} \quad 2Cl^-$$

where X is a monovalent anionic radical. If the chromium has only slight affinity for X, then it possesses considerable reserve valence energy for the other groups; while if X is a radical for which chromium has high affinity, there is only a weak reserve of valence energy for the remaining coordinated groups and, as a consequence, the ol linkage is feeble and easily split.

For the production of a sol in the peptization of a hydrous oxide, one of the best acids to use would be nitric because nitrate ions have but slight tendency to be coordinatively bound and consequently to disrupt ol linkages. An acid such as oxalic would not form a sol owing to the tendency of oxalate ion to disrupt ol linkages and to be bound to the central atom. For each equivalent of hydrogen ion of such an acid reacting with the hydroxo groups, an equivalent of oxalate ion would be coordinatively bound. If the ratio of acid to alumina is low, the acid would be removed from the solution without any dispersing effect upon the alumina and one would say that it was adsorbed by the alumina. A colloidal dispersion of alumina could not arise owing to the disruption of the ol linkages but a crystalloid solution would arise when the ratio of acid to alumina is increased.

The relative peptizing action of several acids upon hydrous alumina has recently been determined[70] under the conditions of agitation of hydrous alumina with aqueous solutions of the acids in the ratio of 30 equivalents of hydrous alumina to 1 of acid. The peptizing order was found to be trichloracetic > dichloracetic > nitric > hydrochloric > monochloracetic > formic > acetic > oxalic > tartaric > sulfuric. With but two exceptions, this order is the reverse of the tendency of the anions to be coordinatively bound as revealed by the effect of their neutral salts in replacing OH groups from the micelles of an aluminum oxysalt hydrosol. Thus in forming aluminum oxysalt, etc., hydrosols, the conditions must be such as to favor a high degree of olation.

Negatively charged aluminum and chromic oxide micelles exist as well as the positively charged ones which have just been so extensively discussed. Our treatment of the negative micelles must be brief because very little is known about them. In view of the reaction $Al(OH)_3 + NaOH \rightarrow NaAlO_2 + 2H_2O$, the writer prefers the following simple (and without doubt too simple) formulation:

$$x\mathrm{Al_2O_3 \cdot AlO_2^- \ Na^+}$$

in which ionization of the sodium aluminate provides the negative charge on the ionic micelle. Some people prefer the scheme

$$x\mathrm{Al_2O_3 \cdot OH^- \ Na^+}$$

on the idea that oxide sol particles are positive or negative depending upon adsorption of H^+ or OH^-, respectively. The amphoteric oxides in general may exist in colloidal solution as positively or negatively charged micelles. Even so weakly amphoteric a substance as iron oxide may be obtained in the state of a negatively charged ionic micelle but in this state the dispersion is of only momentary stability unless other substances such as sugar or gelatin are present. When such substances are added, however, the sol is no longer entitled to the name of "iron oxide."

Hydrosols of the Noble Metals.—Considerable information is now available concerning the nature of platinum hydrosol particles. Beans and Eastlack[42] demonstrated that during the preparation of platinum hydrosols by the Bredig-arc method the conductivity increased, owing to oxidation of the platinum. The stability of the sol was attributed by them to the ions thus formed. The conclusion that platinum oxidizes in the arc is consonant with earlier evidence that finely divided platinum is relatively easily oxidized.[43] The knowledge of the composition of platinum hydrosol particles has been greatly extended by Pennycuick.[44]

Using the Bredig-arc method, this investigator has shown that, on dispersing from 100 to 150 mg. of platinum per liter of water, the specific conductivity attains the magnitude of 6 to 8 reciprocal megohms which increases to 30 or more if the sol is boiled. The sol is acid in reaction (pH = 4.6) and becomes more so upon boiling. By means of conductivity titrations and freezing experiments, Pennycuick showed that the acid is a fairly strong one and identified it as hexahydroxy platinic acid, $H_2Pt(OH)_6$, or one of its dehydration products. His experiments showed that platinum oxides are also present in the micelle. He attributes the clinging of these compounds to the platinum surface to the residual valency forces of the surface of the platinum very much as shown in Fig. 43 for the silver halide particles. His suggestion for a simple formulation of the platinum colloidal electrolyte is

$$[x\text{Pt}.y\text{PtO}_2.\text{Pt(OH)}_6]^= 2\text{H}^+$$

Although the $H_2Pt(OH)_6$ in the foregoing formula is represented as completely ionized, the hydrogen ions form an ionic atmosphere around each particle, and only a fraction can be regarded as actually free.

Pennycuick's formulation for electrically arced platinum hydrosols is generally accepted. There is no such unanimity of opinion concerning electrically synthesized gold hydrosols, however. There are two schools of thought here, one favoring a Werner complex structure and the other denying the existence of gold other than as metal.

Pauli[45] believes that auraates or auriates form during the arcing process and become attached to the gold surface. He confirmed the findings of Beans and Eastlack[42] concerning the necessity for the presence of certain ions in the solution during the arcing and that certain other ions (those which do not form complex auro or auri ions) do not aid in the electrical synthesis of gold hydrosols. He has shown that the red sols made by arcing in the presence of hydrochloric acid and of potassium hydroxide are chemically different. The former are stable when boiled and are unaffected by passage of carbon dioxide through them. The latter turn blue and precipitate either when boiled or when treated with carbon dioxide. He believes that gold is oxidized to AuCl when arced in the presence of hydrochloric acid, resulting in the formation of the chlorido compound $HAuCl_2$. He has found that, if gold is arced to the exhaustion of the hydrochloric acid in the solution, the sol becomes violet in color. It turns red and becomes stable upon subsequent addition of hydrochloric acid. He believes that a hydroxo compound, such as $KAu(OH)_2$, arises upon arcing gold in the presence of traces of potassium hydroxide. The hydroxo gold hydrosol can be converted to a chlorido sol upon addition of the proper amount of hydrochloric acid, the resulting sol being stable to carbon dioxide and to boiling. Nitric acid does not do this and it is significant that crystalloid nitrato auraates or auriates have not been prepared.

It is known that the crystalloid electrolyte is removed from the gold particles upon freezing.[46]   Pauli[47] has obtained a chemical test for gold compounds in the solution and at first thought that the tetrachloridoauriate ion $(AuCl_4)^-$ was attached to the gold particles in the sol.   However, analysis of the solution obtained after freezing these sols showed HCl and $(AuCl_4)^-$ to be present in the ratio of 2 moles of the former to 1 mole of the latter.   This led to the conclusion that the ion actually attached to the particle was the dichloridoauraate.   Now the following reaction is known:[48]

$$3(AuCl_2)^- \rightarrow 2Au + (AuCl_4)^- + 2Cl^- \qquad (8)$$

and consequently Pauli believes that the sol arced in a solution of hydrochloric acid is a complex (water ignored) such as

$$xAu.(AuCl_2)^-\ H^+$$

the tetrachloridoauriate arising in the solution after destruction of the sol by freezing as shown in Eq. (8).

The reader who may doubt the possibility of making the exact quantitative analyses required for these conclusions will be interested to know that Pauli and his colleagues found it possible only through the process which they term *electrodecantation,** enabling them to concentrate the sols to the extent of 6 g. gold per liter.

Pauli's theory of gold hydrosol constitution is opposed by Beans[42] and his coworkers,[46] Zsigmondy,[49] and Thiessen.[50]   The last-named investigator has been unable to detect gold compounds in red hydrosols, although he has obtained positive tests in violet or blue under-reduced sols prepared by the phosphorus, formaldehyde, and hydrazine reduction methods.   He agrees with Steubing[51] that blue or violet sols contain aurous oxide. According to the views of Beans, Zsigmondy, and Thiessen red-gold hydrosol particles formed, for example, by arcing in the presence of hydrogen or potassium chloride would be something like $xAu.Cl^-K^+$ or $xAu.Cl^-H^+$.   In fact Thiessen[52] ascribes the

* See p. 72.

negative charge of the gold micelles to the sorption of hydroxyl ions from water.

Inasmuch as Pauli showed the dissimilarity upon boiling and to the action of carbon dioxide of red gold sols arced in hydrochloric acid and in potassium hydroxide solutions, it is inadvisable to attempt to put all red-gold hydrosols in one category, regardless of the method of preparation, *i.e.*, reduction methods using diverse reducing agents. As Weiser[53] points out, the gold particles in the Zsigmondy formaldehyde hydrosol may be coated with polymerization products arising from formaldehyde.

Bredig-arc silver hydrosols, prepared in the presence of the chlorides of ammonium and of potassium and in the presence of the corresponding hydroxides, resemble the chlorido and hydroxo Bredig gold sols.[54] Pauli therefore believes that the silver ion attached to the metal is a negative Werner complex.

Sulfide Hydrosols.—The sulfide hydrosols have been accepted since 1892[55] to consist of aggregates of insoluble sulfide with sorbed hydrogen sulfide, the particles consisting of $xAs_2S_3.SH_2$, $xHgS.SH_2$, etc., the ionization of the H_2S producing a negative charge on the ionic micelle. A more descriptive name for these would be the "hydrosulfide" hydrosols. By treatment of a solution of arsenious acid with hydrogen sulfide in the dark an orange-red dispersion of arsenious hydrosulfide has been obtained which upon exposure to air and light becomes lemon yellow in color.[56] The reddish sol is claimed to consist of $xAs_2S_2.SH_2$ particles (realgar) which under the influence of oxygen and light are transformed to As_2S_3 particles (orpiment). It has also been suggested[57] that arsenious sulfide hydrosol is

$$[xAs_2S_3.yAs_2S_4H_2.As_2S_4H]^- \ H^+$$

Sulfur Hydrosols.—The Odén type of sulfur hydrosol would be expected to contain polythionates. Freundlich[58] stated that this hydrosol consists of sulfur aggregates attached to pentathionic acid, in the ratio of 0.7 to 1 millimole of pentathionic acid per gram of sulfur.

Bassett and Durant[59] are of the opinion that the polythionate is principally hexathionate. Since the polythionates higher than tetrathionate tend to dissociate rapidly unless something is present to prevent it, the sulfur so disengaged would be expected to separate in mass. But these investigators find that polythionate bound to sulfur is stabilized. They believe that the polythionate molecules coalesce when the concentration is high owing to mutual attraction of the sulfur atoms in the molecules of the polythionic acids and to the tendency for crystalline sulfur to be formed. Thus micelles are formed with an inner nucleus of partly crystalline sulfur atoms, irregularly arranged. The polythionate ions are attached to the edges and corners of these irregular aggregates. As polymerization occurs, polythionate is dislodged mainly as pentathionate if the aqueous medium is sufficiently acid—otherwise as tetrathionate.

As the ions break away in the course of the kinetic equilibrium between the "free" and "bound" polythionate, a few atoms of sulfur are removed each time. This helps to efface the irregularities of the sulfur surface until finally a sulfur particle with completely crystalline structure is obtained, with consequent separation of the particle in the solid state as crystalline sulfur which can be seen under the microscope, as octahedra.

Thus the Odén type of sol may be represented by

$$[xS.S_5O_6H]^- \; H^+ \qquad or \qquad [xS.S_6O_6H]^- \; H^+$$

Miscellaneous Hydrosols.—Since copper ferrocyanide hydrosol requires an excess of ferrocyanide ion for stability, a plausible formulation for this sol would be

$$[xCu_2Fe(CN)_6.Fe(CN)_6]^{==} \; 4K^+$$

Hydrosols of rosin and other gum resins such as shellac and mastic contain negatively charged ionic micelles and are acidic in nature. In fact, rosin consists principally of abietic acid. Schematically the particles are $RCOO^-H^+$ where R represents the water-insoluble organic part, which in the case of abietic acid would be the nonpolar parts of its structure.

Similarly a dispersion of oil droplets in water stabilized by a soap like sodium stearate may be represented by

$$\boxed{(CH_3)[CH_2]_{16}} \; COO^- Na^+$$

the box representing an oil droplet with the hydrocarbon chain of the sodium stearate dissolved in the oil and the polar —COONa group dissolved in the water. This concept will be developed fully in Chaps. X and XVI.

In soap solutions the ionic micelle is, according to McBain,[60] $(NaP)_x.(P)_n^{n-}.(H_2O)_m$ where P represents the palmitate, or any other higher fatty acid radical, and n is small compared to x. Soaps will be discussed further in Chap. XIV.

The Electric Charge of Micelles.—In all the colloidal solutions described in this chapter we see dispersions of massive aggregates ionically charged either positively or negatively, the charge of the colloidal particle or ionic micelle being balanced by crystalloid contra-ions.

Prior to the birth of the theory of ionization it was known that particles suspended in water migrated in an electrical field and it was held that the particles were electrostatically charged by friction with the water in analogy to the rubbing of an ebonite rod with a piece of silk. As has been pointed out by Smoluchowski[61] and by Porter and Hedges,[62] this idea is no longer tenable.

The colloidal or suspension particle is now pictured as a charged particle surrounded by an ionic atmosphere of balancing contra-ions and, as has been mentioned at the outset of this chapter, it is generally taken that the mutual repulsive forces of the like-charged particles are responsible for the stability, for if the charge is suppressed or removed the particles coalesce and settle out. This is a logical theory but is not complete or all-inclusive.

This point of view cannot be accepted as a complete explanation for the stability of all colloidal dispersions because colloidal solutions exist where the dispersed phase does not migrate in an electrical field, *e.g.*, proteins at the isoelectric point,* β-amylose of starch,† and metallic soaps in benzene.[63] In these cases, the stabilizing factors are thought to exist in the polar groups on the particle surface which dip into the dispersion medium. The concept of having a part of a molecule dissolved in a liquid is not novel. Water-insoluble crystalloid compounds such as the higher fatty acids which spread over a water surface are so considered.‡ Polar groups of such substances are said to dissolve

---

* See Chap. XII.
† See Chap. XIII.
‡ This is discussed in Chap. X.

in the water leaving the nonpolar hydrocarbon chains sticking out.

Another fact which demonstrates the insufficiency of a simple electric charge picture of colloid stability is the mutual precipitation of certain like-charged micelles,* e.g., mixtures of sulfur polythionate hydrosols and hydrosulfide hydrosols. For a proper understanding of a sol it is essential to know the chemical composition of the micelle and particularly the identity of the ions responsible for the charge.

Wilson's Hypothesis.—An interesting theory for colloid stability based on the Donnan equilibrium has been proposed by Wilson.[64] As presented here, Wilson's theory is taken from his

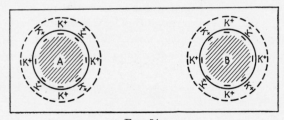

FIG. 54.

book where he uses a gold sol of the assumed composition xAu.ClK as his working model.

In Fig. 54 let A and B represent two gold particles stabilized by potassium chloride. In combining with the gold, the chloride ions have imparted their negative charges to the particles. But the potassium ions are still left in solution, although their field of motion is restricted to the thin film of solution wetting the particles because they must continue to balance the negative charges on the particles. The volume of the film of aqueous solution enveloping a particle will be measured by the surface area of the particle and the average distance that the potassium ions are able to travel from the surface.

Let us now consider the case where a small amount of potassium chloride is present in the sol. The enveloping film will contain potassium ions balancing the charges on the particles as well as ionized potassium chloride. The surrounding solution will have potassium and chloride ions only in equal numbers. In the surrounding solution let

* See Chap. XVII.

$$x = [K^+] = [Cl^-]$$

in the enveloping film let

$$y = [Cl^-]$$

and

$$z = [K^+] \text{ balanced by charges on the particles}$$

whence

$y + z$ represents the total concentration of potassium ion.
As was shown in the discussion of Donnan's theory, the product
$[K^+].[Cl^-]$ must have the same value both in the enveloping
film and in the surrounding solution at equilibrium. Hence

$$x^2 = y(y + z)$$

The surface layer of solution will have a greater concentration
of ions than the surrounding solution by the amount $2y + z - 2x$.
This unequal distribution of ions will give rise to a difference
of potential between the enveloping film and the surrounding
solution whose measure is

$$E = \frac{RT}{F} \log \frac{x}{y} = \frac{RT}{F} \log \frac{2x}{-z + \sqrt{4x^2 + z^2}}$$

But now, if we increase x without limit while z remains constant,
E must decrease, approaching zero as a limit, since

$$x = \overset{\text{limit}}{\infty} E = \frac{RT}{F} \log \frac{2x}{\sqrt{4x^2}} = 0$$

It is thus evident that the difference of potential between the
enveloping film and the surrounding solution will be a maximum
when there is no free potassium chloride present and will decrease,
approaching zero, as the concentration of potassium chloride is
increased without limit.

The particles shown in Fig. 54 are prevented from coalescing
because there is a sufficiently high potential difference of the
same sign between the surrounding solution and each enveloping
film. The force of repulsion is determined by this potential
difference rather than by the absolute electrical charge on the
particles because the surface film completely envelops the particles and endows them with its own properties.

When sufficient potassium chloride has been added to lower
the potential difference to a point where it is no longer able to

overcome the attractive forces between the particles and the surface tension of the enveloping film, the particles move toward each other and the enveloping films of two or more particles blend into one, as shown in Fig. 55. It is at this point that the actual charges themselves come into play and probably determine the nature of the precipitate.

Oakley[65] has extended this idea of colloid stability to include a consideration of the ionization of surface-bound weak acids and bases.

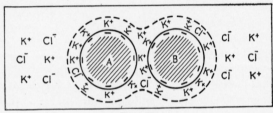

Fig. 55.

Presence of "Protective Colloids."—Any of the dispersions discussed in this and the preceding chapter may have their stability enhanced by the addition of suitable hydrophilic colloids. Likewise suspensions of carbon, silica, etc., may be stabilized. Intermediate colloids have protective power but to a much lower degree. It is known that the stabilizing action is due to the attachment of the stabilizing or protective colloid to the particles, and thus there arises a hydrophilic dispersion where each particle has an insoluble nucleus. While it may be very stable, it cannot perforce be so stable as the hydrophile itself, owing to the extra load of matter which is being held in suspension. The hydrophile constitutes a "solution link" between the insoluble particles and the dispersion medium.

When a small amount of a protein solution is added to a suspension of nitrocellulose particles, the latter then act like the protein itself.[66] When a suitable solution of gelatin is added to a gold hydrosol, no change in appearance of the sol to the eye is observed, yet the sol is no longer hydrophobic; it is hydrophilic. Similarly iron oxychloride sol changes the nature of a platinum sol. Such complicated dispersions are frequently named for convenience after the nature of the less stable sol or suspension, whereas as a matter of fact the particles consist of the hydrophilic particles with inert cores of the named component. More will be said about "protective action" in Chap. XVII.

Shape of Colloidal Particles.—In Chap. III it was remarked that colloidal particles may be rods or disks. It is logical to assume, unless evidence to the contrary is available, that colloidal particles are spherical, or nearly so, inasmuch as a sphere is the shape which exposes the least surface for a given volume, thus permitting the surface energy of the system to approach a low level.

That certain colloids become double refracting in a magnetic field has been known since the observation of Majorana[67] upon an aged ferricoxysalt hydrosol. As a result of studies by several investigators[68] it is now believed that this optical anisotropy is due to the presence of elongated particles. The double refraction is shown also when such sols are subjected to the action of an electric current or are forced through a tube or are stirred. It is manifest to the naked eye by streaks when a suspension of freshly reduced mercurous chloride or a very old vanadium pentoxide sol is stirred. The effect may be lacking in freshly prepared sols (sols which are inclined to show it) but develops upon aging or heating. Flowing double refraction was shown by Zocher to be exhibited by vanadium pentoxide sols, tungstic acid sols, soap solutions, clay suspensions, and aqueous dispersions of benzopurpurin, benzobrown, primulin, sodium alizarin sulfonate, alizarin, p-azoxyphenetol, p-azoxyanisol, anthracene, and aniline blue. Rod-shaped particles orient themselves with their long axes in the direction of the lines of force in a flowing field and disks place themselves with their axis of symmetry perpendicular to these lines.

Aniline blue sols, formed by pouring an alcoholic solution into water, show upon flowing a strong negative double refraction in red, negative pleochroism in orange to green, and positive double refraction in blue. Through this behavior arise anomalous interference colors. The optical anisotropy manifested in a magnetic field has the opposite sign; *i.e.*, the particles are orientated perpendicular to the lines of force, whereas they were oriented parallel to them in a flowing field.

Bergholm and Björnstahl[68] found even gold and silver sols to be doubly refracting in an alternating-current field.

Thus it is seen that dispersed particles exist in a variety of shapes. They may also exist as distinct massive particles, called *primary particles* and as clusters of primary particles called *secondary particles* as illustrated in Figs. 56 and 57.

Zsigmondy[69] offers experimental evidence for distinction between primary and secondary particles in gold hydrosols on the basis of macroscopic and ultramicroscopic color effects. A

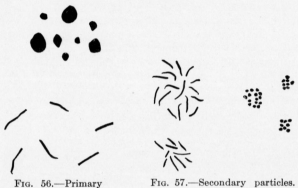

FIG. 56.—Primary particles.   FIG. 57.—Secondary particles.

red-gold hydrosol when subjected to coagulative influences undergoes a change in color through violet to blue, a diminution in number of particles thereby resulting. In the ultramicroscope the primary particles of the red sol appear green and upon uniting to form secondary particles appear brown and more brilliant. Since red hydrosols and ruby glass contain a wide range of sizes of particles which appear green in the ultramicroscope, the conclusion is reached that two types of particles are involved in which they differ by the density of the distribution of the gold, the red sol particles being massive gold while the partly coagulated gold particles consist of clusters of particles.

References

1. SORUM: *J. Am. Chem. Soc.*, **50**, 1263 (1928).
2. SVEDBERG: *Kolloid-Z.*, **2**, 142 (1907).
3. MALFITANO: *Compt. rend.*, **140**, 1245 (1905); **141**, 660, 680, (1905); *Z. physik. Chem.*, **68**, 232 (1909); *Ann. chim. phys.*, (8) **24**, 502 (1911).
4. LANGMUIR: *J. Am. Chem. Soc.*, **38**, 2221 (1916); **40**, 1361 (1918).
5. DUMANSKI: *Kolloid-Z.*, **8**, 232 (1911).
6. ZSIGMONDY: *Z. anorg. allgem. Chem.*, **89**, 210 (1914).

7. VARGA: *Kolloidchem. Beihefte*, **11**, 1 (1919).

8. WINTGEN: *Z. physik. Chem.*, **103**, 238 (1922).

9. WINTGEN and BILTZ: *Z. physik. Chem.*, **107**, 403 (1923).

10. WINTGEN and LÖWENTHAL: *Z. physik. Chem.*, **109**, 378 (1924).

11. THOMAS and FRIEDEN: *J. Am. Chem. Soc.*, **45**, 2522 (1923).

12. HANTZCH and DESCH: *Ann. Chem.*, **323**, 38 (1902).

13. LINDER and PICTON: *J. Chem. Soc.*, **87**, 1919 (1905).

14. NEIDLE: *J. Am. Chem. Soc.*, **39**, 2334 (1917).

15. THOMAS and WHITEHEAD: *J. Phys. Chem.*, **35**, 27 (1931).

16. THOMAS and TAI: *J. Am. Chem. Soc.*, **54**, 841 (1932).

17. TODD, L. J.: Dissertation, Columbia University, 1931.

18. THOMAS and VON WICKLEN: *J. Am. Chem. Soc.*, **56**, 794 (1934).

19. WERNER-PFEIFFER: "Neuere Auschauungen auf dem Gebiete der Anorganischen Chemie," Vieweg und Sohn, Braunschweig, 1923.

20. PFEIFFER: *Ber.*, **40**, 4036 (1907); see also BRONSTED: *J. Phys. Chem.*, **30**, 785 (1926).

21. CUPR: *Collection Czechoslov. Chem. Comm.*, **1**, 467 (1929); through *Chem. Abs.*, **24**, 1013 (1930).

22. KULGREN: *Z. physik. Chem.*, **85**, 472 (1913).

23. PFEIFFER: *Z. anorg. Chem.*, **29**, 107 (1902).

24. WERNER: *Ber.*, **40**, 2113, 4436 (1907).

25. PFEIFFER: *Z. anorg. Chem.*, **56**, 261 (1908).

26. BJERRUM: *Z. physik. Chem.*, **59**, 336 (1907); "Studier over Basike Kromiforbindelser," Kopenhagen, 1908; through STIASNY and GRIMM: *Collegium*, **691**, 505 (1927); *Z. physik. Chem.*, **73**, 724 (1910).

27. RICHARDS and BONNET: *Z. physik. Chem.*, **47**, 29 (1904).

28. STIASNY et al.: *Collegium*, **657**, 190 (1925); **670**, 41; **677**, 413 (1926); **682**, 81; **691**, 505 (1927); **694**, 49, 72; **700**, 389 (1928); **715**, 565 (1929); **737**, 444, 458 (1931); **747**, 543; **752**, 897, 902 (1932); *Z. anorg. Chem.*, **37**, 913 (1929).

29. BRAGG and BRAGG: "X-ray and Crystal Structure," pp. 180–184, George Bell & Sons, London, 1924; PAULING and HENDRICKS: *J. Am. Chem. Soc.*, **47**, 781 (1925).

30. FEIGL and KRAUSS: *Ber.*, **58B**, 398 (1925).

31. SEN: *J. Phys. Chem.*, **31**, 691 (1927).

32. STIASNY: "Gerbereichemie (Chromgerbung)," Chaps. XIV-XVII, T. Steinkopff, Leipzig, 1931.

33. GUSTAVSON: *Ind. Eng. Chem.*, **17**, 945 (1925).

34. Ref. 32 (p. 361).

35. Ref. 32 (p. 339).

36. JORDIS and KANTER: *Z. anorg. Chem.*, **35**, 16 (1903).

37. BRINTZINGER: *Z. anorg. allgem. Chem.*, **159**, 256 (1927); **181**, 237 (1929).

38. NEOGI and MITRA: *J. Chem. Soc.*, **1927**, 1222.

39. Taken from the dissertation of A. P. Tai, Columbia University, May, 1931.

40. MÜLLER: *Z. anorg. Chem.*, **57**, 312 (1908); WINTGEN and KUHN: *Z. physik. Chem.*, **138**, 135 (1928).

41. Ref. 32 (p. 351).

42. BEANS and EASTLACK: *J. Am. Chem. Soc.*, **37**, 2667 (1915).

43. WÖHLER: *Z. anorg. Chem.*, **29**, 1 (1901); **40**, 423 (1904).

44. PENNYCUICK: *J. Chem. Soc.*, **1927**, 2600; **1928**, 551, 2108; **1929**, 618, 623; *Kolloid-Z.*, **49**, 407 (1929); *Z. physik. Chem.*, **148A**, 413 (1930); *J. Am. Chem. Soc.*, **52**, 4621 (1930).

45. PAULI et al.: *Kolloidchem. Beihefte*, **17**, 294 (1923); **21**, 195 (1925); **30**, 113 (1930); *Kolloid-Z.*, **34**, 29 (1924); **38**, 22 (1926); **58**, 22 (1932); summarized by PAULI: *Naturwissenschaften*, **20**, 551, 573 (1932).

46. BEAVER: Dissertation, Columbia University, 1921; SHEAR: Dissertation, Columbia University, 1925; YOUNG: Dissertation, Columbia University, 1931.

47. Ref. 45, *Kolloidchem. Beihefte*, **30**, 113 (1930).

48. GRUBE: *Z. Elektrochem.*, **35**, 703 (1929).

49. ZSIGMONDY-THIESSEN: "Das Kolloide Gold," Akademische Verlagsgesellschaft m.b.H., Leipzig, 1925.

50. THIESSEN: *Z. anorg. allgem. Chem.*, **134**, 393 (1924).

51. STEUBING: *Ann. Physik.*, (4) **26**, 335 (1908).

52. THIESSEN: *Oesterr. Chem.-Ztg.*, **29**, 133 (1926); through *Chem. Abs.*, **21**, 10 (1927).

53. WEISER: "The Colloidal Elements," p. 57, John Wiley & Sons, Inc., New York, 1933.

54. LOFFLER and PAULI: *Kolloid-Z.*, **60**, 146 (1932).

55. LINDER and PICTON: *J. Chem. Soc.*, **61**, 114 (1892); **67**, 63 (1895); PICTON: *J. Chem. Soc.*, **61**, 137 (1892).

56. BHATNAGAR and RAO: *Kolloid-Z.*, **33**, 159 (1923); BHATNAGAR: *J. Phys. Chem.*, **35**, 1803 (1931).

57. PAULI and SEMLER: *Kolloid-Z.*, **34**, 145, 209 (1924).

58. FREUNDLICH and SCHOLZ: *Kolloidchem. Beihefte*, **16**, 234 (1922).

59. BASSETT and DURANT: *J. Chem. Soc.*, **1931**, 2919.

60. MCBAIN: *J. Soc. Chem. Ind.*, **37**, 249 (1918); *J. Chem. Soc.*, **115**, 1279 (1919); *J. Am. Chem. Soc.*, **42**, 426 (1920).

61. SMOLUCHOWSKI: *Z. physik. Chem.*, **92**, 129 (1917).

62. PORTER and HEDGES: *Phil. Mag.*, **44**, 641 (1922).

63. SOYENKOFF: *J. Phys. Chem.*, **34**, 2519 (1930).

64. WILSON: *J. Am. Chem. Soc.*, **38**, 1982 (1916); see also WILSON: "The Chemistry of Leather Manufacture," Vol. I, pp. 173–177, Chemical Catalog Company, New York, 1928.

65. OAKLEY: *J. Phys. Chem.*, **30**, 902 (1926).

66. LOEB: "Proteins and the Theory of Colloidal Behavior," Chap. XVIII McGraw-Hill Book Company, Inc., New York, 1924.

67. MAJORANA: *Compt. rend.*, **135**, 159 (1902).

68. COTTON and MOUTON: *Ann. chim. phys.*, **11**, 145, 289 (1907); FREUNDLICH and DIESELHORST: *Z. Elektrochem.*, **22**, 97 (1916); REINDERS: *Kolloid-Z.*, **21**, 161 (1917); BERGHOLM and BJÖRNSTAHL: *Physik. Z.*, **31**, 137 (1920); ZOCHER: *Z. physik. Chem.*, **98**, 293 (1921); *Kolloid-*

chem. Beihefte, **28**, 167 (1929); FREUNDLICH et al.: *Z. physik. Chem.*, **105**, 119 (1923); **114**, 161, 190 (1924); **119**, 87 (1926); FREUNDLICH: Second Colloid Symposium Monograph, p. 46, Chemical Catalog Company, New York, 1925; THIESSEN: *Z. physik. Chem.*, **156A**, 309, 457 (1931).

69. ZSIGMONDY: *Z. angew. Chem.*, **35**, 449 (1922).
70. VARTANIAN: Dissertation, Columbia University, May, 1934.

CHAPTER VIII

PRECIPITATION BY ELECTROLYTES— HYDROPHOBIC AND INTERMEDIATE DISPERSIONS

When electrolytes are added to colloidal solutions, the stability of the latter is generally decreased, resulting in precipitation provided sufficient electrolyte is added. Occasionally the stability is increased and in certain instances the colloidal dispersion may be converted to a crystalloidal dispersion. No general rule can be given because these effects depend upon the chemical nature of the colloidal dispersion and of the added electrolyte.

In 1851, Scheerer[1] reported that turbid aqueous dispersions could be clarified by the addition of salts. Faraday,[2] in 1856, noted that his gold dispersions were coagulated by traces of salts.

The Valence Rule.—The first important general contribution to the knowledge of the precipitation of colloids was made by Schulze,[3] in 1882. Experimenting upon arsenious sulfide hydrosol, he found that the precipitating effectiveness of salts increased markedly with the valence of the cations. He noted that trivalent cation and divalent cation salts were respectively 1,650 and 30 times as potent precipitants as monovalent cation salts. In other words, only $\frac{1}{1650}$ the concentration of a trivalent cation salt, and $\frac{1}{30}$ the concentration of a divalent cation salt were required to produce the same precipitation effect upon his arsenious sulfide hydrosol as unit concentration of a monovalent cation salt. As a result of this first orderly investigation, one frequently hears of the *Schulze valence rule* in colloid chemistry expressed in terms of the numbers just given. The valence rule was an important discovery but the actual quantitative designations are only of historical interest since they are the result of a particular technique applied to a particular hydrosol.

A more exact study by Hardy[4] confirmed Schulze's experiments and extended the valence rule so that it might be stated generally

178

to the effect that the significant ion in the precipitation of colloids is the ion of charge opposite in sign to the charge of the colloidal ionic micelle and that the precipitating power increases markedly with increase in valence of the significant ions.

Linder and Picton[5] found that the precipitating powers of the cations upon their arsenious sulfide hydrosol were

$$P^+:P^{++}:P^{+++} = 1:35:1,023.$$

These numbers, it is seen, agree qualitatively with those given by Schulze. As one studies the literature, many cases are found supporting qualitatively the valence rule; but just to convince the reader of the validity of the criticism of the quantitative values, the author will cite two more cases. Young and Neal[6] found in the precipitation of copper sulfide hydrosol the values $1:39:875$ for $KCl:CaCl_2:AlCl_3$, while for complex cobalt cation salts acting upon arsenious sulfide hydrosol Matsuno[7] reported $P^+:P^{2+}:P^{3+}:P^{4+}:P^{6+} = 1:16:80:284:1280$.

Whetham,[8] in 1899, attempted to apply the theory of probabilities of contact of charges to the precipitation and stated the ratio of the precipitating powers of the ions, $P':P'':P'''$ to be $x:x^2:x^3$. This rule happened to hold fairly well for the two sets of data available at the time but subsequent accumulation of data has discredited it. There is no quantitative agreement between the various precipitating values of electrolytes published since they are subject to so many variations in conditions of operation, such as the mode of adding the electrolyte, the method of treatment after the addition, *i.e.*, whether quiet or agitated, the temperature of the hydrosol, the concentration of the dispersed phase, the "purity" of the sol, and the time of observation.

Various methods have been devised for the comparison of the precipitation effects of electrolytes upon hydrosols. No matter which method is used, the results are relative only.

A simple method based upon that used by Freundlich[9] is as follows: To a series of carefully cleaned test tubes containing 5 cc. portions of the hydrosol are added 5 cc. portions of different concentrations of the electrolytes. The electrolyte solution is poured quickly into the hydrosol, the mixture quickly poured back into the empty test tube, and then back into the first test tube in order to effect as complete and rapid mixing as possible.

The tubes may then be allowed to stand for 2 hr. or centrifuged for 2 min.; then they are examined for evidence of precipitation. The mean of the concentrations at which precipitation is just complete, as shown by a clear supernatant solution, and the next lowest concentration (where precipitation is not complete) is taken as the precipitation concentration. This concentration is called the *liminal value*. Naturally all must be done under the same conditions.

Some experimental results are given in Tables 23 to 28, inclusive. The letter γ is commonly used to signify the liminal concentration of the mixture in millimoles per liter of the ion of charge opposite to that of the colloidal micelle. The larger this number is, the lower is the precipitating power of the electrolyte.

TABLE 23.—PRECIPITATION OF AN ARSENIOUS SULFIDE HYDROSOL[9]

Electrolyte	γ	Electrolyte	γ
K citrate	>240	$MgCl_2$	0.717
K acetate	110	$MgSO_4$	0.810
LiCl	58.4	$CaCl_2$	0.649
NaCl	51.0	$SrCl_2$	0.635
KNO_3	50.0	$BaCl_2$	0.691
KCl	49.5	$Ba(NO_3)_2$	0.687
$K_2SO_4/2$	65.6	$ZnCl_2$	0.685
NH_4Cl	42.3	$UO_2(NO_3)_2$	0.642
HCl	30.8	$AlCl_3$	0.093
$H_2SO_4/2$	30.1	$Al(NO_3)_3$	0.095
		$Ce_2(SO_4)_3/2$	0.092

TABLE 24.—PRECIPITATION OF A MERCURIC SULFIDE HYDROSOL[10]

Electrolyte	γ	Electrolyte	γ
NaCl	13	$SrCl_2$	0.88
KCl	10	$BaBr_2$	0.68
NH_4Cl	10	$UO_2(NO_3)_2$	0.79
$H_2SO_4/2$	7.8	$CuSO_4$	0.047
NaOH	29	$HgCl_2$	0.11
$AgNO_3$	0.44	$Pb(NO_3)_2$	0.050
$Hg_2SO_4/2$	0.081	$Al_2(SO_4)_3/2$	0.044
$TlNO_3$	0.14	YCl_3	0.073
$Tl_2(SO_4)/2$	0.15	$Ce(NO_3)_3$	0.056

TABLE 25.—PRECIPITATION OF A PLATINUM HYDROSOL[9]

Electrolyte	γ
NaOH	130
NaCl	2.5
KCl	2.2
$AgNO_3$	0.22
$BaCl_2$	0.058
$UO_2(NO_3)_2$	0.065
$Pb(NO_3)_2$	0.011
$Al_2(SO_4)_3/2$	0.013

TABLE 26.—PRECIPITATION OF A GOLD (CO REDUCTION) HYDROSOL[11]

Electrolyte	γ	Electrolyte	γ
LiCl	30	$MgCl_2$	0.15
NaCl	25	$BaCl_2$	0.13
KCl	18	$AlCl_3$	0.0022
CsCl	13	$CeCl_3$	0.0022
HCl	11	$ThCl_4$	0.0014

TABLE 27.—PRECIPITATION OF A FERRIC OXYCHLORIDE HYDROSOL[9]

Electrolyte	γ	Electrolyte	γ
KCl	9.03	$Ba(OH)_2/2$	0.42
KNO_3	11.9	K_2SO_4	0.204
NaCl	9.25	Tl_2SO_4	0.219
$BaCl_2/2$	9.64	$MgSO_4$	0.217
KBr	12.5	$K_2Cr_2O_7$	0.194
KI	16.2	H_2SO_4	About 0.5
HCl	>400		

Inspection of these tables reveals the fact that, while, in general, the precipitating powers of the electrolytes vary as the valence of the ion of charge opposite to that of the colloid, there are, however, variations in precipitation among ions of the same valence, and, indeed, certain exceptions are noted where an ion shows less precipitating effect than one of lower valence. Apparently, there are exceptions to the valence rule.

Order of Alkali and Alkaline-earth Salts.—Arranging the alkali chlorides in Tables 23 and 28 we have the series

$$K^+ > Na^+ > Li^+$$

TABLE 28.—PRECIPITATION OF AN ODEN SULFUR HYDROSOL[12]

Electrolyte	γ	Electrolyte	γ
HCl	6000	$Mg(NO_3)_2$	8.0
LiCl	913	$Ca(NO_3)_2$	4.0
NaCl	153	$Sr(NO_3)_2$	2.5
KCl	21	$Ba(NO_3)_2$	2.2
RbCl	16	$MgSO_4$	9.3
CsCl	9	$CaCl_2$	4.1
NH_4Cl	435	$BaCl_2$	2.1
NH_4NO_3	506	$ZnSO_4$	75.6
$(NH_4)_2SO_4/2$	600	$Cd(NO_3)_2$	49.3
$NaNO_3$	163	$Ni(NO_3)_2$	44.6
$Na_2SO_4/2$	176	$UO_2(NO_3)_2$	13.7
KNO_3	22	$Mn(NO_3)_2$	9.6
$K_2SO_4/2$	25	$CuSO_4$	9.8
		$AlCl_3$	4.4

and

$$Cs^+ > Rb^+ > K^+ > Na^+ > Li^+$$

Using a different method of measuring precipitation powers of electrolytes upon an arsenious sulfide hydrosol, Bach[13] found the order $Cs^+ > Rb^+ > K^+ > Na^+ > Li^+$. The same has been found for gold hydrosol.[14] This order—or parts of it—appears in data for the precipitation of diverse negative ionic micelles. That it is not universally so is indicated by experiments upon a negative micellar "stannic oxide" hydrosol where cesium, rubidium, potassium, sodium, and lithium salts showed practically the same precipitating power.[15] Hence we may say that, for alkali salts with a common ion, the precipitation potency toward negative ionic micelles may be in the order of their atomic weights.

Upon examination of Table 28 the order for the alkaline-earth nitrates is $Ba^{++} > Sr^{++} > Ca^{++} > Mg^{++}$.

Order of Halide Ions.—The precipitation order of the halides upon positive ionic micelles in Table 27 is seen to be

$$Cl^- > Br^- > I^-.$$

This order has been confirmed by Bach.[13] Other orders reported[16] are

$Cl^- > NO_3^- > Br^- > I^-$ and
$$CNS^- > Cl^- > Br^- > NO_3^- > ClO_3^- > I^-.$$

These series, either in the order as given or in the reversed order, have been observed in many physical and physicochemical phenomena.[17]

Fluoride ion is about as powerful as sulfate ion. Fluorides polymerize in aqueous solution.[15,21]

Ions Which Form Insoluble Compounds.—In Table 24 silver, mercurous, and thallous salts are seen to be more powerful precipitants of mercury sulfide sol than barium or strontium salts. This constitutes a striking exception to the valence rule. When one considers the chemical nature of the sol, however, the reason for the potency of these salts is clear. The cations of these salts form insoluble sulfides and consequently their precipitation effectiveness would be expected to be large toward a sol which is $xHgS.SH_2$, or toward any other sol of the H_2S type. In the same table cupric, mercuric, and lead salts are seen to be more potent than the barium, strontium, and uranyl salts and, in fact, they are of the same order of potency as the aluminum, yttrium, and ceric salts.

In Table 25 silver and lead salts are seen to be exceptionally potent. Since Pennycuick has shown platinum hydrosols to consist of complexes of platinum and platinic acids, this behavior indicates that silver and lead platinates are insoluble in water. In Table 27 barium hydroxide is shown to be a much more effective precipitant of the ferric oxychloride hydrosol than barium chloride. Here again the reason is clear; this sol consisting of micelles in hydrolytic equilibrium with hydrochloric acid would naturally be converted to a more basic and less stable dispersion upon the addition of hydroxyl ion.

Reasons for differences between certain salts in Table 28 are not so easily found, owing to the complicated nature of Odén sulfur sols. They contain sulfuric and polythionic acids. The order $Ba^{++} > Sr^{++} > Ca^{++} > Mg^{++}$ might be ascribed to the order of the insolubility of their sulfates. The high precipitating power of the alkaline earths in general might be due to the fact that alkaline-earth polythionates are unstable.[18] Polythionates are known to be quite stable in acid solution while neutral solutions of the polythionates are not so stable and alkaline solutions decompose readily. Consequently, acid-reacting salt solutions should not be so powerful precipitants as neutral-salt solutions owing to the stabilizing action of H^+ ion upon polythionates.

It is evident then that salts containing ions which react with the constituents of the hydrosol in a manner which results in the formation of insoluble compounds or in the decomposition of essential stabilizing parts of the micelle are exceptions to the valence rule and are more potent precipitants of the dispersed phase than other ions of the same valence which do not possess these characteristics. Once one knows the chemical nature of the hydrosol, such potent ions can readily be indicated.

TABLE 29.—PRECIPITATION OF HYDROSOLS BY ORGANIC SALTS

Electrolyte	γ	Electrolyte	γ
Arsenious sulfide sol:[9]		Mercuric sulfide sol:[10]	
NaCl	51.0	NaCl	13
Guanidine nitrate	16.4	Guanidine nitrate	16
Strychnine nitrate	8.0	Morphine chloride	0.14
Aniline chloride	2.52	Strychnine nitrate	0.012
Toluidine sulfate	1.17	New fuchsin	0.019
Morphine chloride	0.425	Crystal violet	0.018
Crystal violet	0.165	Brilliant green	0.011
New fuchsin	0.114	Auramine	0.026
Formol gold sol:[9]		Methylene blue	0.017
NaCl	23	Ferric oxychloride sol:[9]	
SrCl$_2$	0.47	NaCl	300
$\frac{Al_2(SO_4)_3}{2}$	0.025	Sodium formate	56
		Sodium acetate	30
p-chloraniline chloride	6.4	Sodium benzoate	32
Guanidine nitrate	1.7	Sodium salicylate	20
Morphine chloride	1.1	Na$_2$SO$_4$	0.8
Aniline chloride	0.74	Ferric oxychloride sol:[21]	
Strychnine nitrate	0.49	NaCl	230
New fuchsin	0.0004	Sodium acetate	34
		Ammonium benzene sulfonate	44
		Sodium benzoate	8.5
		Sodium maleinate	0.37
		Sodium fumarate	0.24
		Na$_2$SO$_4$	0.21
		Sodium-o-phthalate	0.25
		Sodium-m-phthalate	0.15
		Sodium trimesate	0.08

Freundlich[19] has claimed that precipitation potency of ions is a function of their degrees of sorption by the micelles. In the instances of insoluble-compound formation just discussed, the sorption is readily explained upon a clearer chemical basis. Weiser,[20] who has experimentally investigated this problem, agrees with Freundlich.

Organic Ions.—Salts containing organic ions of sign of charge opposite to that of the micelle are very potent precipitants. Experimental data are given in Table 29.

A study of the precipitating power of the sodium salts of 36 organic acids upon a ferric oxide hydrosol[22] has produced interesting information. The precipitating power increases as CH_3 groups are substituted for H atoms. It increases markedly as phenyl groups are substituted for H atoms. Iodo compounds are more potent than brom, and brom compounds are more potent than chlor compounds. A comparison of the o-, m-, and p-toluates, oxybenzoates, nitrobenzoates, and aminobenzoates showed no consistent order other than the meta compound being between the ortho and para compounds in precipitation power.

Hydrogen and Hydroxyl Ions.—Hydrogen and hydroxyl ions are exceptional in their action upon micelles of opposite charge. Acids in general are much more potent precipitants of arsenious sulfide sol than other inorganic electrolytes with monovalent cations. There are certain exceptions, however, citric acid not acting as a coagulant toward this sol. Acids are potent precipitants of the hydrosulfide type of hydrosols, gold and platinum sols while, on the other hand, H^+ is but a weak precipitant of Odén sulfur sol. In the latter case reference has already been made to the fact that polythionic acids are more stable in acid solution. The hydrosulfide type of hydrosols are sensitive toward added H^+ ion probably because such addition drives back the hydrolysis of the metallic sulfide and represses the ionization of the hydrogen sulfide. The latter suggestion may apply also to the platinic acids of platinum sol.

In the precipitation of a gum mastic hydrosol by hydrochloric, acetic, sulfuric, oxalic, and phosphoric acids, the acids have been shown to be equally effective, all precipitating the gum at pH 2.5.[23] One might expect this since the dispersed phase owes its stability to —COOH groups, but an instance has been pointed out where the anion of the acid is significant.[24] In this instance, hydrochloric, acetic, sulfuric, and nitric acids produced precipitation of a gum mastic hydrosol at pH 2.9, but a pH value of 1 was required for its precipitation by sulfosalicylic acid.

The precipitation effect of acids upon certain clay dispersions also appears to be principally a pH effect.[25] The same has been shown for a Prussian blue hydrosol, with the exception of oxalic acid.[26] It required an abnormally high concentration of oxalic acid and an abnormally low pH value as compared with hydrochloric, sulfuric, acetic, and citric acids. The peculiar effect of oxalate upon Prussian blue hydrosol has been mentioned in Chap. VI. Hydrochloric, hydrobromic, nitric, and sulfuric acids precipitated arsenious sulfide hydrosol at the same pH; oxalic and trichloracetic acids required a lower pH[27]; while acetic acid did not coagulate at all. Pennycuick,[28] experimenting upon a platinum hydrosol, found the pH range of precipitation of hydrochloric, sulfuric, nitric, benzoic, tartaric, salicylic, succinic, and citric acids to be 3.69 to 3.44. He attributed the precipitating action to the repression of the ionization of the micellar platinic acids.

Hydroxyl ion is more potent as a precipitant of the positively charged ionic micelles in ferricoxy, chromicoxy, aluminumoxy, etc., type of hydrosols. The reason for this has been mentioned previously.

Ions of Same Sign of Charge as That of Micelle.—In this discussion only the ions of charge opposite to that of the colloidal micelles have been considered. But the ions of like charge also play a rôle.

The precipitating power of salts diminishes with increase in valence of the ions of the same sign of charge as that of the ionic micelle. In Table 28 it is seen that Na_2SO_4 is weaker than $NaCl$, K_2SO_4 is weaker than KCl or KNO_3, and $MgSO_4$ is weaker than $Mg(NO_3)_2$. The effect of valence is far from being so marked in the "like sign of charge" as in the "opposite sign of charge" case, but it is evident, however.

When the members of a family of anions such as the halides are compared, conflicting results are found:

I > Cl > Br (arsenious sulfide sol)[3]

Br > I > Cl (negative "ferric oxide" sol)[29]

$$Cl > Br > I \quad \text{(selenium sol)}[30]$$
$$Cl = Br > I \quad \text{(tellurium sol)}[30]$$
$$Cl = I \qquad \text{(sulfur sol)}[31]$$
$$Cl > Br = I \quad \text{(gold sol)}[32]$$
$$Cl = Br = I \quad \text{(arsenious sulfide sol)}[27]$$
$$Cl > Br \qquad \text{(gold sol)}[14]$$

Mukherjee[27] states that simple inorganic anions show no differences in precipitating effect upon arsenious sulfide. He found that anion effects became noticeable only with organic and complex inorganic anions. Salts of such ions had lower precipitating powers. This effect is seen in Table 23 where potassium acetate and citrate have much higher liminal values than the other salts. This may be due in part to their tendency to hydrolyze and thus be more alkaline than the other salts. Alkaline reagents are poor precipitants of the sulfide sols as shown by NaOH in Table 24. Hydroxyl ion acts the same upon platinum sol (Table 25), while hydrogen ion is a poor precipitant for ferricoxychloride and similar sols (Table 27). The low precipitating effect of hydroxyl ion upon the sulfide sols is ascribed to its promoting hydrolysis of the sulfide.[33] When added to platinum sol it produces an increased ionization of the micellar platinic acids.[34]

The low precipitating power of monobasic inorganic acids upon ferricoxychloride sols is readily understood because such acids are peptizers of ferric hydroxide. When the pH of ferricoxychloride sol is decreased by addition of acid, increasing amounts of a neutral salt are required to precipitate it.[35] The same is true for chromicoxychloride sol.[36]

Since H^+ and OH^- are so significant, as precipitants or stabilizers of sols depending upon the chemical nature of the latter, it is evident that pH must be controlled when a comparison of ion effects upon sols is under investigation.

The precipitation order of a family of cations upon ferricoxychloride sol has been shown to be[13] $Li^+ > Na^+ > K^+ > NH_4^+$. Quantitatively, while the effect of lithium chloride was about 20 per cent greater than that of sodium chloride, the latter was only 4 per cent more effective than potassium chloride. One might be inclined to generalize and state that the precipitating order of the alkali salts upon a positive ionic micelle is just the reverse of the order for a negative ionic micelle. Such a generalization is dangerous, however, if the following more extensive order found by Jablczynski[16] is correct: $Cs^+ > Rb^+ > Li^+ > Na^+ > K^+ > NH_4^+$. He recalls that cesium and rubidium chlorides readily form complex salts with ferric chloride[37] and suggests this fact as a reason for this peculiar order of the alkali salts. For the alkaline-earth salts he found the order $Mg^{++} > Ba^{++} > Ca^{++} > Sr^{++}$. Taylor[16] reports the order $Li^+ > Na^+ > Mg^{++} > K^+ > Rb^+ > NH_4^+ > Ca^{++}$ for a ferricoxychloride sol.

The order has been found to be $Li^+ > Na^+ > NH_4^+ > K^+$ and $Mg^{++} > Ca^{++} > Sr^{++} > Ba^{++}$ for thorium oxide sols.[39]

Mixtures of Electrolytes.—There is a confused literature upon the precipitation of sols by mixtures of electrolytes.[11,33,36,40] Much is said about the "antagonistic action" of electrolyte pairs. For example, one finds that a mixture of sodium and hydrogen chlorides exerts a greater precipitating effect upon arsenious sulfide sol than is expected from the value obtained with each alone. This is not surprising if one will admit that added hydrochloric acid represses the hydrolysis of arsenious sulfide and the ionization of hydrogen sulfide, thus rendering the sol less stable.[33] Furthermore, conversion of amicroscopic to submicroscopic particles has been observed as a result of the addition of small amounts of hydrochloric acid to an arsenious sulfide sol.[38] Likewise a mixture of sodium hydroxide and chloride is less potent on arsenious sulfide sol than would be expected because alkalinity favors hydrolysis of arsenious sulfide and thus converts the micelles into particles containing more sulfide ions.[33] When small quantities of potassium ferrocyanide are added to copper ferrocyanide sol, larger amounts of potassium chloride and of barium chloride are required to precipitate it than in the absence of the added ferrocyanide.[36] This is due to the fact that ferrocyanide is the stabilizing ion in this sol.

Influence of Concentration of Dispersed Phase.—In 1919, it was shown that an arsenious sulfide sol upon dilution required more monovalent cation salt, less trivalent cation salt, and about the same amount of divalent cation salt for precipitation.[41,42] In the cases of copper sulfide and mercuric sulfide sols[42] and of ferricoxychloride sol,[41] decreasing amounts of even monovalent ion electrolytes gave precipitation of increasingly diluted sols. Burton and Bishop[43] confirmed the first-mentioned behavior for arsenious sulfide, gum mastic, and copper hydroxide sols. For example, their liminal values for a gum mastic hydrosol were KCl, 205; $CaCl_2$, 11.5; $Al_2(SO_4)_3$, 0.061 millimoles, while after dilution of 1 volume of the sol with 19 volumes of water the values were KCl, 632; $CaCl_2$, 14.4; $Al_2(SO_4)_3$, 0.009. In the first instance, $P':P'':P''' = 1:17.4:3,333$ and in the second, $= 1:44:52,000$, thus again showing the valence rule to be merely of qualitative significance. This effect of dilution is generally called the "Burton-Bishop rule" in the American literature on colloid chemistry.

Weiser and Nicholas[44] confirmed the Burton-Bishop rule for arsenious sulfide sol but found that chromic oxide, ferric oxide, and Prussian blue hydrosols required less of all electrolytes for precipitation after dilution. They pointed out that the manner in which the precipitation value of an electrolyte varies with the concentration of the colloid is determined to a large extent by the relative sorptive property of the ion of opposite charge (precipitating ion) and of the ion of like charge (stabilizing ion). If the adsorption of the stabilizing ion of an electrolyte is negligible and the adsorption of the precipitating ion is very large, the liminal value varies almost directly with the concentration of the colloid. If the adsorption of the stabilizing ion is appreciable, the liminal value is increased upon dilution.

The behavior toward electrolytes upon dilution obviously depends upon the nature of the colloid also. An arsenious sulfide hydrosol may become more stable upon dilution owing to hydrolysis[45] and increase in degree of dispersion.[46] This would be manifested upon treatment with a salt such as potassium chloride while not upon treatment with powerful precipitants such as copper, lead, and aluminum salts.

Ferric oxychloride sols as already mentioned show normal effects upon dilution. It has been shown, however, that Sorum's chloride-free ferric oxide sol follows the Burton-Bishop rule upon dilution; but when ferric chloride is added to it in small quantities, it assumes the normal property.[47] This has been shown to be the case for thorium oxide sols, also.[39]

The Irregular Series.—When two extremes of electrolyte concentration produce precipitation and intermediate concentrations do not, the effect is called the *irregular series* in precipitation. This effect is encountered generally with salts containing polyvalent or heavy metal cations in the precipitation of negative micelles. Tables 30 and 31 summarize two typical irregular-series experiments.

TABLE 30.—BREDIG PLATINUM HYDROSOL PRECIPITATED BY FERRIC CHLORIDE[80]

Millimolar Concentration of $FeCl_3$	Effect
0.021 to 0.056	No precipitate. Particles migrated to anode
0.083 to 0.222	Complete precipitation
0.333 to 6.67	No precipitate. Particles migrated to cathode
16.3 to 667	Complete precipitation

TABLE 31.—MERCURIC SULFIDE HYDROSOL[10]

Millimolar Concentration of $AgNO_3$	Effect
0.23 to 0.26	No precipitation
0.27 to 0.64	Complete precipitation
0.89 to 14.9	No precipitation
17.8	Partial precipitation
22.3 to 44.6	Complete precipitation

The generally accepted explanation for the irregular series has been that of mutual colloid reaction; *i.e.*, in the first precipitation zone the flocculation is caused by the positively charged colloidal oxide arising from hydrolysis of the salt, and the zone of no precipitation following is a result of the fact that there is sufficient colloidal oxide not only to neutralize the charge of the negative colloid but to carry it as part of the positive complex, *i.e.*, to protect it. When oppositely charged colloids are mixed together, there is no precipitation if there is a large excess of one of them. The second and final zone of precipitation is simple salting-out.

This theory is questioned by Kruyt and van der Spek[41] because they obtained the following irregular series in the precipitation of a ferric oxychloride hydrosol with sodium hydroxide (Table 32).

It is evident that the colloidal oxide peptization theory for the mid-zone cannot be applied to this case. The experi-

TABLE 32.—FERRIC OXIDE HYDROSOL TREATED WITH NaOH[41]

Millimolar Concentration of NaOH	Effect after 3 Hr. Standing
1.27 to 1.4	Incompletely precipitated
1.55 to 2.8	Completely precipitated (immediate)
3.1	Almost completely precipitated
3.99	Turbid
5.59 to 8.36	Scarcely any precipitate
13.9	Turbid
20.9 to 27.9	Incompletely precipitated
30.3 to 32.4	Completely precipitated

menters ascribe the "tolerance" region to peptization of the particles by hydroxyl ion due to its great "electrocapillary" activity and, since the charge of the particles is reversed thereby, then the final precipitation zone is due to sodium ion. They obtained a similar series when they used disodium phosphate as coagulant, owing to the hydroxyl ion arising from the hydrolysis of the salt.[48]

Kruyt and van Arkel-Adriani[49] offer evidence in the reaction between gold hydrosol and thorium nitrate to show that both theories may obtain depending upon the conditions of the experiment. They prepared a gold sol by reduction of chlorauric acid with hydrogen peroxide and exactly neutralized it with alkali. This was termed "neutral" sol. To another portion,

TABLE 33.—NEUTRAL GOLD SOL AND THORIUM NITRATE

Concentration of $Th(NO_3)_4$, Millimoles per Liter	Condition after 5 Min.
Up to 0.00084	Red
0.00086 to 0.00088	Red-blue
0.00090 to 0.0028	Blue
0.003	Violet-blue
0.004 to 15.0	Red
15.5	Violet-red
17 to 19	Violet
20 to 26	Blue

TABLE 34.—ALKALINE GOLD SOL AND THORIUM NITRATE

Concentration of $Th(NO_3)_4$, Millimoles per Liter	Condition after 5 Min.
0.0005 to 0.02	Red
0.03 to 0.05	Red flocks
0.10 to 2.5	Red
3.0	Violet-red
5.0	Blue

a slight excess of alkali was added—"alkaline" sol. The behavior of both sols when treated with thorium nitrate is shown in Tables 33 and 34.

It is evident that in the alkaline sol the flocculating agent in the first zone is colloidal thoria formed by the alkaline reaction, especially since the red flocks are formed instead of a blue color. This flocculation is analogous to the formation of purple of Cassius. They prepared thoria hydrosol and upon mixing it with the alkaline gold sol obtained the following results:

Concentration of ThO_2,
Millimoles per Liter   Condition after 5 Min.
   0.002 to 0.10.............................. Red sol
   0.25 to 0.50.............................. Red flocks
   0.60 to 7.0.............................. Red sol

Accordingly they admit that in the case of the alkaline gold sol the mid-zone is due to peptization of the gold particles by the colloidal thoria but state that such is not true with the neutral sol. In the latter instance, it is contended that the tolerance zone is a result of the very high electrocapillary activity of the polyvalent cation which reverses the sign of the charge of the colloidal particles just as such an ion reverses the sign of the charge of glass capillaries against water.

The possibility of reversing the sign of charge of colloidal gold is disputed. Gold sols prepared by the Bredig-arc method are always negative, regardless of whether gold wires are sparked in solutions containing sodium hydroxide, sodium chloride, or hydrochloric acid, and the addition of acid to a gold sol always results in precipitation of the gold. It never reverses the charge.[50] Burton claims to have reversed the charge of gold sols by the addition of an aluminum salt and Kruyt and van Arkel-Adriani obtained a tolerance zone when precipitating gold sols with an aluminum salt, but in the opinion of the author it was not a simple reversal of sign of charge but a peptization of gold particles by the colloidal hydrous oxide resulting from hydrolysis of the aluminum salt. In the exceedingly low concentrations of the salt used, such hydrolysis surely does take place without the aid of hydroxyl ions in excess of those already present in pure water and therefore this view appears reasonable.

Like Powis, Kruyt and van Arkel-Adriani were unable to reverse the sign of charge of arsenious sulfide hydrosol no matter how they manipulated, nor could they get an irregular series with vanadium pentoxide hydrosol. This lends support to the view favoring the mutual colloid effect for polyvalent-cation salts; for if the tolerance zone were due to selective sorption of a polyvalent ion, it should be general.

Herstad[51] like Morawitz[52] found that colloidal gold made by the formol method is very sensitive to mercuric chloride but that, when a little hydrochloric acid is added, the gold is no longer precipitated by mercuric chloride. Hydrogen ion activity measurements showed that the sol was sensitive to the action of the mercuric chloride when it was slightly alkaline. The unneutralized gold sol precipitated at 0.03 to 0.10 millimole per liter of mercuric chloride, beyond which concentration there was a zone of no precipitation. A second precipitation zone could not be obtained possibly due to the limited solubility of mercuric chloride. Herstad explains the precipitation in the first instance as due to the formation of mercuric oxide by the alkali, the mercuric oxide in turn being reduced by the formaldehyde to mercurous oxide, which is sufficiently ionized to produce sufficient mercurous ions to coagulate the gold. The zone of no precipitation is due to the formation of sufficient mercuric oxide sol to peptize the gold. When hydrochloric acid is added, these substances cannot be formed and hence there is no precipitation.

An irregular series has been observed in the reaction between typhoid bacilli and immune serum.[53]

Ionic Interchange in Precipitation.—Linder and Picton,[5] 1895, were the first to give a chemical explanation of the precipitation of sols by electrolytes and to show that the coagulum carried down that ion of the added electrolyte which was of opposite sign of charge to that carried by the micelle. The view that colloid coagulation was in this sense very similar to the precipitation of ordinary insoluble salts was strongly supported by Duclaux.[54]

In 1901, Whitney and Ober[55] found that an arsenious sulfide sol becomes acid when precipitated by a neutral salt and that equivalent amounts of cations of different salts are fixed in the resulting gel. They added a constant volume of salt solution to

100 cc. of sol which contained 10 g. arsenious sulfide per liter. The precipitate was filtered and washed until no test for chloride was obtained in the washings. By analysis of the filtrate, the amount of metallic ion held by the gel was calculated. In this manner 7.6 mg. of barium and practically chemical equivalent amounts of calcium, strontium, and potassium were found to be fixed by the gel obtained from 100 cc. of the sol. The amounts of hydrochloric acid produced were chemically equivalent also, leading Whitney and Ober to the conclusion that the colloid caused hydrolysis of the salt and carried the base down in the gel.

This explanation was disputed by Duclaux[56] who found that, after coagulation of an arsenious sulfide hydrosol by barium chloride, the supernatant solution contained arsenious acid, despite the fact that the original sol contained an excess of hydrogen sulfide. He suggested that the sorbed barium replaced "a monovalent arsenious radical such as (AsO) preexisting in the sulfide." In concluding his paper he remarked as follows:

It is certainly very convenient to consider only the valence or the electric charge of ions and to neglect their chemical affinities; unfortunately the theories thus arrived at and which are so widespread are contradicted by the simplest experiments.

The problem has been studied by Rabinowitsch[57] using conductometric measurements. These measurements confirmed the previously reported facts of acidification of the solution and sorption of cation which Rabinowitsch attributes to the following reaction (*e.g.*, when using barium chloride):

$$nAs_2S_3.SH_2 + BaCl_2 = nAs_2S_3.SBa + 2HCl$$

He proved quantitatively for Pb^{++} and Ag^+ and qualitatively for Cu^{++} and Hg^{++} that these cations also replace the arsenic from the arsenious sulfide, *e.g.*,

$$As_2S_3 + 3Pb(NO_3)_2 + 3H_2O = 3PbS + As_2O_3 + 6HNO_3$$

Odén[12] found 1.9 gram equivalents of sodium, potassium, rubidium, and cesium sorbed in 1,000 g. of precipitated sulfur from sulfur hydrosol when precipitated by the corresponding chlorides. Bassett and Durant[58] demonstrated that the cations carried down in the gel from a sulfur sol were chemically equivalent to the polythionate of the sol. They believe that the sulfur gel in all cases is just an insoluble salt complex, the precipitation of the sulfur being an exact chemical process.

Weiser[59] does not believe that sorption of ions by the coagulum is always equivalent; his experiments upon aluminum and chromic oxide hydrosols gave the sorption order: ferrocyanide > ferricyanide > oxalate > sulfate > chromate > dithionate > dichromate.

By means of the calomel electrode, Rabinowitsch[60] showed that chloride is removed from an internally bound state to the free ionic condition when a ferricoxychloride sol is titrated with sulfate, chromate, phosphate, oxalate, hydroxide, and nitrate. This has been confirmed by Weiser.[61] The conversion of internally bound hydroxo groups in aluminumoxy salt hydrosols to free hydroxyl ions by neutral salt anions has been discussed in Chap. VII.

Polyvalent precipitating ions are held very tenaciously in the gel. It has been found[62] that a copper oxide hydrosol precipitated by a chloride formed a gel which could be redispersed by repeated washings which removed the sorbed chloride. If precipitated by a sulfate, however, washing would not redisperse the gel until an excess of sodium chloride had been added. The latter displaced the sulfate and then subsequent washing with water resulted in repeptization. Similarly a silica gel formed by the precipitation of silica hydrosol by means of aluminum chloride has been reported[63] to hold the aluminum so tenaciously that water would not wash it out. If washed with a potassium chloride solution, however, potassium would be sorbed and some of the aluminum washed out.

The Influence of Surface Tension.—It is generally agreed that the addition of crystalloid surface-tension-lowering substances such as alcohols, urethanes, phenol, camphor, and thymol to arsenious sulfide, gold, silver, copper ferrocyanide, chromicoxy, and ferricoxy salt hydrosols renders these sols more sensitive toward monovalent ions.[64] The reports of their effects upon the precipitating powers of higher valence ions are conflicting. Weiser[65] ascribes the sensitizing action of these substances to their sorption by the colloidal particles which tends to lower the concentration of electrolyte essential for precipitation, the amount of the lowering being greatest for electrolytes with weakly sorbed precipitating ions that precipitate only in relatively high concentration.

The precipitating effects of a series of organic ions which diversely affect the surface tension of water have been found to bear no relationship to the surface tension when tried upon ferric oxide, zirconium oxide, cerium oxide, gold, arsenious sulfide, Victoria blue, and Congo red hydrosols,[66] although in the precipitation of mastic hydrosols the precipitating powers paralleled the lowering of the surface tension.

More recently, however, Freundlich[67] has produced the information in Table 35.

TABLE 35.—PRECIPITATION OF AN ARSENIOUS SULFIDE HYDROSOL

Electrolyte	Liminal value	Electrolyte	Liminal value
NH_4Cl	51	NH_4Cl	51
CH_3NH_3Cl	30	$(C_2H_5)NH_3Cl$	17.5
$(CH_3)_2NH_2Cl$	14.5	$(C_2H_5)_2NH_2Cl$	5.3
$(CH_3)_3NHCl$	6.9	$(C_2H_5)_3NHCl$	1.5
$(CH_3)_4NCl$	4.8	$(C_2H_5)_4NCl$	0.85
NH_4Cl	51		
$(C_3H_7)NH_3Cl$	9.8		
$(C_3H_7)_2NH_2Cl$	2.3		
$(C_3H_7)_3NHCl$	0.34		
$(C_3H_7)_4NCl$	0.155		

The alkyl amine salts increasingly lower the surface tension of water and the ζ-potential* of the particles with increasing numbers of alkyl groups.

Using a ferric oxide sol (made by action of hydrogen peroxide upon iron carbonyl) the order was p-ethylbenzene sodium sulfonate $>$ p-toluene sodium sulfonate $>$ benzene sodium sulfonate for precipitating power, lowering of the surface tension and for decreasing the ζ-potential.[67] In both series, it will be observed that the electrolytes are in the order of molecular weight.

Kinetics of Precipitation.—A theory for the coagulation of colloidal dispersions was developed by von Smoluchowski[68] in 1917, in which he considered the probability of collision and

* See Chap. IX for definition of ζ-potential.

adhesion of particles resulting in the formation of aggregates large enough to settle out rapidly. The probability of collision is a function of the Brownian movement and of the distance between the particles. The probability of adhesion is a result of the mutual attractive forces of one particle for another and the diminution of surface energy resulting upon union, which is greater when the repulsive forces of the electric double layer have been diminished by the addition of electrolyte.

In considering the case of *rapid coagulation*, *i.e.*, where the sol particles have been robbed of all stabilizing factors, each collision will result in adhesion. Smoluchowski assumes that around each particle there is a sphere of attraction of radius R' so that the center of any particle entering this sphere is firmly bound and R' must be at least twice the radius of the particle. The probability of a particle getting within the sphere of attraction of another particle (assumed to be motionless) is

$$p = 4\pi D R' \nu_0$$

where D is the velocity constant of the Brownian motion,

$$D = \frac{RT}{N} \frac{1}{6\pi\eta r}$$

The "coagulation time" (T'), in which, on an average, the moving particle sticks to the motionless one, is

$$T' = \frac{1}{4\pi R' D \nu_0} = \frac{1}{\beta}$$

where ν_0 is the number of particles originally present in the unit of volume. But now it must be taken into consideration that the selected particle is not at rest but is also subjected to the Brownian motion. This is done by doubling D. The decrease of the number of the simple primary particles is given by

$$\nu_1 = \frac{\nu_0}{1 + 8\pi R' D \nu_0 t} = \frac{\nu_0}{1 + \dfrac{2t}{T'}}$$

But here only the uniting of simple particles into doublets has been considered, whereas, in reality, the formation of multiple particles must be taken into account. The double and treble particles already formed act in their turn as nuclei of coagulation, unfortunately in such a manner as cannot be exactly calculated,

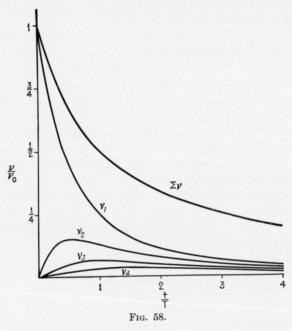

Fig. 58.

the form of the multiple particles being in all probability not spherical. The total decrease of the primary particles is

$$\frac{1}{8\pi DR'}\frac{1}{\nu_1}\frac{d\nu_1}{dt} = -\nu_1 - \nu_2 - \nu_3 - \cdots \nu_n$$

By integration, the total number of particles, *i.e.*, the sum of all singles, doublets, triplets, etc., is

$$\sum \nu = \nu_1 + \nu_2 + \nu_3 + \cdots = \frac{\nu_0}{1 + \beta t}$$

or

$$\sum \nu = \frac{\nu_0}{1 + \dfrac{t}{T'}}$$

From this equation it is seen why T' is called the "coagulation time" for, when $t = T'$, the number of particles is just halved. T' is then a good characteristic for the rate of coagulation.

In Fig. 58 are plotted the ratios $\Sigma\nu/\nu_0$, ν_1/ν_0, ν_2/ν_0, ν_3/ν_0, and ν_4/ν_0 as a function of t/T'. Originally there are present only single particles and consequently $\Sigma\nu$ and ν_1 start at the same point. As the coagulation proceeds, $\Sigma\nu$ and ν_1 diminish. Concomitantly the doublets increase to a maximum and, while decreasing, the triplets increase to a maximum and then decrease, and so on, until all of the particles have coagulated and settled out.

Smoluchowski's equation for rapid coagulation was first verified by Zsigmondy[69] for gold sols and subsequently by others,[39,70,71] Kruyt and van Arkel having made a total count of 200,000 particles in their experimental work!

For the case of *slow coagulation*, *i.e.*, coagulation produced by the addition of a small amount of electrolyte which Smoluchowski theorized would result in only partial annihilation of the repulsing, electric double layers, he proposed a modified formula. This has been shown not to hold.[71] A suggested reason is that the electric charge is not uniformly distributed on the particle surface. Consequently when two particles touch each other at the uncharged spots, they adhere and can thus form clusters like a bunch of grapes.[72]

Heat of Coagulation.—The literature concerning the heat exchanges in the precipitation of colloids by electrolytes is rather meager. Berthelot[73] concluded from his measurements that the heat evolved in the coagulation of ferric oxyacetate hydrosol by potassium sulfate was very slight. Linder and Picton[74] noted no heat evolved in the coagulation of arsenious sulfide hydrosol, but their measurements were crude. Graham noted a temperature rise in the coagulation of silicic acid hydrosol by electrolytes and so did Wiedemann and Lüdeking.[75] Doerinckle[76] noted a positive heat change in the coagulation of silicic acid, ferric oxide, and silver hydrosols and showed that the amount of heat evolved was a function of the concentration and kind of coagulating electrolyte. While he noted that after dialysis the sols evolved less heat upon electrolyte coagulation, he did not seem to attach much significance to this important fact.

Kruyt and van der Spek[77] measured the heat interchanges upon the coagulation of arsenious sulfide and ferric oxychloride hydrosols. After correcting for the heats of dilution they found a positive heat evolution upon the precipitation of ferric oxychloride but none in the case of arsenious sulfide and concluded that the evolution of heat upon coagulation is a property peculiar to the highly hydrated dispersions like silicic acid and ferric oxide. They also noted an expansion of the solution upon addition of sodium chloride and of ammonium nitrate in the precipitation of ferric oxychloride but none in the reaction with arsenious sulfide sol.

Browne and Mathews[78] performed a careful investigation upon the heat of precipitation of ferric oxide hydrosol and criticized Kruyt and van der Spek's belief that it was due to a dehydration. They studied ferric oxychloride sols of varying "purity," *i.e.*, of varying ferric chloride content, and attempted to correct for the heats of dilution and of hydrolysis of the ferric chloride present. They found that, if the heat of dilution per gram equivalent of chlorin in the sol is plotted against the chlorin content, the curve is of the same nature as that for the heat of dilution of ferric chloride solutions of varying concentrations. The heats of coagulation of sols of varying purity with sodium oxalate, sulfate, chloride, potassium ferricyanide, sodium hydroxide, and sulfuric acid were all positive and decreased as the purity of the sol increased to a purity ratio $Fe/Cl = 14$, beyond which either there was no heat evolved or it was negative. The amount of heat liberated varied with the kind of electrolyte. They conclude that the heat effects observed on coagulating ferric oxide sols with electrolytes are to be attributed to the action of the electrolytes in the coagulants upon the peptizing electrolytes, particularly ferric chloride, present in the sol. They also found that the change in dispersity of the ferric oxide on coagulation does not involve a heat change greater than 1 to 2 cal. per gram equivalent of ferric oxide, the limit of accuracy of their method. With Odén sulfur sol, a similar effect was found.[79]

In this chapter, the precipitation of hydrophilic dispersions and the Hofmeister series has not been mentioned. This subject will be discussed in a subsequent chapter.

References

1. SCHEERER: *Ann. Chem.*, **82**, 419 (1851).

2. FARADAY: *Phil. Trans. Roy. Soc. London*, **147**, 145 (1857).

3. SCHULZE: *J. prakt. Chem.*, **25**, 431 (1882); **27**, 320 (1883); **32**, 390 (1884).

4. HARDY: *Proc. Roy. Soc. (London)*, **66**, 110 (1899); *J. Phys. Chem.*, **4**, 235 (1900); *Z. physik. Chem.*, **33**, 385 (1900).

5. LINDER and PICTON: *J. Chem. Soc.*, **67**, 63 (1895).

6. YOUNG and NEAL: *J. Phys. Chem.*, **21**, 14 (1917).

7. MATSUNO: *J. Tokyo Chem. Soc.*, **39**, 908 (1918).

8. WHETHAM: *Phil. Mag.*, **48**, 474 (1899).

9. FREUNDLICH: *Z. physik. Chem.*, **44**, 129 (1903).

10. FREUNDLICH and SCHUCHT: *Z. physik. Chem.*, **85**, 641 (1913).

11. FREUNDLICH and SCHOLZ: *Kolloidchem. Beihefte*, **16**, 267 (1922).

12. ODÉN: Der Kolloide Schwefel, *Nova Acta Regiae Soc. Sci. Upsala*, (4) **3**, 1–193 (1913).

13. BACH: *J. chim. phys.*, **18**, 46 (1920).

14. LAGEMANN: *Kolloidchem. Beihefte*, **32**, 212 (1931).

15. GHOSH and DHAR: *Kolloid-Z.*, **44**, 149 (1928).

16. JABLCZYNSKI and KAWENOKI: *Bull. soc. chim.*, **39**, 1322 (1926); TAYLOR: *Proc. Roy. Soc. Edinburgh*, **49**, Pt. 3, 198 (1928–1929).

17. For summaries on this point the reader is referred to:
    DHAR: *Z. Elektrochem.*, **20**, 57 (1914); DRUCKER: *ibid.*, **20**, 80 (1914); FRICKE: *ibid.*, **28**, 161 (1922); TRAUBE: *Arch. ges. Physiol. (Pflüger's)*, **132**, 511 (1910); *J. Phys. Chem.*, **14**, 452 (1910).

18. For the chemistry of the polythionates the reader will find the following helpful: EPHRAIM: "Anorganische Chemie," T. Steinkopf, Dresden and Leipzig, pp. 468–472, 1929; KURTENACKER: *Z. anorg. allgem. Chem.*, **148**, 43 (1925); **174**, 179 (1928); **175**, 367 (1928); FOERSTER. *ibid.*, **141**, 228 (1924); **144**, 337 (1925); JOSEPHY: *ibid.*, **135**, 21 (1924).

19. FREUNDLICH: *Z. physik. Chem.*, **73**, 385 (1910).

20. WEISER: *J. Phys. Chem.*, **24**, 630 (1920); **25**, 399, 665 (1921); **28**, 232 (1924); **29**, 955 (1925).

21. WEITZ and STAMM: *Ber.*, **61B**, 1144 (1928).

22. HERRMANN: *Helvetica Chim. Acta*, **9**, 785 (1926).

23. TARTAR and GAILEY: *J. Am. Chem. Soc.*, **44**, 2212 (1922).

24. MICHAELIS and HIRABAYASHI: *Kolloid-Z.*, **30**, 209 (1922).

25. BRADFIELD: *J. Am. Chem. Soc.*, **45**, 1243 (1923).

26. WEIR: *J. Chem. Soc.*, **127**, 2245 (1925).

27. MUKHERJEE and CHAUDHURI: *J. Chem. Soc.*, **125**, 794 (1924).

28. PENNYCUICK: *J. Chem. Soc.*, **1928**, 551.

29. SEN and DHAR: *Kolloid-Z.*, **34**, 262 (1924).

30. DOOLAN: *J. Phys. Chem.*, **29**, 178 (1925).

31. DORFMAN: *Kolloid-Z.*, **52**, 66 (1930).

32. HENRY and MORRIS: *Trans. Faraday Soc.*, **20**, 30 (1924).

33. GHOSH and DHAR: *Kolloid-Z.*, **39**, 346 (1926).

34. PENNYCUICK: *J. Chem. Soc.*, **1929**, 623; **1930**, 1447.

35. FREUNDLICH and LINDAU: *Kolloid-Z.*, **44**, 198 (1928); HAZEL and SORUM: *J. Am. Chem. Soc.*, **53**, 49 (1931).

36. SEN and MEHROTRA: *Z. anorg. allgem. Chem.*, **142**, 345 (1925).

37. WALDEN: *Z. anorg. Chem.*, **7**, 331 (1894).

38. COWARD: *Trans. Faraday Soc.*, **9**, 142 (1913).

39. DESAI: *Kolloidchem. Beihefte*, **26**, 357 (1928).

40. DORFMAN: *Kolloid-Z.*, **46**, 186 (1928); FREUNDLICH and TAMCHYNA: *Kolloid-Z.*, **53**, 288 (1930); GHOSH and DHAR: *J. Phys. Chem.*, **29**, 659 (1925); **31**, 649 (1927); *Kolloid-Z.*, **38**, 141; KRUYT and VAN DER WILLIGEN: *Proc. Acad. Sci. Amsterdam*, **29**, 484 (1926); MUKHERJEE and GHOSH: *Quart. J. Indian Chem. Soc.*, **1**, 213 (1924); *Chem. Abs.* **19**, 1801; NEUSCHLOSS: *Kolloid-Z.*, **27**, 292 (1920); RABINERSON: *ibid.*, **42**, 50 (1927); SEN: *Kolloid-Z.*, **39**, 324 (1926); WEISER: Ref. 20; also *J. Phys. Chem.*, **30**, 1527 (1926); BUXTON and TEAGUE: *Z. physik. Chem.*, **57**, 76 (1907).

41. KRUYT and VAN DER SPEK: *Kolloid-Z.*, **25**, 1 (1919).

42. MUKHERJEE and SEN: *J. Chem. Soc.*, **115**, 461 (1919).

43. BURTON and BISHOP: *J. Phys. Chem.*, **24**, 701 (1920); BURTON and MACINNES: *J. Phys. Chem.*, **25**, 517 (1921).

44. WEISER and NICHOLAS: *J. Phys. Chem.*, **25**, 742 (1921).

45. GHOSH and DHAR: *J. Phys. Chem.*, **31**, 187 (1927).

46. ROSSI and MARESCOTTI: *Gazz. chim. Ital.*, **59**, 319 (1929); *Chem. Abs.*, **23**, 5379.

47. JUDD and SORUM: *J. Am. Chem. Soc.*, **52**, 2598 (1930).

48. TAYLOR: *Proc. Roy. Soc. Edinburgh*, **45**, 323 (1926).

49. KRUYT and VAN ARKEL-ADRIANI: *Rec. trav. chim.*, **39**, 609 (1920).

50. BEAVER: Dissertation, Columbia University, 1921.

51. HERSTAD: *Kolloidchem. Beihefte*, **8**, 399 (1916).

52. MORAWITZ: *Kolloidchem. Beihefte*, **1**, 323 (1909).

53. EISENBERG and VOLK: *Z. Hygiene*, **40**, 155 (1902).

54. DUCLAUX: *J. chim. phys.*, **5**, 29 (1907); **7**, 405 (1909).

55. WHITNEY and OBER: *J. Am. Chem. Soc.*, **23**, 842 (1901); *Z. physik. Chem.*, **39**, 630 (1902).

56. DUCLAUX: *J. chim. phys.*, **6**, 592 (1908).

57. RABINOWITSCH: *Z. physik. Chem.*, **116**, 97 (1925); RABINOWITSCH and DORFMANN: *ibid.*, **131**, 313 (1928).

58. BASSETT and DURANT: *J. Chem. Soc.*, **1931**, 2919.

59. WEISER: *J. Phys. Chem.*, **29**, 955 (1925).

60. RABINOWITSCH and KARGIN: *Z. physik. Chem.*, **133**, 203 (1928).

61. WEISER: *J. Phys. Chem.*, **35**, 1, 1368 (1931).

62. PAINE: *Kolloidchem. Beihefte*, **4**, 24 (1912); *Proc. Cambridge Phil. Soc.*, **16**, 430 (1912); *Kolloid-Z.*, **11**, 115 (1912).

63. VAN BEMMELEN: *J. prakt. Chem.*, **23**, 324 (1881).

64. KRUYT and VAN DUIN: *Kolloidchem. Beihefte*, **5**, 269 (1914); VAN DUIN: *Kolloid-Z.*, **17**, 123 (1915); FREUNDLICH and RONA: *Biochem. Z.*, **81**, 87 (1917); BOUTARIC and SEMELET: *Rev. gén. colloides*, **4**, 268 (1926); CHAUDHURY and CHATTERJEE: *J. Phys. Chem.*, **33**, 244 (1929);

JANEK and JIRGENSONS: *Kolloid-Z.*, **41**, 40 (1927); LACHS and CHWA-
LINSKI: *Z. physik Chem.*, **A159**, 172 (1932); MATSUNO: *Biochem.
Z.*, **150**, 159 (1924).

65. WEISER: *J. Phys. Chem.*, **28**, 1253 (1924).
66. SHRYVER and SPEER: *Proc. Roy. Soc. (London)*, **90B**, 400 (1918).
67. FREUNDLICH and SLOTTMAN: *Z. physik. Chem.*, **129**, 305 (1927).
68. VON SMOLUCHOWSKI: *Z. physik. Chem.*, **92**, 129 (1917).
69. ZSIGMONDY: *Z. physik. Chem.*, **92**, 600 (1917); *Z. Elektrochem.*, **23**, 148
   (1917).
70. WESTGREN and REITSTÖTTER: *Z. physik. Chem.*, **92**, 750 (1917); EHRING-
   HAUS and WINTGEN: *Z. physik. Chem.*, **104**, 301 (1923).
71. KRUYT and VAN ARKEL: *Rec. trav. chim.*, **39**, 656 (1920); **40**, 916 (1921);
   Kolloid-Z., **32**, 29 (1923).
72. DE JONG: *Z. physik. Chem.*, **130**, 205 (1927).
73. BERTHELOT: *Ann. chim. phys.*, **30**, 178 (1873).
74. LINDER and PICTON: *J. Chem. Soc.*, **61**, 114 (1892).
75. WIEDEMANN and LÜDEKING: *Ann. Physik*, **25**, 145 (1885).
76. DOERINCKLE: *Z. anorg. Chem.*, **66**, 20 (1910).
77. KRUYT and VAN DER SPEK: *Kolloid-Z.*, **24**, 145 (1919).
78. BROWNE and MATHEWS: *J. Am. Chem. Soc.*, **43**, 2336 (1921); BROWNE:
   ibid., **45**, 311 (1923).
79. BROWNE: *First Colloid Symposium Monograph*, p. 7 (1923).
80. BUXTON and TEAGUE: Ref. 40.

CHAPTER IX

ELECTROKINETICS

Whenever two phases come into contact, there generally arises a stratification of balanced electrical charges between the two. If electrodes are placed at the ends of the tube shown in Fig. 59a and an electric field is impressed, the water moves

(a)- Water in a Glass Tube

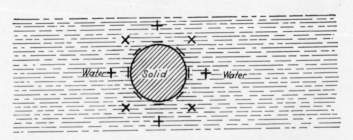

(b)- A Solid Particle Suspended in Water

Fig. 59.

and, conversely, if the water is forced through the tube, a difference in potential is set up. Likewise, the particle shown in Fig. 59b moves in an electric field and, conversely, a potential difference results if the particle is moved through the water. Thus there are four phenomena involving the electrical forces set up by the relative motion of solids and liquids, or, of such relative motions set up by applied e.m.f.

204

These phenomena are correlated as follows:[1]

Motion Caused by Applied E.M.F.	E.M.F. Set Up by Impressed Motion
1. Liquid moves along stationary walls of tubes. *Electroosmosis*	1. Liquid is forced through stationary tubes. *Stream* or *flow potentials*
2. Solid particles move through stationary liquids. *Electrophoresis*	2. Solid particles are dropped through liquids. *Dorn effect*[2]

The classical observation was made by Reuss, in 1808. Inserting electrodes in water contained in two tubes which were inserted upright in a mass of moist clay, he noticed that, when the electrical potential was applied, the water rose in one tube and fell in the other while fine particles of clay detached themselves and migrated in the opposite direction, rendering turbid the contents of the tube wherein the water level fell. In 1816, Porret showed that water could be "entrained by the electric current" across layers of sand and across animal membranes. Analogous observations were made later by Becquerel, Armstrong, and Daniel.

Methods of Measurement of Electrophoresis.—Three general methods are available for measuring the velocity of micelles in an electric field. These are the moving boundary, the Hittorf transference, and the observation of the motion of a single particle under the microscope.

Moving Boundary.—The measurement of the mobility of a colloidal particle by observation of the velocity of a moving boundary in an electric field was first done in a rudimentary form by Picton and Linder[3] (1892). This was six years after Lodge[4] measured the velocity of hydrogen ion by means of the moving-boundary technique. After making a series of qualitative measurements upon a variety of colloidal solutions, Picton and Linder described "a remarkable property which consists in the repulsion of the substance as a whole from one pole to another when one immerses the electrodes connected with a galvanic battery." These experiments combined with their other observations led them to "consider that we have made out good *prima facie* case for the belief that there is a continuous series of grades of solution passing without break from suspension to crystallisable solution." In a later paper[5] they stated, "It will be at once apparent that we have here a remarkable mimicry of ionic dissociation." In 1904, Whitney and Blake[6] found that the rate of migration of the micelles in gold, platinum, and Prussian blue hydrosols approximated that of inorganic crystalloid ions.

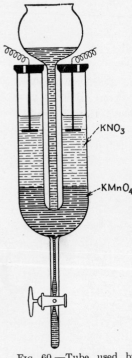

FIG. 60.—Tube used by Nernst for measurement of ionic mobilities.

Hardy[7] should be credited with the first quantitative electrophoretic measurements. He used a U-tube practically identical with that shown in Fig. 60. This is the tube used by Nernst[8] to measure ionic mobilities. Hardy dipped the electrodes into an overlying aqueous solution of the same conductivity as that of the hydrosol. He showed that the overlying liquid must not react with the sol and that merely having an equally conducting overlying liquid did not necessarily make the measurement correct.

The Nernst-Hardy tube is commonly referred to as the "Burton tube," owing to the more widely known experiments performed by Burton[9] upon a number of inorganic hydrosols and suspensions. As used by Burton, its limbs are 12 cm. long and 1.5 cm. in diameter. In the bend is sealed a small-bore delivery tube provided with a stopcock and funnel. With the cock closed, the funnel tube is filled with colloidal solution. A solution of potassium chloride having the same conductivity as that of the hydrosol is put in the U-tube to a height of a few centimeters. After the apparatus has been submerged in a thermostat for a while, the cock is opened allowing the colloidal solution to rise in the limbs. Platinum electrodes are inserted, dipping in the supernatant solution, and are connected to a source of *constant* voltage. Under the action of the current, the boundary between the hydrosol and the overlying liquid falls in one limb and rises in the other. From these displacements in a given time the velocity of the motion of the boundary is calculated. In order to evaluate the mobility of the colloidal particles, the potential gradient must be known. Burton obtained this value by dividing the voltage drop across the electrodes by the *effective* length of the U-tube. It is required, however, for this to be valid, that the field be uniform throughout the system, *i.e.*, that the conductivity of the medium remain the same throughout the determination. The velocity of migration divided by the potential gradient gives the mobility.

Burton noted that the downward displacement was always greater than the upward motion. He referred to this as the "settling of the colloid" and ascribed it to the action of gravity,[10] which is open to question.

The results obtained by means of this method have varied so widely[11] that most workers have found it necessary to alter the apparatus and particularly the nature of the overlying solution. Different values for the mobility are obtained according to the nature of the overlying liquid.[11]

In order to avoid the complications arising from electrolysis products, nonpolarizable electrodes have been used. Electrodes have also been inserted in U-shaped side tubes.[12] Subsidiary electrodes have also been fitted in the main vessel near the boundaries in order to measure and to control the potential drop at the boundary.[13]

In those cases where the colloidal solution is not colored, the motion of the boundary may be followed by use of a Tyndall beam.[14] Since protein solutions fluoresce in ultraviolet light, this may be employed[15] or the absorption of ultraviolet light by the dispersed protein may be photographed.[16]

Different types of overlying or indicating liquids have been used by various workers. Mukherjee[11,17] gives reasons for use in some cases of a suitably chosen solution of the same conductivity as that of the hydrosol. Pennycuick[18] uses the solution obtained by freezing platinum sols in the study of the mobility of platinum micelles. Some workers use an ultrafiltrate as indicating solution. At the present time it is recognized that the constituents of the overlying liquid should not react with the micelles or change their environment, while permitting the calculation of the potential gradient at the boundary.

The intermicellar liquid meets the first requirement and, if its conductivity is the same as that of the sol, the potential gradient problem is eliminated. Within the precision of the ultimate measurements this condition has been fulfilled by certain sols.[19] In the case of proteins it may be realized by using a buffer of sufficient concentration for the foregoing to hold.

The case where the conductivity of the ultrafiltrate differs from that of the original sol has been treated by Kruyt and van der Willigen.[12] They assumed that a boundary finally located above its initial position moves in a medium of conductivity equal to that of the supernatant liquid (*i.e.*, ultrafiltrate), whereas the movement of the micelles below the initial position takes place in a medium of conductivity equal to that of the original sol. This assumption has been shown by Henry and Brittain[13] not to be strictly valid. However, the mobility values obtained by the latter authors for a silver hydrosol, using the method of Kruyt (in both procedure and calculation of results), can be related to the true mobility, obtained by the transference method, by the theoretical treatment given by Henry and Brittain. This treatment is based on the Kohlrausch-Weber theory of moving boundaries.[20]

Hacker[19] shows how one can arrive at the concentration of the indicating solution having ions in common with that of the sol. His treatment is based also on the Kohlrausch-Weber theory.

Henry and Brittain[13] suggest the following simple calculation of the mobility when the change in concentration of the moving sol column is not considered important, the ultrafiltrate being used as the indicating or overlying liquid.

$$U = \frac{v\kappa}{i}$$

where U = mobility of the colloidal micelle.

v = velocity of the advancing sol column.

κ = conductivity of the sol measured during its motion by means of suitably placed side tube electrodes.*

i = current density.

* See description of such a cell by Mukherjee.[17]

Some simple and perhaps obvious rules about the method of moving boundaries are the following:

1. The mobility of the particle must be independent of the nature of the indicating solution. Thus if one uses a potassium chloride solution as an overlying liquid in the case of an oxide hydrosol, chemical changes will invalidate the results. The ultrafiltrate will affect the sol least, if at all.

2. The mobility of the micelle should be independent of the field. This is in fact true for all electrophoretic measurements.

The reader seeking a review of the theory and mechanism of moving boundaries is referred to the comprehensive and authoritative article by MacInnes and Longsworth.[21]

Transference.—The transference method is identical with the Hittorf method of determining ionic transference numbers. This method was first applied to colloidal solutions by Duclaux[22] in 1909 and the method has since been used by several investigators[13,19,23,24] with various modifications of apparatus. One

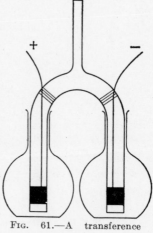

Fig. 61.—A transference apparatus.

of these, the apparatus used by Paine,[24] may be considered. As shown in Fig. 61 it consists of two flasks connected by means of an inverted U-tube. The electrodes are strips of platinum foil wrapped tightly around the outside of the leg of each tube. Platinum wires welded to these strips are passed along the outside of each tube, being fastened at the top. The hydrosol is placed in each of the two flasks and drawn up into the U-tube. A potential difference to produce a current of a few tenths of a milliampere is applied to the electrodes. The current is permitted to flow until a desired amount of the dispersed phase has migrated from one flask to the other; then the stopcock is opened allowing the liquid to flow back into the flasks. The contents of the flasks are analyzed for the mass of the migrating constituent which is *assumed* to be entirely a part of the micelle. Since the mass of the dispersed phase present in an electrode chamber before the application of the current is known, the mass which has migrated from one vessel to the other is readily calculated.

The mobility of the colloidal micelle is given by the equation

$$U = \frac{m\kappa}{MIt} \tag{1}$$

where U = mobility (velocity in centimeters per second under a potential gradient of 1 volt per centimeter).

I = current in amperes.

t = time in seconds.

M = mass of dispersed phase per cubic centimeter of the original hydrosol.

m = mass of dispersed phase transported from one compartment to the other.

κ = specific conductivity of the original hydrosol.

A derivation of this equation is as follows. Consider the area (A) of the cross section of that part of the U-tube where the sol remains unaltered during the electrolysis. If the colloidal particle moves at the velocity v, under a potential gradient of X volts per centimeter, and M is the mass of the particles per cubic centimeter, the amount passing through the cross section A in 1 sec. will be vAM. In t sec.,

$$m = AvMt \tag{2}$$

The current I flowing across A will be

$$I = \kappa XA \text{ or } A = \frac{I}{\kappa X} \tag{3}$$

Replacing A in Eq. (2) one has

$$m = \frac{IvMt}{\kappa X} \tag{4}$$

Since, by definition $v = U$ when $X = 1$ volt per centimeter,

$$U = \frac{m}{M} \frac{\kappa}{I} \frac{1}{t} \tag{5}$$

If it is assumed that the potential gradient is uniform throughout the entire length of the U-tube, it can be said that

$$E = \frac{Ip}{\kappa} \tag{6}$$

where $E =$ the potential drop across the electrodes.

$p =$ the "cell constant" of the apparatus.

This cell constant is determined in the same manner as in the case of a conductivity cell. Thus, substituting for κ/I in Eq. (1),

$$U = \frac{mp}{MEt} \tag{7}$$

the form which Paine used for calculating the mobility of the particles in "copper oxide" hydrosols. The conductivities of these sols were so low that the assumptions may have held. The assumptions were shown not to hold for sols of higher conductivity, *viz.*, certain silver hydrosols. Henry and Brittain[13] found in the latter case that the resistance of the system dropped during the course of the experiment owing to the accumulation of products of electrolysis, which did not, however, reach the topmost portion of the U-tube. Some typical results obtained by the investigators just mentioned are to be found in Table 36.

TABLE 36.—MOBILITIES OF COLLOIDAL PARTICLES

	Conductivity, mhos $\times 10^6$	Mobility, cm. per sec. per volt per cm. $\times 10^5$	
		By Eq. (1)	By Eq. (7)
"Copper oxide" hydrosol→.	2.03	....	39.5
	2.12	....	39.0
	2.11	....	39.0
"Silver" hydrosol→........	16.9	36.3	36.5
	16.6	36.8	36.8
	16.6	35.3	34.8
	16.6	37.3	36.7

The mobilities given in the table are of the same order of magnitude as those of simple ions. For comparative purposes one might cite the following mobilities ($\times 10^5$) determined by Kohlrausch many years ago (at 18°):

Cu^{++}...	31
Li^+..	36
Ag^+..	57
Na^+..	45

The transference method is more time consuming than the moving-boundary technique and its use is restricted to dispersions where the element analyzed for, in order to measure the transference, is present in the micellar form only. For example, if one were measuring the mobility of an aluminumoxychloride micelle, aluminum ion must not be present, inasmuch as the transference of the micelle would be measured by determination of aluminum. The precision of the transference method is set by analytical considerations. An advantage of the method is that the uncertainty concerning the potential gradient, the chief source of error in the moving-boundary method, is absent.

If the theoretical treatment of the various methods of measuring mobility is sound, then the mobility should be independent of the method. In the case of crystalloids, data obtained by means of the improved moving-boundary technique of MacInnes and coworkers differed so widely from the results of earlier investigators who used the Hittorf method that the latter method was questioned. The refinements in the Hittorf technique produced by MacInnes and Dole,[25] however, result in complete agreement between the two methods when applied to a crystalloid. Agreement between these two methods when applied to colloids has recently been established.

Hacker,[19] employing an apparatus which measured the mobility by transport and by motion of the boundary, obtained concordant results in a formol gold hydrosol. Henry and Brittain,[13] studying a Kohlschütter type of silver hydrosol, applied the transference and moving-boundary techniques separately "to the same sol as nearly as possible at the same time" and obtained the results set down in Table 37 upon four hydrosols.

TABLE 37.—MOBILITY OF SILVER MICELLES

Mobility in centimeters per second $\times 10^5$

By Transference	By Moving Boundary
37.7	38.5
36.8	38.3
34.7	34.7
$\begin{cases} 37.2 \\ 33.8 \end{cases}$	36.6

The Microscope-cell Method.—This method consists in the observation of the motion of an individual particle in an electric field using a microscope or an ultramicroscope. It is not applicable either to amicroscopic particles or to concentrated dispersions. In order to minimize the error introduced by the Brownian movement, the mean of many observations is taken.

The observed velocities of the particles vary according to their distance from the cell walls owing to the electroosmotic flow of the dispersion medium along the cell walls (in the opposite direction). Quincke,[26] who is credited with being the first to use this method, called attention to the fact that lycopodium particles suspended in water in proximity to the cell walls moved in the opposite direction to their motion in the center of the liquid.

In a study of the electrophoresis of oil globules in water, Ellis[27] developed a method for the true mobility of the dispersed particles. He assumed that for a flat closed cell the observed velocity (v_0) at a particular level (*i.e.*, the velocity of the particle with respect to a given fixed point on the cell wall) is equal to the algebraic sum of the true velocity of the particle (v_t), *i.e.*, with respect to the suspending liquid, and of the velocity of the liquid (v_l). Thus for a particular level

$$v_0 = v_t + v_l$$

or

$$v_t = v_0 - v_l \tag{8}$$

Integrating over the entire depth (x) of liquid in the cell

$$\int_0^x v_t dx = \int_0^x v_0 dx - \int_0^x v_l dx \tag{9}$$

but $\int_0^x v_l = 0$ for the closed cell and $\int_0^x v_t dx = v_t x$ since v_t is constant and is a function of the potential gradient only. Thus

$$v_t = \frac{1}{x} \int_0^x v_0 dx \tag{10}$$

Equation (10) then simply expresses the true velocity of the particle as the mean velocity in the cell. By plotting the observed values of v_0 as a function of the depth of the cell, a curve as shown in Fig. 62 results, from which the value of v_t is found. The area under the curve divided by x is v_t.

Smoluchowski[28] by deriving the formula for the velocity of the liquid medium in the electrophoretic cell (as a function of the distance from the cell walls) enables one to calculate the true electrophoretic velocity merely by observing the velocity of the particle at two different levels. His equation for the electro-osmotic velocity is

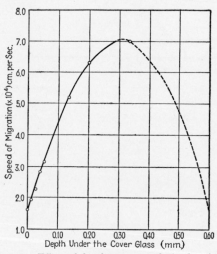

FIG. 62.—Effect of depth upon speed of migration.

$$v_l = v_l'\left[1 - 6\left(\frac{l}{D} - \frac{l^2}{D^2}\right)\right] \tag{11}$$

where v_l' = the velocity of the liquid at the wall of the cell.

l = the depth at which the liquid travels at the velocity v_l.

D = the total depth of the cell.

Thus by observing the velocity of a particle at the levels (l/D) $\frac{1}{6}$ and $\frac{1}{2}$ one obtains by simple algebra two equations [Eqs. (8) and (11)] where the two unknowns are now v_l' and v_t. Thus

$$v_t = 0.75v_{\frac{1}{6}} + 0.25v_{\frac{1}{2}} \tag{12a}$$

where $v_{\frac{1}{6}}$ and $v_{\frac{1}{2}}$ are the observed electrophoretic velocities at the levels $\frac{1}{6}$ and $\frac{1}{2}$, respectively. From Eq. (11) it follows that $v_l = 0$ when $l/D = \frac{1}{2} \pm 1/\sqrt{12}$. Thus, approximately,

$$v_t = v_{\frac{1}{6}} = v_{\frac{4}{6}} \tag{12b}$$

These measurements are valid only where the flat cell is very thin with respect to its width, *i.e.*, where the depth is so small compared with its width that flow may be treated as taking place between infinite parallel planes.

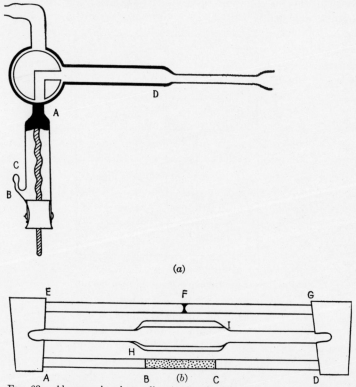

Fig. 63.—Abramson's micro cell. (*a*) is scheme of apparatus in longitudinal section. *A* is the agar plug and *B* is the outlet sealed off at *C*. The cell itself is fused to the electrode arm at *D*. (*b*) is a schematic view from above. *ABCD* and *EFG* are solid-glass supporting rods. Part of the bar *BC* (stippled) is curved to render possible the dark-field illumination from the side. Shaded *F* of the rear supporting rod is a break in *EFG* which is sealed with cement. By cementing glass plates above and below at the sides *H* and *I* of the cell itself, surfaces are obtained for both manual and mechanical manipulation.

Both treatments just discussed have been confirmed[29,30] for flat cells in which the depth is small in comparison with the width. For deep cells, the Smoluchowski formula does not apply.[31] While Ellis's method would apply to these cells, the large number of observations required at the various levels to establish the curve would render it so laborious as to be practically inapplicable. Sumner and Henry[31] have derived formulas for electroosmotic flow in strictly rectangular cells of any ratio of depth to width.

While a variety of cells for the microscope electrophoresis method have been devised, it will suffice here to describe one used by Abramson,[32] whose experimental results have an important bearing upon the theory of electrokinetics. Abramson's cell, shown in Fig. 63[30] is 3.5 cm. long, 0.99 cm. wide, and has a mean depth of 0.081 cm. Reversible electrodes (Cu in saturated $CuSO_4$ solution) are inserted in electrode vessels which are fused to the cell. The agar-agar plugs prevent streaming of liquid from the electrode system into the system being measured.

Abramson calculated the actual velocity of migration of the particle from the observed velocity by means of Ellis's and Smoluchowski's methods and then calculated the mobility, determining the potential gradient as follows:

$$X = \frac{IR}{A} \tag{13}$$

where X = potential gradient.

I = current flowing through the apparatus.

R = specific resistance of the colloidal solution.

A = cross section of the electrophoresis cell.

Figure 64 shows the results obtained by Abramson for the mobility of serum albumin particles* using this technique compared with the values found by Tiselius[33] by means of the moving-boundary method applied to solutions of this protein. The results are seen to be identical. Freundlich and Abramson[34] likewise produced results for egg albumin which were identical with those of Svedberg and Tiselius.[35] At the time of writing these remarks, there is only one other case in the literature bearing on this problem. Kruyt[36] by means of the moving-boundary technique obtained mobilities for gold and selenium particles which were about one-half those found by his use of a van der Grinten[37] microscope cell. This led Kruyt to the belief that the two methods yielded divergent results. In this respect he was

---

* Quartz particles coated with serum albumin were used.

misled owing to an erroneous calculation applied to the van der Grinten cell.[38] By eliminating this mistake, which underestimated the actual mobility by roughly one-half, the abovementioned apparent divergence can be reconciled.

Thus on the basis of these three instances it may be said that, when properly carried out, the "micro" and moving-boundary

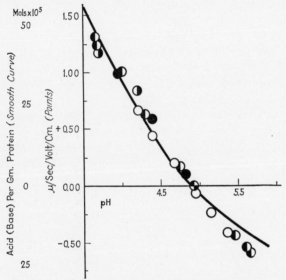

Fig. 64.—The open circles are the values of electric mobility of dissolved serum albumin. The other points are the mobilities of microscopically visible quartz particles covered with an adsorbed film of the same protein. The line is the titration curve of a sample of serum albumin.

techniques give identical values for the mobilities of colloidal particles.

Electrophoresis—Qualitative.—Obviously, the electrophoresis cells already discussed are serviceable for the qualitative purpose of determining the sign of the charge of micelles. Usually a different type of U-tube known as a "Coehn" or "Michaelis tube" is employed. It is merely a U-tube with a stopcock in each limb just above the bend. The drawing in Fig. 65 illustrates such a tube with electrodes and leveling device used in the determination of the change in the direction of migration of the enzyme malt amylase with change in pH.[39] Since the method employed in this particular instance is applicable to all amphoteric colloids, the details of the measurement are given in full.

The connecting flasks (D) served as a leveling device. The electrodes were placed in cells (C and A) which dipped into the connecting flasks and which have stopcocks in the connecting tubes or salt bridges. These stopcocks (4 and 5) were greased in such a way that the current would still be carried by a film of the liquid when they were closed. Diffusion of the solutions surrounding the electrodes into the rest of the apparatus was thus

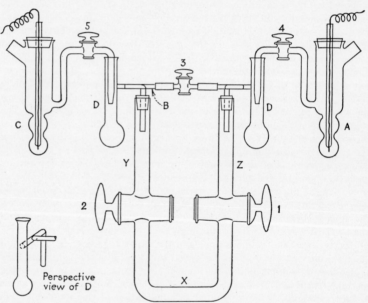

FIG. 65.—An apparatus for the determination of the sign of the charge of micelles.

decreased and further guarded against by the presence of the connecting flasks (D), which acted as traps as well as leveling devices. Changes in the level of the liquid in the U-tube, which may be caused by the evolution of gases at the electrodes and which, even when slight, give rise to noticeable errors, were also thus minimized.

Buffer solutions of the desired hydrogen ion concentrations were prepared by mixing molar monosodium phosphate with 0.5 M disodium phosphate according to electrometric titrations. The enzyme preparation was dissolved in a small portion of buffer solution containing 2 per cent of pure sucrose to increase its density. The bend (X) and stopcocks (1 and 2) of the U-tube were filled with this weighted solution, the stopcocks (1 and 2) were then closed with the careful exclusion of all bubbles, and the arms

(*Y* and *Z*) thoroughly washed. The U-tube was then securely fastened in an ice bath, the arms (*Y* and *Z*) of the tube were filled with buffer solution containing no sucrose, the connecting flasks and leveling bridge (*B*) inserted, and the whole was filled with the same buffer solution, care being taken to exclude all bubbles and to adjust the level of the solution in the connecting flasks. The electrode vessels (*C* and *A*) with their salt bridges were also filled with the same buffer solution and inserted in the connecting flasks (*D*). Solid copper sulfate and an electrode made by enclosing a copper wire in glass were placed in the electrode vessel (*C*) on the cathode side, and solid monosodium phosphate and a platinum electrode in the electrode vessel (*A*) on the anode side. In adjusting the level of the whole apparatus, care was taken always to have the solution pass from the connecting flasks into the electrode vessels rather than in the opposite direction, in order to avoid contamination of the solutions with the electrode reagents. A 220-volt direct current was then turned on while the stopcocks of the calomel-cell salt bridges and of the leveling bridge were open and those of the U-tube closed. The stopcocks 4 and 5 were then closed in such a manner as to have the current conducted by a film of the buffer solution around them. The stopcock (3) of the leveling bridge was next closed as tightly as possible and those in the U-tube (1 and 2) were opened simultaneously, thus allowing the current to pass through the whole system. An ammeter was inserted to give indications of the amount of current obtained during the setting up of the apparatus and during the experimental period. Experience showed that 24 to 36 hr. was a satisfactory length of time for the electrophoresis. At the expiration of this time stopcocks 1 and 2 were simultaneously closed, the current discontinued, and the solutions in the arms (*Y* and *Z*) and in the bend (*X*) were tested for enzymic activity. Since inconsistencies due to changes in level and to the tipping of the apparatus were eliminated, and since the enzyme was originally confined to the bend of the U-tube and the possibility of its diffusion into the arms of the U-tube is equal on both sides, any differences in enzymic activity found in the solutions in the arms of the U-tube can properly be attributed to a migration of the active material caused by the electric current, provided these solutions are tested for amylolytic power under strictly comparable conditions.

It was found that the enzyme migrated into the cathode arm when the solution was more acid than pH = 4.3, and to the anode when more alkaline than pH = 4.5. Hence this enzyme had an isoelectric point between these pH values in the particular environment described.

If the colloid is not amphoteric, one omits the buffer solutions and puts a very dilute solution of potassium chloride in the arms *Y* and *Z*. If the colloid is colored, the direction of migration is perceptible to the eye but when it is not colored a suitable analytical test must be applied to the contents of *Y* and *Z* after a suitable time of application of the current, provided the Tyndall-beam or ultraviolet-light methods are not convenient or applicable.

A method known as *capillary analysis* is an alluring substitute for the troublesome electrophoresis just described owing to its simplicity. A strip of filter paper is dipped into the colloidal solution and the rise of the micelles noted. Negatively charged micelles are reputed to rise by capillarity in the paper, while positively charged micelles are stated not to do so. This has been shown to be erroneous.[40] A dilute hydrosol ascends the strip of paper, while a concentrated one does not, regardless of the sign of the charge of the micelle. Despite the fact that this attractive technique has long been known to be worthless, it is still recommended[41] by some writers.

Sign of the Charge of Some Micelles.—Dispersions containing positively charged micelles are the hydrous "oxides" such as ferric oxysalt, aluminum oxysalt, chromium and thorium, silver halides in presence of a slight excess of silver ion, colloidal basic dyes such as Victoria blue, and proteins on the acid side of their isoelectric points. Dispersions in which the colloidal particles bear a negative charge are hydrous oxides such as of silicon, tin, and vanadium, dispersions of noble metals such as gold, platinum, and palladium, silver halides in the presence of a slight excess of halide ion, sulfides, hydrosols of sulfur, selenium, alkali soaps, caramel, gum arabic, shellac, rosin, mastic, colloidal acid dyes such as Congo red, and proteins on the alkaline side of their isoelectric points.

The reasons for most of the foregoing charges have been discussed in Chap. VII. Basic and acid dyes have positive and negative micelles, respectively, because the complex organic radicals are, respectively, the cations and anions.

Thornton[42] showed that watery suspensions of vegetable microorganisms such as diatoms and algae migrate to the cathode, while animal microorganisms migrate to the anode. This is probably due to the fact that the vegetable microorganisms investigated by Thornton were living in a medium which was on the acid side of the isoelectric point of the protoplasm of the organism, while the animal microorganisms existed in solutions on the alkaline side of the isoelectric point of their protoplasm.

A rather prevalent illusion concerning the sign of charge is that, when a liquid is in contact with some other nonmiscible phase, the substance with the higher dielectric constant is positive toward the substance of lower dielectric constant. This is known as "Coehn's rule."[43] While there are experimental data in confirmation of this rule, there are likewise contrary data. Pure benzene or pure carbon tetrachloride in contact with various diaphragms fails either to electroosmose upon application of an e.m.f. or to develop a stream potential upon application of pressure. Consequently it is apparent that dielectric constants of the phases in contact have nothing to do with the sign of the charge.

Measurement of Electroosmosis.—Following the first quantitative measurements made by Wiedemann[44] and by Quincke,[26] nothing of note seems to have been done upon electroosmosis until 1904. In that year, Perrin[45] devised a method of measuring this phenomenon through diaphragms consisting of plugs filled with small particles instead of the traditional porous-clay diaphragms. Thus the study of electroosmosis through a variety of materials was made possible. Perrin found that the direction of flow of the water was markedly influenced by acids and bases (0.002 to 0.02N) in the case of diaphragms of alumina, carborundum, sulfur, graphite, naphthalene, and gelatin, but not with diaphragms of cotton, glass, and iodoform. In the former cases the water flowed to the anode in acid solutions, to the cathode in alkaline solutions and not at all at a certain intermediate pH value, depending upon the chemical nature of the diaphragm. Perrin concluded that the electrical potential of a surface in aqueous solution is made more positive, or less negative, by the addition of an acid and more negative, or less positive, by the addition of a base.

Experimenting with salts, he found that one-one salts did not affect electroosmosis to any appreciable extent. Salts with one ion of valence higher than that of the other were influential— the higher the valence of the ion of charge opposite to that of the diaphragm, the greater was the lowering of the velocity of flow through the diaphragm, *i.e.*, the lowering of the charge of the diaphragm.

A refinement in technique wherein the electroosmotic flow was followed by means of an air bubble in a single capillary tube was developed by Elissafoff.[46] This investigator found that certain monovalent organic cations were quite as effective in reducing the charge of negatively charged glass and quartz walls as divalent alkaline-earth cations and that heavy metal cations were also very potent in this respect, e.g., Ag^+ as effective as the alkaline-earth cations and Hg^{++} much more effective than the latter. He found also that the valence and nature of the anion were significant toward negatively charged surfaces, salts with

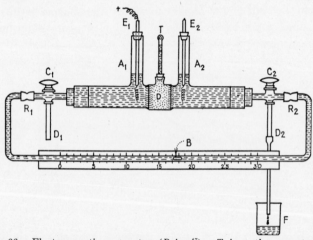

FIG. 66.—Electroosmotic apparatus (*Briggs*[47]). T is a thermometer. A_1 and A_2 are electrode tubes holding platinum electrodes E_1 and E_2 10 cm. apart. D is the chamber containing the porous diaphragm. R_1 and R_2 are rubber connections. D_1 and D_2 are exit tubes. F is a beaker. By manipulation of the stopcocks C_1 and C_2 a bubble is introduced at B.

potent anions not having appreciable charge-lowering quality. Thorium nitrate and the basic dye methyl violet reversed the sign of the charge of glass and quartz walls when present in sufficiently high concentration.

An improved apparatus developed by Briggs[47] is shown in Fig. 66. The volume of liquid which flows through the diaphragm in a given time is measured by the velocity of motion of the bubble. Among other measurements with this apparatus, Briggs determined the effect of temperature and of voltage upon the rate of flow. Figure 67 shows the relation between rate of flow and the applied voltage.

Several modifications of the apparatus and discussions of technique have appeared since Briggs's work, but these will not be discussed here.[48]

Measurement of Stream Potentials.—In the study of this phenomenon, capillary tubes[49] or porous diaphragms[50] have been used. Kruyt's[49] measurements of the potentials set up by the flow of aqueous solutions through a glass capillary are plotted in Fig. 68. It is seen that a negative current of 350 millivolts arose per centimeter of mercury pressure of pure water flow against the wall of the capillary. This was sharply reduced by very small amounts of potassium and of barium chloride, the

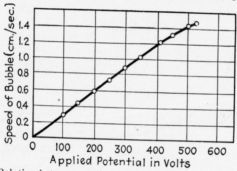

Fig. 67.—Relation between applied voltage and rate of electroosmosis.[47]

latter being the more effective. Minute quantities of aluminum chloride, on the other hand, rendered the glass wall positive, the extent of this positive charge diminishing markedly with increased additions of the aluminum chloride.

Briggs[50] used diaphragms of cellulose and of protein-coated quartz particles in the apparatus which was previously used for electroosmosis experiments. The reader will observe that this apparatus becomes a stream-potential device when, instead of applying a potential to the electrodes, one measures the potential set up when liquid is forced under a definite pressure through the diaphragm. This was done by connecting the electrodes to a quadrant galvanometer. Briggs introduced a method for measuring the specific conductivity of the liquid as it exists in the pores of the diaphragm* as follows. The material of the dia-

*This is important because the conductivity of the liquid in the capillaries may differ from its conductivity in bulk form.

phragm is packed between two perforated gold plates which are connected to nonpolarizable subsidiary electrodes. The "cell constant" of this portion of the diaphragm is measured by means of an electrolyte (0.1N potassium chloride) whose surface con-

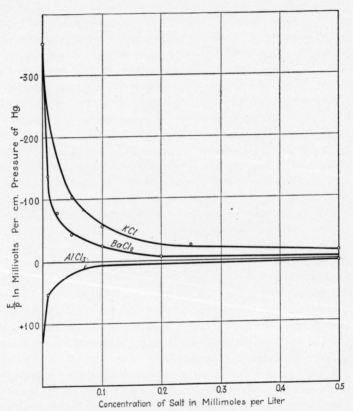

Fig. 68.—Stream potentials arising through the flow of aqueous solutions through glass capillaries.[49]

ductance can be neglected. If the cell constant is known, the specific conductivity of any other liquid as it exists in the diaphragm may be measured. This method is essentially that used by Gortner[50,51] and his coworkers in measuring the potential difference at cellulose-organic liquid and at alumina-organic liquid interfaces.

Theory of Electrokinetics.—The various phenomena already discussed were first theoretically treated by Helmholtz[52] and later modified, although not materially altered, by Lamb,[53] Smoluchowski,[28] and Perrin.[45] This treatment was based upon the concept of an electrical double layer forming a sort of parallel-plate condenser with one laminar distribution of charge residing in the rigid phase and the other equal and opposite layer of charges residing in the mobile phase. The present concept of the double layer is different, in that the outer sheath is conceived as a diffuse layer of charges. The charge density of this layer is conceived to diminish from a maximum in the immediate neighborhood of the fixed inner layer to a negligible value in the bulk of the liquid. The distance over which the net electric density of this double layer reaches a negligible value is a function of the concentration and valence of the ionic species in the solution and may lie between about 1μ (pure water at 20°) and molecular dimensions.

The idea of a diffuse double layer of charges was originated by Gouy[54] in 1910. It has since been developed by other investigators, particularly by Debye and Hückel.[55]

The following simple derivations (according to Perrin) of the electrokinetic formulas are those generally known to colloid chemists. For a rigorous treatment of the theory of electrokinesis, which is beyond the scope of this book, the author recommends the article by Henry.[56]

Consider a cylindrical capillary of radius r, with an electrode inserted at each end, through which water is flowing at the steady rate of volume V per second as a result of an impressed electrical field. The water moves owing to the double layer of charges, those of one sign adhering to the wall, while at the slight distance δ therefrom in the liquid are aligned an equal number of charges of opposite sign. The layer of liquid with its charge moves along the walls to the electrode of opposite sign of charge. Opposing this motion is the force of friction.

The frictional force is proportional to the viscosity η of the liquid, to the area of the surface of contact, and to the velocity gradient. If u represents the mean velocity of a particle of the liquid moving through the capillary,

$$V = \pi r^2 u \tag{14}$$

Since the liquid particles away from the wall are moving at this velocity u, while the particles of opposite charge adhering to the wall do not move, there is a velocity gradient from the value u to zero over the distance z perpendicular to the wall. Then in the confines of the double layer, the velocity gradient is du/dz which is equal to u/δ. If this is combined with Eq. (14), the frictional resistance per unit area is

$$\frac{\eta V}{\pi r^2 \delta}$$

If X represents the potential gradient per centimeter resulting from the applied e.m.f. E, and e represents the density of the charge, *i.e.*, the quantity of electricity per square centimeter of surface, Xe is the electrical force. Since at constant velocity this is equal to the viscous resistance, we have

$$Xe = \frac{\eta V}{\pi r^2 \delta} \tag{15}$$

If we consider the double layer as a condenser with the potential ζ between the plates, the following relation holds:

$$\zeta = \frac{4\pi \delta e}{K} \tag{16}$$

where K is the dielectric constant of the medium between the plates. Combining Eqs. (15) and (16), we get

$$V = \frac{r^2 \zeta X K}{4\eta} = \frac{r^2 \zeta E K}{4\eta l} \tag{17}$$

where l is the distance between the electrodes $(Xl = E)$.

If, instead of a single capillary, we apply the reasoning to a porous diaphragm, we may assume that such a diaphragm consists of a bundle of capillaries, with A the cross section of the diaphragm equal to πr^2. Then Eq. (17) becomes

$$V = \frac{A \zeta X K}{4\pi \eta} = \frac{A \zeta E K}{4\pi \eta l} \tag{18}$$

which states that the volume of liquid electroosmotically transported across the diaphragm is directly proportional to the cross section, to the potential difference of the double layer, to the impressed e.m.f., to the dielectric constant, and inversely proportional to the viscosity of the liquid.

According to Ohm's law, $E = IR$, and since R may be expressed by the quotient of the length of the capillary l over the specific conductivity* κ times the cross section A, then $E = Il/A\kappa$. Substituting for E in the second quotient of Eq. (18), we have

$$V = \frac{\zeta IK}{4\pi\eta\kappa} \tag{19}$$

Equation (19) shows that, for constant current, the volume of liquid transported is independent of the cross section of the diaphragm and of the length of the capillaries.

Poiseuille's law states

$$V = \frac{\pi P r^4}{8\eta l} \tag{20}$$

where P is the pressure applied. Combining Eq. (20) with Eq. (17), we get

$$P = \frac{2\zeta EK}{\pi r^2} \tag{21}$$

which states that the hydrostatic head brought about by an applied e.m.f. is proportional to the e.m.f.

Equation (19) may be written

$$\zeta = \frac{4\pi\eta\kappa}{K}\frac{V}{I} \tag{22}$$

Since the applied mechanical work PV is equal to the electrical work EI produced, then

$$\frac{V}{I} = \frac{E}{P} \tag{23}$$

and, combining Eqs. (22) and (23), we get

$$E = \frac{PK\zeta}{4\pi\eta\kappa} \tag{24}$$

an equation for the stream potential produced when a liquid is forced through a capillary.

In the discussion of electroosmosis we analyzed the action of an electrical field parallel to the surface of contact of a solid and a liquid and set the conditions so that only the liquid could move. Now, instead of imagining a rigid and stationary capillary

* The specific conductivity of the liquid system in the capillaries.

tube, let us assume that the latter is converted to very small pieces which we suspend in the liquid. Now when the electric field is applied, the layer of charges drags the particle through the liquid just as the water was carried in the electroosmotic case. Since, in the electroosmosis of water $u = V/\pi r^2$, then by combination of this expression with Eq. (17) we have

$$u = \frac{\zeta X K}{4\pi\eta} \qquad (25)*$$

which is the equation for the electrophoretic velocity of a suspended particle of cylindrical shape. The equation states that the electrophoretic speed of migration of such a particle is proportional to the difference in potential between the layers constituted by the charges affixed to the particle and the layer of balancing charges contiguous thereto in the liquid bathing the particle, to the applied field, to the dielectric constant of the medium between the charged layers, and inversely proportional to the viscosity of the medium through which the particle is moving.

It will be observed that Eq. (25) is not concerned with the size of the particle. Smoluchowski claimed that u was independent also of the shape of the particle. Debye and Hückel,[57] however, maintained that Eq. (25) is correct only for a cylindrically shaped particle and that the equation should be written in the general form

$$u = \frac{C\zeta X K}{\eta} \qquad (26)$$

where C depends upon the shape of the particle, being $1/6\pi$ for a sphere.[58] While experimental evidence pointed to the correctness of Smoluchowski's conclusion, it was Henry[56] who showed that both Smoluchowski and Debye and Hückel were theoretically correct provided that the conductivity of the particle substance was considered. If the particle substance has the

---

* The reader may be more familiar with Eq. (25) in the form

$$\zeta = \frac{4\pi\eta u(300)^2}{KX} \text{ volts}$$

Since 1 electrostatic unit = 300 volts, the result is obtained in volts by dividing ζ and X each by 300.

same conductivity as the medium, then the Debye-Hückel formulas would obtain, while Smoluchowski's conclusion would apply to insulating particles. By showing that Eq. (25) holds for the case of a nonconducting sphere and also for a non-conducting cylinder oriented either axially or broadside to the applied field, Henry infers that "the result lends considerable support to the view that the same equation holds for any shape of particle."

The assumptions[56,59] underlying the electrokinetic formulas derived for a rigid, electrically insulating particle with respect to its medium, and *vice versa*, are:

1.* The usual hydrodynamic equations for the motion of a viscous fluid may be assumed to hold both in the bulk of the liquid and within the double layer.

2.† The motion is "stream line" and so slow that the "inertia terms" in the hydrodynamic equations may be neglected.

3.‡ The applied electric field may be taken as simply superimposed upon the field of the double layer.

4.§ The thickness of the double layer (*i.e.*, the distance over which the potential differs appreciably from that of the bulk of the liquid) is small compared with the radius of curvature at any point on the surface.

Experimental Results.—The formula for electrophoresis [Eq. (25)] states among other things that the velocity of a particle is independent of its shape or size. This has been tested experimentally and shown to be true[60] in many instances. According

---

* This assumption is probably justified although it is possible that the appropriate values of the dielectric constant and the coefficient of viscosity will not be those which apply to the liquid in bulk.[56]

† For velocities encountered in electrophoresis and in electroosmosis this assumption holds well except in the case of an irregular particle with sharp edges or pronounced reentrant angles. Since, however, such particles are often highly solvated, it is at least possible that the attached shell of solvent molecules will produce a particle of "easy" shape.[56]

‡ This assumption is open to question since it is certain that the application of an external field and the migration of the particle will disturb the symmetry of the ionic atmosphere about the particle. Mooney[59] discusses this assumption and Henry[56] agrees that "it is not easy to estimate the magnitude of the error introduced."

§ In order to estimate the error involved in this assumption, one would have to have some law for the thickness of the double layer. One might use the Debye and Hückel first approximation. For a treatment of this question see the paper by Henry.[56]

to the formula for electroosmosis [Eq. (19)] it is seen that the volume of liquid (V) transported is proportional to the current (I) irrespective of the dimensions of the capillaries. This is generally referred to as "Wiedemann's first law" and in general it is obeyed.

If Smoluchowski's equation [Eq. (25)] for electrophoresis is correct, then the ratio of electroosmotic to electrophoretic mobility should equal 1. For a direct comparison of these mobilities, the micro method has been utilized. The reader will recall that the observed velocity of a particle at a given level in the cell consists of the algebraic sum of the actual velocity

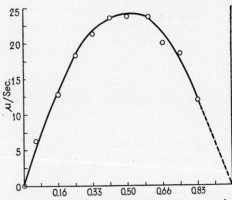

Fig. 69.—Observed electrophoretic mobilities of protein-covered particles. The abscissas are the levels in the electrophoresis cell.

of the particle and of the electroosmotic velocity of the liquid. Since the actual velocity of the particle can be calculated, then the velocity of the flow of the liquid along the wall of the cell can be obtained.

Since protein coats a solid surface in contact with a protein solution, Abramson[30] used protein solutions in order to obtain similar surfaces. Observing the velocity of protein-coated quartz particles in protein solutions, he found electroosmotic and electrophoretic mobility to be identical. This relationship can be seen in one of his graphs where the *observed* electrophoretic velocity is plotted as a function of the depth of the microscope cell (Fig. 69). It is to be noted that, at the walls of the cell, the velocity of the liquid must have been equal to the velocity of the suspended particle* in order to produce an observed velocity of zero for the particle.[61]

The fact that some workers studying this problem without the use of protein solutions have not obtained the above-noted concordance is due to the fact that the surface of a particle produced by fracture of a cell wall is not identical with that of the surface of the unfractured material. Sumner and Henry[31]

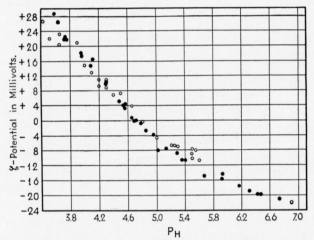

FIG. 70.—Variation of the ζ potential of albumin with pH. ● By stream potential (*Briggs*). ○ By electrophoresis (*Abramson*).

obviated this difficulty by employing a method which enabled them to use a glass cylinder drawn from the same glass as the cell.

The derivation of Eq. (24) for the stream potential involved the statement that $E/P = V/I$. This was experimentally verified by Saxén,[62] in 1892.

Additional proof of the theory was provided by Briggs,[63] who measured the potentials set up by the flow of protein solutions at various pH values through a diaphragm of protein-coated quartz particles.† He obtained values for ζ almost

* The reader will recall that the liquid moves in the direction opposed to that of the suspended particle.

† The isoelectric points of proteins can be accurately determined by this method.

identical with those found by Abramson[64] who used the electro-phoretic method. Figure 70 shows the concordance of these methods in this instance.

The experimental work cited thus far is the essence of the proof of the theory of electrokinesis. However, there are numerous examples which are not in accord with the theory, some of which will now be mentioned. The value for ζ obtained by the stream-potential method has been stated to be independent of the pressure for aqueous solutions but not for methyl alcohol solutions.[65] White, Urban, and van Atta[66] show that the stream potentials of "0.005 mm. diameter are from 0 to 25 per cent as great as with large capillaries." Further, they state: "These low figures cannot be accounted for by the classical stream potential equation or any modification so far proposed." A summary of data showing variance between the influence of electrolytes upon ζ as determined by the stream-potential and electrophoretic methods has been published by Thon.[67]

Significance of the Electrokinetic Potential (ζ) to the Stability of Colloidal Dispersions.—Inasmuch as the mobility u changes when electrolyte is added to hydrosols, then according to Eq. (25), the ζ *potential** likewise changes. Since decrease in mobility is generally effected by ions of charge opposite to that of the micelles in a fashion qualitatively proportional to their potency in pre-cipitation of the micelles, colloid chemists have been in the habit of ascribing the stability of colloidal dispersions to the ζ potential. The value of ζ calculated from the value of u where the micelles precipitate has been called the *critical potential*.

The author is of the opinion that this habit is not based upon a sound foundation. There are stable colloidal dispersions wherein the micelles do not migrate in an electric field and hence in these cases $\zeta = 0$. Further, Kruyt, and van der Willigen[68] have found in experimentation upon hydrosols of selenium, arsenious sulfide, and mercuric sulfide that the electrophoretic mobility of the micelles *increases* upon addition of potassium chloride and of potassium ferrocyanide *until the micelles flocculate*. The same sort of behavior has been shown to occur when sodium hydroxide is added to platinum hydrosol.[18]

* It is common usage in the colloid literature to express the electrokinetic potential (ζ) by the term "zeta potential."

The ζ potential is evaluated through the theoretical electrokinetic formula. It has never been measured *per se*. Laing[69]
and McBain[70] present a more general theory of electrokinesis
without the concept of the double layer, portraying electrokinetic
phenomena as a "particular case of electrolytic migration . . .
without reference to the many hypothetical assumptions usually
introduced in the evaluation of the electrical phenomena of
colloids."

References

1. BURTON: Fourth Colloid Symposium Monograph, p. 132, Chemical
   Catalog Co., New York, 1926.
2. DORN: *Ann. Physik*, **5**, 20 (1878); **9**, 513 (1880); **10**, 46 (1880).
3. PICTON and LINDER: *J. Chem. Soc.*, **61**, 148 (1892).
4. LODGE: *Brit. Assoc. Advancement Sci., Birmingham Rept.*, 389 (1886).
5. PICTON and LINDER: *J. Chem. Soc.*, **71**, 568 (1897).
6. WHITNEY and BLAKE: *J. Am. Chem. Soc.*, **26**, 1339 (1904).
7. HARDY: *J. Physiol.*, **29**, 26 (1903); **33**, 251 (1905).
8. NERNST: *Z. Elektrochem.*, **3**, 308 (1897).
9. BURTON: *Phil. Mag.*, **11**, 436 (1906); see also BURTON: "The Physical
   Properties of Colloidal Solutions," Longmans, Green & Co., New
   York, 1916.
10. BURTON and REID: *Phil. Mag.*, **50**, 1221 (1925).
11. MUKHERJEE: *Proc. Roy. Soc. (London)*, **103A**, 102 (1923); ENGEL and
    PAULI: *Z. physik. Chem.*, **126**, 247 (1927).
12. KRUYT and VAN DER WILLIGEN: *Kolloid-Z.*, **44**, 22 (1928).
13. For improvements in apparatus see KRUYT: Ref. 12; HENRY and BRIT-
    TAIN: *Trans. Faraday Soc.*, **29**, 798 (1933); PRICE and LEWIS: *ibid.*,
    775.
14. KRUYT: *Kolloid-Z.*, **37**, 358 (1925); DUMANSKI and KNIGA: *ibid.*, **39**,
    40 (1926); KRUYT and TENDELOO: *Kolloidchem. Beihefte*, **29**, 413
    (1929).
15. SVEDBERG and JETTE: *J. Am. Chem. Soc.*, **45**, 954 (1923); SCOTT and
    SVEDBERG: *ibid.*, **46**, 2700 (1924).
16. SVEDBERG and TISELIUS: *J. Am. Chem. Soc.*, **48**, 2272 (1926).
17. MUKHERJEE: *J. Phys. Chem.*, **36**, 595 (1932).
18. PENNYCUICK: *J. Chem. Soc.*, **1930**, 1447.
19. HACKER: *Kolloid-Z.*, **62**, 37, 66 (1933).
20. KOHLRAUSCH: *Ann. phys.*, **62**, 209 (1897); WEBER: Sitz. Berlin Akad.,
    936 (1897).
21. MACINNES and LONGSWORTH: *Chem. Rev.*, **11**, 171 (1932).
22. DUCLAUX: *J. chim. phys.*, **7**, 405 (1909).
23. VARGA: *Kolloidchem. Beihefte*, **11**, 1 (1919); WINTGEN: *Z. physik. Chem.*,
    103, 238 (1922); **107**, 403 (1923); **109**, 378 (1924); ENGEL and PAULI:
    Ref. 11; MCBAIN and BOWDEN: *J. Chem. Soc.*, **123**, 2417 (1923).

24. PAINE: *Trans. Faraday Soc.*, **24**, 412 (1928).
25. MacINNES and DOLE: *J. Am. Chem. Soc.*, **53**, 1357 (1931).
26. QUINCKE: *Ann. phys.*, **113**, 513 (1861).
27. ELLIS: *Z. physik. Chem.*, **78**, 321 (1912).
28. SMOLUCHOWSKI: *Bull. acad. sci. Cracovie*, 182 (1903); see GRAETZ: "Handbuch der Elektrizität und des Magnetismus," Vol. 2, p. 366, Leipzig, 1914.
29. SVEDBERG and ANDERSSEN: *Kolloid-Z.*, **24**, 156 (1919).
30. ABRAMSON: *J. Gen. Physiol.*, **12**, 469 (1929); **13**, 657 (1930).
31. SUMNER and HENRY: *Proc. Roy. Soc. (London)*, **133A**, 130 (1931).
32. ABRAMSON and GROSSMAN: *J. Gen. Physiol.*, **14**, 563 (1931).
33. TISELIUS: "The Moving Boundary Method of Studying the Electrophoresis of Proteins," Dissertation, Upsala, 1930.
34. FREUNDLICH and ABRAMSON: *Z. physik. Chem.*, **133**, 51 (1928).
35. SVEDBERG and TISELIUS: *J. Am. Chem. Soc.*, **48**, 2272 (1926).
36. KRUYT and VAN DER WILLIGEN: *Kolloid-Z.*, **44**, 22 (1928).
37. VAN DER GRINTEN: *J. chim. phys.*, **23**, 209 (1926).
38. ABRAMSON: *J. Phys. Chem.*, **35**, 289 (1931).
39. SHERMAN, THOMAS, and CALDWELL: *J. Am. Chem. Soc.*, **46**, 1711 (1924).
40. THOMAS and GARARD: *J. Am. Chem. Soc.*, **40**, 101 (1918).
41. FINDLAY: "Practical Physical Chemistry," p. 294, Longmans, Green & Co., New York, 1931.
42. THORNTON: *Proc. Roy. Soc. (London)*, **82B**, 638 (1910).
43. COEHN: *Ann. Physik*, **64**, 217 (1898); *Z. Elektrochem.*, **16**, 586 (1910).
44. WIEDEMANN: *Ann. phys.*, **87**, 321 (1852); **99**, 177 (1856).
45. PERRIN: *J. chim. phys.*, **2**, 601 (1904).
46. VON ELISSAFOFF: *Z. physik. Chem.*, **79**, 385 (1912).
47. BRIGGS, BENNETT, and PIERSON: *J. Phys. Chem.*, **22**, 256 (1918); see also STRICKLER and MATHEWS: *J. Am. Chem. Soc.*, **44**, 1647 (1922).
48. See the following for additional apparatus and technique for measurement of electroosmosis: GYEMANT: *Kolloid-Z.*, **28**, 103 (1921); *Z. physik. Chem.*, **103**, 260 (1922); FAIRBROTHER and MASTIN: *J. Chem. Soc.*, **125**, 2495 (1924); **127**, 32 (1925); FAIRBROTHER and BALKIN: *ibid.*, **1931**, 389; HEPBURN: *Proc. Phys. Soc. London*, **38**, 363 (1926); **39**, 99 (1927); **43**, 524 (1931); GLIXELLI and WIERTELAK: *Kolloid-Z.*, **43**, 85 (1927); HARKEVITSCH: *ibid.*, **47**, 101 (1929); ANDRIANOV: *ibid.*, **61**, 46 (1932). For some practical applications see BARY: *Chimie & Industrie*, **7**, 640 (1922); PRAUSWITZ: *Kolloid-Z.*, **31**, 319 (1922); FRYDLENDER: *Rev. prod. chim.*, **25**, 721 (1922); ILLIG: *Z. angew. Chem.*, **39**, 1085 (1926); SCHÖNFELDT: *Z. Elektrochem.*, **38**, 744 (1932).
49. KRUYT: *Kolloid-Z.*, **22**, 81 (1918); FREUNDLICH and RONA: *Sitzb. preuss. Akad. Wiss.*, **20**, 397 (1920); LACHS and BICZYK: *Z. physik. Chem.*, **148**, 441 (1930).
50. BRIGGS: *J. Phys. Chem.*, **32**, 641 (1928); MARTIN and GORTNER: *ibid.*, **34**, 1509 (1930); JENSEN and GORTNER: *ibid.*, **36**, 3138 (1932).
51. BULL and GORTNER: *J. Phys. Chem.*, **35**, 700 (1931).
52. HELMHOLTZ: *Ann. phys.*, **7**, 337 (1879).

53. LAMB: *Phil. Mag.*, **25**, 52 (1888).
54. GOUY: *J. phys.*, **9**, 457 (1910).
55. DEBYE and HÜCKEL: *Physik. Z.*, **24**, 185 (1923).
56. HENRY: *Proc. Roy. Soc. (London)*, **135A**, 106 (1931); also see BIKER-MAN: *Z. physik. Chem.*, **163A**, 378 (1932).
57. DEBYE and HÜCKEL: *Physik. Z.*, **25**, 49 (1924).
58. HÜCKEL: *Physik. Z.*, **25**, 204 (1924).
59. MOONEY: *J. Phys. Chem.*, **35**, 331 (1931).
60. ABRAMSON and MICHAELIS: *J. Gen. Physiol.*, **12**, 587 (1929); ABRAMSON: *J. Phys. Chem.*, **35**, 289 (1931).
61. See also DANIEL: *J. Gen. Physiol.*, **16**, 457 (1933).
62. SAXÉN: *Ann. Physik*, **47**, 46 (1892).
63. BRIGGS: *J. Am. Chem. Soc.*, **50**, 2358 (1928).
64. ABRAMSON: *J. Am. Chem. Soc.*, **50**, 390 (1928); see also Ref. 32.
65. ETTISCH and ZWANZIG: *Z. physik. Chem.*, **147A**, 151 (1930).
66. WHITE, URBAN, and VAN ATTA: *J. Phys. Chem.*, **36**, 3152 (1932).
67. THON: *Z. physik. Chem.*, **147A**, 147 (1930).
68. KRUYT and VAN DER WILLIGEN: *Z. physik. Chem.*, **130**, 170 (1927).
69. LAING: *J. Phys. Chem.*, **28**, 673 (1924).
70. MCBAIN and LAING-MCBAIN: *Z. physik. Chem.*, **161A**, 279 (1932).

CHAPTER X

SURFACE PHENOMENA—GAS-LIQUID AND LIQUID-LIQUID INTERFACES—WETTING

Some of the characteristic properties of colloidal dispersions may be attributed to their great development of surface. As particles of matter are progressively subdivided, the amount of surface increases. Inasmuch as the surface is the capacity factor of surface energy and since the amount of chemical change in unit time is proportional to the surface of contact between the reacting phases, the system is the more reactive according as the particles are more finely subdivided.

The development of surface upon subdivision of a particle is shown by Table 38 where a cube of 1 cm. side length is pro-

TABLE 38.—DEVELOPMENT OF SURFACE UPON COMMINUTION

Length of side		Number of cubes	Total surface	Specific surface
1 cm.	10^0 cm...............	1	6 sq. cm.	6
1 mm.	10^{-1} cm...............	10^3	60 sq. cm.	6×10
0.1 mm.	10^{-2} cm...............	10^6	600 sq. cm.	6×10^2
0.01 mm.	10^{-3} cm...............	10^9	6,000 sq. cm.	6×10^3
1 μ	10^{-4} cm...............	10^{12}	6 sq. m.	6×10^4
0.1μ	10^{-5} cm...............	10^{15}	60 sq. m.	6×10^5
0.01μ	10^{-6} cm...............	10^{18}	600 sq. m.*	6×10^6
1 mμ	10^{-7} cm...............	10^{21}	6,000 sq. m.	6×10^7

* Equal to about $\frac{1}{7}$ acre.

gressively divided into cubes with sides one-tenth as large. According to Ostwald,[1] the effects produced by extension of surface do not become noticeable until a specific surface† of 10,000 or more is reached.

Influence of Extension of Surface upon Properties.—It is well-known that, while hydrogen peroxide may be concentrated

† Specific surface = surface area/volume.

by evaporation in a smooth platinum vessel, the addition of a small amount of platinum black or of colloidal platinum causes rapid decomposition.

Upon subdivision of a sphere of water 1 cm. in diameter into a fog of droplets 0.1 μ in diameter, the total surface energy increases from 9×10^{-5} to about 9 cal., which is nearly one-fourth the latent heat of fusion for this amount of liquid.[2] For

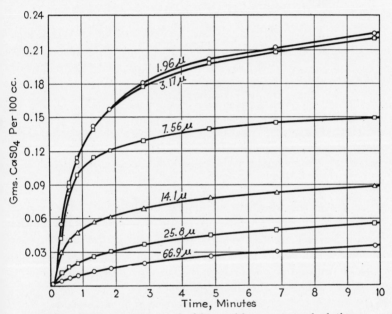

Fig. 71.—Influence of size of anhydrite particles upon rate of solution.

particles 10 mμ in diameter the surface energy becomes more than twice the latent heat of fusion. Harkins[2] suggests that a colloidal system may be defined as one in which the surface energy is appreciable in comparison with the heat of fusion or of vaporization of the material present as the dispersed phase.

The influence of the degree of subdivision upon the properties of solids has been recognized for a long time. Stas, in 1870, reported that the solubility of silver chloride varied according to the method of forming it, depending upon whether it was finely granular, coarsely granular, or gelatinous.

The influence of the size of particles of anhydrite upon rate of its solution in water at 20° has been shown by Roller[3] (Fig. 71). The numbers on the curves are the surface mean diameters of the particles. By taking the relative specific surface and the relative rate of solution of the largest particles equal to unity, the relative rate of solution per unit of surface may be calculated for each particle size as set down in Table 39.

TABLE 39.—RELATIVE RATES OF SOLUTION OF ANHYDRITE PARTICLES AT 20°C.[3]

Surface mean diameter, microns	Relative specific surface	Relative rate of solution	Relative rate of solution per unit surface
66.9	1.00	1.00	1.00
25.8	2.59	2.66	1.03
14.1	4.74	9.54	2.01
7.56	8.82	66.7	7.55
3.17	21.1	364	17.2
1.96	34.1	382	11.2

It is seen that down to a diameter of about 25 μ, the rate of solution per gram for different particles is proportional to the specific surface, and the relative rate of solution per unit surface is constant. This is to be expected if, as in the usual case, the rate of solution is proportional to the surface exposed. Below 25 μ, however, the rate increases more rapidly than the surface exposed up to 3.17 μ, at which a maximum is reached. Here the rate of solution of the anhydrite is 17.2 times the proportional increase in surface. The range for particle diameters for which the phenomenon occurs is less than the thickness of the diffusion film, 20 to 50 μ, calculated according to the theory of Noyes and Whitney,[4] and Nernst,[5] from the monomolecular dissolution rate of a plane surface in water.[6] The reason for the maximum at a surface mean diameter of 3.17 μ is not clear.

The relation between surface energy and crystal growth was developed by Curie,[7] who showed that, in a mixture of different-sized crystals under a mother liquor, the small ones dissolve and the large ones grow so that the total surface of the solid phase decreases.

Hulett[8] reasoned that, from analogy between the vapor pressure of solutions and the solution tension of solids, one would expect the solution tension of a solid, and hence its solubility, to be a function of the surface energy and, therefore, the solubility of a substance must increase with decrease in size of the particles. He verified this experimentally using gypsum, barium sulfate, and mercuric oxide (Table 40).

TABLE 40.—INFLUENCE OF PARTICLE SIZE UPON SOLUBILITY

Size of Particles, μ	Solubility at 25°C.
(CaSO₄)	
2	2.085 g. per liter*
0.3	2.476 g. per liter
(BaSO₄)	
1.8	2.29 mg. per liter*
0.1	4.15 mg. per liter
(HgO)	
Coarse red powder	50 mg. per liter*
Very fine yellowish powder	150 mg. per liter

* These are the permanent saturated solutions. The more concentrated solutions, obtained from contact with the more finely ground particles, slowly revert to the normally saturated solutions and the particles grow to 2 μ in size.

By shaking a normally saturated solution of gypsum with coarse particles of gypsum, the concentration was raised about 5.5 per cent owing to the mechanical comminution of the particles from the abrasion. Upon grinding barium sulfate with quartz powder in order to get very fine particles, Hulett obtained a solubility of 4.6 mg. per liter, or about double that of the normally saturated solution.

This subject has been investigated by Dundon and Mack,[9,10] who offer new calculations of the surface energy of certain relatively insoluble powders obtained from the second equation below. The increase in solubility of a difficultly soluble substance as a function of the increase in surface energy due to the subdivision of the substance into small particles is given by the equation

$$\frac{RT}{M} \ln \frac{S_2}{S_1} = \frac{2\gamma}{\rho}\left(\frac{1}{r_2} - \frac{1}{r_1}\right) \qquad (1)$$

where γ = surface tension.

ρ = density of particle substance.

R = gas constant.

T = absolute temperature.

M = molecular weight of the solid in solution.

S_1 = solubility of the large particles of radius r_1.

S_2 = solubility of the small particles of radius r_2.

This is the Ostwald-Freundlich equation which was first derived in its most general form by Willard Gibbs in 1876.

Since for large crystals $1/r_1 = 1/\infty$, and correcting for the degree of ionization of the electrolytes studied, Dundon and Mack arrived at the following expression which they found to approximate quite closely the more rigorous equation of Jones[11]:

$$\frac{2\gamma}{\rho r} = \frac{iRT}{M} \ln \frac{S_r}{S} \qquad (2)$$

where S_r = the solubility of the small particles of radius r, S = the solubility of the substance in large particles (*i.e.*, the equilibrium solubility), and i = the van't Hoff factor, *i.e.*, $i = (1 - \alpha + n\alpha)$ where α = the degree of ionization of the substance.

The increased solubilities of a number of finely ground compounds, as found by Dundon, and the surface-energy values calculated therefrom using the foregoing equation are given in Table 41. Molecular volumes and hardness values are included, showing that a rough proportionality exists between surface energy and hardness, while surface energy and molecular volumes are inversely proportional.

This inverse relation between surface energy and molecular volume is approximately true for the fused lithium, sodium, potassium, rubidium, and cesium compounds of fluorin, chlorin, bromin, and iodin, and their nitrates and sulfates. Of all these alkali salts[12] lithium fluoride has the smallest molecular volume and consequently the largest surface energy. At 1270° it is 201 ergs per square centimeter, at 1000° it is 237, and at 870° it is 250, making an extrapolated value of about 350 at 25°, for the supercooled liquid. Dundon found that by substituting 350 for γ in the first equation the calculated increase in solubility for particles of lithium fluoride 0.3 μ in diameter would be only about

1 per cent. As a matter of fact, it was not possible with the methods employed by him to detect an effect with lithium fluoride as great as 0.5 per cent, thus showing the very slightly increased solubility of fine powders of substances of small molecular weight.

TABLE 41.—CALCULATED VALUES FOR SURFACE ENERGY

Substance	Molecular weight	Density	Molecular volume	Diameter of particles, μ	Per cent solubility increase	Temperature °C.	i	γ	Hardness
PbI₂............	461.04	6.16	74.8	0.4	2	30	1.97	130	Very soft
CaSO₄.2H₂O......	172.16	2.32	74.2	0.2 to 0.5	4.4 to 12*	30	1.56	370	1.6 to 2
Ag₂CrO₄..........	331.76	5.52	60.1	0.3	10	26	1.95	575	About 2
PbF₂.............	245.20	8.24	29.7	0.3	9	25	1.70	900	About 2
SrSO₄............	183.69	3.96	46.4	0.25	26	30	1.82	1,400	3.0 to 3.5
BaSO₄†	233.43	4.5	52.	0.1	80	25	1.96	1,250	2.5 to 3.5
				0.2	90	30	1.96	3,000	2.5 to 3.5
CaF₂.............	78.07	3.18	24.6	0.3	18	30	1.97	2,500	4

* Due to variations in water content.

† The reason for the large difference in the two values of γ lies in the difference in the estimated size of the particles. This value was taken from Hulett.

Dehydrated and apparently insoluble aluminum oxide and zirconium oxide, when ground to less than 2.5 μ size have been found to dissolve appreciably in hydrochloric acid solution.[13] The surface attack of various gases and acid solutions upon metals has been found to be greatest in the regions of greatest curvature.[14]

When finely divided to an impalpable powder, quartz is converted to silicic acid gel by boiling with water.[15]

The dissociation pressure of silver carbonate, Iceland spar, and mercuric oxide decidedly increases when the particles are of the order of 1 μ.[16]

The melting points of highly subdivided particles of azobenzene, *p*-chloraniline, tristearin, stearic acid, and myristic acid have been found to be a few tenths of a degree lower than the normal melting points.[17]

The heat of solution of finely ground sodium chloride (particles of about 1.3 μ average diameter) has been found to be about -900 cal. per mole, while that of coarse crystals is -928.6 cal. per mole.[18]

Gibbs's Law of Surface Concentration.—Surface energy is a function of the capacity factor (surface area) and the intensity factor (surface tension). Since the energy of a system tends to flow to a minimum level, the only way possible for a chemically homogeneous liquid to decrease its surface energy, since the intensity factor is constant at constant temperature, would be to diminish its surface. This is evidenced by the tendency of droplets of a liquid to coalesce to form larger drops.

In the case of a solution, however, there is the additional possibility of decreasing the surface energy by means of solute moving into or out of the interface according to whether the solute lowers or raises the surface tension of the solvent. This actually does happen and was predicted by Willard Gibbs, in 1878.[19] Gibbs deduced from his theoretical treatment of the effect of capillary forces on phase equilibria that, if a substance (a gas or a dissolved substance) possesses the property of lowering the interfacial tension which exists between the gaseous or solution phase and some second phase which may be either liquid or solid, then the substance will be attracted to the interface, so that its concentration in the interfacial layer becomes greater than its average concentration through the bulk of the gaseous or solution phase. If, on the other hand, the substance considered possesses the property of raising the interfacial tension, the substance will be repelled from the surface and its concentration in the surface layer will be less than that in the bulk of the homogeneous phase.

The quantity concentrated in the surface, denoted by Γ, is defined as the mass of the substance per unit area of the interface in excess of the mass which would be there if capillary effects were absent.

This conclusion was expressed by Gibbs in a generalized equation involving the chemical potentials of the substances present, the masses concentrated at the interface, the surface tension, and the entropy. For the case of the concentration of water vapor at a water-mercury surface, we have in Gibbs's own words:

If liquid mercury meets the mixed vapors of water and mercury in a plane surface, and we use μ_1 and μ_2 to denote the potentials of mercury and water respectively, and place the dividing surface so that $\Gamma_1 = 0$, *i.e.*, so that the total quantity of mercury is the same as if the liquid mercury reached this surface on one side and the mercury vapor on the other without change of density on either side, then $\Gamma_{2(1)}$ will represent the amount of water in the vicinity of this surface, per unit of surface, above that which there would be, if the water vapor just reached the surface without change of density, and this quantity (which we may call the quantity of water condensed upon the surface of the mercury) will be determined by the equation

$$\Gamma_{2(1)} = -\frac{d\gamma}{d\mu_2} \qquad (3)$$

where γ is the interfacial tension.

Since the chemical potential $\mu = RT \, ln \, a$ where a is the activity, we have

$$\Gamma = -\frac{1}{RT}\frac{d\gamma}{dlna} \qquad (4)$$

or

$$\Gamma = -\frac{a}{RT}\frac{d\gamma}{da} \qquad (5)$$

For dilute solutions, we may substitute concentration for activity:

$$\Gamma = -\frac{c}{RT}\frac{d\gamma}{dc} \qquad (6)$$

Equation (6) has also been derived by the process of a thermodynamic cycle.[20] The student should note that Eq. (6) will apply only to a thermodynamically reversible system in mobile equilibrium where the interfacial concentration is sufficiently dilute for the gas law to be applicable.

The formula contains the differential coefficient of the surface tension with change in concentration, which is positive if these change in the same and negative when they change in opposite directions. This in conjunction with the minus sign shows that there will be a "negative excess," *i.e.*, a lower concentration in the surface layer as the surface tension increases with increase in concentration of the solute. If the surface tension decreases with increasing concentration, the slope of the curve is negative, and this in conjunction with the minus sign means that an increase in concentration in the surface layer as compared with that of the bulk of the solution will result, or that there will be an actual excess concentration in the surface layer.

Quantitative Tests of Gibbs's Law.—The situation in regard to the experimental verification of Gibbs's law by direct measurement of the interfacial concentration of solute is rather confused. Donnan and Barker[21] obtained results by the aspiration of air bubbles up a vertical column of nonylic acid solution which are in fair agreement with those calculated by means of the surface tension and Eq. (6). Table 42 gives their results which they

TABLE 42.—CONCENTRATION OF NONYLIC ACID AT AIR-WATER INTERFACE

Grams nonylic acid in 100 g. solution ($\times 10^5$)	Surface tension, dynes per cm. at 20°C.	Γ observed in g. per sq. cm. ($\times 10^7$)	Γ calculated ($\times 10^7$)
0	72.91		
243	67.97	0.95	0.58
500	57.33	1.52	1.23
759	50.24	1.09	1.58
806	49.09	0.92	1.63

believed supported the equation. The same authors experimented with saponin solutions but the results were poor.

By means of a more highly developed air-bubble technique, McBain[22] finds two to eight times as much surface concentration of surface-active* solutes as predicted by Eq. (6). Aqueous solutions of iso-amyl alcohol, acetic, butyric, caproic acids, phenol, *p*-toluidine, resorcinol, thymol, and camphor were studied. McBain contends that Gibbs's law is not quantitatively valid for such solutions. On the other hand, by assuming the validity of Eq. (5), Harkins[23] has calculated from surface-

* For convenience, we shall denote substances which lower surface tension as *surface-active* substances. In the German literature the term *capillary active* is used.

tension and activity data that a monomolecular film of butyl
alcohol forms on the surface of a 0.85 M aqueous solution of butyl
alcohol.

Quantitative investigation of the concentration of a solute at
liquid-liquid interfaces was made by Lewis.[24] His systems consisted of a series of aqueous solutions which were brought into
contact with large surfaces of hydrocarbon oil. The solutes
employed were sodium glycocholate, Congo red, methyl orange,
sodium hydroxide, silver nitrate, potassium chloride, barium

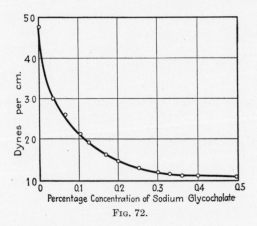

Fig. 72.

chloride, cupric chloride, and caffein. All of these were found to
lower the oil-water interfacial tension (the first four exerting a
very marked depressing action upon the interfacial tension) and
hence all should be concentrated in the interface.

The technique employed with sodium glycocholate, which is
typical of all, was as follows. The interfacial tensions between
the oil phase and solutions of varying concentrations of the salt
were determined and plotted as shown in Fig. 72.[24]

To calculate the adsorption (surface concentration) in the
case of a 0.2 per cent solution of sodium glycocholate, the tangent
to the curve corresponding to this bulk concentration must be
taken and calculated in absolute units.

$$- \frac{d\gamma}{dc} = \frac{9.5 \text{ dynes per cm.}}{0.002 \text{ g. per cc.}} = 4{,}750$$

With $T = 289$ and R in ergs 83.2×10^6, the value for Γ becomes 5.5×10^{-8} g. per square centimeter.

The experimental method of measurement was carried out (1) by forming an emulsion of the oil in the glycocholate solution and (2) by passing droplets of oil of 1- to 2-mm. radius through the solution and estimating the change in bulk concentration which took place.

The method of determining the diminution in concentration was by means of measuring the interfacial tension and then reading the concentration from the curve given above. The changes were so small that the experimental error was as great as 25 per cent.

By the emulsification method, using a 0.2 per cent solution of the glycocholate, in the first instance Γ was found to be 4.7×10^{-6} g., and by the second method 3 to 5×10^{-6} g. Hence there is a great discrepancy between the calculated and experimentally determined values.

With solutions of methyl orange, Congo red, and sodium hydroxide the observed concentrations were twenty to eighty times those calculated, and in the case of caffein and the inorganic salts there appeared to be an agreement at least in order of magnitude; but since the change in concentration was so slight, no great accuracy can be claimed for the observed values. Lewis ascribes the discrepancy in the cases of sodium glycocholate, Congo red, and methyl orange to their colloidal nature, which produces a layer of coagulated material at the interface.

In another method, using a fine spray of falling mercury droplets as adsorbing surface, Lewis obtained certain interesting results. Employing as solvent a mixture of water 80 per cent and alcohol 20 per cent in order to avoid the disturbance due to dissolved oxygen and, as solute, aniline in 0.007 per cent concentration, the surface concentration was found to be 2 to 3×10^{-8} g. per square centimeter. The calculated value was 1×10^{-8} g. This is at least an agreement in order of magnitude; but when this method was applied to solutions of sodium glycocholate, the surface concentration was about twenty-five times that calculated.

The adsorption of mercurous sulfate from water by a mercury surface has been shown to agree with the values calculated by

Gibbs's equation.[25] Patrick[26] found the order for adsorption of
a series of solutes at a mercury-water interface to be $Hg_2SO_4 >$
salicylic acid > picric acid > new fuchsin. This is also the order
for their lowering of the $Hg-H_2O$ interfacial tension.

An appreciable length of time is required for surface equilibrium. This is shown in Fig. 73.[27,28] The phenomenon is most
striking in the case of exceedingly dilute solutions. At sodium
oleate dilutions greater than 1 part in 100,000 of water, it is

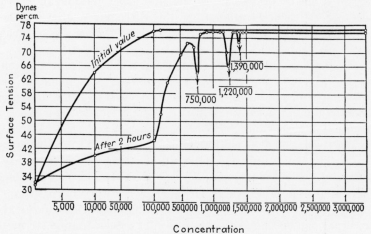

FIG. 73.—Surface tension of aqueous sodium oleate solutions.

seen that the initial surface tension is that of pure water, but
after 2 hr. the presence of the oleate in the surface layer is manifested. The significance of the three points of minimum will be
discussed later in this chapter.

The time factor in surface concentration of proteins is shown
in Fig. 74.[28,29] This curve shows how the surface orientation is
disturbed by stirring.

In the case of solutions containing solutes which raise the
surface tension, interesting results are obtained if it is assumed
that they are covered by a surface layer of pure water. If it is
assumed that such a solution remains constant in composition
right up to the boundary of this layer of pure water t, the thickness of this layer may be calculated by means of

$$t = -\frac{1,000\Gamma}{m} \qquad (7)$$

where $-\Gamma$ is the deficiency of solute per square centimeter and m is the molality of the solution. Langmuir[30] calculated the thickness of the pure water layer in this way and found values from 3.3 to 4.2 Å. If the water molecule is assumed to be cubical in

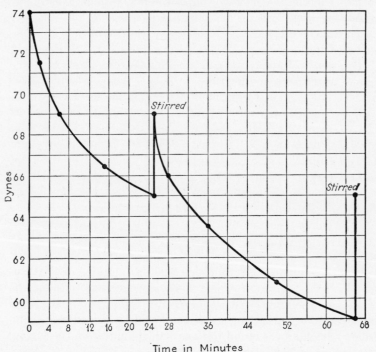

Fig. 74.—Effect of stirring upon solutions of serum; dilution 1: 10,000.

shape, the length of its side is 3.1 Å. Consequently, the assumption of the existence of a superficial film of water seems to be justified. This is so for dilute solutions. As the solution of a surface tension raising salt is concentrated, the calculated thickness of the pure water layer diminishes.[31,32] At 0.1 molal concentration of sodium chloride, the thickness was calculated[32] as 4.00 Å. At 5 molal it fell to 2.30 Å, which shows that the ions must diffuse into the surface film here and there as the concentration in the solution is increased.

Qualitative Verification of Gibbs's Law and Phenomena for Which It Offers an Explanation.—The deposition of a solid substance on the surface of aqueous solutions of albumin upon shaking or aspiration of air through them was reported in 1851.[33] Plateau[34] noted that the viscosity of surface films on a 1 per cent saponin solution was considerably greater than that of the bulk of the solution. Ostwald[35] in discussing similar results on *mechanical coagulation* of albumin, obtained by Ramsden,[36] stated that he considered it to be a physical equilibrium explainable by Gibbs's theory.

Ramsden[37] studied aqueous dispersions of various surface-active substances, finding that many of them, when shaken, concentrate to such an extent in the liquid-air interfaces of the bubbles that they precipitate out, frequently forming very viscous surface skins. A solution containing 1 part of albumin in 1,000,000 parts of water showed marked surface concentration. The precipitation upon shaking is due to increase of the total surface concentration resulting from the large development of surface by the air bubbles. When these rise and break, the material is deposited on the surface of the solution.

"Mechanical coagulation" of albumin solutions may also be effected by shaking the solutions with an immiscible liquid such as chloroform, isoamyl alcohol, heptylic acid, or nonylic acid.

It was also shown by Ramsden that in solutions of mixtures of substances, both of which lower the surface tension, the substance which lowers it to the greater extent will concentrate in the surface layer, driving out the less active substance therefrom. Saponin was found to force egg albumin from the surface of solutions of the latter.

The optimum pH value for the mechanical coagulation of albumin and of hemoglobin has been found to be that of the isoelectric point.[38] Since conalbumins are not mechanically coagulated, a method of separation of conalbumin from albumin has been devised based on shaking.[39]

The inactivation of enzyme solutions upon shaking[40] is an illustration of mechanical coagulation. The presence of saponin has been found to prevent such inactivation.

Since the surface concentration results in stiff viscous films, high pressure is required to force a solution of saponin or of albumin through a capillary tube in which an air bubble is formed, because it is so difficult to change the shape of the rigid air-bubble film.

In the filtration of a hydrophilic colloid solution, unless the filter paper is previously wet with water, it soon clogs and the filtration becomes very slow owing to this surface deposition filling up the pores. When a solution of a gum or protein is filtered through cotton, the latter must be wet with water first; otherwise the skin formed is so thick that filtration is effectively arrested.

An investigation of the formation of skins on peptone solutions[41] showed that, when a drop of a concentrated solution of peptone is let fall upon water, it spreads over the surface of the damp glass walls of the container as well as over the water surface. It will not spread on dry glass. The film becomes stiffer on aging but permits water to evaporate through it. The minimal weight of peptone which is necessary to form a solid skin is about 4×10^{-7} g. per square centimeter. Less peptone than this may be spread upon the water surface without any noticeable change on the surface viscosity.

Further qualitative verification of Gibbs's law was provided by Hall[42] and Clara Benson.[43] The former found that the froth from a soap solution was more concentrated than the bulk of the solution; the latter's analysis of bubbles from an aqueous solution of amyl alcohol showed more amyl alcohol in the surface layer than in the bulk of the solution.

Spreading of Liquid over Liquid Surfaces.—The spreading of liquids over the surface of a liquid with which they are immiscible or in which they are but slightly soluble has been studied notably by Quincke (1868–1894), Lord Rayleigh (1890–1899), Devaux (1903–), Hardy (1912), Marcelin (1914), Langmuir (1916–), Harkins (1917–) and Adam (1921–).

It was not until about 1870 that systematic attempts were made to distinguish clearly between the properties of water surfaces when clean, and when covered by a film of contamination. In 1890, Rayleigh[44] measured the amount of olive oil necessary to check the motions of camphor which take place on a clean-water surface, and the amount of the diminution of the surface tension caused by the minimum quantity of oil required to stop the camphor movements.[45]   The amount of olive oil required was 0.81 mg. for 555 sq. cm., lowering the surface tension about 16 dynes per centimeter.   If olive oil is assumed to be triolein (it actually consists of about 90 per cent triolein), a molecule of oil covered 100 Å² in Rayleigh's experiment.[46]   From modern measurements it is known that one molecule of triolein covers an area of 97 Å².

A clever and outstanding contribution was made in 1890 by Agnes Pockels,[47] who showed that a film on a water surface may be mechanically removed or concentrated in any desired part of the surface, leaving the remainder clean, by raking the surface, just as large objects floating on water may be pushed aside.   By the use of barriers working on the surface of water contained in a trough filled to the brim, she was able to vary the surface available for a given amount of oil present as a film.   She found that, when the area available exceeded a certain amount, there was no perceptible diminution of surface tension; but as soon as the area was diminished below this, a rapid fall of surface tension began.

Rayleigh[48] confirmed Pockels's observation and suggested that, at the point of the first fall in surface tension, the molecules of the film were just crowded together in mutual contact to form a layer one molecule thick.

The next advance in our knowledge of the structure of surface films was made by Langmuir.[49]   He accepted the monomolecular layer idea, postulating that liquids which spread out into thin films on the surface of water contain active groups which dip into the aqueous surface.   For example, when a drop of oleic acid is placed on water, it forms a film one molecule deep, in which, if the film is compact, the hydrocarbon chains stand on the surface of the water with the —COOH groups dissolved in water. While a —COOH group can by virtue of its strong attraction for water drag a few water-insoluble hydrocarbon groups under the surface, as in acetic, propionic, butyric acids; when the hydrocarbon chain is sufficiently long, only the —COOH dissolves leaving the remainder sticking out.   Pure paraffin oil, having no water-soluble groups, does not spread at all over water.

Langmuir built an apparatus embodying the idea of the Pockels's surface scraper.   It was a rectangular shallow trough, at one end of which was a balance so connected with a float on the surface that measurement of the surface pressure of the film could be made.*

A drop of a solution of fatty acid or oil in a volatile solvent was then placed on the surface of the water in the trough and the scraper moved along the surface in order to push the oleaginous contamination toward the float. The float was unaffected until suddenly it showed a sharp diminution in surface tension. At this point, the area covered by the film was recorded and then on the assumption that it consisted of a monomolecular layer the data in Table 43 were calculated.

TABLE 43.—CROSS SECTIONS AND LENGTHS OF MOLECULES†

Substance	Formula	(I) Cross section, $\mathring{A}^2$	(II) $\sqrt{\text{Cross section}}$, $\mathring{A}$	(III) Length, $\mathring{A}$
Palmitic acid	$C_{15}H_{31}COOH$	21	4.6	24.0
Stearic acid	$C_{17}H_{35}COOH$	22	4.7	25.0
Cerotic acid	$C_{25}H_{51}COOH$	25	5.0	31.0
Tristearin	$(C_{18}H_{35}O_2)_3C_3H_5$	66	8.1	25.0
Oleic acid	$C_{17}H_{33}COOH$	46	6.8	11.2
Triolein	$(C_{18}H_{33}O_2)_3C_3H_5$	126	11.2	13.0
Trielaidin	$(C_{18}H_{33}O_2)_3C_3H_5$	120	11.0	13.6
Cetyl palmitate	$C_{15}H_{31}COOC_{16}H_{33}$	23	4.8	41.0
Myricyl alcohol	$C_{30}H_{61}OH$	27	5.2	41.0
Cetyl alcohol	$C_{16}H_{33}OH$	21	4.6	21.9
Ricinoleic acid	$C_{17}H_{32}(OH)COOH$	90	9.5	5.8
Linoleic acid	$C_{17}H_{31}COOH$	47	6.9	10.7
Linolenic acid	$C_{17}H_{29}COOH$	66	8.1	7.6

† Langmuir.

Dividing the area covered by the number of molecules of oil on the surface, the area of water covered by each molecule is obtained. This must also equal the cross section of the molecules. The results are given in column I of Table 43. The number of molecules of oil on the surface is found by multiplying the number of gram-molecules of added substance by 60.6×10^{22}. It is seen that the cross sections of the molecules vary over quite

* Detailed description of a sensitive apparatus for measuring surface pressures is given by Adam.[50]

a wide range—from 21 to 126 Å². The three saturated acids—palmitic, stearic, and cerotic—all occupy nearly the same areas, notwithstanding the fact that the number of carbon atoms in the molecules increase from 16 to 26. Each tristearin molecule covers a space which is three times that of a stearic acid molecule and the molecule of cetyl palmitate takes up an area about the same as that of stearic acid.

Thus each $-\overset{\displaystyle O}{\overset{\displaystyle \|}{C}}-O$ group occupies an area of about 23 Å², no matter whether it occurs in an acid or in an ester, and this area is substantially independent of the length of the hydrocarbon chain to which the active group is attached.

The length of the molecules in a direction perpendicular to the surface is calculated as follows: The volume of each molecule is found by dividing the "molecular volume" of the oil (M/ρ) by the Avogadro number N. By dividing this volume by the cross section of each molecule, the length of the molecule in a direction perpendicular to the surface is obtained. The results are given in column III of Table 43.

It is interesting to compare these lengths with the cross sections. As a rough approximation it may be assumed that the dimensions of the molecule in directions parallel to the surface can be found by taking the square root of the cross section. This is equivalent to assuming that each molecule in the surface film occupies a volume represented by a square prism with its axis vertical. The length of the square side, or the "average diameter," is given in column II of Table 43.

It is seen at once that the molecules are very much elongated. Thus the length of the palmitic acid molecule is about 5.2 times the average diameter.

The molecule of tristearin has the same length (perpendicular to the surface) as the stearic acid molecule, but three times the cross section. Thus each of the three active groups has been drawn down on to the surface of the water while the hydrocarbon chains are packed in side by side and are erect upon the surface.

In the case of cetyl palmitate the length of the molecule is shown to be 41 Å, or nearly twice that of the palmitic acid molecule, while the average diameter is only 4.8 Å, or about the same as the palmitic acid molecule. The molecule contains two long hydrocarbon chains connected by a —CO.O— group. In palmitic acid the length of such a chain is 24 Å. If the length of this chain were nearly a constant quantity, then one would have to assume that in the cetyl palmitate film the two chains in each molecule are arranged one above the other with the carboxyl in the middle. On this assumption, however, the only part of the molecule in contact with the water would be the CH₃ on the end of one of the hydrocarbon chains, so that there should be no

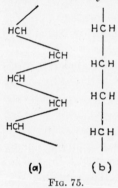

(a) (b)
Fig. 75.

tendency for this substance to form a monomolecular film on water. Solid paraffin, for example, dissolved in benzene and placed on water does not give a monomolecular film but gives a film of variable thickness (10 to 40 molecules) depending on the rate at which the benzene is allowed to evaporate.

Langmuir's theory therefore compels us to conclude that the —CO.O— group of the cetyl palmitate is on the surface of the water and that both hydrocarbon chains are packed in side by side above the —CO.O— group. The area of water covered by the —CO.O— is the same as the carboxyl in the palmitic acid so that the two hydrocarbon chains side by side do not have any greater cross section than the one in the palmitic acid. But each chain is extended to nearly twice the length in the first case than it is in the second.

This led Langmuir to suggest a zigzag orientation of the palmitic acid chains (Fig. 75a), the two chains of the cetyl palmitate being straight (Fig. 75b). He submitted as added evidence the fact that in the diamond, the carbon atoms are 1.54 Å apart. This is probably the minimum distance within which carbon atoms can approach each other. In a substance as soft as a hydrocarbon molecule one would expect that they would be considerably farther apart than this.

If the lengths of the molecules in column III of Table 43 are divided by the number of carbon atoms in the chain, the average vertical distance between adjacent carbon atoms in the chain is obtained. In all cases except that of cetyl palmitate the distance is less than the distance between atoms in the diamond. This is a clear indication that the atoms cannot be arranged linearly but rather must be arranged along a zigzag or curved line. The observed cross section (23 Å²) is ample to allow the carbon atoms to be arranged in some such manner and still be separated from each other by distances greater than 1.54 Å.

The results obtained with the substances containing unsaturated hydrocarbon chains afford confirmation of Langmuir's belief that the double bond is to be regarded as an active group. Each oleic acid molecule covers a surface of twice that of the saturated acids. This same difference is manifest in triolein and trielaidin when compared with tristearin.

The zigzag structure of the fatty acid and glyceride films postulated by Langmuir has since been substantiated by X-ray examination.[50] It is believed by Adam, however, that the molecular chains are tilted at an angle instead of being oriented vertically.

If molecules of fatty acids or soaps are considered square prisms, it is apparent that a continuous film might consist (1) when closely crowded together, of the molecules standing vertically on the surface, (2) when less crowded, of the molecules lying flat on the surface on their narrow sides, and (3) when still less crowded, lying on their wider sides. Du Noüy[27] postulated this as an explanation for the three minima in the surface tension of sodium oleate solutions shown in Fig. 73, where the concentrations are sufficiently low for all of the sodium oleate to be deposited in the surface.

Du Noüy placed 2-cc. portions of sodium oleate solutions in watch glasses of such a size that the total surface area (water-glass plus water-air) was 26.4 cm.². At the first minimum of the surface tension, $1/750,000 \times 2 = 26.7 \times 10^{-7}$ g. sodium oleate present. This weight of oleate was spread evenly on an area of 26.4 cm.². Thus the weight of oleate per square centimeter was $26.7 \times 10^{-7} \div 26.4 = 1.01 \times 10^{-7}$ g. This divided by the specific gravity of sodium oleate (0.821) gives 12.3×10^{-8} cm.* or the thickness of the film in centimeters.

---

* Langmuir's measurements indicate that the length of an oleic acid molecule is 11.2×10^{-8} cm. The replacement of hydrogen by sodium increases the length of the molecule apparently.

Let us now consider the second minimum at $1/1,220,000$. The same calculation yields the thickness of the layer, which is 7.56×10^{-8} cm. This minimum can occur only if a critical organization of molecules takes place. Consequently, in this case, we have another monomolecular layer, but the molecules are horizontally arranged, and 7.56×10^{-8} cm. is one of the dimensions of the base of the molecule.

The third minimum, at $1/1,390,000$, corresponds to a third monomolecular layer, the thickness of which is 6.64×10^{-8} cm. This is the third dimension of the molecule, which at this dilution lies flat on the surface, occupying a rectangular area 7.56×12.30 cm.$^2 \times 10^{-16}$. [In the second position (at a dilution of $1/1,220,000$) it occupies, in the horizontal plane, an area equal to 6.64×12.30 cm.$^2 \times 10^{-16}$, and in the first position (vertical molecules, at a dilution of $1/750,000$) it occupies in the horizontal plane an area equal to 7.56×6.64 cm.$^2 \times 10^{-16}$.] This may be true, regardless of the real shape of the molecule, since we are concerned only with the space occupied by one molecule when symmetrically packed with others.

These three dimensions make it possible now to compute the volume of the molecule to be 617.44×10^{-24} cm.^{3}, and, from the specific gravity of the substance (0.821) its mass is found to be 507×10^{-24} g. Dividing the molecular weight of sodium oleate (304.35) by the mass of one molecule we obtain a value for the Avogadro number,

$$N = 6.003 \times 10^{23}$$

which is within 1 per cent of Millikan's value (6.062×10^{23}).

It has also been shown[51] that the rate of evaporation of such very dilute solutions decreases at the concentrations of sodium oleate corresponding to the minima shown in Fig. 73. Films of fatty acids also retard the evaporation of water.[52]

The idea of the spreading of films of insoluble substances as just developed is frequently called the Langmuir-Harkins theory because Harkins published his first paper[53] presenting a similar picture shortly after Langmuir.

Harkins has developed a general method for prediction of the spreading tendencies of liquids upon water based upon the works of adhesion and of cohesion. The work of adhesion W_a is the

work required to pull apart a bar of unit cross section of two
immiscible liquids which are in contact. The work of cohesion
W_c is the work required to pull apart a bar of unit cross section of
a pure liquid.

A liquid will spread if its work of surface cohesion W_c is less,
and will not spread if its work of surface cohesion is greater, than
its work of adhesion W_a with respect to the surface of the liquid
or solid upon which the spreading is to occur. The *spreading
coefficient* is defined as

$$S = W_a - W_c$$

Harkins points out that the *polar theory* holds only in the case
of the formation of monomolecular films and that nonpolar liquids
may spread also while forming thicker films. That is, there is a
gradual transition from highly spreading liquids, which are polar,
to those which do not spread at all.

The relation $S = W_a - W_c$ is derived by Harkins[2] as follows:

When a drop of liquid b is placed upon the surface of another
liquid a, spreading may occur. If it does, the surface of the liquid
a disappears, while its place is taken by substantially an equal
area of the surface b plus an equal area of the interface ab, provided the surface of b and the interface ab do not lose their identity. If they do, then only one composite surface c takes the
place of the surface a.

The spreading coefficient may be developed by thermodynamic
reasoning, provided the former of the two hypotheses of the
preceding paragraph is used as a basis. Since only large-scale
motion is of importance in spreading, only the *free* surface
energies are involved. The free energy decrease S which occurs
in spreading is obviously given by the expression

$$S = \gamma_a - (\gamma_b + \gamma_{ab}) \tag{8}$$

where γ_{ab} represents the free energy of the surface or interface,
since the right-hand side of this equation gives merely the net
amount of free energy which disappears when the spreading
occurs. The work of adhesion W_a, or the work necessary to
pull apart the 1 sq. cm. of the interface ab, is given by the equation of Dupré as

$$W_a = \gamma_a + \gamma_b - \gamma_{ab} \tag{9}$$

since all that occurs is the disappearance of the surfaces a and b and the appearance of the interface ab. The work of cohesion is that necessary to create inside a liquid an area equal to 2 sq. cm. or, more specifically, to break apart a bar of liquid 1 sq. cm. in area and is given as

$$W_c = 2\gamma_b \tag{10}$$

A combination of Eqs. (8), (9), and (10) gives

$$S = W_a - W_c \tag{11}$$

One of the principal effects of the presence of a polar group is to increase the work of adhesion—much more than the work of cohesion. The dissymmetry of the molecule is one of the most important factors in spreading tendencies of a liquid, the spreading coefficient increasing generally as the electromagnetic field of force around the molecule becomes more unsymmetrical. This is due to the fact, according to Harkins, that with unsymmetrical molecules the work of adhesion toward water is much greater, in comparison with the work of cohesion, than in the case of symmetrical molecules since, when the liquid is torn from water, the strongest field must be ruptured, while when it is separated from itself only the weakest field is broken.

Nonspreading is usually due to a high value of the work of cohesion of the substance and seems to accompany the presence of the $=S$ or $=CS$ or phenyl groups, or that of chlorin, bromin, or iodin, as substituents in paraffins, in benzene, or in naphthalene, even when the unsubstituted compound spreads easily. When only one chlorin atom is present in a paraffin derivative, it seems to be polar and increases the spreading coefficient, while with several chlorin atoms the spreading coefficient is decreased. Bromin and especially iodin are much more effective than chlorin as substituents for producing nonspreading.

The spreading coefficients of some organic liquids, as measured by Harkins, are given in Table 44.

Adam[54] states that surface films cannot be stable unless the molecules contain groups which normally promote solution in water, thus providing a firm anchorage for the lower end of the molecules. Partial obstruction of such groups diminishes or

TABLE 44.—THE SPREADING COEFFICIENT OF ORGANIC LIQUIDS ON WATER*
AT 20°

(From W. D. Harkins[2])

A. Spreading Liquids

	S or $W_a - W_c$		S or $W_a - W_c$
Ethyl alcohol	50.40	Ethyl capronate	25.64
Methyl alcohol	50.10	Mercaptan	24.86
Propyl alcohol	49.10	Oleic acid	24.62
Dipropylamine	48.60	Isoamyl butyrate	24.61
Butyl alcohol	48.30	Aniline	24.45
Isobutyl alcohol	48.20	Heptane	22.40
Propionic acid	45.77	Ethyl nonylate	20.88
Butyric acid	45.66	Trimethyl ethylene	18.85
Ethyl ether	45.50	Methylene chloride	17.97
Acetic acid	45.20	Ethyl bromide	17.44
Acetonitrile	44.40	Benzaldehyde	17.25
Isoamyl alcohol	44.30	Isoamyl nitrate	14.82
Isovaleric acid	43.89	Chloroform	13.04
Methyl ketone	42.37	Anisole	11.76
Diisobutyl amine	40.47	Phenetole	10.66
Methylbutyl ketone	37.58	p-Cymene	10.10
Sym-octyl alcohol	37.32	Isopentane	9.44
Heptylic acid	37.12	Benzol	8.94
Methylhexyl carbinol	36.67	o-Xylene	6.85
n-octyl alcohol	35.74	Toluene	6.84
Formic acid	35.50	"Higher" paraffin	6.72
Butyronitrile	34.36	p-Xylene	6.70
Isoamyl chloride	33.88	Tetrachloroethane	6.44
Ethylpropyl ketone	33.75	m-Xylene	6.19
Ethyl carbonate	33.63	Ethyl benzol, mesitylene	5.59
Isovaleronitrile	32.63	Trichloroethylene	5.09
Heptaldehyde	32.22	o-Nitrotoluene	4.15
Undecylenic acid (at 25°)	32.02	m-Nitrotoluene	4.13
Methylhexyl ketone	31.92	Nitrobenzene	3.76
Ethyl isovalerate	30.71	Diisoamyl (decane)	3.76
Monochloroacetone	30.42	Hexane	3.41
Tert-butyl chloride	29.46	Chlorobenzene	2.31
Asym-dichloroacetone	26.46	β, β'-Dichloroethyl sulfide	1.62
Isobutyl chloride	26.43	Pentachloroethane	0.67
Nitromethane	26.32	Octane	0.22

* The values of W_c, from which the spreading coefficients were calculated, relate to the pure dry organic liquids, but the latter in spreading become saturated with water; therefore still more exact information in regard to spreading would be given if W_c were determined by the use of liquids saturated with water.

TABLE 44.—THE SPREADING COEFFICIENT OF ORGANIC LIQUIDS ON WATER*
AT 20°—(*Continued*)

B. Liquids Which Form Lenses in Water

Carbon tetrachloride...	1.06(?)	Tribromohydrin..........	−11.06
p-Bromotoluene.......	−1.29(30°)	"Stanolax"..............	−13.44
Ethylene dibromide....	−3.19	Liquid petrolatum, Squibbs	−13.64
Monobromobenzene...	−3.29	α-Monobromonaphthalene.	−13.86
o-Monobromotoluene..	−4.20	Acetylene tetrabromide....	−15.64
Perchloroethylene.....	−6.42	Methylene iodide.........	−26.46
Carbon disulfide......	−6.94	Diphenyl methane	
Phenyl mustard oil....	−7.68	Diphenyl dichloromethane	
Monoiodobenzene.....	−8.74	Tribromoethylene	
Bromoform..........	−9.58	p-Bromotoluene at 30°. ...	− 1.29
α-Monochloronaphtha-lene................	−9.74		

* The values of W_c, from which the spreading coefficients were calculated, relate to the pure dry organic liquids, but the latter in spreading become saturated with water; therefore still more exact information in regard to spreading would be given if W_c were determined by the use of liquids saturated with water.

destroys the stability of the film. He gives a rough classification[55] of these groups as follows:

a. Very weak attraction, no film formed; hydrocarbon, $-CH_2I$, $-CH_2Br$, $-CH_2Cl$.

b. Weak attraction, unstable films (groups in increasing order of attraction); $-CH_2OCH_3$, $-C_6H_4OCH_3$, $-COOCH_3$.

c. Strong attraction, stable films (but inappreciable solution with a 16 carbon chain); $-CH_2OH$, $-COOH$, $-CN$, $-CONH_2$, $-CH:NOH$, $-C_6H_4OH$, $-CH_2COCH_3$, $-NHCONH_2$, $-NHCOCH_3$.

d. Very strong attraction, substances dissolve with a 16 carbon chain; $-C_6H_4SO_3H$, $-SO_3H$.

The areas of groups as packed in films as given by Adam are tabulated in Table 45.

Experiments with mercury[56] show that the spreading coefficient for water over mercury is high (32) and much higher (from 60 to 137) for all of certain 29 organic liquids tested. These liquids presumably spread upon the surface of other metals as well. The failure of water ordinarily to spread upon mercury is due to contamination of the mercury. It is interesting to learn that the presence of bromin or of iodin in the molecule, which results in nonspreading on water, enhances the tendency to spread on mercury.

TABLE 45.—AREAS OF GROUPS PACKED IN FILMS

	Å^2
Hydrocarbon chains	20.4
—CH$_2$.CH$_2$.COOH	25.1
—CH$_2$.OH	21.7
—CH$_2$.CH$_2$.COOR*	22
—CH:CHCOOH	28.7
—CH:CHCOOR*	28.7
—CONH$_2$	< 21
—CN	27.5
—C$_6$H$_4$OH, —OCH$_3$ or —NH$_2$	23.8
—C$_6$H$_4$NHCOCH$_3$	28.2 or 25.8
—NHCONH$_2$	26
—NHCOCH$_3$	24.2
—CHBrCOOH	26 to 32
—CH$_2$CH:NOH	25
Hydrolecithin	52
Cholesterol	39
Triglycerides	63
Glycol dipalmitate	42

* R may be methyl, ethyl, or allyl.

Spreading of Liquids over Solid Surfaces.—When powdered or porous solids are thrown into liquids, there is an evolution of

TABLE 46.—HEAT OF SORPTION
(In small calories)

Substance	Fuller's earth	Bone charcoal	Kaolin	Dispersive power, per cent
Amylene	57.1	....	78.8	1.54
Water	30.2	18.5	....	2.82
Acetone	27.3	19.3	....	1.72
Methyl alcohol	21.8	17.6	27.6	1.60
Ethyl acetate	18.5	16.5	....	1.05
Ethyl alcohol	17.2	16.5	24.5	
Aniline	13.4			
Amyl alcohol	10.9	10.6	20.4	
Ethyl ether	10.5	....	....	0.90
Chloroform	8.4	14.0	15.7	0.86
Benzene	4.6	11.1	9.9	0.39
Carbon disulfide	4.6	8.4	9.9	
Carbon tetrachloride	4.2	13.9	9.4	0.27
Hexane	3.9	8.9	7.2	0.22

heat accompanying the sorption of liquid by the solid. Table 46 shows results obtained by Gurvich.[57]

Gurvich observed that when fuller's earth is shaken up with hexane it settles out rapidly, leaving a nearly clear liquid, but with acetone the liquid remains turbid. The disintegration of aggregates of fuller's earth particles could be observed under the microscope. By determining the percentage of the earth which remains suspended in different liquids he determined the dispersive powers as given in the last column of Table 46. The closeness of the parallelism between dispersive power and heat of sorption is striking, and in general the liquids showing high heats of sorption have high dielectric constants.

Langmuir points out that the heat of sorption is determined in general by the interaction of the active groups and the atoms of the solid body. Thus in Table 46 it is seen that those groups which cause oils and other liquids to spread on water surfaces are just those which cause an increase in the reaction between the liquids and fuller's earth, kaolin, and bone charcoal.

Measurements of the heat liberated when powdered titanium dioxide, stannic oxide, and zinc oxide were immersed in various liquids[58] show similar results. In fact the surface relations between these oxides and organic liquids are very similar to those of water, but polar groups such as —OH, —COOH, —COONa, are much more strongly attracted by these solid oxides than by water. The presence of as little as 0.03 per cent water in benzene increases the heat evolution to almost the value obtained in pure water. A trace of butyric acid in benzene produces a similar result. These measurements indicate that a monomolecular layer of polar molecules forms on the surface of the oxides.

The spreading of liquids upon metals or upon solid surfaces is generally called *wetting* of the solid by the liquid. When the liquid does not spread over such surfaces, it is referred to as *nonwetting*.

Liquid B will spread over the liquid or solid A if $\gamma_{a,g} > \gamma_{b,g} + \gamma_{a,b}$ where $\gamma_{a,b}$ represents the interfacial tension between A and B, $\gamma_{a,g}$ is the surface tension of A, $i.e.$, the interfacial tension between A and the air or gas (g) over its surface, and $\gamma_{b,g}$, the same for B. The condition for nonspreading is $\gamma_{a,g} < \gamma_{b,g} + \gamma_{a,b}$.

This cannot be experimentally verified for the spreading of a liquid over a solid, owing to the lack of a method for measurement of the surface tension at a solid surface. Indirect methods have been resorted to which have produced results of practical value, however. Obviously, the lubricating quality of an oil is a direct function of its wetting or spreading power over the metallic surfaces which are to be lubricated. The more the interfacial tension between metal and oil is lowered, the better is the spreading. The interfacial tension between steel or brass and oil cannot be measured, but that between mercury and oil can.* If it is assumed that the mercury-oil interfacial tensions are analogous to solid metal-oil interfacial tensions, the lubricating qualities of oils may be studied and improved.[59,60] For example, the addition of organic acids lowers the interfacial tension between oil and mercury (and also mineral oil-water interfacial tension), and the addition of as little as 0.1 per cent fatty acids to a mineral oil markedly lowers the coefficient of static friction between metallic surfaces, *i.e.*, increases the lubricating value.[61] The heat of wetting of copper powder by oils known to be excellent lubricants has been shown to be greater than that obtained with oils of poor lubricating power.[62] The addition of a small amount of oleic acid to petroleum produces a relatively large rise in the heat of wetting.

X-ray spectrographs show that, when greases are rubbed between two smooth surfaces, the molecules become oriented,[63] thus verifying the suggestion of Bragg that the mechanism of lubrication consists of the production of a leaflike orientation of the molecules which permits them to glide past each other with little friction.

The spreading power of paints over wood surfaces should increase with decreased interfacial tension between wood and the paint oil. Since wood surfaces carry a film of moisture, the conditions for a good spreading paint should be predicted from a study of linseed-oil-water interfacial tensions. It has been found that this interfacial tension is lowered (the Donnan drop number is raised) by the presence of a small amount of fatty acid. Hence it would be expected that the presence of certain amounts of fatty acid in linseed oil should cause the paint to spread better.[64]

* By the Donnan drop pipette.

Wetting power is of the greatest importance in the use of insecticidal sprays used in agriculture. Obviously, the more thoroughly the aqueous phase containing the poison spreads over the leaves and the bodies of insects, the more effective it will be. Leaf and certain insect surfaces are waxy. Hence the wetting power of a spray liquid ought to be determinable by means of measurement of the interfacial tension between water and a heavy mineral oil. Soaps have been found to lower this interfacial tension and likewise to increase the wetting power of the spray liquid.

The use of soap-oil emulsions in sprays is due to their wetting power. An instance of their value is reported by Nuttall.[65] In tropical and subtropical countries, stock breeding is only possible if insect parasites which infest the cattle are kept down. According to Nuttall, the usual method of protection is by systematic dipping in a solution of sodium arsenite, but in South Africa it was found that the concentration of the arsenite necessary to kill the "bont" tick frequently led to fatal injury to the cattle. By incorporating a soap-oil emulsion with the arsenite, and thus increasing the wetting power over the greasy hides of the animals, it proved possible materially to reduce the arsenite content of the dip and yet accomplish destruction of the tick without injury to the cattle.

The effect of castor-oil soap in lowering the surface tension and the interfacial tension of its aqueous solutions toward a specimen of heavy petroleum oil is shown in Table 47.[65]

TABLE 47.—SURFACE TENSION AND INTERFACIAL TENSION OF SOLUTIONS OF CASTOR OIL SOAP TOWARD "LIQUID VASELINE"

Concentration percentage of fatty acid	Surface tension of soap solution γ_s, dynes per cm.	Interfacial tension γ_{vs}, dynes per cm.	$\gamma_v - (\gamma_s + \gamma_{vs})$,* dynes per cm.
2.0	33.45	8.23	−10.57
1.0	33.45	10.93	−13.27
0.5	33.45	11.98	−14.32
0.1	33.45	27.39	−29.73
0.01	33.45	76.46	−45.35
0.001	56.61	108.43	−77.32
0.0001	70.76	129.28	−98.17

* Surface tension of "vaseline" $\gamma_v = 31.11$.

While low surface tension means better wetting of greasy surfaces by aqueous solutions, there is an additional factor; the wetting ability is greater if the substance which lowers the surface tension of water forms a viscous film. Saponins and proteins, it will be recalled, form viscous surface layers on water. Saponin solutions wet a paraffin surface better than soap solutions do owing to the fact that the surface film of a saponin solution is rendered so viscous that it will not break up into droplets. The addition of saponin to ink will make it spread better on greasy paper.

The principles of wetting power have been employed in the separation of bitumen from finely divided mineral matter.[66] Washing with water does not work. The addition to 1,000 parts of water of 1 part of alkali soap or of sodium carbonate which forms soaps with acids in the bitumen or of saponin produces a solution which is successful.

The hydrolysis of fatty oils is readily accomplished by treatment with sulfonated aromatic compounds known as "Twitchell's reagents." The efficient action of a Twitchell reagent is due to the lowering of the oil-water interfacial tension. This favors emulsification of the oil, thereby increasing the oil surface exposed to the hydrolytic action of the aqueous acid phase.[67] Weston[68] states that colloidal clay acts similarly.

The spreading of water in a film over surfaces of glass and celluloid rather than its accumulation as a misty surface is desirable on automobile windshields, eyeglasses, and gas-mask windows. Various preparations used for these purposes known as *antidimmers* have been investigated by the Chemical Warfare Service of the U. S. Army.[69] Mixtures of soaps of sulfonated oils with glycerol and caustic soda were found to be the best antidimming preparations.

The reverse of wetting is the aim in the manufacture of rainproof fabrics. The fibers are coated with an aluminum soap, or wax, without affecting the porosity of the fabric. Raindrops run off as drops without spreading to a film.

Bartell and his colleagues have made many measurements of the wetting of solids by liquids [70] and have proposed some new definitions for the fundamental types of wetting.[71]

Distribution of a Coarse Powder.—If three immiscible liquids are shaken together, then according to the values of the interfacial tensions $\gamma_{1,2}$, $\gamma_{2,3}$, and $\gamma_{3,1}$, there are two possibilities: either the phases form a common network or one separates out and spreads itself between the two others.

If gravity is ignored, the first case is realized when none of the three interfacial tensions is greater than the sum of the two others, and the second case when one is greater than the sum of the others, i.e., if $\gamma_{1,2} > \gamma_{2,3} + \gamma_{3,1}$, then phase 3 separates out between phases 1 and 2, thereby establishing a minimum energy level for the system.

If phase 3 is solid and the two others liquid, then the same possibilities are to be noted with the distinction that if $\gamma_{1,2} > \gamma_{2,s} + \gamma_{s,1}$ a spreading out of the solid (S) between phases 1 and 2 is not possible. The solid (S) will collect in the interface of partition of phases 1 and 2.

When $\gamma_{2,s} > \gamma_{1,2} + \gamma_{1,s}$, the solid will be completely surrounded by liquid (1); i.e., it will be drawn into or held in liquid (1), while if $\gamma_{1,s} > \gamma_{1,2} + \gamma_{2,s}$, the solid will be wetted by liquid (2).

In the latter instance, the solid is said to be *preferentially wetted* by liquid (2).

The principle of preferential wetting is involved in ore flotation and may be useful for rough analytical separations. For example, when a mixture of powdered galena and quartz is shaken with water and butyl alcohol, the galena lodges quantitatively in the interface of the two liquids while the quartz remains in the water layer.

A study of the distribution of various powders when shaken with a number of water-organic-liquid combinations is shown in Table 48.[72]

In this table w signifies that the powder practically completely remained in the water phase after shaking with the organic liquid; o signifies that it went into the organic liquid or, if it was originally present in the organic liquid, it remained there after shaking with water, and only a very small fraction adhered to the interface. The initial i shows quantitative adhesion at the interface, while in the case of partial interfacial adhesion, oi means interfacial plus organic-liquid distribution, and iw that it went into the water layer as well as into the interface. A case marked such as $w(i)$ indicates that, while a portion went into

TABLE 48.—DISTRIBUTION OF POWDERS BETWEEN WATER AND ORGANIC LIQUIDS

Suspended powder	Water-ether	CHCl₃	i-butyl alcohol	Benzol and xylol	Petroleum	i-amyl alcohol	Paraffin oil
CaSO₄	w	w	w(i) w	w(i) w	w(i) w	w(i) w	wi w
SnO₂	w(i)	wi	i wi	i i(w)	i i(w)	i iw	iw
Al(OH)₃	w(i)	wi	wi	i	i i(w?)	iw	i i(w)
SnS	wi	i wi	i wi	i i(w)	i i(w)	i	wi
BaSO₄	wi	wi	wi	i	i	i i(w?)	i i(w?)
ZnS	w(i)	wi	i wi	i	i(w?)	i	i(w?)
ZnO	wi	wi	i i(w)	i	i	i	i
CaCO₃	wi	wi	i	i	i	i	i
Mg(OH)₂	i(w?)	wi	i	i	i	i i(w)	o iw
Al	oi iw	i i(w)	i i(w)	i	i	i i(w)	o(i) i
BaCO₃	wi	wi	i	i	oi i	i iw	o(i) i
CuS	wi	i i(w)	i	i	i	i	o i
PbCrO₄	wi	i i(w?)	i	i	i	i	o(i) i
Cu₂O	wi	i	i	i	i	i(o?) i	o i
MoS₂	i(w?)	i	i	i	i	i(o) i	o i
PbS	wi	i	i	i	i	oi i	o i
Fe₃O₄	wi	i	i	i	i	oi i	o i
BaCrO₄	wi	i	i	i	i(o) i	oi i	o(i) i
Pb₃O₄	i iw	i	i	i	i	oi i	o i
C	i iw	i	i	i	i(o?) i	i(o) i	o i
PbI₂	i	i	o oi	i	i	oi	o i
HgS	i	i	i(o) i	i	i(o?) i	i(o) i	o i
HgO	i	i	oi i	i	oi i	o i	o o
HgI₂	i	i	oi i	i	oi i	o	o oi
AgI	i	i	o	i	oi i	o	o oi

the interface, it is relatively small compared with the amount that was found in the water layer, etc.

There are two rows of key letters which require explanation: If upon 1 to 2 min. of boiling in the organic liquid before shaking with water, the powder behaved differently from when it was first boiled with water previous to shaking with the organic liquid, this is shown in the lower of each pair of rows of initials. If no difference in behavior was noted, the initial in the upper row describes both cases.

It is seen that the silicates, sulfates, carbonates, and oxides of the lighter metals are wetted best by water, while the heavy-metal compounds carbon, sulfur, and selenium are preferentially wetted by organic liquids.

Less extensive experiments were performed by Reinders,[73] who included, however, sulfur and selenium and certain hydrosols. Sulfur and selenium went into the organic-liquid layers.

When a red-gold hydrosol[75] was shaken up with isobutyl alcohol, amyl alcohol, benzene, benzin, carbon tetrachloride, carbon bisulfide, and ether, a layer separated out in the interface which was violet-blue in transmitted light and gold colored in reflected light. Ferric oxychloride hydrosol always remained in the aqueous phase when shaken up with immiscible liquids. When arsenious sulfide hydrosol was shaken with paraffin oil, carbon tetrachloride, benzene, and ether, the dispersed phase remained in the water layer, while with amyl or isobutyl alcohol it separated out in the interface. Addition of isobutyl alcohol had no effect until its solubility in the water was exceeded, when two layers are formed. The arsenious sulfide particles then deposited out in the interface. Colloidal tellurium separated out in the interface with all solvents mentioned, while colloidal selenium acted in practically the same manner except with amyl alcohol, where part went into the alcohol phase and part deposited in the interfacial layer.*

---

* P. Klein[74] obtained results just like those of Reinders when gold, ferric oxide, and arsenious sulfide hydrosols were shaken with organic liquids. He attributed the effect to the decrease in charge of the gold and arsenious sulfide sols by the low dielectric constant of the sorbed organic liquid causing coagulation. Since negative albumin hydrosol was also coagulated by shaking with organic liquids, he stated that this phenomenon of coagulation by organic liquids is limited to "negatively charged" colloids, the charge apparently being undiminished in the positive iron oxide sol. Had he tried positive albumin hydrosol, he would have found it to coagulate as well and his hypothesis would have been ruined.

The presence of traces of organic acids may result in better wetting of hydrous ferric oxide by organic liquids than by water. This has been shown by Fair[75] in the writer's laboratory. A simple demonstration is as follows: Some freshly precipitated and thoroughly washed hydrous ferric oxide is placed in each of two bottles. Distilled water is added to both, followed by a layer of ether. A drop of hydrochloric acid is added to one and a crystal or two of benzoic acid to the other. Then the mixtures are shaken violently for a few moments and allowed to come to rest. The ferric oxide in the bottle to which the benzoic acid was added will be in the ether layer, while in the other bottle it will be in the water layer.

References

1. OSTWALD: "Handbook of Colloid Chemistry," P. Blakiston's Son & Co., Philadelphia, 1915.
2. HARKINS: "Bogue's Colloidal Behavior," Vol. I, Chap. VI, McGraw-Hill Book Co., Inc., New York, 1924.
3. ROLLER: *J. Phys. Chem.*, **35**, 1133 (1931).
4. NOYES and WHITNEY: *Z. physik. Chem.*, **23**, 689 (1897).
5. NERNST: *Z. physik. Chem.*, **47**, 52 (1904).
6. BRUNNER: *Z. physik. Chem.*, **47**, 56 (1904); WAGNER: *ibid.*, **71**, 434 (1910).
7. CURIE: *Bull. soc. franc. minéral*, **8**, 145 (1885).
8. HULETT: *Z. physik. Chem.*, **37**, 385 (1901); **47**, 357 (1904).
9. DUNDON and MACK: *J. Am. Chem. Soc.*, **45**, 2479 (1923).
10. DUNDON: *J. Am. Chem. Soc.*, **45**, 2658 (1923).
11. JONES: *Ann. Physik*, **41**, 441 (1913); *Z. physik. Chem.*, **82**, 448 (1913).
12. JAEGER: *Z. anorg. allgem. Chem.*, **101**, 1 (1917).
13. PODSZUS: *Z. physik. Chem.*, **92**, 227 (1917).
14. REBOUL: *Compt. rend.*, **155**, 1227 (1912); **156**, 549 (1913); LUCE: *Ann. Physik*, **11**, 167 (1929).
15. DESCH: "The Chemistry and Testing of Cement," E. Arnold, London, 1911.
16. TZENTNERSHYER and KRUSTINSONS: *Z. physik. Chem.*, **130**, 187 (1927); **132**, 185 (1928); KRUSTINSONS: *ibid.*, **150A**, 310 (1930).
17. MEISSNER: *Z. anorg. allgem. Chem.*, **110**, 169 (1920); see also PAVLOV: *Kolloid-Z.*, **6**, 37 (1910).
18. LIPSETT, JOHNSON, and MAAS: *J. Am. Chem. Soc.*, **50**, 2701 (1928).
19. J. WILLARD GIBBS: "Collected Works," Vol. I, p. 235, Longmans, Green & Co., New York, 1928.
20. FREUNDLICH: "Kapillarchemie," 2d ed., p. 65, Akademische Verlagsgesellschaft m.b.H., Leipzig, 1922; MILNER: *Phil. Mag.*, (6) **13**, 96 (1907); HARLOW and WILLOWS: *Trans. Faraday Soc.*, **11**, 53 (1915); ADAMS: Ref. 50.

21. DONNAN and BARKER: *Proc. Roy. Soc. (London)*, **A85**, 557 (1911).

22. McBAIN and DAVIES: *J. Am. Chem. Soc.*, **49**, 2230 (1927); McBAIN and DUBOIS: *ibid.*, **51**, 3534 (1929).

23. HARKINS and WAMPLER: *J. Am. Chem. Soc.*, **53**, 850 (1931).

24. W. C. LEWIS: *Phil. Mag.*, **15**, 499 (1908); **17**, 466 (1909); *Z. physik. Chem.*, **74**, 619 (1910); *Science Progress*, **11**, 198 (1916).

25. SCHOFIELD: *Phil. Mag.*, (7) **1**, 641 (1926).

26. PATRICK: *Z. physik. Chem.*, **86**, 545 (1913).

27. DU NOÜY: *Phil. Mag.*, **48**, 665 (1924).

28. DU NOÜY: "Surface Equilibria of Biological and Organic Colloids," A.C.S. Monograph, Chemical Catalog Co., New York, 1926.

29. DU NOÜY: *J. Exptl. Med.*, **35**, 707 (1922); *Phil. Mag.*, **48**, 264 (1924).

30. LANGMUIR: *J. Am. Chem. Soc.*, **39**, 1848 (1917).

31. HARKINS and McLAUGHLIN: *J. Am. Chem. Soc.*, **47**, 2083 (1925); HARKINS and GILBERT: *ibid.*, **48**, 6047 (1926).

32. GOARD: *J. Chem. Soc.*, **127**, 2451 (1925).

33. MELSENS: *Ann. chim. phys.*, (3) **33**, 170 (1851); SMEE: *Proc. Roy. Soc. (London)*, **12**, 399 (1863).

34. PLATEAU: *Ann. chim. phys.*, (4) **17**, 260 (1869); *Ann. Phys. Chem.*, **141**, 44 (1870).

35. WILHELM OSTWALD: *Z. physik. Chem.*, **15**, 703 ref. (1894).

36. RAMSDEN: *Arch. Anat. Physiol.*, Physiol. Abt. 517 (1894).

37. RAMSDEN: *Proc. Roy. Soc. (London)*, **72**, 156 (1903); *Z. physik. Chem.*, **47**, 336 (1904).

38. WU and LING: *Chinese J. Physiol.*, **1**, 407 (1927); through *Chem. Abs.*, **22**, 1987.

39. WU and LING: *ibid.*, 431; through *Chem. Abs.*, **22**, 1988.

40. ABDERHALDEN and GUGGENHEIM: *Z. physiol. Chem.*, **54**, 331 (1908); SHAKLEE and MELTZER: *Am. J. Physiol.*, **25**, 81 (1909); HARLOW and STILES: *J. Biol. Chem.*, **6**, 359 (1909).

41. METCALF: *Z. physik. Chem.*, **52**, 1 (1905).

42. HALL: *Proc. Roy. Dublin Soc.*, **9**, 56 (1899).

43. BENSON: *J. Phys. Chem.*, **7**, 532 (1903).

44. LORD RAYLEIGH: *Proc. Roy. Soc. (London)*, **47**, 364 (1890).

45. LORD RAYLEIGH: *Phil. Mag.*, **30**, 386 (1890).

46. ADAM: *Chem. Rev.*, **3**, 163 (1926).

47. POCKELS: *Nature*, **43**, 437 (1891).

48. LORD RAYLEIGH: *Phil. Mag.*, **48**, 334 (1899).

49. LANGMUIR: *Chem. Met. Eng.*, **15**, 468 (1916); *J. Am. Chem. Soc.*, **39**, 1848 (1917).

50. ADAM: "The Physics and Chemistry of Surfaces," Clarendon Press, Oxford, 1930.

51. DU NOÜY: *Compt. rend.*, **184**, 1062 (1927).

52. RIDEAL: *J. Phys. Chem.*, **29**, 1585 (1925). LANGMUIR and LANGMUIR: *ibid.*, **31**, 1719 (1927).

53. HARKINS, BROWN, and DAVIES: *J. Am. Chem. Soc.*, **39**, 354 (1917); HARKINS, DAVIES, and CLARK: *ibid.*, **39**, 541 (1917). The reader will

find a subsequent series of papers by Harkins and colleagues in the *J. Am. Chem. Soc.* on this subject.

54. ADAM: *Trans. Faraday Soc.*, **24**, 149 (1928).
55. ADAM: Ref. 50.
56. HARKINS and EWING: *J. Am. Chem. Soc.*, **42**, 2439 (1920).
    HARKINS and FELDMAN: *ibid.*, **43**, 2665 (1921).
57. GURVICH: *J. Russ. Phys.-Chem. Soc.*, **47**, 805 (1915); through Langmuir, Ref. 30.
58. HARKINS and DAHLSTROM: *Ind. Eng. Chem.*, **22**, 897 (1930); see also BARTELL and HERSHBERGER: *Ind. Eng. Chem.*, **22**, 1304 (1930).
59. W. C. LEWIS: *Phil. Mag.*, (6) **15**, 499 (1908).
60. BHATNAGAR and GARNER: *J. Soc. Chem. Ind.*, **39**, 185 (1920).
61. ARCHBUTT: *J. Soc. Chem. Ind.*, **39**, 55 (1920); **40**, 287 (1921); WELLS and SOUTHCOMBE: *J. Soc. Chem. Ind.*, **39**, 51 (1920).
62. BACHMANN and BRIEGER: *Kolloid-Z.*, Special No., p. 142 (April, 1925).
63. TRILLAT: *Compt. rend.*, **182**, 843 (1926).
64. GARDNER and HOLDT: *U. S. Paint and Varnish Mfrs. Assoc. Circ.* 124 (1921).
65. NUTTALL: *Fifth Report on Colloid Chemistry, Brit. Assoc. Advancement Sci.*, p. 41 (1923).
66. EYLEMAN: *J. Soc. Chem. Ind.*, **41**, 14 (1922).
67. NUTTALL: *J. Soc. Chem. Ind.*, **39**, 67 (1920).
68. WESTON: *Chem. Age (London)*, **4**, 604 (1921).
69. CARLETON: *J. Ind. Eng. Chem.*, **11**, 1105; HOLMES: *ibid.*, 1111 (1919).
70. BARTELL et al.: *Z. physik. Chem.*, **130**, 715 (1927); *Ind. Eng. Chem.*, **19**, 1277 (1927); *ibid.*, **20**, 738 (1928); *ibid.*, **21**, 1102, 1248 (1929); *ibid.*, **22**, 1304 (1930); *J. Rheol.* **2**, 177 (1931).
71. OSTERHOF and BARTELL: *J. Phys. Chem.*, **34**, 1399 (1930).
72. HOFMANN: *Z. physik. Chem.*, **83**, 385 (1913).
73. REINDERS: *Kolloid-Z.*, **13**, 235 (1913).
74. KLEIN: *Kolloid-Z.*, **29**, 247 (1921).
75. FAIR: Dissertation, Columbia University, 1930.

CHAPTER XI

SORPTION

The verb *adsorb* is derived from the Latin *ad*, meaning *to*, and *sorbere*, meaning *suck in*. Consequently, in chemistry the noun *adsorption* is defined as the gathering or accumulation of a gas, liquid, or dissolved substance at a surface. The surface concentrations discussed in the preceding chapter are frequently called adsorption. The term *absorption* is used to describe the phenomenon where a substance penetrates a liquid or massive solid structure, producing an intimate intermingling of its atoms with those of the absorbing liquid or solid. Thus when a gas dissolves in a liquid, it may be said to be absorbed by the liquid, and likewise, perhaps, hydrogen is absorbed by platinum. When a vapor or liquid is sucked in by charcoal or by silica gel, one might imagine that an absorption has taken place, but actually, inasmuch as charcoal and silica gel are extremely porous bodies, possessing great extension of surface, the vapor or liquid is adsorbed.

McBain[1] has argued that adsorption of a substance is in some cases accompanied or followed by a slow penetration of the massive structure by the adsorbed substance. Firth,[2] observing the taking up of iodin from a benzene and from a chloroform solution by charcoal, has shown that a rapid removal of iodin occurs in the first few minutes, followed by a very slow removal of iodin from the solvents named over a period of many months. He calls the rapid removal "true adsorption" and the slow secondary removal "absorption." Others take the position that the slow secondary process is actually adsorption; it is slow because it is so difficult for the substance to penetrate the ultramicroscopic pores or capillaries of the charcoal. As a consequence of all this, McBain recommended that the non-committal terms *sorb* and *sorption* be used.

When one examines the journal literature of colloid chemistry, he finds that the term adsorption is applied to any phenomenon involving a change in concentration without an *obvious* primary valence reaction. For example, if the pressure of a gas is diminished by the introduction of a solid phase, if a vapor is condensed upon a solid surface, if a liquid is imbibed by a porous solid, if the concentration of a solution is altered by the introduction of a solid, or if suspended particles adhere to solid surfaces, the term adsorption is used to describe the case. In view of this state of affairs, it is probably advisable to adopt McBain's suggestion concerning the terminology.

Sorption was put to practical use by ancient peoples in the clarification of water by percolation through broken stone and shells. Plinius mentioned that water could be purified for drinking purposes by pouring it through wool. About 1777, Scheele and Fontana independently discovered that wood charcoal sorbs gases. The first systematic and quantitative investigation was de Saussure's study[3] of the sorption of gases published in 1812.

Sorption of Gases.—Unless the molecules of a gas which may strike a solid surface all rebound elastically, there will necessarily be a higher concentration of molecules of the gas at the surface layer of the solid than in the body of the gas. If any molecules impinging on the surface of the solid are condensed, a certain time interval must elapse before they can evaporate. This time lag will bring about the accumulation of molecules in the surface layer and may thus be looked upon as the cause of sorption. Langmuir[4] showed that the collisions of the molecules of a vapor with a solid surface are inelastic, so that every molecule striking the surface condenses. Considering that the surface of a crystal is a sort of checkerboard of active and inactive areas and that the layer of sorbed gas is only one molecule thick, Langmuir[5,6] developed the following theory for sorption of gases at solid surfaces.

The rate at which the molecules of a gas come into contact with the solid surface is according to the kinetic theory,[5]

$$m = p\sqrt{\frac{M}{2\pi RT}} \qquad (1)$$

where m = rate at which gas molecules strike against the surface, expressed in grams of gas per square centimeter per second.

M = molecular weight of the gas.

R = gas constant, 83.2×10^6 ergs per degree.

T = absolute temperature.

p = pressure of the gas in bars.

Letting μ represent the number of gram molecules of gas striking each square centimeter of surface per second, then

$$\mu = \frac{m}{M} = \frac{p}{\sqrt{2\pi MRT}} = 43.75 \times 10^{-6} \frac{p}{\sqrt{MT}} \tag{2}$$

If α represents the fraction of the impinging molecules which stick to the surface, $\alpha\mu$ represents the rate at which the gas condenses on the bare surface. If θ represents the fraction of the surface which is bare, the rate of condensation of the gas upon a partially saturated surface is

$$\alpha\mu\theta$$

The rate of evaporation from the surface is

$$\nu_1\theta_1$$

where ν_1 is the rate at which the gas would evaporate if the surface were completely covered and θ_1 is the fraction of the surface actually covered by the sorbed molecules. When a gas is in equilibrium with a solid surface, these two rates must be equal, so that

$$\alpha\mu\theta = \nu_1\theta_1 \tag{3}$$

Since

$$\theta + \theta_1 = 1$$

Then

$$\theta_1 = \frac{\alpha\mu}{\nu_1 + \alpha\mu} \tag{4}$$

θ_1, a measure of the amount of gas sorbed, is proportional to the pressure at low gas pressures, but as the pressure increases θ_1 increases more slowly until finally it reaches 1; i.e., the surface becomes saturated. Further, it is seen that at small values of ν_1 (at low temperatures) the sorption should be large and nearly independent of the pressure, while at large values of ν_1 (at high temperatures) the sorption should be small and should be proportional to the pressure. These deductions were shown by Langmuir to be in accord with experimental facts.

Equation (4) shows that the tendency of a gas to be sorbed on a surface is determined by ν_1, the rate of evaporation from the surface. This in turn depends on the secondary valence forces acting between the atoms of the solid surface and those of the sorbed gas. Thus what may properly be termed *chemical forces* enter the picture.

If n is the number of gram molecules of a gas sorbed per square centimeter of the surface, then nN is the number of molecules (N = Avogadro number) sorbed per square centimeter. Assuming that the molecules of gas are sorbed only in the active spaces of the surfaces, *i.e.*, only where there are unsatisfied valence forces, then nN must be equal to the number of secondary valence bonds of the surface which are saturated. The latter is equal to $\theta_1 N_0$, where N_0 is the number of these bonds per square centimeter of surface.

Hence

$$n = \theta_1 \frac{N_0}{N} = \frac{N_0}{N} \frac{\alpha\mu}{\nu_1 + \alpha\mu} \tag{5}$$

If $\alpha/\nu_1 = \beta$,

$$n = \frac{N_0}{N} = \frac{\beta\mu}{1 + \beta\mu} \tag{6}$$

where β may be termed the "average life" of the molecules on the surface.

Since μ is proportional to the pressure of the gas, we may write Eq. (6) in a simpler form as follows:

$$q = \frac{abp}{1 + bp} \tag{7}$$

where q = the quantity of gas sorbed by a solid surface.

p = the pressure of the gas.

a and b are constants.

Rewriting Eq. (7):

$$\frac{p}{q} = \frac{1}{ab} + \frac{p}{b} \tag{8}$$

where it is seen that if the theory holds, a straight line with the slope $1/b$ intercepting the p/q axis at $1/ab$ is obtained when p/q is plotted as a function of p.

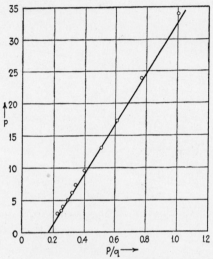

Fig. 76.—Sorption of nitrogen on mica.

A typical result obtained by Langmuir is given in Table 49, the data of which are plotted in Fig. 76.

Table 49.—Sorption of Nitrogen on Mica at 90°K.
q is expressed in cubic millimeters at 20°C., and 760 mm. pressure.
p is expressed in bars.
$a = 0.156 \qquad b = 38.9$

p	q obs.	q calc.	p/q
34.0	33.0	32.8	1.03
23.8	30.8	30.7	0.77
17.3	28.2	28.4	0.61
13.0	25.5	26.0	0.51
9.5	23.9	23.2	0.40
7.4	21.6	20.8	0.34
6.1	19.0	19.0	0.32
5.0	17.0	17.0	0.29
4.0	15.1	15.0	0.26
3.4	13.4	13.5	0.25
2.8	12.0	11.8	0.23

Hitchcock[7] has shown that an equation of the same form as Langmuir's equation for sorption would result from the application of the law of mass action to a reversible combination between two substances, one at a fixed total concentration, the other variable. Consider a reversible reaction between two substances, A and B, to form a compound, AB. From the mass law

$$[A] \cdot [B] = k[AB]$$

$$\frac{[A]}{[AB]} = \frac{k}{[B]}$$

$$\frac{[A] + [AB]}{[AB]} = \frac{k + [B]}{[B]}$$

$$[AB] = \frac{\dfrac{[A] + [AB]}{k}[B]}{1 + \dfrac{[B]}{k}} \tag{9}$$

For an experiment in which the total A (*i.e.*, the sum of the concentrations of A and AB) is kept constant, Eq. (9) is of the same form as Eq. (7). The variables $[AB]$ and $[B]$ correspond to q and p respectively, while the constant $1/k$ corresponds to a, and the constant $[A] + [AB]$ corresponds to b.

The chemical nature of the sorption of certain gases by certain hot filaments has been experimentally demonstrated by Langmuir. A tungsten filament heated to 2700°K. in a bulb containing a low pressure of carbon monoxide, and cooled by an outer bath of liquid air, sorbed carbon monoxide evidently by primary valence forces, since not CO but the compound WCO distilled off the filament at a constant rate, independent of the pressure of the carbon monoxide. Figure 77 is a picture of the tungsten surface with sorbed carbon monoxide.

He showed also that the sorbed film of oxygen on a hot carbon filament is so stable as to suggest a primary valence union. This film was so stable as to require heating of the filament at 2300°K. in a good vacuum for nearly half an hour in order to distill it off. Langmuir's picture of this sorbed film is given in Fig. 78.

He found that the catalytic action of hot platinum on the reaction between oxygen and hydrogen is poisoned by traces of cyanogen. He cites this as evidence for the covering of the platinum by an exceedingly stable sorbed film of cyanogen and ascribes it to the well-known chemical facts concerning strong development of primary and secondary valence forces in the cyanogen radical and its marked tendency to form very stable and complex compounds with metals. When such a poisoned platinum surface is heated so high that the cyanogen reacts with hydrogen, forming hydrogen cyanide, then the hot platinum resumes its property of catalyzing the combination between the remaining hydrogen and oxygen. Likewise, a trace of cyanogen poisoned the catalysis of the reaction between carbon monoxide

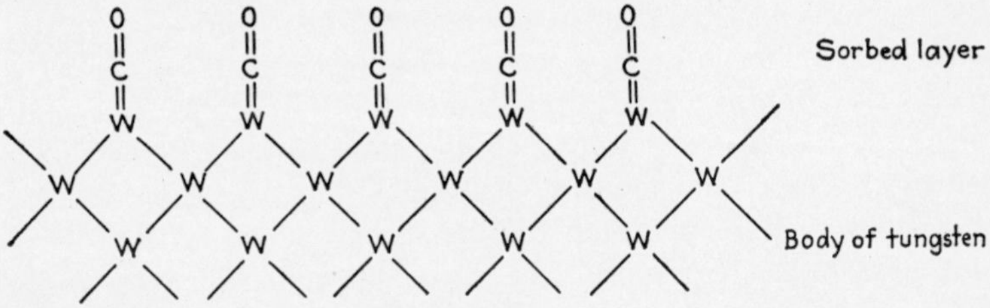

Fig. 77.

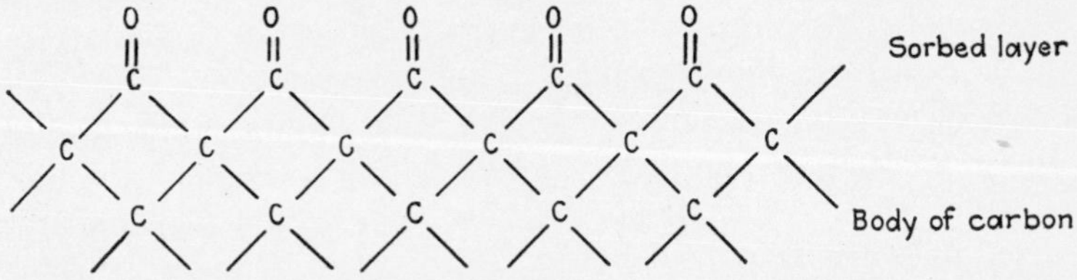

Fig. 78.

and oxygen to carbon dioxide by a platinum filament at 900°K. By raising the temperature of the filament to 1000°K., the cyanogen reacted with the oxygen to form nitrogen and carbon monoxide. As soon as all the cyanogen was oxidized, the catalytic activity of the platinum was restored, with the result that the remaining oxygen reacted rapidly with the carbon monoxide to form carbon dioxide.

Langmuir made some very interesting experiments upon the passivation of a hot tungsten filament by traces of oxygen. Oxygen was shown to stop completely this filament's property of causing dissociation of hydrogen molecules to atoms. As little as 0.001 bar of oxygen lowered the electron emission from a hot tungsten filament to a very small fraction of its normal value.

He points out that the inability of the hydrogen to react with the oxygen in such a case is strong evidence against a sorption theory which postulates merely a condensed layer of oxygen molecules as sorbed at the surface. It is evidence to the effect that the valence bonds of the oxygen are intimately combined with those of the tungsten atoms on the surface of the filament.

These experiments and their theoretical interpretation by Langmuir laid the foundation for rapid development in the knowledge of contact catalysis.

What has been said above applies to experiments at very low gas pressures but Langmuir contends that his theory of sorption (adsorption) is applicable to gases at atmospheric pressures. He points out, in the case of the sorption of vapors at such high pressures that as they approach the state of saturated vapors, there will be a tendency for the sorbed film to become several molecules deep. According to this theory, however, it is very improbable that films more than one or two molecules deep would ever be held on a surface by sorption, except with nearly saturated vapors, for the reason that the rate of evaporation of additional molecules would be nearly identical with that from the liquefied or solidified gas. If the vapor pressure were well below saturation, the rate at which such additional molecules would condense on the surface would be much less than the rate at which they would evaporate. He cites one of his measurements upon the amount of water vapor sorbed by a glass surface in which he found about fifty-five times as much water sorbed as the monomolecular-layer theory predicted. He ascribes this to solution in or absorption of the water by the glass. In defense of this view he cites the extreme slowness at which water is removed from glass upon heating and the length of time required for the resorption of the moisture by the glass.

Much has been written on sorption of gases by solids. McBain[8] has published a bibliography of about six thousand papers. A recent symposium held by the Faraday Society is recorded in some three hundred printed pages.[9]

Sorption from Solutions.—When charcoal is placed in a solution, a change in concentration results. If the solution is not too concentrated, the concentration of the solute is diminished owing to the greater sorption of the solute by the charcoal than of the solvent. Freundlich[10] showed that the sorption from many solutions by charcoal could be expressed by the equation

$$a = kC^{\frac{1}{n}} \tag{10}$$

where a = amount of solute sorbed by the sorbent.

C = equilibrium concentration of solute in the solution.

k and $1/n$ are constants.

This is called the Freundlich adsorption equation.* When $n = 2$, it is the equation for a simple parabola. The results of one of Freundlich's typical experiments are given in Table 50.

TABLE 50.—ONE OF FREUNDLICH'S MEASUREMENTS OF THE SORPTION OF ACETIC ACID FROM AQUEOUS SOLUTION BY BLOOD CHARCOAL AT 25°C.

C, moles per liter	a, millimoles per gram charcoal obs.	a calc.
0.018	0.47	0.47
0.031	0.62	0.60
0.062	0.80	0.80
0.126	1.11	1.08
0.268	1.55	1.49
0.471	2.04	1.89
0.882	2.48	2.47
2.785	3.76	4.01

The data are plotted in Figs. 79 and 80. It is seen that the logarithmic plot

$$\log a = \log k + \frac{1}{n} \log C \tag{11}$$

is a straight line with the slope $\frac{1}{n}$ (0.425), intercepting the log a axis at log k ($k = 2.606$).

Freundlich's sorption equation has been erroneously mistaken by some people for a fundamental expression evolved from Gibbs's law of surface concentration. It is, on the contrary, merely an empirical relationship and was so announced by its originator. As stated by Procter,[11] "The 'adsorption formula, just quoted is absolutely void of theoretical basis, as regards

* Actually first proposed by Boedecker (an agricultural chemist) in 1858.[12]

adsorption, but is a mathematical expression which will closely represent any chemical or physical phenomenon which proceeds at a diminishing ratio.''

The Freundlich equation reminds one of Henry's law as applied to the distribution of a solute between two immiscible

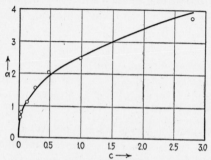

Fig. 79.—Sorption of acetic acid from aqueous solution by blood charcoal.

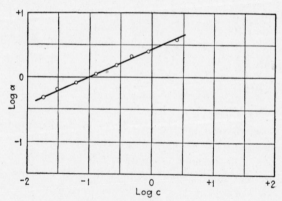

Fig. 80.—Logarithmic plot of Fig. 79.

liquids.[13] For example, succinic acid is distributed between ether and water as follows. The concentrations C_w and C_e represent grams of succinic acid dissolved in 10 cc. of solvent:

C_w	C_e	$\dfrac{C_w}{C_e} = K$
0.024	0.0046	5.2
0.070	0.013	5.2
0.121	0.022	5.4

The constancy of the partition is to be expected because succinic acid has its normal molecular weight both in ether and in water, disregarding its slight dissociation in the latter.

When a substance has different molecular weights in the two solvents, then the results obtained are very different, as in the case of the distribution of benzoic acid between water and benzene.

C_w	C_b	$\dfrac{C_w}{C_b}$	$K = \dfrac{C_w}{\sqrt{C_b}}$
0.0150	0.242	0.062	0.0305
0.0195	0.412	0.048	0.0304
0.0289	0.970	0.030	0.0293

Benzoic acid shows a normal molecular weight in water, while in benzene double molecules predominate; and since the number of these molecules in benzene, according to the mass law, is proportional to the square root of the concentration, then the law of distribution requires a proportionality between C_w and $\sqrt{C_b}$. It is seen that the ratio $C_w/\sqrt{C_b}$ is constant.

Therefore, where association takes place in one phase, Henry's law becomes

$$C_1^p = kC_2 \text{ or } C_1 = kC_2^{\frac{1}{p}},$$

where p is the association factor. Since in the Freundlich equation the exponent $1/n$ always has a value of less than 1—in fact, it is frequently in the neighborhood of 0.5—it is plain that, if the sorption by the solid sorbent is looked upon as solid solution, the molecular weight of the sorbed substance would be indicated as one-half its molecular weight in water, which when applied to the sorption of acetic acid, as shown above, is absurd since acetic acid cannot exist in a smaller molecular magnitude than it does in water. It is apparent, therefore, that the resemblance between Freundlich's adsorption equation and Henry's law of partition of a solute between two immiscible solvents is accidental.

Freundlich found the sorptions by charcoal of the solutes which he worked with to be reversible, submitting the following typical data as evidence therefor:

	C, moles
Experiment	per liter

1 g. charcoal shaken 20.5 hr. with 100 cc. of 0.0688 M aqueous
solution acetic acid.................................... 0.06078

1 g. charcoal shaken with 50 cc. of 0.1376 M acetic acid solution
for 21 hr., then diluted with 50 cc. water and shaken 3 hr.... 0.06064

1 g. charcoal shaken with 100 cc. of 0.1321 M solution of benzoic
acid in benzene.. 0.1177

1 g. charcoal shaken with 50 cc. of 0.2642 M solution of benzoic
acid in benzene, after 2 hr. diluted with 50 cc. benzene and
shaken again... 0.1179

While this finding by Freundlich applied to the charcoals
used by him, we now know that charcoals "purified" in a certain
manner irreversibly sorb solutes at very low concentrations.
This will be discussed later. It is also obvious that the Freundlich equation cannot hold over a wide range of concentration
because, as one would suspect, the sorbing surface finally becomes
saturated.

Since there is a limiting maximal amount of sorbate that can
be sorbed, the curve should flatten out and finally become
parallel to the C-axis. Schmidt,[14] assuming that the amount of
sorption would depend upon the free unsaturated surface of the
sorbent, suggested the relation

$$\frac{dx}{dC} = K(S - x) \tag{12}$$

where x = sorbed amount, C = concentration, S = limiting
value of x or the saturation limit, and K is a constant. Upon
integration,

$$\ln \frac{S}{S - x} = KC \tag{13}$$

This equation did not hold because K was found to be a function of x. Then assuming that with increase of the amounts
sorbed, the activity decreases proportionately, he postulated:

$$\frac{dx}{dC} = K_0(S - x)^{e^{-Ax}} \tag{14}$$

which integrates to

$$\ln \frac{S}{S - x} - Ax = KC \tag{15}$$

But this was found to be only an approximation which fails for small amounts of sorbent. Then after taking cognizance of all these effects he developed the general formula

$$\frac{a - x}{v} S = K e^{\frac{A(S-x)}{S}} x \qquad (16)$$

where a = mass of solute originally present.

x = amount sorbed from the volume v.

Hence

$\dfrac{a - x}{v}$ = final concentration.

S = limiting value of x.

A, K are constants.

Arrhenius[15] proposed the formula

$$k \frac{dx}{dc} = \frac{S - x}{x^n} \qquad (17)$$

which, when $n = 1$, integrates to

$$\log \frac{S}{S - x} - 0.4343 \frac{x}{S} = \frac{c}{K} \qquad (18)$$

Evidently this is only a special case of the earlier Schmidt formula where $0.4343/S$ appears instead of A.*

Negative Sorption.—The experimental technique of sorption measurement consists in setting up a series of equal volumes of solution of differing and measured concentration C_o. Then equal masses of the sorbent are placed in each solution and the systems are agitated until equilibrium is reached. After the sorbent has settled out, portions of the supernatant solution are analyzed to determine the equilibrium concentration C_e. The amount of solute sorbed in each case is then taken to be $C_o - C_e$. Obviously, this yields the true value for the sorbed amount provided none of the solvent is sorbed. In certain cases the solvent is actually sorbed to a greater extent than the solute with the result that the equilibrium solution is more concentrated than the original. Thus $C_o - C_e$ becomes a negative number and hence the origin of the term *negative sorption*. A

---

* A review of a wide variety of proposed sorption formulas is available in the paper by Swan and Urquhart.[16]

negative sorption may be expected from rather concentrated solutions. The type of curve[17] obtainable is shown in Fig. 81. Obviously, the technique employed in such sorption experiments actually measures only a change in concentration in the liquid phase.

The results of an experiment[18] which shows the difference between the actual amounts of chromium removed from aqueous solutions of basic chromic sulfate by hide powder and the amounts calculated by means of $C_o - C_e$ are plotted in Fig. 82. The amounts of chromium actually fixed by the hide powder could be measured on account of its irreversibility.

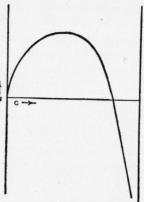

Fig. 81.—Negative sorption.

Hence, after the sorption, the chromium-tanned piece of skin could be washed free of adhering solution and analyzed for the

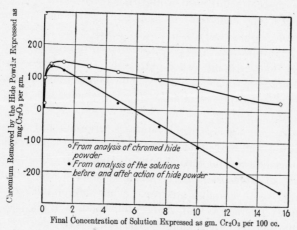

Fig. 82.—Removal of chromium compounds from basic chromic sulfate solutions by cowhide powder.

chromium and protein contents. Here the usual sorption technique yielded absurd results because of the tendency of the hide protein to sorb increasing amounts of water from increasingly concentrated solutions of the basic chromic sulfate.

Discontinuities in Sorption Isotherms.—Until recently it has been customary to regard the relationship between the sorbed amounts and the equilibrium concentrations as a uniformly varying one. Consequently, smooth curves have always been drawn through the experimentally measured points. Discontinuities in sorption curves, however, constitute one of the latest discoveries. These discoveries were made at the University of London where Professor Allmand and his colleagues have shown discontinuities in the sorption of several vapors at low pressures by charcoals and by silica gel.[19] Benton and White[20] have found similar effects in the sorption of hydrogen and nitrogen on nickel, copper, and iron, while Burrage[21] has shown discontinuities in the sorption of water by charcoal. This phenomenon is not restricted to the sorption of gases and vapors since Chaplin[22] has shown that it is also obtained in the sorption of phenol from aqueous solution by a commercial charcoal.

Sorptive Carbons.—Before proceeding farther with the subject of sorption from solution it would be well to pause and examine the nature of charcoals or sorptive "carbons." Charcoals made from bones and from woody matter are of tremendous commercial importance. They are used to remove objectionable coloring matters and other impurities from liquid systems. Their action is rather complex, not being limited to simple surface or adsorptive action, however, owing to their very heterogeneous nature.

Bone charcoal necessarily contains a large amount of calcium, phosphate, iron, and other inorganic matter present in bones, as well as organic matter incompletely carbonized. Likewise blood charcoal, so often used for the establishment of the "adsorption equation," is a complex mixture. Charcoals made from vegetable matter, such as nut shells and wood, like the ash of all vegetable matter, are alkaline. Certain wood charcoals render distilled water strongly alkaline. Thus all sorts of chemical reactions are to be expected when such heterogeneous mixtures are put into solutions.

Attention was called to this[23] in 1919 by the effect of charcoal upon solutions of acid and basic dyes. The addition of sufficient charcoal to decolorize a basic dye solution left the anion of the dye salt in solution. The solution was not acid; hence a "hydrolytic adsorption" had not taken place. Analysis revealed the presence of calcium ions which had come from the charcoal. Thus a simple double-decomposition reaction was demonstrated. A similar effect was found with an acid dye, the cation of which remained in solution balanced by chloride ion which came from the charcoal.

One naturally turns to a method of purification, such as digestion with acid in order to remove the extraneous inorganic matter. Odén[24] extracted blood charcoal repeatedly with dilute hydrochloric acid, washed repeatedly with hot water, and finally dried the charcoal at 125°C. He found that such charcoal had a marked sorptive action upon potassium hydroxide solutions. It sorbed neutral salts also, although to a much less extent.

Judged by the experiments made by Bartell and Miller[25,26,27] Odén's acid extracted charcoal was not pure but held a firmly bound film of hydrogen chloride. Such a charcoal does not sorb alkali; its sorbed film of hydrogen chloride is removed and the neutralization accounts for the apparent sorption of alkali. Bartell and Miller prepared the purest form of sugar charcoal hitherto known by charring recrystallized sucrose, followed by heating about 48 hr. at about 1000°C., in silica vessels with access to a small amount of air. The resulting product had a soft velvety-black appearance* in contrast to the hard gray cokelike appearance of the material prior to the *activation, i.e.,* the 48 hr. treatment at 1000°C. with access to a little air. The ash content was 0.01 per cent. This *activated* sugar charcoal sorbed acids but not bases. In fact, it produced negative sorptions from solutions of alkalies.

Such activated charcoal appears to sorb acids irreversibly from very dilute solutions. For example, Miller[27] found that when 2.3 g. activated charcoal (which had sorbed 0.294 millimole of hydrochloric acid) was suspended in 200 cc. of conductivity water, the aqueous phase remained strictly neutral in reaction. Upon 15 extractions each with 200 cc. of boiling water, a total of 0.15 millimole of hydrochloric acid was recovered from the charcoal. Charcoal containing such sorbed acid has no hydrolytic action on sucrose.[28]

* The presence of graphite has been demonstrated by X-ray spectra.[32]

These investigators found that blood charcoal and Norite charcoal, when purified, acted like the activated sugar charcoal. The purification involved first several digestions with hydrofluoric acid, then with hydrochloric acid solutions, followed by washing with water and drying, when the 48-hr. heat treatment was applied.

Next we learn that activated charcoals, like those just discussed, sorb acids on account of the oxygen film held on their surface.[29,30,31] When such activated charcoal is heated for several hours *in vacuo* at 1000°, its sorptive affinity for hydrochloric acid is diminished. Upon exposure to air after the evacuation, the sorptive affinity for hydrochloric acid returns.

Frumkin[30] has demonstrated that ash-free sugar charcoal activated at 1000° in carbon dioxide followed by thorough evacuation has no effect upon solutions either of hydrochloric acid or of sodium hydroxide. When the activation is carried out in an atmosphere of hydrogen, it does not sorb hydrochloric acid but does sorb sodium hydroxide, provided contact with oxygen is prevented. Such charcoal, upon exposure to air, assumes the properties of an oxygen-activated charcoal. On the other hand, exposure to hydrogen does not influence an oxygen-activated carbon. Frumkin postulates that the activated charcoals act as gas electrodes when placed in water, the oxygen-activated charcoal sending hydroxyl ions into the water at the carbon-water interface and the hydrogen-activated charcoal sending hydrogen ions into the aqueous side of the interface. He found that small amounts of platinum in the charcoal enhanced the activity of the hydrogen-activated product and it has been found[31] that the volume of hydrogen gas taken up by the platinized charcoal is proportional to the hydrogen ion activity of the surrounding solution.

Hydrolytic Sorption.—Neutral solutions of electrolytes become acid or alkaline after contact with certain sorbents. It has been customary to call this *hydrolytic adsorption*, because it was believed that OH^- or H^+ was preferentially sorbed. Many of the so-called hydrolytic sorptions reported in the literature have been shown to be mere displacements from the sorbent of bound acid or alkali by the neutral electrolyte solution.[14,24] This is another example of the confusion in the literature of colloid chemistry resulting from so many publications upon experimentation with inadequately defined systems and upon substances whose purity is neither established nor investigated.

Bartell and Miller[25,26] have demonstrated that their oxygen-activated sugar charcoal sorbs hydrolytically from dilute neutral salt solutions, always rendering these solutions alkaline. Inasmuch as their charcoal irreversibly sorbs a certain amount of acid from dilute aqueous solutions of acids (but never alkali), its above-mentioned behavior is readily understood. By analogy, one would expect that Frumkin's[30] hydrogen-activated charcoal would, in the absence of oxygen, sorb base hydrolytically from neutral salt solutions.

Inasmuch as charcoals have a greater sorptive affinity for organic than for inorganic compounds, marked hydrolytic sorption is encountered with solutions of electrolytes where one ion is organic and the other is inorganic.

Effect of Solvent upon Charcoal Sorption.—Freundlich[10] called attention to the different degrees of sorption of a given solute from different solvents (Table 51) and looked unavailingly

TABLE 51.—INFLUENCE OF SOLVENT UPON SORPTION[10]

Solvent	Sorbate	a^*
Water	Benzoic acid	3.27
Benzene	Benzoic acid	0.54
Ethyl ether	Benzoic acid	0.30
Acetone	Benzoic acid	0.30
Water	Picric acid	1.31
Ethyl alcohol	Picric acid	0.77
Benzene	Picric acid	0.49
Water	Bromin	4.73
Concentrated H_2SO_4	Bromin	2.48
Ethyl ether	Bromin	1.36

* a = millimoles sorbed per gram blood charcoal when the equilibrium concentration = 0.01 mole per liter.

for an explanation based upon surface tension. Using acid extracted blood charcoal, Lundelius[33] showed a quantitative relationship between the sorption of iodin from carbon tetrachloride, chloroform, and carbon bisulfide and the solubility of iodin in these liquids. The ratios of the equilibrium concentrations were $C(\text{in } CS_2) : C(\text{in } CHCl_3) : C(\text{in } CCl_4) = 4.5 : 2 : 1$. These values are close to the ratios of the solubility of iodin in these liquids.

Gurvitsch[34] found an inverse qualitative relationship between heat of wetting of the solvent and the sorption of benzoic acid, as shown in Table 52. The inference gained from this work is

TABLE 52.—INFLUENCE OF SOLVENT UPON SORPTION OF BENZOIC ACID[34]
Sorption by 10 g. sorbent from 100 cc. of 1 volume per cent benzoic acid solution

| Solvent | Sorbent | | | |
| | Charcoal | | Floridin earth | |
	$a*$	H.W.†	a	H.W.
Acetone..........................	0.99	19.3	0.00	27.3
Ethyl acetate.....................	1.02	16.5	0.22	18.5
Chloroform.......................	5.19	14.0	3.50	8.4
Benzene..........................	6.04	11.1	3.64	5.6
Carbon tetrachloride.............	7.20	8.4	3.95	4.6
Carbon bisulfide.................	5.02	13.9	3.94	4.2
Benzin (80 to 82°)...............	7.11	9.5	4.01	4.2

* a = amount of benzoic acid sorbed in percentage of the weight of the sorbent.
† H.W. = heat of wetting of 1 g. of sorbent in calories by an excess of the liquid.

that liquids showing high heats of wetting are highly sorbed and thus hinder the sorption of the solute. He found[34] that a sorbate could best be extracted from a sorbent by a liquid possessing high heat of wetting; and if the sorbate were but slightly soluble in this liquid, the extraction could be effected by using a mixture of the high heat of wetting liquid and one in which the sorbate was readily soluble.

Heymann and Boye,[35] using highly purified beechwood charcoal, have investigated the degrees of sorption of formic, acetic, butyric, benzoic, and picric acids and of iodin from a wide variety of solvents in the search for a relationship between sorptive affinity for the solute and dipole moment (and molecular polarization) of the solvent. While from certain liquids of weak dipole moment and low molecular polarization the sorption was very much higher than from liquids of the opposite type, there were inconsistencies which showed that a general rule could not be formulated. They concluded that specific chemical properties overcome the purely physical properties in certain instances. Hence they decided to use a series of chemically similar liquids and chose the alcohols with the results set down in Table 53.

TABLE 53.—INFLUENCE OF MOLECULAR POLARIZATION OF SOLVENT UPON SORPTION[35]

Sorption (1) from 25 cc. 0.01 N benzoic acid by 2 g. charcoal; (2) from 25 cc. 0.033 N picric acid by 1 g. charcoal

Solvent	Percentage sorption		Molecular polarization	Molecular refraction
	Benzoic acid	Picric acid		
Methyl alcohol.........	82	98	36.8	8.1
Ethyl alcohol...........	72	91	39.8	10.3
Propyl alcohol..........	66	75	65.1	16.9
Isobutyl alcohol........	62	64	78.4	27.5
Isoamyl alcohol........	55	50	90.6	31.4
Sec. octyl alcohol.......	..	41	....	40.4

The alcohols have nearly the same dipole moment but progressively different deformability, as shown by their molecular polarization. The results show diminishing sorption with increasing molecular polarization. This has been true also for the sorption of tetraethyl ammonium iodide from water and from ethyl and methyl alcohols, where the sorption is greatest from water and least from ethyl alcohol.[36]

Rather extensive experimentation upon sorption of fatty acids in the homologous series from formic to stearic by unpurified blood charcoal has been made with a wide variety of solvents.[37] When the sorbed amounts of the fatty acids were charted against their numbers of carbon atoms, as done in Fig. 83, the solvents could be put in two groups. From those containing oxygen—alcohols, acetone, and ether—the sorption sharply dropped from formic to valeric, followed by a sharp rise. From the other solvents—benzene, toluene, chloroform, carbon tetrachloride, and carbon bisulfide—the amounts of fatty acid sorbed, dropped very gradually with increasing molecular weight. The crossing of the lines for fatty acids of eight and more carbon atoms in Fig. 83 demonstrates the difficulty or impossibility of generalizing.

Experimental studies of sorption from mixtures of solvents[35,37,38] have produced very complicated pictures. It is impossible to generalize about them, except, perhaps, for the sorption of benzoic and picric acids from mixtures of two nonpolar solvents[35] the amount sorbed was a straight-line function of the composition of the binary solvent.

The Lundelius rule, once thought quite general, is now known also to be a qualitative relationship[39] to which there are excep-

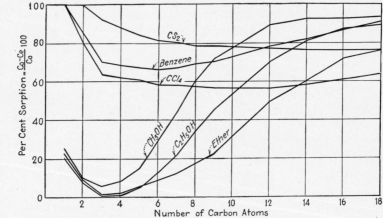

Fig. 83.—Sorption of fatty acids from different solvents by blood charcoal.

tions.[35,40] However, fair guesses may be made, as a result of the experimentation cited; a solute will be apt to be weakly sorbed from solvents in which it is very soluble, from solvents which wet the sorbent with high energy, and from solvents possessing weak dipole moments.

The difference in degree of sorption from different solvents may be used advantageously in the recovery of various substances from solutions. A dilute solution of a dye, like crystal violet, can be readily and completely decolorized by charcoal. If the charcoal is then placed in alcohol, from which crystal violet is sorbed less than from water, the surface concentration of the dye in the charcoal is in excess of that which will establish equilibrium, and consequently a large amount of it goes into solution in the alcohol. Similarly a dilute aqueous solution of an alkaloid may be concentrated. The aqueous solution of the alkaloid salt is treated with commercial charcoal and made slightly alkaline to liberate the free alkaloid base which is strongly sorbed. The charcoal is removed and treated with some organic solvent which extracts a large part of the alkaloid from the charcoal.

Relative Sorptive Affinities of Charcoals.—Researches upon the relative sorptions of different compounds by charcoal have provided useful information, especially for the organic chemist. Experimental data on the sorption of various acids[25] from aqueous solution by oxygen-activated sugar charcoal are tabulated in Table 54. This table shows the following general effects:

1. Sorption of organic acids was greater than the sorption of inorganic acids.

2. Sorption of aromatic acids was greater than the sorption of aliphatic acids.

3. Substituents such as —OH and —NH_2 lowered the sorptive affinity.

TABLE 54.—SORPTION OF ACIDS FROM 100 CC. 0.01 N AQUEOUS SOLUTION BY 0.25 g. OXYGEN-ACTIVATED SUGAR CHARCOAL

Acid	Percentage Sorbed
Benzoic	75.8
Salicylic	73.8
Anthranilic	67.0
Succinic	48.0
Malic	35.9
Tartaric	31.8
Aspartic	8.8
Formic	15.7
Acetic	16.4
Propionic	24.4
Butyric	35.5
Lactic	17.9
Aminoacetic	0.0
Hydrochloric	11.2
Perchloric	10.9
Nitric	10.1
Sulfuric	9.7
Hydrobromic	8.5

Tables 55 and 56 contain data on the sorption of organic acids from alcoholic solution.[41] The charcoal was commercial "animal

TABLE 55.—RELATIVE SORPTION OF ORGANIC ACIDS BY CHARCOAL[41]
(50 cc. 0.05 N alcoholic solutions and 5 g. charcoal)

Acid	Relative sorption	Acid	Relative sorption
Acetic	1.00	Lactic	0.58
Propionic	0.65	Phenylacetic	3.26
Butyric	0.87	Phenylpropionic	4.04
Isobutyric	0.27	Cinnamic	6.25
Isovaleric	0.21	Mandelic	2.29
Hexoic	1.13	Succinic	1.44
Heptoic	0.92	Adipic	1.05
Octoic	1.50	Sebacic	2.30
Nonoic	1.32	Monobromsuccinic	1.77
Lauric	2.15	Ethyl succinic	0.85
Stearic	2.32	Malic	1.22
Monochloracetic	2.31	Tartaric	1.60
Trichloracetic	0.27	Fumaric	4.15
Monobromacetic	2.70	Citraconic	5.54
α-Brompropionic	1.92	Mesaconic	3.41
α-Bromisobutyric	1.38		

TABLE 56.—RELATIVE SORPTION OF AROMATIC ACIDS BY CHARCOAL[41]
(50 cc. 0.05 N alcoholic solutions and 5 g. charcoal)

Acid	Relative sorption	Acid	Relative sorption
Benzoic	1.00*	p-Nitrobenzoic	3.64
o-Toluic	0.97	o-Chlorbenzoic	0.86
m-Toluic	1.19	Salicylic	1.64
p-Toluic	1.36	o-Acetoxybenzoic	0.75
o-Brombenzoic	1.01	p-Methoxybenzoic	2.30
m-Brombenzoic	2.10	Phthalic	2.30
p-Brombenzoic	2.42	o-Aminobenzoic	2.91
o-Nitrobenzoic	1.34	o-Acetamidobenzoic	2.30
m-Nitrobenzoic	3.32	s-Tribrombenzoic	2.51

* The relative sorption of benzoic acid, in terms of acetic = 1, was approximately 5.5.

charcoal, acid-free," which the experimenters extracted with hot water until no longer alkaline to phenolphthalein and "heated

to redness for some hours in a Vitreosil tube, a steady stream of
dry nitrogen being passed through towards the end of the operation and continued until the tube was cold."

In tracing the effects of the substituents in Table 55, it is
seen that small alkyl groups and the hydroxyl group reduce sorption, while halogen (except in trichloracetic acid) and phenyl
groups increase it.   Unsaturation causes a marked increase in
sorption.   From Table 56 it may be said generally that the
relative sorption of the aromatic acids is five to twenty times
that of the aliphatic acids.   Substituents in the para position
increase the relative sorption, the effect of the groups being in
the order alkyl, halogen, nitro; in the meta position there is a
corresponding but smaller enhancement; and ortho substitution
has usually a smaller or even a depressing effect.   The enhancement attributable to *o*-hydroxy and *o*-amino groups was reduced
by acetylation.

It is to be noted that what has just been said applies to ethyl
alcohol solutions.   All of these relative effects may not hold in
aqueous solution.   For example, double bonds cause a marked
increase in sorption from alcoholic solution, a fact which has
been found by another investigator[42] using similar charcoal.
But this investigator found that double bonds decrease sorption
from aqueous solution.

Fumaric acid is sorbed to a greater extent than maleic acid
at pH values less than 5 from water by oxygen-activated sugar
charcoal.[43]   This may be accepted as verified since other investigators using different charcoal have found the same result.[42]
The same order is true for methyl alcohol solutions but reversed
in ethyl alcohol.[42]   The trans isomer of hydrobenzoin has been
found to be sorbed more than the cis isomer.[44]

The sorption of organic acids and of organic bases has been
studied as a function of the pH of the solution by Phelps.[45,46]
Using Norite charcoal, extracted with hydrochloric acid and
hydrofluoric acid, washed with hot water and ignited to bright
red heat *in vacuo* (ash = 0.07 per cent), he obtained the result
shown in Fig. 84.   The same relationship was found when using
charcoal prepared from "ashless" filter paper by activating the
charcoal at 1200°C. for ½ hr. in a silica vessel, digesting with
the acids, washed, etc., just like the Norite.

The proportion of propionic acid sorbed falls off almost to zero between pH 3.5 and 5.5. This region covers almost exactly the ionization range for this acid. The same is true for succinic acid, in the range pH 4 to 7. In the case of caproic acid, a similar effect was noted, the sudden drop in sorption being between pH 4.8 and 7.5. Hence Phelps held that only the undissociated acid is sorbed, in confirmation of Fromageot and Wurmser.[47] Using the charcoal made from filter paper (without the acid extraction), he found the same principle to hold for butylamine and propyl-

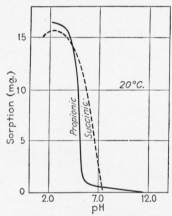

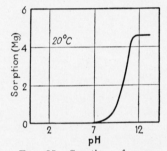

Fig. 84.—Sorption of acids from 20 cc. of solution by 0.2 g. charcoal. $C_o = 1.8$ mg. per cubic centimeter for propionic and 1.3 mg. per cubic centimeter for succinic acid.

Fig. 85.—Sorption of n-propylamine from 20 cc. of 0.2 per cent solution by 0.2 g. charcoal.

amine (Fig. 85). The acid-purified and activated Norite did not yield so close a relation to the ionization curve, owing probably to a trace of sorbed acid. Information concerning the sorption of organic bases furnished by another investigator[48] may well be mentioned here. Using sugar charcoal, heated in a silica crucible with a loose cover over a gas burner for 20 hr., followed by heating in an open porcelain tube at 1000°C. for 20 hr., he obtained a charcoal which would not sorb strong inorganic bases. The sorption order for weak bases was dimethylaniline > aniline > secondary aliphatic amines > propylamine > ammonia. While coniine, arecoline and nicotine were markedly sorbed; codeine, morphine, quinine, brucine, cytisine, methyl cytisine, hydrastinine, pelleterine, and pseudopelleterine were not sorbed.

Phelps found that the amino acids glycine and alanine were not sorbed at any pH value. The dicarboxylic amino acids aspartic and glutamic were only slightly sorbed with a tendency to a minimum at pH 5. A ring-structured amino acid, histidine, was sorbed as shown in Fig. 86 which shows also the curve for the base histamine. It is seen that the sorption rises steeply for both with increasing alkalinity, while that for the amino acid shows an abrupt fall, starting at pH = 7.3.

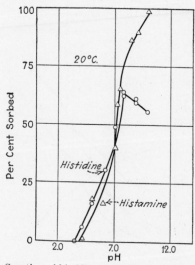

Fig. 86.—Sorption of histidine and of histamine by charcoal.

Based upon the older experience with unpurified charcoals, there is rather widely stated in the literature of colloid chemistry "Traube's rule," *viz.*, that when the sorptions of the members of an homologous series from aqueous solutions are compared, the sorptions increase with increasing molecular weight. If they lower the charcoal-water interfacial tension in the same order as they lower the air-water interfacial tension, then this sorptive order can be accounted for by means of Gibbs's law. In recent years, however, owing to experimentation with "purified" charcoals, the validity of this rule has been questioned. Figure 87 offers an illustration taken from the work of Nekrasov.[49] Here we see Traube's rule holding for four specimens of charcoal, while it is reversed for charcoal V. These charcoals were described as follows:

I = blood charcoal. Ash content, 7.2 per cent.

II = I purified by the method of Dubinin. Ash content, 6.4 per cent.

III = gas-mask wood charcoal. Ash, 4.2 per cent.

IV = III purified by same method as II. Ash, 1.4 per cent.

V = activated sugar charcoal (Dubinin). Ash, 0.08 per cent.

The sorptions by the same charcoals from alcoholic solutions are charted in Fig. 88. Here again, charcoal V, the activated

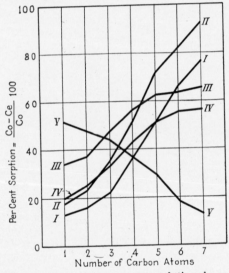

Fig. 87.—Sorption of fatty acids from aqueous solutions by various charcoals.

sugar charcoal shows a reversal of Traube's rule, while the others give a "mixed series," *i.e.*, from formic to propionic or butyric acid the sorption diminishes with increasing molecular weight and from butyric to stearic it increases with increasing molecular weight.

Likewise the strong acids have been reported on an equivalent basis to be sorbed in the order $H_3PO_4 > H_2SO_4 > HCl$. This order also has been found to be reversed.

Dubinin,[50] who has concerned himself with these orders and their reversals, has found that sugar charcoal activated by heating at 550°C. sorbed the aliphatic acids in the order propionic > valeric > heptylic and the strong acids HCl > H_2SO_4 > H_3PO_4. When the same sample of original sugar charcoal was activated at 800°C., both sorptive orders were reversed. He prepared an extensive number of charcoals activated with oxygen, with carbon dioxide, with and without evacuation, heating at different temperatures for various lengths of time and with different rates of gas flow. His experiments with these charcoals produced

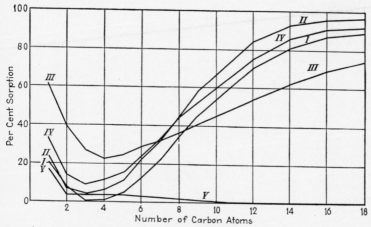

FIG. 88.—Sorption of fatty acids from ethyl alcohol solutions by various charcoals.

normal Traube series, also reversed and "mixed" series. Summarizing his experience in these complex experiments, he stated that the less highly activated charcoals possess very fine ultrapores, while the more highly activated charcoals possess larger pores. Hence since the smaller sorbate molecules can penetrate the ultrapores which are too small for the larger sorbate molecules, a reason for the reversal of the Traube rule becomes apparent. He points out further that finer pores in the charcoal introduce a time factor which has not been appreciated. In Table 57 are described five charcoals and their sorptive effects are given in Table 58.[51] It is seen that the sorptive order for the finer pored charcoals (A and B), where sorption is slow, is propionic > valeric > heptylic acid, although the relative values after 31 days sorption are less different from one another than

TABLE 57.—DESCRIPTION OF ACTIVATING TREATMENTS (SUGAR CHARCOAL)[51]

Activating gas	Grams charcoal used	Temperature, °C.	Time, hours	Volume of gas per hour	Final yield of charcoal, per cent	Designation of charcoal*
Air..........	10	850	4	0.82	92.5	B
Air..........	10	850	8	1.03	86.2	C
CO₂..........	10	1000	8	3.54	54.8	D
Air..........	4	500	4	1.93	83.0	E†

* Charcoal A consisted of sugar charcoal merely pulverized and heated *in vacuo* at 850°.
† Charcoal E was made from D.

TABLE 58.—RESULTS* OBTAINED WITH CHARCOALS DESCRIBED IN TABLE 57

Acid	Percentage sorbed by charcoal				
	A	B	C	D	E
Propionic:					
1 hr.......................	4	10	32	52	29
1 day......................	7	24	43	52	31
31 days....................	15	29	47	55	†
Valeric:					
1 hr.......................	1	4	26	86	68
1 day......................	2	9	44	86	69
31 days....................	5	..	58	88	†
Heptylic:					
1 hr.......................	0.8	3	18	98	94
1 day......................	2	4	30	99	94
31 days....................	5	11	45	98	†

* Technique: 25 cc. of 0.01 N aqueous solution, 0.1 g. charcoal.
† Measured at 5 days and found practically same as at 1 day.

those measured after 1 hr. sorption. On the other hand, the larger pored charcoals (D and E), where the sorption equilibrium is fast, give the order heptylic > valeric > propionic, while charcoal C gives a "mixed series." A similar result was obtained in the sorption of hydrochloric acid, sulfuric acid, and phosphoric acids. Dubinin's idea is shared by other investigators.[52] Bruns[53] showed that, excluding formic acid, an activated sugar charcoal which showed reversal of Traube's rule gave the normal series after grinding.

Incidentally, it is obvious that there is no answer to the question, How long does it take for sorptive equilibrium with charcoal? It may be mentioned in passing, though, that with crystals as sorbents equilibrium is practically instantaneous, provided the system is stirred with great rapidity.[54]

The sorption order for the urethanes[55] by charcoal has been reported isobutyl > propyl > ethyl > methyl.

Studies on the relative sorptions of inorganic salts from water by Odén[56] have produced the following information (acid extracted blood charcoal):[24]

Alkaline-earth nitrates: $Ba^{++} > Sr^{++} > Ca^{++} > Mg^{++}$

Alkali nitrates: $Cs^+ > NH_4^+ > Rb^+ > K^+ > Na^+ > Li^+$

Potassium salts at 0.01 M concentration: $I^- > CrO_4^= > CNS^- > Fe(CN)_6^{4-} > Br^- > ClO_3^- > NO_3^- > SO_4^= > Cl^- > F^-$.

Potassium salts at 0.2 M concentration: $CNS^- > I^- > ClO_3^- > NO_3^- > CrO_4^= > Br^- > Cl^- > Fe(CN)_6^{4-} > F^- > SO_4^=$.

It should be recalled that the above-mentioned charcoal sorbed alkali strongly, owing to the presence of the tenaciously sorbed hydrochloric acid. The order $I^- > Br^- > Cl^-$ has been confirmed[57,58] by use of blood charcoal and of Dubinin's activated sugar charcoal.[59] The sorption of the alkaline-earth cations by the activated sugar charcoal was ascribed[57] to precipitation of their carbonates in the pores of the charcoal owing to carbon dioxide present there. Other investigators,[60] also using acid washed charcoal, do not confirm Odén's order for the alkali cations, finding $Li^+ > Na^+$.

Ammino complexes of copper and of cobalt are decomposed by activated charcoal, splitting off NH_3 molecules.[61] The platinichlorides likewise are split upon sorption.[62]

Sorptions from Mixtures.—If a given charcoal sorbs A to a greater extent than B from their individual solutions at equal concentration, one would expect that A would be sorbed to a greater extent than B from their mixed solution. Likewise one would expect the addition of A to the system charcoal-solution-B to effect a marked displacement of some sorbed B from the charcoal into the liquid phase. Conversely, B should displace some sorbed A, but to a much less extent. This has been found experimentally for several mixtures. In the older literature[63] one finds that fatty alcohols, acetone, and surface-active substances in general diminish the sorption of iodin, of inorganic electrolytes, etc. Further it was shown that the effectiveness of the alcohols was in the order amyl > propyl > ethyl > methyl.

The reverse, *i.e.*, the effect of salts upon surface-active substances, is an exception to the general rule. The addition of inorganic salts to solutions of acetic, propionic, and butyric acids, acetone, and alcohol has been found to effect an increase in the sorption of these by charcoal.[64] In comparing the effects of alkali and alkaline-earth chlorides, the sorption-promoting influence was in inverse ratio to their atomic weights; *i.e.*, the higher the atomic weight of the cation, the lower was the sorption increment. The air-water interfacial tension is lowered in proportion to the sorption increment. Thus the added inorganic electrolyte increased the activity of the surface-active substance in solution.

The sorption of dextrose from aqueous solution by blood charcoal is not influenced by even 2 M concentration of sodium chloride, but neither does this salt markedly affect the surface tension of a solution of the surface-inactive dextrose. The influence of added surface-active substances upon sorption of dextrose, however, is shown in Table 59.

TABLE 59.—DEPRESSION OF SORPTION OF DEXTROSE BY URETHANES[55]
(100 cc. aqueous solution, 3 g. blood charcoal. In each case the original solution was 0.07 M with regard to the urethane and 0.90 per cent with respect to dextrose)

Added urethane	Percentage sorbed	
	Urethane	Dextrose
None............................	..	38
Methylurethane..................	57	26
Ethylurethane...................	72	20
Propylurethane..................	87	8
Butylurethane...................	94	2

In using modern purified charcoal, it has been shown that added phenol diminishes the sorption of hydriodic acid from water, and that added amyl alcohol inhibits somewhat the sorption of phenol.[48]

A study of the sorption from the following mixtures has afforded a quantitative relationship:[65] $HCl-H_2C_2O_4$, $HNO_3-H_2-C_2O_4$, $HBr-HNO_3$, $HCl-HNO_3$, HCl-acetone, CH_3COOH-acetone. The first substance was kept at constant concentration, with the second at varying concentration. Typical results are plotted in Fig. 89. The sorbent was sugar charcoal which had been heated with $4N$ nitric acid for several hours, carefully washed with water, dried, heated at $850°C$. *in vacuo*, washed again with water, and reheated at $850°C$. *in vacuo*. Wood charcoal, purified in the same manner, gave similar results. In Fig. 89, it

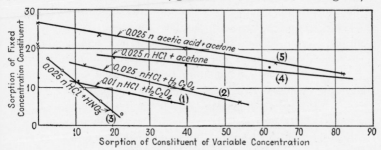

Fig. 89.—Sorption from mixtures; 1 g. charcoal in 25-cc. solution. Ordinates and abscissas = milliequivalents when multiplied by 2×10^{-2}.

is seen that a straight line is obtained when the sorbed amounts of the fixed-concentration substance are plotted against the sorbed amounts of the variable-concentration substance. Hence

$$\frac{-y}{x} = k$$

or

$$y = b - kx \tag{19}$$

where y = amount of constituent A sorbed in the presence of constituent B.

b = amount of constituent A sorbed from solution in the absence of constituent B.

x = amount of constituent B sorbed from solution in the absence of constituent A.

When, of course, chemical interaction intervenes, the prediction of relative sorptive affinities cannot be based upon simple rules. For example, mercuric chloride is strongly sorbed by charcoals, but its sorption from mixtures containing alkali chlorides is diminished. This has been ascribed[66] to the formation of compounds such as $NaHgCl_3$ or Na_2HgCl_4. The toxicity of mercuric chloride is also decreased by the presence of sodium chloride.

Inorganic Sorbents.—Earths, clays, zeolites, and oxides have wide use industrially. Earths are extensively used with charcoals in the decolorizing of oils. The zeolites ("Permutit") are employed in water softening, the action consisting in an equivalent replacement of sodium ion in the zeolite by calcium in the water.[67] "Silica gel," a dried silicic acid, is extensively employed for sorption of liquids and vapors.[68]

The sorption of ionizable substances by mineral sorbents is traceable in most cases to simple chemical reactions. For example, commercial silica (which does not sorb acid dyes) sorbs basic dyes by formation of dye-cation silicate on the surface, a cation such as iron or calcium being released. Ferric oxide containing occluded ferric salt (which does not sorb basic dyes) sorbs an acid dye by formation of a ferric dye-anion complex on the surface.[69,70] Quartz surfaces which are inert may be sorptively activated by a brief bath in hydrofluoric acid, or treatment with fused potassium hydroxide at 350° for a few minutes, followed by boiling in hydrochloric acid.[71]

Kaolin (a hydrous aluminum silicate) sorbs basic dye cations but not acid dye anions.[70] Here again the formation of dye-silicate has been noted. Kaolins are excellent sorbents for alkaloids; the specially prepared hydrous aluminum silicate known as *Lloyd's reagent*[72] is very active.

The pH value of the solution markedly affects the degree of sorption of an alkaloid by kaolin. In the case of quinine the optimum value was at pH 6 to 7, the sorption falling off somewhat in more acid solutions, but falling abruptly to zero at pH 8 to 9.[73]

In Table 60, the sorption[74] of some acidic and basic substances by some inorganic sorbents shows interesting chemical relationships. Sorption by alumina is most marked in the case of the acidic compounds, though the most basic substance—piperidine—is also sorbed appreciably. These results are not unexpected in view of the well-known amphoteric character of alumina. Although the hydrous iron oxide used was apparently an excellent sorbent, the sorption was very irregular, being strongest in the

TABLE 60.—SORPTION BY INORGANIC SORBENTS[74]
(25 cc. of 0.01 M aqueous solutions, 0.5 g. sorbent)

Substance	pH	By silica, per cent	By alumina, per cent	By iron oxide, per cent	By fuller's earth, per cent
Piperidine	11.46	94.5	5.7	25.2	73.8
Nicotine	10.6	87.3	1.5	2.2	43.7
Arginine	9.5	72.5	1.2	34.2	31
Quinoline	8.6	47	2	1	71.2
Adenine	8.4	10.6	2	60	21.2
Caffein	7.8	11.2	0.5	0	87
Creatine	7.2	4.7	1.3	3	7.4
Betaine	7.5	5.5	0	0	5.1
Acetanilid	7.2	2.4	1.8	12.3	3.1
Urea	7.1	1.9	2.94	0.3	5
Acetamide	7.1	1.1	3.7	1	5.4
Glucose	7.1	0.7	1.0	11.0	0
Succinimide	6.0	0.7	0.5	0.0	0.5
Glycine	6.1	0.7	3.0	15.9	0
Vicine	6.0	0.7	13.9	20.3	2.4
Asparagine	5.4	0.7	11.0	44.8	0
Glutamic acid	3.2	0.6	74.3	81.6	0
Aspartic acid	3.1	0	84.5	87.5	0

case of acid substances, as might be expected, but also taking place markedly in the case of certain of the neutral and basic compounds. The sorption by fuller's earth parallels very roughly the sorption by silica. One striking exception appears in the case of caffein. Approximately eight times as much of this substance was sorbed by fuller's earth as by silica.

The use of alumina gel by Willstätter in enzyme purifications has excited interest in its properties as influenced by mode of preparation.[75] It sorbs basic and acidic substances because it reacts chemically with them. For example, the sorption of nucleic acid[76] increases with increasing acidity of the solution from almost zero at pH 8. The sorption of phosphate is at a maximum at about pH = 3, falling off on either side thereof.[76] The effectiveness of salts in displacing sorbed malt amylase from alumina gel[77] has been shown by Caldwell and Doebbling to be phosphate > citrate > tartrate > sulfate > oxalate > acetate >

chloride, which is the order for the "penetration" of these ions into the ionic micelle of basic aluminum complexes. The displacement of chromate from alumina gel likewise is effected by powerful penetrating ions but not by halides and nitrates.[78]

The order of sorption of silver salts by silver iodide has been found to be[79] benzoate > acetate > nitrite > bromate > naphthalene sulfonate > nitrate > chlorate > ethyl sulfate > perchlorate. While this order is not exactly the reverse order of the solubilities of the corresponding silver salts, in general the less soluble are sorbed more than the more soluble ones. The sorptive capacity of lead chromate for potassium salts has been indirectly determined to be[80]

$$CrO_4^= > IO_3^- > NO_3^- > I^- > SO_4^= > Cl^-,$$

which, with the exception of the nitrate and iodide, is in the order of the insolubility of the corresponding lead salts in water. The order for the sorption of salts of a given anion was found to be $Pb^{++} > Ba^{++} > Ca^{++} > K^+$.

During its formation, barium sulfate is a good sorbent of ions. Its sorption of the anions of sodium and potassium salts is given in the order:[81] $Cr_2O_7^= > S_2O_3^= > BrO_3^- > AsO_3^{3-} > C_2O_4^= > IO_4^- > IO_3^- > MnO_4^- > NO_2^- > Fe(CN)_6^{4-} > Fe(CN)_6^{3-} > Cl^- > CNS^- > Br^- > I^-$. Tezak[82] states that such occurs in the presence of excess barium ions, his series being $Fe(CN)_6^{4-} > Fe(CN)_6^{3-} > NO_3^- > Cl^- > Br^- > I^-$. He holds that sorption of ions from solutions increases as the sorbed ion resembles more closely an ion of the heteropolar crystal. Thus the Ba^{++} ion resembles xenon, and sorption on barium sulfate follows the series $Ba^{++} > Hg^{++} > Pb^{++} > Ca^{++} > Mn^{++} > Zn^{++} > Cu^{++} > Ni^{++} > Mg^{++}$ which corresponds to the series $Xe > Kr > A > Ne$ in atomic similarity. Miss de Brouckere[83] has published several papers on sorption by barium sulfate. She states that both ions of a salt are sorbed, and that the sorption of iron from dilute ferric chloride is ten to two hundred times that of nonhydrolyzing salts because of the presence of ferric oxy micelles.

The sorption of fatty acids by silica gel from toluene[84] and from carbon tetrachloride gives the reverse of Traube's rule. This is accounted for in the following manner.[84] The highly polar —COOH end of the fatty-acid molecules orients toward the polar silica and the nonpolar alkyl groups orient toward the toluene. Hence since fatty acids of higher molecular weight are less polar, they are more and more attracted to the toluene and less strongly sorbed by the silica. The sorption of formic, acetic, propionic, butyric, and caproic acids from CCl_4, C_6H_6, C_2H_5OH, $(CH_3)_2CO$, and water by metallic gold[85] is also a reverse of Traube's rule, caprylic, myristic, and stearic not being sorbed at all. This also is said to show that the —COOH groups are oriented toward the sorbent—in this case gold.

The sorption of the saturated aliphatic monohydric alcohols from benzene by silica is also in inverse order of the molecular weights.[86]

Silica does not sorb strong acids from water[87] but does sorb alkalies in the order LiOH > NaOH > KOH > NH_4OH. Consequently, hydrolytic sorption is observed when silica is added to neutral salt solutions.

Platinum black which is charged with hydrogen hydrolytically sorbs base and not acid from a neutral salt solution.[88]

The sorption by platinum black from ether and water solutions of organic acids has been investigated.[89] Sorption of the monobasic fatty acids increased with increasing molecular weight. Normal acids were sorbed more than acids with branched chains of carbon atoms. Cis isomers were sorbed better than trans isomers. Double bonds increased sorption. Parallelism of magnitudes of sorptions and velocities of hydrogenation was observed in cis and trans isomers and in isomers forming the same hydrogenation product.

Blue Iodo Complexes.—The blue complex formed upon contact of starch with iodin is called a *sorption complex*. Chemical compound formation is generally believed to be absent. Mylius,[90] in 1887, thought that it was a chemical compound of the formula $(C_{24}H_{40}O_{20}I)_4.HI$. While as yet there is insufficient knowledge concerning starch to settle the arguments—chemical *versus* physical—it is interesting to note that Mylius found hydriodic acid or alkali iodide to be an essential part of the blue complex. He pointed out that, if the blue iodostarch solution is treated with silver acetate to remove the iodide, it becomes yellow in color. This yellow solution, he found, turns dark blue when treated with hydrogen iodide so dilute as 1 part in 1,000,000 of water. Thus it is an exceedingly sensitive reagent for the detection of iodide ion. Mylius found[91] also that cholic acid* yields a blue iodo complex with the formula $(C_{24}H_{40}O_5I)_4KI$. Again iodide ion must be present; in its absence a brown complex is formed.

Bergmann[92] has shown stoichiometric relations in the combination of iodin and potassium iodide with the compounds

$$\left[\begin{array}{c} CH_3C(OCH_3).CH_2 \\ \underline{\hspace{1cm}}O\underline{\hspace{1cm}} \end{array} \right]_2 \qquad \left[\begin{array}{c} CH_3.C(OCH_3).CH.CH_3 \\ \underline{\hspace{1cm}}O\underline{\hspace{1cm}} \end{array} \right]_2$$

methylcycloacetal of acetol   methylcycloacetal of acetoin

The former yields, upon treatment with iodin and potassium iodide, deep blue-black metallic-looking prisms, the latter steel-blue prisms. Analysis showed four atoms of iodin and one formula weight of potassium iodide per formula of each as pictured above. Bergmann believes that, since in the starches, as in the cycloacetals, there are oxygen bridges and since these oxygen bridges possess known and pronounced residual valence forces, in both cases the binding of the iodin and potassium iodide is at such oxygen bridges. He postulates that the apparent, simple sorption-curve effects measured with starch and iodin are the result of the facile dissociation of the iodostarches. In this connection it is interesting to note that the ethyl ester of euxanthic acid† forms a blue complex with iodin[93] and potassium iodide, the maximum amount of iodin fixed being two atoms per molecule of the ester.

Barger and Field[94] reported that the glucoside saponarin, $C_{21}H_{24}O_{12}$, first isolated from *Saponaria officinalis* by Barger[95] forms the blue complex under certain conditions. Saponarin crystallizes from water and from pyridine in minute needles and is soluble to the extent of 1 part in 7,100 parts of water at 18°. Neither the solution nor the crystals react with iodin, but a colloidal dispersion of it, formed either by peptizing with alkali followed by acidification or by boiling with water, yields the blue complex upon addition of iodin. Iodin added to concentrated colloidal dispersions results in the formation of a blue

* Cholic acid is $C_{24}H_{40}O_5$. Its structural formula is unknown.

† Euxanthic acid is $C_6H_3(OH) \begin{array}{c} O \\ < > \\ O \end{array} C_6H_3O.CH(OH)(CHOH)_4COOH$.

jelly. When the colloidal dispersion of the blue compound is diluted with water, the blue color vanishes when the dilution of 1 part in 7,100 parts of water is reached. The blue dispersion has all the properties of a hydrophobic dispersion and is negatively charged. Just as a blue iodostarch changes to a red complex upon addition of a large excess of potassium iodide, so does the saponarin iodide complex.

Barger and Starling[96] found some fifty compounds which form blue complexes upon the addition of iodin. The reaction with naphthaflavone is even more delicate than with starch; a blue coloration is produced by solutions containing 1 part of iodin in 800,000 parts of water. The reaction is produced by 2- and 4-pyrone derivatives but is not confined to them. It is greatly increased by the presence of benzene nuclei, as in the coumarins, chromones, xanthones, and flavones. Alkyl and hydroxy groups diminish it. Thus coumarin fixes iodin slightly, hydrocoumarin and hydroxycoumarin not at all, while naphthacoumarins, phenylcoumarins, and benzoylcoumarins are colored blue by very dilute iodin solutions. In no case was the iodin found combined in stoichiometrical proportions, although many of the blue substances could be obtained crystalline.

Further investigations[97] on this problem have demonstrated that the presence of iodide ion is necessary for the formation of the blue complex.

The addition of 0.04 cc. of 0.2N alcoholic iodin solution to 2 cc. of cold saturated thallous chloride gives a clear-brown solution, but the further addition of a few drops of potassium iodide solution produces at once an intense grayish-black precipitate which disappears on warming and reappears on cooling, as with iodostarch.[98] The composition of the precipitate is approximately Tl_6I_8.

In 1857, Damour[99] reported that the slimy precipitate formed upon precipitation of lanthanum acetate by ammonium hydroxide becomes dark blue upon treatment with iodin. This effect is not obtained when lanthanum nitrate is used instead of the acetate; but once the blue complex is obtained with the basic acetate, the addition of potassium nitrate does not affect it.[100]

The reaction seems to depend upon the physical condition of the precipitate; it must be gelatinous. Colloidal dispersions of lanthanum hydroxide peptized by acetate give the blue compound, but a pulverulent white precipitate formed by precipitation of a boiling solution of lanthanum acetate by alkali takes up but a small amount of iodin and is brownish black in color, whereas, once the blue complex is formed, boiling does not decompose it. The blue complex is obtained when lanthanum chloride or nitrate is treated with ammonium hydroxide in the presence of propionate ion as well, but not in the presence of many other organic ions,[101] and consequently a method for testing for these two organic ions is indicated. Other rare earths do not react as lanthanum does.[101]

Sorption of Colloids.—The literature contains very little information on sorption from colloidal solutions. The sorption of albumin from water by ferric oxide hydrogel, cellulose and kaolin appears to be irreversible,[102] the same as in the sorption of proteoses by kaolin and charcoal.[103] Added acetone has no effect upon this sorption of proteoses, whether added prior or subsequent to the sorption. Acetone is sorbed by charcoal covered by proteose as well as by free charcoal.[103] "Animal charcoal" sorbs albumin irreversibly, as does kaolin, although the latter's sorptive capacity is low.[104] Aluminum hydroxide also sorbs albumin irreversibly,[105] its sorbing power being markedly diminished by ignition. Animal charcoal is reported[106] not to sorb gum arabic from aqueous solution, whereas hydrous alumina does markedly and irreversibly sorb it.

The sorption of albumin and gelatin by nitrocellulose has already been mentioned in the chapter on dialysis, Hitchcock[107] showing the sorption maximum to be at the isoelectric point. In addition he proved that the sorption of these proteins by nitrocellulose sheets followed Langmuir's but not Freundlich's equation (Fig. 90).

Abderhalden and Fodor[108] find that the sorption of proteins from their aqueous dispersions is greatest in the region of the isoelectric point, departure from the isoelectric hydrogen-ion concentration causing diminution in sorption. The maximum degree of sorption is thus found under the conditions of minimum degree of stability in solution. When increasing concentrations of potassium chloride were added to a slightly acid solution of yeast-juice protein, there resulted an increasing degree of turbidity leading finally to flocculation. The sorption from these solutions ran parallel with the turbidity, from which they conclude that the dehydrating effect of the added salt on the protein displaces it from the water phase into the charcoal surface.

The degree of acidity of the medium is of importance in the decolorization of sugar-cane juice. It has been shown that such solutions are better decolorized by commercial charcoal at increasing acidities and not decolorized at all when alkaline.[109] There are, of course, practical limitations since the "bone blacking" in sugar refineries is carried out at elevated temperatures where

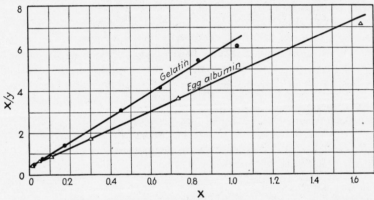

Fig. 90.—Sorption of proteins from aqueous solution by nitrocellulose follows the equation $\dfrac{x}{y} = \dfrac{1}{ab} + \dfrac{x}{b}$.

slight increases in hydrogen-ion activity would cause considerable loss of sucrose due to conversion to invert sugar.

When commercial charcoals are placed in inorganic hydrosols, an apparent sorption is noted. It is merely precipitation by electrolytes however. Thomas and LeCompte[110] found that various charcoals purified by extraction with hydrochloric acid followed by washing to negative test for chloride did not sorb the micelles of Bredig gold or of ferric oxychloride hydrosols. Later experience in the author's laboratory has yielded interesting information on this point. When a specimen of "purified" charcoal (*A*) used by Thomas and LeCompte had been activated by heating in an electric furnace for several hours at about 1000°C., the resulting product (charcoal *B*) showed an apparent sorptive affinity for the hydrosols mentioned. Then samples of the charcoals A and B and of a commercial animal charcoal (C) were placed in nitrocellulose bags containing distilled water which were lowered into specimens of ferric oxychloride sol. The sols in contact with the bags containing B and C precipitated while that one in contact with A did not. In the case of C, the precipitation is ascribed to electrolyte which dialyzed from the charcoal through the bag. In the case of B, the precipitation is due to the strong irreversible affinity of this activated charcoal for hydrochloric acid, thus abstracting it from the sol. Charcoal A, undoubtedly having an irreversible bound film of hydrochloric acid, exerted no influence upon the sol for that reason.

References

1. McBain: *Phil. Mag.*, **18**, 916 (1909); *Z. physik. Chem.*, **68**, 471 (1909).
2. Firth: *Trans. Faraday Soc.*, **16**, 434 (1921).
3. See the paper by Chappuis: *Ann. Physik u. Chem.*, (N.F.) **8**, 1 (1879).
4. Langmuir: *Phys. Rev.*, **8**, 149 (1916).
5. Langmuir: *Phys. Rev.*, **2**, 331 (1913); **6**, 79 (1915).
6. Langmuir: *J. Am. Chem. Soc.*, **38**, 2221 (1916).
7. Hitchcock: *J. Am. Chem. Soc.*, **48**, 2870 (1926).
8. McBain: "The Sorption of Gases and Vapours by Solids," G. Routledge Sons, Ltd., London, 1931.
9. Papers on sorption of gases by solids: *Trans. Faraday Soc.*, **28**, 131–447 (1932).
10. Freundlich: *Z. physik. Chem.*, **57**, 385 (1907); **73**, 385 (1910).
11. Procter: *Brit. Assoc. Advancement Sci.*, *First Report on Colloid Chemistry* (1917).
12. Ostwald and de Izaguirre: *Kolloid-Z.*, **30**, 279 (1922).
13. Nernst: "Theoretical Chemistry," 3d English ed., p. 496, Macmillan & Co., Ltd., London, 1911.
14. G. C. Schmidt: *Z. physik. Chem.*, **74**, 689 (1910); **77**, 641 (1911); **78**, 667 (1912); **83**, 674 (1913); **91**, 103 (1916).
15. Arrhenius: *Meddel. Vetenskapsakad. Nobelinst.*, (7) **2** (1911).
16. Swan and Urquhart: *J. Phys. Chem.*, **31**, 251 (1927); see also Kruyt and Modderman: *Chem. Review*, **7**, 259 (1930).
17. A. M. Williams: *Meddel. Vetenskapsakad. Nobelinst.*, (27) **2** (1913); *Trans. Faraday Soc.*, **10**, 155 (1914).
18. Thomas and Kelly: *J. Ind. Eng. Chem.*, **13**, 31 (1921).
19. Allmand and Burrage: *Proc. Roy. Soc.* (*London*), **130A**, 626 (1931); Allmand, Burrage, Chaplin: *Trans. Faraday. Soc.*, **28**, 218 (1932); Burrage: *J. Phys. Chem.*, **37**, 33 (1933).
20. Benton and White: *J. Am. Chem. Soc.*, **53**, 3301 (1931).
21. Burrage: *J. Phys. Chem.*, **37**, 41 (1933).
22. Chaplin: *J. Phys. Chem.*, **36**, 909 (1932).

23. MICHAELIS and RONA: *Biochem. Z.*, **97**, 57 (1919).

24. ODÉN and ANDERSSON: *J. Phys. Chem.*, **25**, 311 (1921).
    ODÉN and LANGELIUS: *ibid.*, **25**, 385 (1921).

25. BARTELL and MILLER: *J. Am. Chem. Soc.*, **44**, 1866 (1922); **45**, 1106 (1923); *J. Phys. Chem.*, **28**, 992 (1924); MILLER: *J. Am. Chem. Soc.*, **46**, 1150 (1924).

26. MILLER: *J. Phys. Chem.*, **30**, 1031, 1162 (1926); **31**, 1197 (1927).

27. MILLER: *J. Am. Chem. Soc.*, **47**, 1270 (1925).

28. MILLER and BANDEMER: *J. Am. Chem. Soc.*, **49**, 1686 (1927).

29. SHILOV et al: *Z. physik. Chem.*, **133A**, 188 (1928); **143A**, 41 (1929); **148A**, 233; **149A**, 211; **150A**, 31 (1930); *Kolloid-Z.*, **52**, 107 (1930).

30. FRUMKIN et al: *Z. physik. Chem.*, **141A**, 141, 158, 219 (1929); **147A**, 125 (1930); *Kolloid-Z.*, **46**, 89 (1928); **51**, 123 (1930).

31. BRETSCHNEIDER: *Z. physik. Chem.*, **159A**, 436 (1932).

32. BARKER: *Ind. Eng. Chem.*, **22**, 926 (1930); HOFMANN, GROLL, and LEMCKE: *Z. angew. Chem.*, **44**, 841 (1931).

33. LUNDELIUS: *Kolloid-Z.*, **26**, 145 (1920).

34. GURVITSCH: *Kolloid-Z.*, **32**, 80 (1923); **38**, 247 (1926); see also HEYNE and POLANYI: *Z. physik. Chem.*, **132**, 384 (1928).

35. HEYMANN and BOYE: *Z. physik. Chem.*, **150A**, 219 (1930).

36. SUIRKIN and POLIAKOV: *Kolloid-Z.*, **55**, 33 (1931).

37. NEKRASOV: *Z. physik. Chem.*, **136**, 18 (1928).

38. SHILOV and PEVSNER: *Z. physik. Chem.*, **118**, 361 (1925).

39. SATA: *Kolloid-Z.*, **49**, 275 (1929).

40. BERGER: *Rec. trav. chim.*, **50**, 377 (1931).

41. GRIFFIN, RICHARDSON, and ROBERTSON: *J. Chem. Soc.*, **1928**, 2705.

42. ALEKSEEVSKII: *J. Russ. Phys.-Chem. Soc.*, **59**, 1033 (1927); through *Chem. Abs.*, **22**, 3328.

43. PHELPS: *J. Chem. Soc.*, **1929**, 1724.

44. HERMANS: *Z. physik. Chem.*, **113**, 385 (1924).

45. PHELPS and PETERS: *Proc. Roy. Soc. (London)*, **A124**, 554 (1929).

46. PHELPS: *Proc. Roy. Soc. (London)*, **A133**, 155 (1931).

47. FROMAGEOT and WURMSER: *Compt. rend.*, **179**, 972 (1924).

48. KOLTHOFF: *Rec. trav. chim.*, **46**, 549 (1927).

49. NEKRASOV: *Z. physik. Chem.*, **136**, 18, 379 (1928).

50. DUBININ: *Z. physik. Chem.*, **140A**, 81 (1929); **150A**, 145 (1930).

51. DUBININ: *Z. physik. Chem.*, **155A**, 116 (1931).

52. LANDT and KNOP: *Z. Elektrochem.*, **37**, 645 (1931).

53. BRUNS: *Kolloid-Z.*, **54**, 33 (1931).

54. ARENDT: *Kolloidchem. Beihefte*, **7**, 212 (1915).

55. RONA and VON TOTH: *Biochem. Z.*, **64**, 288 (1914).

56. Ref. 24; see also RONA and MICHAELIS: *Biochem. Z.*, **94**, 240 (1919).

57. SHILOV and CHEPELEVETSKII: *Z. physik. Chem.*, **123**, 248 (1926).

58. CHEPELEVETSKII: *Z. physik. Chem.*, **136**, 34 (1928).

59. DUBININ: *Z. physik. Chem.*, **133**, 122 (1928).

60. ZELINSKY and BALANDINE: *Bull. soc. chim.*, **39**, 1508 (1926).

61. NEKRASOV: *J. Russ. Phys.-Chem. Soc.*, **58**, 207 (1926); through *Chem. Abs.*, **21**, 682. SHILOV and NEKRASOV: *Z. physik. Chem.*, **118**, 79 (1925).

62. ZHUKOV and SHIPULINA: *Kolloid-Z.*, **49**, 126 (1929).

63. MICHAELIS and RONA: *Biochem. Z.*, **15**, 196 (1909).
    ESTRUP: *Kolloid-Z.*, **14**, 8 (1914).
    BERCZELLER and HETENYI: *Biochem. Z.*, **84**, 118 (1917).

64. WIEGENER et al: *Kolloid-Z.*, **28**, 51 (1921).

65. DUBININ: *Z. physik. Chem.*, **135**, 24 (1928).

66. MICHAELIS and RONA: *Biochem. Z.*, **97**, 85 (1919).

67. GUNTHER-SCHULZE: *Z. Elektrochem.*, **27**, 402 (1921).
    VOGTHERR: *Z. angew. Chem.*, **33**, 1, 241 (1920).
    ROTHMUND and KORNFELD: *Z. anorg. Chem.*, **103**, 129 (1918).

68. MILLER: *Chem. Met. Eng.*, **23**, 1155, 1219, 1251 (1920).
    PATRICK: *Trans. Am. Inst. Chem. Eng.*, **15**, I, 283 (1923).
    PARTRICK et al.: *J. Phys. Chem.*, **29**, 1, 220, 336, 601 (1925).
    WILLIAMS: *J. Soc. Chem. Ind.*, **43**, 97T (1924).

69. MICHAELIS and RONA: *Biochem. Z.*, **97**, 57 (1919); *Kolloid-Z.*, **25**, 225 (1919).

70. RHEINBOLDT and WEDEKIND: *Kolloidchem. Beihefte*, **17**, 115 (1923). This paper extensively reviews previous work on sorption of dyes by inorganic substances.

71. NUTTING: *Science*, **72**, 243 (1930).

72. LLOYD: *J. Am. Pharm. Assoc.*, **5**, 381 (1916).

73. GUERRANT and SALMON: *J. Biol. Chem.*, **80**, 67 (1928).

74. GRETTIE and WILLIAMS: *J. Am. Chem. Soc.*, **50**, 668 (1928).

75. WILLSTÄTTER et al.: *Ber.*, **57B**, 1082 (1924); **58B**, 2448 (1925); **64B**, 1697 (1931).

76. EULER and ERIKSON: *Z. physiol. Chem.*, **128**, 1 (1923).

77. CALDWELL and DOEBBELING: *J. Biol. Chem.*, **98**, 553 (1932).

78. CHARRIOU: *Compt. rend.*, **176**, 1890 (1923).

79. BEEKLEY and TAYLOR: *J. Phys. Chem.*, **29**, 942 (1925).

80. MUKHERJEE and RAY: *Quart. J. Indian Chem. Soc.*, **1**, 173 (1924); through *Chem. Abs.*, **19**, 1800 (1925).

81. GHOSH and DHAR: *Kolloid-Z.*, **35**, 144 (1924).

82. TEZAK: *Kolloid-Z.*, **59**, 158 (1932).

83. DE BROUCKERE: *Bull. sci. acad. roy. Belg.*, **13**, 415, 827, (1927); **15**, 170 (1929); **16**, 1263 (1930); **17**, 1249 (1931); *Rev. gen. colloides*, **7** 250 (1929); *J. chim. phys.*, **26**, 250 (1929); **29**, 108 (1932); *Bull. soc. chim. Belg.*, **38**, 409 (1929); **39**, 174 (1930).

84. HOLMES and McKELVEY: *J. Phys. Chem.*, **32**, 1522 (1928).

85. HEYMANN and BOYE: *Kolloid-Z.*, **59**, 153 (1932).

86. BARTELL and SCHEFFLER: *J. Am. Chem. Soc.*, **53**, 2507 (1931).

87. BARTELL and FU: *J. Phys. Chem.*, **33**, 676 (1929).

88. FRUMKIN and DRUDE: *Ber.*, **60B**, 1816 (1927).

89. PLATONOV: *J. Russ. Phys.-Chem. Soc.*, **61**, 1055 (1929); **62**, 1975 (1930), through *Chem. Abs.*, **24**, 539 (1930); **25**, 16 (1931).

90. MYLIUS: *Z. physiol. Chem.*, **11**, 306 (1887); *Ber.*, **20**, 688 (1887).

91. Ref. 90; also KÜSTER: *Z. physik. Chem.*, **16**, 156 (1895).

92. BERGMANN: *Ber.*, **57B**, 753 (1924).

93. GRAEBE: *Ber.*, **33**, 3360 (1900).

94. BARGER and FIELD: *J. Chem. Soc.*, **101**, 1394 (1912).

95. BARGER: *J. Chem. Soc.*, **89**, 1210 (1906).

96. BARGER and STARLING: *Proc. Chem. Soc.*, **29**, 128 (1913).

97. BARGER and EATON: *J. Chem. Soc.*, **125**, 2407 (1924).

98. See also GRAMENITZKI: *Biochem. Z.*, **185**, 427 (1927).

99. DAMOUR: *Compt. rend.*, **43**, 976 (1857); see also LOTTERMOSER and HERRMANN: *Z. physik. Chem.*, **122**, 1 (1926); LOTTERMOSER: *Kolloid-Z.*, **33**, 271 (1923).

100. BILTZ: *Ber.*, **37**, 719 (1904).

101. KRÜGER and TSCHIRCH: *Ber.*, **62B**, 2776 (1929); **63B**, 826 (1930); *Pharm. Zentralhalle*, **71**, 145 (1930).

102. BILTZ and STEINER: *Biochem. Z.*, **23**, 27 (1910).

103. MICHAELIS and RONA: Ref. 63.

104. RAKUZIN: *J. Russ. Phys.-Chem. Soc.*, **48**, 709 (1916); through *Chem. Abs.*, **11**, 2984 (1917).

105. RAKUZIN: *J. Russ. Phys.-Chem. Soc.*, **48**, 95, 711 (1916); through *Chem. Abs.*, **11**, 736, 817 (1917).

106. RAKUZIN: *J. Russ. Phys.-Chem. Soc.*, **53**, 1 (1921); through *Chem. Abs.*, **17**, 3635 (1923).

107. HITCHCOCK: *J. Gen. Physiol.*, **8**, 61 (1925).

108. ABDERHALDEN and FODOR: *Kolloid-Z.*, **27**, 49 (1920).

109. WIJNBERG: *Intern. Sugar J.*, **17**, 70 (1915); BREWSTER and RAINES: *J. Ind. Eng. Chem.*, **13**, 1043 (1921).

110. THOMAS and LECOMPTE: Fourth Colloid Symposium Monograph, p. 328, Chemical Catalog Co., New York, 1926.

CHAPTER XII

PROTEINS

When proteins are hydrolyzed, the ultimate products are mainly α-amino acids. This fact, together with other evidence, indicates that the amino group of one amino acid is condensed with the carboxyl group of its neighbor in the following fashion where an imaginary protein consisting only of glycine radicals is used as an example:

$$
\begin{array}{ccc}
\text{H} & \text{H H} & \text{H H} \\
\text{H}_2\text{N-C-CO-(N} \cdot \text{C-CO-)}_n\text{-N-C-COOH} \\
\text{H} & \text{H} & \text{H}
\end{array}
$$

This theory of the structure of the protein molecule is due to Emil Fischer, who in support thereof synthesized a polypeptide containing as many as 19 molecules of amino acids. It resembled the peptones in properties.

Some biochemists have suggested that the straight-chain polypeptide theory of protein structure may have to be modified to include ring structures.[1] For example, two molecules of glycine can be condensed to form 2, 5-diketopiperazine:

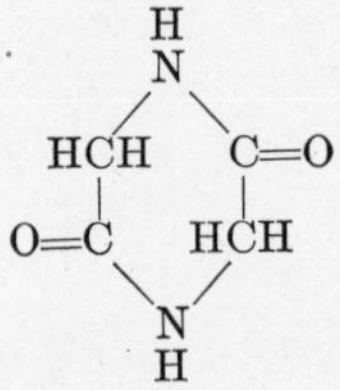

$$
\begin{array}{ccc}
 & \text{H} & \\
 & \text{N} & \\
\text{HCH} & & \text{C=O} \\
\text{O=C} & & \text{HCH} \\
 & \text{N} & \\
 & \text{H} &
\end{array}
$$

Abderhalden and his coworkers have searched for the presence of dioxopiperazine nuclei in proteins and they believe as a result of experimental evidence that such structures exist therein because of their presence in the degradation products of suitably hydrolyzed proteins. Many workers in the field of protein chemistry, however, are of the opinion that the piperazine nuclei found among the hydrolysis products may have been formed during the hydrolysis, rather than having existed as such in the original protein.

Amphoteric Properties of Amino Acids.—Amino acids have the property of neutralizing both acids and alkalies. This property has been explained for many years in the following manner:[2]

$$H_2C \Big\langle \begin{array}{c} COOH \\ NH_2 \end{array} + HCl \rightarrow H_2C \Big\langle \begin{array}{c} COOH \\ NH_3{}^+ \end{array} \quad Cl^-$$

$$H_2C \Big\langle \begin{array}{c} COOH \\ NH_2 \end{array} + NaOH \rightarrow H_2C \Big\langle \begin{array}{c} COO^- \quad Na^+ \\ NH_2 \end{array} + H_2O$$

According to these pictures, the amino acid exists in pure aqueous solution in a completely or nearly completely un-ionized form, acids reacting with the —NH₂ group forming the —NH₃⁺ ion, and bases with the —COOH group forming the —COO⁻ ion. But biochemists now seriously doubt the validity of this concept and are finding evidence in support of the suggestion made by Adams[3] and by Bjerrum[4] that an amino acid exists in pure aqueous solution in a completely ionized form:

$$H_2C \Big\langle \begin{array}{c} COO^- \\ NH_3{}^+ \end{array}$$

The German name *Zwitterion* applied to this structure is widely used in English, although some use the term *amphoteric ion.* According to this hypothesis the reactions of amino acids in acid and alkaline solutions are described on page 318.

As the formulas show, there is no disagreement between the two hypotheses regarding the results obtained upon neutralization, but the mechanisms are different. According to the older view, the effect of increasing alkalinity is to permit the ionization of the weak —COOH group. Similarly the —NH₂ is so weak as a base that it dissociates only in acid solutions.

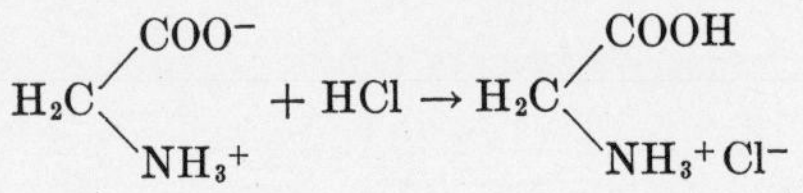

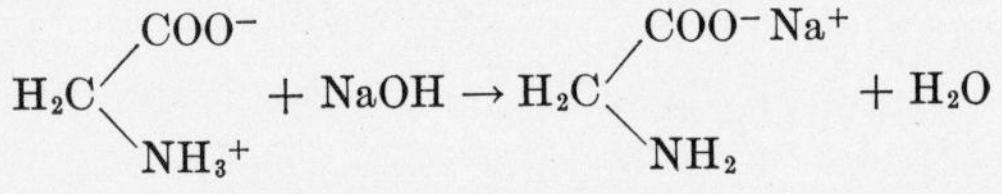

$$H_2C \begin{matrix} COO^- \\ \\ NH_3^+ \end{matrix} + HCl \rightarrow H_2C \begin{matrix} COOH \\ \\ NH_3^+ Cl^- \end{matrix}$$

$$H_2C \begin{matrix} COO^- \\ \\ NH_3^+ \end{matrix} + NaOH \rightarrow H_2C \begin{matrix} COO^- Na^+ \\ \\ NH_2 \end{matrix} + H_2O$$

According to the new, or *zwitter-ion*, hypothesis the effect of the addition of an acid is to repress the ionization of the carboxyl group, leaving the —NH₃⁺ radical free, electrostatically balanced by the anion of the added acid. Similarly the effect of the addition of a base is to repress the ionization of the amino group, thus leaving the —COO⁻ radical free, electrostatically balanced by the cation of the added base.

An essential difference between the two hypotheses consists in the strengths to be ascribed to the acidic and basic groups. According to the older view the acidic and basic groups of glycine, for example, are many times weaker than acetic acid and ammonia, while according to the zwitter-ion hypothesis they are each slightly stronger.

The student will recall the following method of estimation of the k_a of a weak acid and of the k_b of a weak base. According to the law of mass action, the degree of dissociation of the very weak acid HA is

$$[H^+] \cdot [A^-] = k_a[HA] \tag{1}$$

hence

$$[H^+] = k_a \frac{[HA]}{[A^-]}$$

or

$$\log [H^+] = \log k_a + \log \frac{[HA]}{[A^-]} \tag{2}$$

If this acid is being progressively neutralized by titration with a base, then assuming that the salt formed is completely ionized,

[HA]/[A$^-$] is the ratio of the concentration of the unneutralized acid to that of the salt formed, or [acid]/[salt]. Since this ratio is equal to 1, when one-half of the acid has been neutralized by the added base, Eq. (2) becomes

$$\log [H^+] = \log k_a \tag{3}$$

or

$$pH = pk_a \tag{4}*$$

From the mid-point of the titration curve for the titration of glycine by sodium hydroxide, its k_a has been estimated as 1.8×10^{-10}.

Similarly for the weak base BOH:

$$[B^+] \cdot [OH^-] = k_b[BOH]$$

since

$$[H^+] \cdot [OH^-] = k_w$$

then

$$\frac{1}{[H^+]} = \frac{k_b}{k_w} \cdot \frac{[BOH]}{[B^+]}$$

or

$$- \log [H^+] = \log \frac{k_b}{k_w} + \log \frac{[BOH]}{[B^+]}$$

and at half neutralization:

$$pH = pk_w - pk_b \tag{5}$$

By means of Eq. (5) at the half-neutralization of glycine by hydrochloric acid, k_b has been estimated as 2.7×10^{-12}.

The fact that such dissociation constants are so small in comparison with those of organic acids or bases of similar structure led Bjerrum to postulate that the constant obtained when an amino acid is titrated with an acid is not the dissociation constant of the amino group but is the hydrolysis constant of the acid group. Likewise, the constant obtained upon titration with a base is not the dissociation constant of the —COOH group but is the hydrolysis constant of the amino group. Thus, according to Bjerrum, the equilibria in solution are represented by the equations

* In conformity with the "pH" precedent, $- \log k_a$ and $- \log k_b$ are now generally written as pk_a and pk_b in the biochemical literature.

$$K_A = \frac{[NH_3^+ \cdot R \cdot COO^-][H^+]}{[NH_3^+ \cdot R \cdot COOH]} \qquad (6)$$

$$K_B = \frac{[NH_3^+ \cdot R \cdot COO^-][OH^-]}{[NH_2 \cdot R \cdot COO^-]} \qquad (7)$$

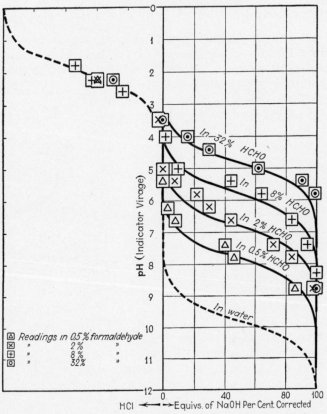

FIG. 91.—Effect of formaldehyde upon the titration curves of glycine.

where K_A is the hydrolysis constant of the acid group and K_B is the hydrolysis constant of the basic group.* Hence,

$$K_A = \frac{k_w}{k_b} \text{ and } K_B = \frac{k_w}{k_a}$$

* In this book k_a and k_b are used to signify the classical acidic and basic dissociation constants, while K_A and K_B represent Bjerrum's zwitter-ion constants according to Eqs. (6) and (7).

Experimental support for the zwitter-ion hypothesis has been provided by Harris[5,6] by the titrations of several amino acids in the presence of formaldehyde. Since formaldehyde reacts with —NH₂ groups according to the equation

$$R \cdot NH_2 + OCH_2 \rightarrow R \cdot N{:}CH_2 + H_2O$$

and not with the carboxyl groups, any modification found in the titration curve in the presence of formaldehyde should be ascribed to the amino groups. One of Harris's experiments is shown in Fig. 91. It is seen that the titration of glycine by hydrochloric acid is not affected by the presence of formaldehyde, while the titration by sodium hydroxide is markedly affected. Hence when glycine is titrated with an acid, it is the carboxyl group and not the amino group which is involved. Likewise in the titration of glycine by a base, the amino group is concerned but not the carboxyl. Harris obtained similar results with other naturally occurring amino acids, with gelatin, and with a tripeptide, the latter being shown in Fig. 92.

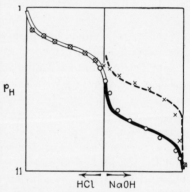

Fig. 92.—Titration curves of glycylglycylglycine in water (o) and in 1 per cent formaldehyde solution (x).

Further experimental evidence for the zwitter-ion hypothesis has been found by investigation of the effect of glycine and of alanine upon the pH values of phosphate buffer solutions interpreted according to the modern physical chemistry of solutions.[7] A comparison between the values of heats of dissociation of amines, organic acids, and amino acids also supports the zwitter-ion hypothesis.[8] Recently the ratio of zwitter-ion to neutral molecules in solution has been found to range from 40,000 (for glycylglycine) to nearly 1,000,000 (for ε-aminocaproic acid).[9] Since the ratio diminishes with rise in temperature (approximately halved for a rise of 10°), the formation of a zwitter-ion from a neutral molecule is an exothermic process.[9] The ratio is also lower in solvents of low dielectric constant. Not all amino-acidic compounds can be assumed to exist in the zwitter-ion form, however. Titration of p-aminophenol and of p-amino-benzoic acid in the presence of formaldehyde[6] produces a significant shift of the hydrochloric acid curve but not of the sodium hydroxide curve. Hence these compounds must be assumed to exist in the un-ionized or nearly un-ionized form in pure aqueous solution. In an acid such as aspartic, one of the carboxyl groups is un-ionized at the isoelectric point and at lower pH values. Similarly one of the —NH₂ groups in an acid like lysine remains in the un-ionized form at the isoelectric point and at higher pH values. In view of the above-mentioned facts and until sufficient experimental evidence is available, we are obliged to consider amino acids and proteins from both viewpoints.

Isoelectric Point of Amino Acids.—Since an ampholyte may exist as a cation or as an anion, there must be a hydrogen ion activity at which its positive and negative charges are equal to each other, *i.e.*, a region of electrical neutrality. The hydrogen ion activity (or pH value) at which the ampholyte is in this condition is called the *isoelectric point*. The location of this value and the amount of undissociated ampholyte (adopting here the classical viewpoint) in solution at the isoelectric point or range depend upon the relative values of k_a and k_b and their orders of magnitude.

According to Michaelis,[10] who is the originator of the following derivations and definitions, let us define the ratio of the undissociated portion, $[U]$, to the total concentration, $[A]$, of an ampholyte as the "undissociated fraction" ρ, and let the concentrations of ampholyte cations and anions be represented by $[A^+]$ and $[A^-]$.

By definition, then,

$$\frac{[U]}{[A]} = \rho = \frac{[A] - [A^+] - [A^-]}{[A]}$$

According to the mass law,

$$[A^-] = k_a \frac{[U]}{[H^+]} \text{ and } [A^+] = k_b \frac{[U]}{[OH]}$$

$$[U] = [A] - [A^+] - [A^-] = [A] - k_a \frac{[U]}{[H^+]} - k_b \frac{[U]}{[OH^-]}$$

dividing by $[U]$,

$$\frac{[A]}{[U]} = 1 + \frac{k_a}{[H^+]} + \frac{k_b}{[OH^-]}.$$

substituting $k_w/[H^+]$ for $[OH^-]$ we get

$$\frac{[U]}{[A]} = \rho = \frac{1}{1 + \dfrac{k_a}{[H^+]} + \dfrac{k_b[H^+]}{k_w}} \tag{8}$$

The relation between ρ and the product of the constants k_a and k_b for a series of hypothetical ampholytes is shown in Fig. 93. When the product $k_a \cdot k_b$ is very small, 10^{-30}, it is seen that the maximum elevation of the curve spreads over a very wide range.

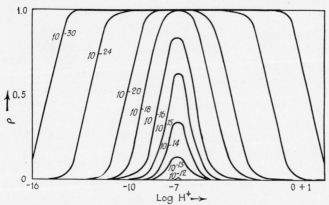

FIG. 93.—Undissociated fraction curves. The numbers on the curves represent the product $k_a \cdot k_b$.

As $k_a \cdot k_b$ becomes larger, the maximum range for the undissociated fraction becomes narrower, being reduced to a point when $k_a \cdot k_b = 10^{-18}$. With products larger than this the maximum point falls below the ordinate value of 1, showing that all of the ampholyte does not exist in the undissociated form at pH 7. For the case where $k_a \cdot k_b = 10^{-14}$, the maximum value is only about ⅓ but ampholytes with the product so large do not exist.

In Fig. 93, the values of k_a and k_b were taken as equal. For a given product, but with different magnitudes of k_a and k_b, the curves are identical in shape but shifted along the pH axis to the acid side when $k_a > k_b$ and to the basic side when $k_b > k_a$.

The hydrogen ion activity corresponding to the maximum of the undissociated fraction curve is defined by Michaelis as the *isoelectric point*. This can readily be defined in terms of k_a, k_b, and k_w in the following manner. For ease of calculation, consider the condition for the minimum of the reciprocal $1/\rho$ as follows:

$$\frac{1}{\rho} = 1 + \frac{k_a}{[H^+]} + \frac{k_b}{k_w}[H^+]$$

Its derivative with respect to $[H^+]$ is

$$\frac{d\frac{1}{\rho}}{d[H^+]} = -\frac{k_a}{[H^+]^2} + \frac{k_b}{k_w}$$

by setting this derivative $= 0$, one has the minimum of $1/\rho$ or the maximum of ρ which is the hydrogen ion concentration for the isoelectric point (I):

$$[H^+] = \sqrt{\frac{k_a k_w}{k_b}} \tag{9}$$

Since the cations and anions yielded by an ampholyte are equal in numbers at the isoelectric point,* the latter can be determined by adding portions of the ampholyte (if it is readily soluble) to a series of dilute buffer solutions. The buffer with pH equal to the isoelectric point of the ampholyte will suffer no change in pH. The ampholyte acts as a base toward buffers of lower pH values tending to raise the pH, and as an acid to buffers of higher pH values tending to lower the same.

By this method the isoelectric point of glycine was located to be between pH 6.3 and 5.8.[12] Its isoelectric point, calculated from $k_a = 1.8 \times 10^{-10}$ and $k_b = 2.7 \times 10^{-12}$ at 25°C., is pH 6.09.

Michaelis[13] showed that the solubility of a difficultly soluble amino acid in water is lowest at or very near the isoelectric point. Consequently the region of the isoelectric point has since been estimated by means of the location of the pH for the solubility minimum.

* For proof, see Michaelis.[11]

An equal and ample amount of the ampholyte is added to each of a series of hot buffer solutions and examined for bulk of crystals upon cooling. The following values were found[13] by this method:

Acid	k_a	k_b	I.E.P. (calc.)	[H$^+$] at lowest solubility
o-Aminobenzoic........	1.21×10^{-5}	2.33×10^{-12}	1.7×10^{-4}	1.6×10^{-4}
m-Aminobenzoic.......	1.63×10^{-5}	1.22×10^{-11}	8.8×10^{-5}	6.3×10^{-5}

When the product $k_a \cdot k_b$ is very small, such as 10^{-20} in the case of tyrosine, there is a long range of minimum solubility. This corresponds to the range, rather than point, for the *undissociated fraction* of such an ampholyte as shown in Fig. 93. The isoelectric point calculated from the dissociation constants of tyrosine ($k_a = 4.0 \times 10^{-9}$, $k_b = 2.6 \times 10^{-12}$) is pH = 5.4. This is, however, the mid-point of the isoelectric range and is not a point of sharp change. One should therefore speak of the isoelectric range of such a substance.

The formula $I = \sqrt{\dfrac{k_a}{k_b} k_w}$ applies rigidly only to a simple monobasic, monoacidic ampholyte. For a polybasic, polyacidic ampholyte the following is more exact:[14]

$$I = \sqrt{\frac{k_{a_1} + k_{a_2} + k_{a_3} \cdots + k_{a_n} k_w}{k_{b_1} + k_{b_2} + k_{b_3} \cdots + k_{b_n}}} = \sqrt{\frac{\Sigma k_a}{\Sigma k_b} k_w} \qquad (10)$$

Generally, however, the second dissociation constant is so small as to make but a negligible difference in the calculation. For example, the case of aspartic acid may be cited. Its constants at 30°C. have been determined to be[14]

$$k_{a_1} = 2.35 \times 10^{-4}$$
$$k_{a_2} = 3.39 \times 10^{-10}$$
$$k_b = 1.50 \times 10^{-12}$$

and

$$k_w \text{ at } 30° = 1.89 \times 10^{-14}$$

Calculation of I by both formulas gives pH 2.76. No difference is found to the second decimal of pH because k_{a_2} is negligible in comparison with k_{a_1}.

It should be carefully noted that the isoelectric point and the pH of a solution of pure ampholyte are not the same.[14]

At the isoelectric point,

$$\alpha_{b_1}C + \alpha_{b_2}C + \alpha_{b_3}C \cdots + \alpha_{b_n}C = \alpha_{a_1}C + \alpha_{a_2}C + \\ \alpha_{a_3}C \cdots + \alpha_{a_n}C$$

or

$$\Sigma\alpha_b = \Sigma\alpha_a \tag{11}$$

i.e., the sum of the ionized fractions of basic groups equals the sum of the ionized fractions of the acid groups of an ampholyte at its isoelectric point. On the other hand, the $[H^+]$ of a solution of an ampholyte is represented by

$$[H^+] + \Sigma\alpha_b C = [OH^-] + \Sigma\alpha_a C \tag{12}$$

(For the sum of the positive ions in a solution must equal the sum of the negative ions.)

It is seen that the isoelectric point as defined is constant and independent of the concentration, while the pH of the pure ampholyte solution is obviously a variable since it is a function of the concentration. Except in the special case where $\alpha_a = \alpha_b$ $[H^+]$ does not equal $[OH^-]$ and the pH of a pure aqueous solution of an ampholyte lies between its isoelectric point and the pH of pure water. The more concentrated the solution, the nearer its pH value approaches that of the isoelectric point.

Neutralization of Acids and Bases by Proteins.—In 1898, Bugarsky and Lieberman[15] demonstrated by e.m.f. measurements that egg albumin combines with acids and bases and, in 1899, Osborne[16] showed that various amounts of acids are required to neutralize the basic groups of a number of proteins. In 1900, Hardy[17] reported that the direction of migration of proteins in an electrical field depended upon the acidity or alkalinity of the solution. Later[18] he attributed this behavior to the fact that proteins are amphoteric substances which react with acids or bases to form salts, the positively charged protein in acid solutions being the cation and the negatively charged protein in alkaline solutions constituting the anion of the salt produced.*

The first titration curve of a protein was published in 1912.[19] The protein studied was serum albumin. The data of several investigators obtained for this protein have been plotted by Cohn[20] (Fig. 94), who found that essentially the same curve can be drawn through the experimental points obtained by several investigators, thus demonstrating that the titration curve is an accurate method of defining the acid- and base-combining proper-

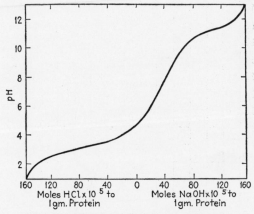

Fig. 94.—Titration curve of serum albumin.

ties of a protein. The curves of egg and serum albumin are steeper than those of serum globulin, edestin, and casein.[22] The neutralization curves of proteins for acids and bases are not surprising in view of their composition and of the behavior of amino acids.

* It is now common practice to refer to such salts as "protein chlorides," "protein sulfates," etc., and as "sodium proteinates," etc., as the case may be. There are several objections to the use of such terms since they infer definite chemical composition. For example, the term *gelatin* is not the name of an individual but is used to denote a group of an unknown number of chemical individuals or a mixture formed by peptization of another indefinite group, the collagens, but possessing certain common properties which distinguish them from other types of proteins. For the sake of brevity it is convenient to use these terms and defensible in view of the evidence, provided it is understood that they are employed under the premises stated.

Different acids react with proteins in stoichiometrical proportions. This was shown by Loeb.[21] The particular case for egg albumin is given in Fig. 95 where the amount of acid required to produce a certain pH value is corrected for the amount necessary to confer the same pH value on pure water.

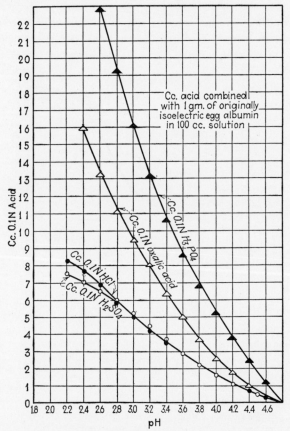

FIG. 95.—The neutralization of acids by albumin.

Since sulfuric acid is completely ionized at the dilutions used, just as many equivalents should be required as for hydrochloric acid. Three times as many equivalents of phosphoric acid are required to bring albumin to a given pH value as compared with hydrochloric or sulfuric acid. This is due to the fact that, in the pH range shown in Fig. 95, phosphoric acid is ionized appreciably only into H^+ and $H_2PO_4^-$ ions, *i.e.*, it reacts as a monobasic acid. The reason for this is apparent upon inspection of the titration curve of phosphoric acid shown in Fig. 96. The curve shows that, in the range from about pH 4 and lower, H^+ and $H_2PO_4^-$ only are found in the solution, the $HPO_4^=$ ion appearing appreciably only above pH 4.6.

In Fig. 95 it is seen that, at pH values lower than 3.2, twice as much oxalic acid as hydrochloric acid is combined with the protein as expected, since the acid solutions are of equal nor-

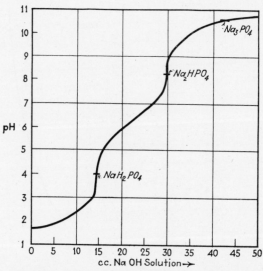

FIG. 96.—Titration of 200 cc. of 0.0143 M H_3PO_4 with 0.2 M NaOH[24].

mality. Above pH 3.2, it is less than twice because in this range the ions H^+, H^+ and $C_2O_4^=$ are arising, while below pH 3.2, the ions present are H^+ and $HC_2O_4^-$.

The stoichiometrical nature of the combination between bases and a protein is shown in Fig. 97, taken from the experiments of Loeb.[21]

The point has been raised by Hoffman and Gortner[22] that simple chemical neutralization by proteins occurs only in the pH range between 2.5 and 10.5, and that at pH values beyond these limits all proteins bind acid and alkali to the same extent, the nature of the combination being a physical adsorption.

This conclusion has been set aside by Cohn[20] because the error in estimating combined acid or alkali becomes greater, the greater the concentration, for two reasons. The activity coefficient is more variable in concentrated than in dilute solu-

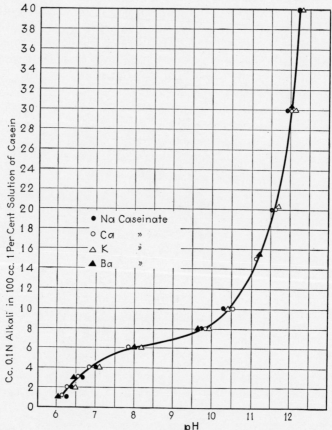

Fig. 97.—The neutralization of bases by casein.

tion; and furthermore since the amount of acid combined with a protein is determined by the difference between the total acid (or base) and the free acid (or base), the error in calculating acid- (or base-) combining capacity is least in systems containing relatively small amounts of free acid (or base).

Certain of the measurements which led Hoffman and Gortner to raise this question have been recalculated by Cohn over the range in which the amount of free acid increased from one-half to more than eight times that bound by the protein, using activity coefficients. So calculated, the measurements are not very different from those of other investigators. Irregularities in acid- or base-combining capacity of proteins in strongly acid and alkaline solutions cannot be correctly interpreted until more is known concerning the effect of proteins upon the activity coefficients of the hydrogen and hydroxyl ions. Further, the matter is complicated by incipient hydrolysis of proteins in strongly acid or alkaline solutions.[22,23] The change in protein aggregation produced by high and low pH values will be shown by Svedberg's work later in this chapter.

The maximal combining capacities of some proteins for H^+ and OH^- ions as determined are shown in Table 61. From studies

TABLE 61.—ACID- AND BASE-COMBINING CAPACITY OF PROTEINS
[Expressed in equivalents ($\times 10^5$) per gram of protein]

Protein	Acid-combining capacity	Base-combining capacity
Albumin (egg).........	80 (20)*	80 (20)
Albumin (serum)......	155 (20)	
Bence-Jones...........	92 (20)	
Casein...............	{ 80 (26) { 90 (20)	140† (25) 180‡ (25)
Edestin..............	{127 (20) {134 (27)	
Gelatin..............	{ 89 (20) } 96 (28) { 94 (29) { 92 (30)	57 (20) 73 (31) 33 at pH 7.9 (28) About 90 at pH 12 (28)
Gliadin..............	34 (20)	30 (20)
Zein.................	0 (20) (32)	{34 (32) {30 (20)

* Numbers in parentheses are literature references.

† Casein isolated and purified without alkaline treatment.

‡ Casein subjected to alkaline reaction or prepared by Hammarsten's method, thus rendering it "unnatural" and more reactive.

of the quantitative amino-acid constitution of these proteins, the values can be satisfactorily accounted for in most cases on the basis of the free amino groups of the diamino and of the free carboxyl groups of the dicarboxylic acids, and of the terminal amino and carboxyl groups. Zein is extraordinary in its behavior. It neither neutralizes acids nor dissolves in them, although small amounts of histidine and of arginine are part of its molecule. Apparently the extra amino groups of these acids are firmly bound.[32]

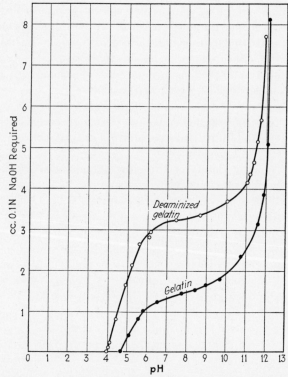

Fig. 98.—Titration of gelatin and of deaminized gelatin with sodium hydroxide.

It is commonly said that proteins combine only with the hydrogen ion in acid solutions. More accurately stated, however, proteins combine preponderantly with the hydrogen ion in acid solutions. Hitchcock[27,28] has reported the following amounts of chloride ion removed from hydrochloric acid solutions: by edestin, 39×10^{-5} equivalent per gram of protein; by gelatin, 20×10^{-5}.

The relationship between acid-binding and amino groups is well illustrated by one of Hitchcock's[33] experiments. Taking a specimen of gelatin which neutralized 89×10^{-5} equivalent of hydrochloric acid per gram and treating it in the cold with nitrous acid followed by dialysis, he produced a "deaminized" gelatin which contained 40×10^{-5} equivalent less of nitrogen than the original gelatin. The deaminized specimen neutralized only 44×10^{-5} equivalent of hydrochloric acid, the difference (45×10^{-5}) being reasonably equal to the loss of nitrogen when the experimental hazards are understood. It has since been shown[34] that Hitchcock's deamination process removed the free amino groups of the lysine part of the gelatin without affecting the arginine or histidine groups.

More sodium hydroxide is required to titrate deaminized gelatin to a given pH value than to titrate the original gelatin. This is illustrated by the experiments of Loebel[35] plotted in Fig. 98.

The Isoelectric Points of Proteins.—The isoelectric point of a protein is that pH value or hydrogen ion activity of its solution at which it does not migrate in an electrical field. The concept of the isoelectric point had its origin in Hardy's[17] experiments with the migration of aqueous suspensions of denatured egg albumin in an electrical field. While it was found later[36,37] that serum albumin also migrated to the cathode in acid solutions and to the anode in alkaline solutions, Michaelis[38] was the first to determine accurately the pH values at which the migration of a protein reversed its direction. In using serum albumin, the change was found to be quite abrupt, migration being to the anode at pH = 4.72 and greater, to the cathode at pH = 4.68 and less.

It has since been established that the majority of the physical and chemical properties of protein solutions, such as osmotic pressure, solution stability, swelling, membrane potential, and conductivity, are at a minimum at or very close to the isoelectric point. When the values of these properties are plotted as a function of pH, the curves show a sharp drop at or near the isoelectric point, as shown in Fig. 99.

One of Loeb's original experiments[39] by means of which Fig. 99 was evaluated, may serve as an illustration.

A number of 1-g. portions of powdered gelatin was soaked for 30 min. at 15°C. in 100-cc. portions of 0.125 M and weaker solutions of hydrobromic

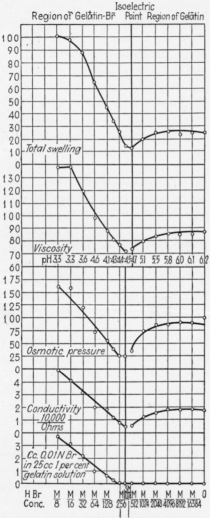

acid. Each portion was then filtered through small pads in cylindrical funnels. The gelatin granules in each of the funnels were then perfused about six times with equal portions of cold water. After the final portion of liquid drained through the filter, the volume (*i.e.*, the relative swelling of the gelatin) was measured; then the gelatin was melted by warming and water was added to bring the volume in each case to 100 cc. Then the conductivity, osmotic pressure, and viscosity were measured and the pH values of the solutions also determined.

A glance at Fig. 99 shows that the curves drop very sharply at pH 4.7.

The lowest curve in Fig. 99 represents titration for Br⁻. Gelatin should exist in the form of gelatin bromide only on the acid side of the isoelectric point and titration for Br⁻ should be negative when the pH is above 4.7. The curve shows that no Br⁻ was found when the pH was equal to or greater than 4.7, while it was found on the acid side in increasing quantity with decreasing pH value.

Fig. 99.—The properties of gelatin are at a minimum at the isoelectric point.

Sorensen[40] found that the optimum condition for crystallization of egg albumin from solutions containing the protein and ammonium sulfate coincided with a pH value of 4.58. By electrophoresis technique he established the isoelectric point to be at pH = 4.8. The minimum solubility was thus slightly on the acid side of the isoelectric point. Albumins can be crystallized in the neighborhood of the isoelectric point only from concentrated solutions of salts. Hemoglobin, however, which is less soluble than the albumins, crystallizes from pure water solutions in the region of its isoelectric point.[41,42]

The isoelectric point of globulins cannot be so accurately determined as that of albumins by the method of electrophoresis because the pH range in which they remain motionless is relatively wide. By definition, the globulins are proteins which are insoluble in water but soluble in neutral salt solutions in the neighborhood of their isoelectric points. Globulins are also dissolved by water containing acids or bases. Consequently, if a salt solution of a globulin is dialyzed, the protein will flocculate. By electrical migration, the isoelectric point of serum globulin was found to be at pH = 5.52 and the optimum for its flocculation at pH = 5.44.[43]

The vegetable globulin, edestin, gives a wide flocculation zone because it not only is relatively insoluble but it also forms a relatively insoluble acid compound.[16] The pH for maximum precipitation has been given as 6.89 from phosphate buffers[43] and 5.60 from acetate buffers.[44] In such a case the pH of maximum insolubility may be quite far removed from the isoelectric point and vary with the nature of the anions present.

Gliadin, a prolamin, is insoluble in water over the pH range of 6 to 10. As a result, values for the isoelectric point of gliadin have been reported at pH 6.5 and at 9.2.

Proteins like gelatin and casein, although they are very nearly as insoluble as the prolamins, have very much narrower precipitation zones. The pH values for the isoelectric condition of casein and for its maximum degree of precipitation from solution coincide,[45] provided ions of high valence are absent. The precipitation of casein at its isoelectric point is most complete and clean cut. Its purification, depending upon its relative insolubility at pH = 4.6, was utilized long before the development of the theory of the isoelectric point.

Table 62 contains values for the isoelectric points of a number of proteins and other bodies. Only part of the values were measured by electrical migration but the values obtained by other methods are probably not far removed from the true ones, however. The isoelectric point is influenced by the nature and amount of the ions present in the solution.

TABLE 62.—ISOELECTRIC POINTS OF PROTEINS AND OF SOME OTHER AMPHOTERIC BODIES*

Ampholyte	Isoelectric point	Ampholyte	Isoelectric point
Albumin (cows' milk)....	4.6	Glutelins..............	6.2 to 6.5
Albumin (hens' eggs)....	4.6 to 5.0	Glutenin..............	5.3 to 5.4
Albumins (seeds)........	4.2 to 5.1	Hemocyanins..........	4.3 to 5.3
Albumins (serum).......	4.7 to 5.2	Hemoglobins..........	6.8
Amylase (barley malt)...	4.4	Hide powders (limed cow hide)...........	4.8 to 5.5
Bence-Jones protein.....	4.0 to 6.7	Histone...............	8.5
Casein (cows' milk)......	4.6 to 4.9	Insulins...............	5.0 to 5.7
Casein (human milk)....	4.1 to 4.7	Lecithin (hens' eggs) ...	2.6 to 2.7
Catalase (liver).........	5.4 to 5.6	Livetin (hens' egg)	4.8 to 5.0
Erythrocruorins.........	4.6 to 5.1	Myogens..............	6.3
Esterase (canine enteric secretion)............	4.5 to 5.0	Myosins...............	4.8 to 6.6
Fibrins................	4.7 to 7.2	Pepsins...............	2.5 to 3.3
Fibrinogens............	4.9 to 5.5	Phycocyans...........	4.5 to 4.9
Gelatins...............	4.4 to 5.6	Protamines...........	10.0 to 12.4
Gliadin................	5.8 to 6.6	Sericins..............	3.8 to 4.6
Globins................	6.9 to 8.1	Silk fibroins..........	2.1 to 5.1
Globulins (seeds)........	4.5 to 5.5	Trypsin...............	7.0 to 8.0
Globulins (serum).......	5.1 to 5.5	Wools................	3.4 to 4.8

* Since the isoelectric point varies somewhat with the nature and concentration of the ions other than H+, together with the facts that many proteins are ill-defined and the methods of isolation and purification may alter them, it is not surprising to find a range of values reported for a supposedly definite protein. In order to condense this table, the author has reported the range for a series of proteins under a general classifying name in several instances. The reader who desires a list of individual proteins with details of method of measurement and literature citations is referred to the review by A. W. Thomas, *J. Am. Leather Chem. Assoc.*, **29**, 3 (1934).

Chemical treatment which alters the acidic or basic nature of a protein should likewise alter the isoelectric point. For example, treatment of a protein with formaldehyde would be expected to produce a shift of the isoelectric point to lower pH values in view of the reaction

$$HOOC \cdot R \cdot NH_2 + O:CH_2 \rightarrow HOOC \cdot R \cdot N:CH_2 + H_2O.$$

The isoelectric point of a gelatin shifted from pH = 4.75 to pH = 4.3 as a result of treatment with formaldehyde.[46] Similar experience has been reported in the cases of egg and of serum albumin.[47]

Nitrous acid treatment should produce a similar effect according to the reaction of this acid with primary amines:

$$R \cdot NH_2 + HONO \rightarrow R \cdot OH + N_2 + H_2O.$$

"Deamination" of gelatins has shifted the isoelectric point from pH = 4.7 to 4.0.[33,35]

Change of Property with pH.—An explanation for the change in certain properties of protein solutions with change in pH based on the Donnan equilibrium was given by Jacques Loeb in 1920. One of his experimental series on osmotic pressure of protein solutions is plotted in Fig. 100.[48] The experimental technique by means of which these data were obtained was briefly as follows. A nitrocellulose bag was filled with an acidified 1 per cent gelatin solution and tied tightly on to a rubber stopper pierced by a long glass tube. The bag was suspended in a beaker of water containing acid so that the pH value was the same as that of the protein solution inside the bag. A series of these containing increasing amounts of acid were let stand at 24°C. until equilibrium was established (after about 6 hr.) when the heights of solution in the glass tubes were measured.

Figure 100 shows that the osmotic rise increased to a maximum and then fell with increase in H^+ activity, and that the curves for the completely dissociating dibasic acids are much lower than those for the monobasic acids. One curve serves for a variety of monobasic acids and another single curve for sulfuric and sulfosalicylic acids.

After some acid has been added to isoelectric protein, the compositions of the solutions inside and outside the bag are as follows:

$$a \begin{cases} P^\circ \\ P^+ \end{cases} \quad Cl^- \quad H^+ \quad \bigg| \quad H^+ \quad Cl^-$$

$$\underset{\text{inside}}{y+z \qquad y} \qquad \underset{\text{outside}}{x \qquad x}$$

where x = concentration of H⁺ and of Cl⁻ ions in the outside
    solution.
    y = concentration of H⁺ in the inside solution.

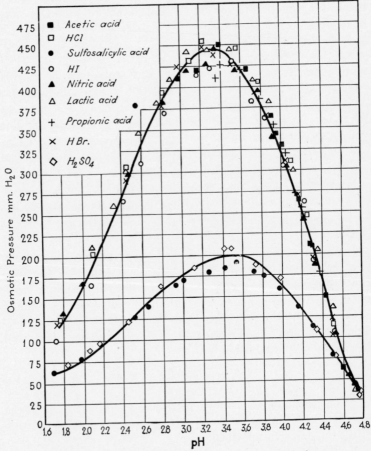

Fig. 100.—Osmotic pressure of 1 per cent gelatin solutions.

z = concentration of Cl⁻ balancing the plus charge of the
    protein *i.e.*, equal to the H⁺ which combined with the
    protein.
Hence $y + z$ = concentration of Cl⁻ in the inside solution.
    a = concentration of protein.

For the sake of simplicity, complete ionization of the hydrochloric acid and gelatin chloride is assumed. The osmotic pressure of the inside solution is determined by $a + 2y + z$. But against this there is the counter osmotic pressure of $2x$. Hence the osmotic pressure of the gelatin chloride solution may be expressed by

$$P = (a + 2y + z - 2x)RT \tag{13}$$

Since y and x may be determined by measurement of the pH values of the inside and outside solutions, respectively, and z may then be calculated from the Donnan equation, $x^2 = y(y + z)$, the values for P in Eq. (13) may be calculated, ignoring a. The values so calculated by Loeb agreed reasonably well with the observed values, allowing for the simplifying assumptions and crudity of the osmotic-pressure apparatus.

Since, from the Donnan equation of products, $x = \sqrt{y^2 + yz}$, substituting this value for x in Eq. (13) and ignoring a,* we get

$$P = (\sqrt{4y^2 + 4yz + z^2} - \sqrt{4y^2 + 4yz})RT \tag{14}$$

Equation (14) shows that $P = 0$ when no acid is present, that inasmuch as the values of z increase at a greater rate than those of y as acid is added, P rises, reaching a maximum value for the maximum value of z, i.e., at the maximal acid-combining capacity of the protein. From this point, added acid increases y while z remains constant (assuming no mass-action effect) and the value for P diminishes, or

$$P_{\substack{\overline{\text{limit}} \\ y = \infty}} (\sqrt{4y^2} - \sqrt{4y^2})RT = 0 \tag{15}$$

When the anion of the protein-acid salt is bivalent, as in the case of gelatin sulfate, with $x =$ the hydrogen ion concentration of the outside solution, then

$x/2 =$ the $SO_4^=$ concentration of the outside solution.

$y =$ H^+ concentration of the inside solution.

$y/2 =$ concentration of $SO_4^=$ of the free acid.

$z/2 =$ concentration of $SO_4^=$ balancing the plus charge of the protein.

* a is small and, provided the acid does not alter the size of the protein micelles, is constant throughout.

Thus the counterpart of Eq. (13) is

$$P = \left(a + \frac{3y}{2} + \frac{z}{2} - \frac{3x}{2}\right)RT \qquad (16)$$

showing that P is lower in the case of a gelatin sulfate solution as compared with a gelatin chloride solution of the same pH value. By means of the Donnan equation $x^3 = y^2(y + z)$ applicable to the gelatin sulfate case, third-degree equations analogous to Eqs. (14) and (15) are readily developed leading to an identical conclusion.

Loeb demonstrated that similar curves are obtained for alkaline solutions of a protein, the sodium proteinate being like the gelatin chloride curve and the calcium proteinate resembling the gelatin sulfate curve.* The application of the Donnan equilibrium to the elucidation of the rise and fall of the volume of gelatin jellies with change in pH value will be made in Chap. XVIII.

When even small amounts of a neutral salt are added to an acid or to an alkaline protein solution, the osmotic pressure drops. Upon comparison of the effects of different salts it has been found that the fall in the osmotic pressure is nearly identical for a given concentration of ions of charge opposite to that of the protein, practically regardless of the valence of the like-charged ion. Further, it is found that increase in valence of these ions produces an increased fall in the osmotic pressure. This is illustrated by Fig. 101.[49] Inasmuch as neutral salts cannot increase z [Eqs. (13) to (16)] while they do increase the concentration of the ions not bound to the protein, the effect produced by their addition is analogous to that of increasing y while keeping z constant.

The depressing influence of neutral salts was likewise shown and accounted for by Loeb[21] for certain other properties of aqueous protein systems. Additions of nonelectrolytes such as sugar or glycerol were without effect. Since these exert no appreciable effect upon either y or z, this result is expected from Eqs. (13) to (16).

The Combination of Proteins with the Ions of Salts.—The formation of crystals of glycine neutral-salt addition compounds

* The student will find this treated in detail in Loeb's book.[21]

was reported about ninety years ago[50,51] but nothing further seems to have been done about it until 1912 when Pfeiffer[52] isolated a number of crystalline compounds of glycine, glycylglycylglycine, alanine, and betaine with certain halides of the alkaline earths, lithium and lanthanum. The zwitter-ion

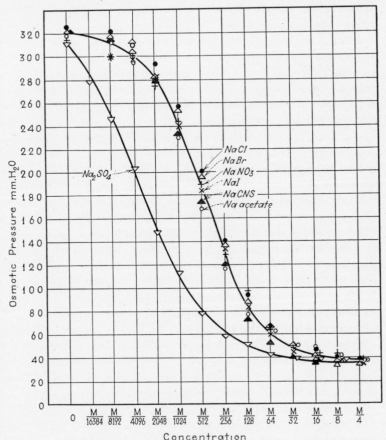

FIG. 101.—The effect of salts upon the osmotic pressure of gelatin chloride solutions (at pH 3.8).

hypothesis enables one to account for such neutral salt compounds. Pfeiffer[53] suggested the following mechanism for the combination with a neutral salt of type MeX:

$$Me^+(^-OOC \cdot R \cdot NH_3^+)X^-$$

Neutral-salt combination with amino acids may be expected to influence certain properties. The titration curve of glycine has been shown to shift to lower pH values when glycine is titrated in 1 M solution of magnesium chloride.[54]

The tendency for egg albumin to combine with ammonium sulfate is illustrated by the well-known fact of crystalline albumin being obtained in this form.

Loeb[55] discovered that lanthanum chloride and sodium ferrocyanide, when added to solutions of isoelectric gelatin, caused the gelatin to migrate to the cathode and to the anode, respectively. The effect reached a maximum at about 0.00013 M concentration of these salts. He did not find this effect with Ca^{++}, Na^+, Cl^-, or $SO_4^=$ ions. Hexammine cobalti chloride charges isoelectric albumin positively.[56] Careful experiments with gelatin revealed combination with La^{+++}, Al^{+++}, and Ca^{++} at the isoelectric point and that Cl^- combined to a less extent inasmuch as the protein became positively charged.[57] Attention must be directed toward the nature of other ions present when the isoelectric point of a protein is being measured.[58]

Even small amounts of heavy-metal cations or of anions such as ferrocyanide, picrate, dichromate, tannate, tungstate, phosphotungstate, phosphomolybdate very strikingly precipitate proteins from aqueous solution provided the pH value of the mixture is right, *e.g.*, on the alkaline side of the isoelectric point for precipitation by the heavy-metal cations and on the acid side for precipitation by the anions named. Care must be exercised when attempting to precipitate a protein by heavy-metal salts lest the pH be lowered past the isoelectric point owing to the hydrolysis of such salts. In Fig. 102,[59] one sees that the volume of precipitate from an albumin solution increased with addition of zinc chloride up to about 5×10^{-3} M zinc chloride, then decreased to a minimum at about 0.1 M, followed by a second rise. The albumin solution was originally at pH 6.1. Hence it was possible for zinc albuminates to precipitate as long as the mixture did not become too acid. It is seen that, as the pH value became less than 5.6, the volume of precipitate diminished approaching zero at about pH = 4. It is safe to say that heavy-metal proteinates precipitate on the alkaline side of the isoelectric point, at the isoelectric point, and at a few tenths of a pH on the acid side thereof. One cannot be more definite inasmuch as the combination between any one protein and a metallic ion is a specific chemical case.

The second rise in the curve is a result of the precipitation of denatured albumin. This will be discussed later. Figure 102 is in general typical of the results obtained when heavy-metal salts are added to solutions of proteins which denature, *e.g.*, the albumins and globulins.

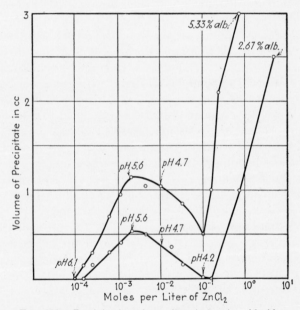

Fig. 102.—Precipitation of egg albumin by zinc chloride.

The metal-proteinate precipitate has in it some of the anion[60,61] of the precipitating salt as well as the cation, although the latter predominates.

Stoichiometric relations in the binding of metallic ions have been found by Northrop and Kunitz.[57] Copper was bound by gelatin to the extent of 9×10^{-4} equivalent per gram of gelatin, the same as for hydrogen ion. The lowered binding capacity of a "deaminized" gelatin for cupric ion equaled exactly that for hydrogen ion. La^{+++} and Al^{+++} were bound to a less extent by this gelatin, 5×10^{-4} equivalent per gram.

Owing to a mistake of Loeb's, the erroneous impression was created that combinations between proteins and cations (or anions) were sharply delimited at the isoelectric point. That this is not so has been demonstrated by experiment.[57,62,63]

The formation of insoluble protein complexes with the anions previously mentioned has not been carefully studied. It is known that, if the protein is in the form of a cation, precipitation takes place. Whether or not precipitation takes place at the isoelectric point or slightly on the alkaline side has not yet been determined.

Dyestuff ions appear to combine very firmly with proteins, which results in the formation of insoluble complexes in many instances.[64,67,68] The combination between certain proteins and a variety of dyes has been found to be stoichiometric[65,66] and in the case of a deaminized gelatin the decreased binding power of two dyes was accounted for quantitatively through the loss of the lysine amino groups.[67] The chemical nature of the combination between dyes and proteins has also been indicated by pronounced shifts in the absorption bands.[68] True chemical reaction, with resulting dye formation, is also known to take place in neutral aqueous mixtures of diazotized aromatic amines and proteins.[69]

The Salting-out of Proteins.—In 1888, Hofmeister[70] found the following order for the salting-out of "natural" egg albumin from aqueous solution:

$$SO_4 > PO_4 > acetate > citrate > HCO_3 > CrO_4 > Cl > NO_3 > ClO_3$$

$$Li > Na > K > NH_4 > Mg$$

the cations not showing as marked differences as the anions. Later Pauli[71] reported the following order:

$$F > SO_4 > PO_4 > citrate > tartrate > acetate > Cl > NO_3 > ClO_3 > Br > I > CNS$$

with the cation order the same as Hofmeister's. But he found that, if the egg-albumin solution were acidified, the orders were reversed. As a consequence of Pauli's findings, the specific case of albumin is frequently generalized to cover all proteins—

an unwarranted assumption. Pauli's finding of a reversal in acid solution may pertain to denaturation of albumin rather than to simple salting-out. The Hofmeister series is common to a variety of phenomena in colloid chemistry, crystalloid chemistry, and biology. An extensive review of these cases was made by Traube.[72] The physical chemist generally refers to such as *specific ion effects* rather than as the *Hofmeister series*. The name *lyotrope series* is also used.

The order for peptizing action on the globulins of wheat flour has been found to be[73]

$$I > Br > tartrate > Cl > SO_4 > F$$
$$Ca > Mg > Sr > Ba > Li > K > Na$$

and for the peptization of collagen:[74]

$$CNS > I > Br > Cl > SO_4 > S_2O_3$$
$$Ca > Sr > Mg > Na > K$$

Thus the reverse anion order for the salting-out of albumin on the alkaline side of its isoelectric point closely follows that for peptization of these two water-insoluble proteins. It is now believed that dilute salt solutions dissolve globulins because they form globulin-salt complexes which are soluble in water. Also it is obvious that, since salts in low concentration form complexes with proteins, the substances salted out by high concentrations of salts must be protein-salt complexes.

The solubility of amino acids in water is influenced in the lyotrope order.[52,75] For very dilute solutions the "salting-in" orders found were

$$\left. \begin{array}{l} ClO_4 > NO_3 > I > Br > CNS > Cl \\ Ca > Sr,\ Ba\text{—}Li > Na > K \end{array} \right\} \text{glycine and leucine}$$
$$\left. \begin{array}{l} NO_3 > I > Br > Cl \\ Ba > Sr > Ca\text{—}K > Na > Li \end{array} \right\} \begin{array}{l} \text{aspartic acid} \\ \text{glutamic acid} \end{array}$$

whereas for higher concentrations of the neutral salts, the salting-out orders for both of the foregoing series were reversed.

The Hofmeister series effect, so universal in chemical phenomena, has been studied by many investigators, but a satisfactory explanation is still lacking. When Loeb undertook his famous researches in 1918, the Hofmeister series (lacking, of course, any fundamental basis) was pointed out as the crux of protein behavior. He showed that alteration in protein properties was predominantly controlled by the H^+ activity and he so vigorously criticized the Hofmeister-series explanation that the impression was created in the minds of some people that he doubted its existence. This impression is erroneous because the specific ion effects are shown in his data. The effects were so small in comparison with the H^+ ion effects, however, for the low concentrations of electrolyte studied by him, that he was justified in practically ignoring them.

Denaturation.—It has long been known that certain proteins (albumins, globulins, and globins) coagulate when their aqueous solutions are heated. The "heat coagulation" of proteins has been shown to consist of two distinct processes:[76] First the protein is *denatured* and then, provided conditions are right, the denatured substance flocculates. The process of denaturation involves an as yet unsolved internal reaction. It is known that nitrogen is not split off,[77] that the acid- and base-combining capacities are unchanged,[78,79] and that sulfhydryl groups not detectable in the native protein are found in the denatured protein.[80]

The temperature coefficient for the denaturation of egg albumin is enormous,[76] about 600 for 10°; and since the coagulation is so sudden and copious when a certain temperature is reached, the "temperature of heat coagulation" has frequently been wrongly regarded as a physical constant. When a protein is denatured, it flocculates if the pH is at or close to the isoelectric point, or over a broader pH range if salts are present. Consequently, denaturation may occur without being visually obvious. However, if a dispersion of denatured protein is brought to the isoelectric point, flocculation takes place.*

Denaturation is catalyzed by increase in acidity† or alkalinity, by alcohol, acetone, urea, thiocyanate, iodide, and salicylate. As stated in Chap. X, albumin and hemoglobin denature when

---

* If one thoroughly dialyzes a solution of egg albumin against distilled water, no visual change will be observed when it is heated in boiling water or when an excess of ethyl alcohol is added. The moment a trace of electrolyte is added, however, a dense white flocculation forms.

† The influence of pH on rate of denaturation of egg albumin in aqueous solution by hydrochloric acid is shown in Fig. 103.[59]

concentrated at interfaces. Heavy-metal ions catalyze denaturation in acid solution.[59] X-rays,[81] radium emanation,[82] and ultraviolet light[83] also cause denaturation.

Denaturation is a reversible reaction.[84,85]

Molecular Weights of Proteins.—Protein chemistry has been greatly advanced in recent years by the ultracentrifugal measurements of the molecular (or micellar) weights of proteins made by Svedberg and his associates, using centrifugal machines the construction of which involved great mechanical skill and ingenuity. An oil turbine-driven machine[86] capable of running

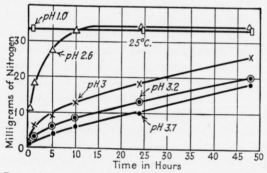

FIG. 103.—Rate of denaturation of egg albumin. The ordinates represent the amounts of denatured protein.

at a speed of 42,000 r.p.m. and giving an effect 104,000 times that of gravity* requires a flow of 240 liters of cooled oil per minute through the turbines, and 7 liters of oil per minute to lubricate and cool the bearings. The rotor, cylindrical in shape, 15 cm. in diameter, and 6 cm. thick, made of chrome nickel steel has openings drilled through it in which are inserted quartz cells containing the protein solution. The motion of the protein particles may be observed colorimetrically, by refractive index, or by absorption of ultraviolet light. The last-named process is used by Svedberg. The light rays directed upward under the rotor pass through the rotating cells and strike

* In *Science*, **79**, 327 (1934), Svedberg summarizes his ultracentrifugal technique with a description of his low- and high-speed machines. He states that the latest machine runs at speeds up to 75,000 r.p.m. and that he has found it feasible to make quantitative measurements in centrifugal fields up to 400,000 times the force of gravity.

a photographic plate above the rotor at the instant an exposure is made. Inasmuch as protein particles absorb ultraviolet rays, the concentration of protein at any point is determinable from measurements of the relative opacity at that point in comparison with protocols. For this purpose Svedberg has devised a photo-electric cell and galvanometer system for reading mechanically the density of the photographic plate. It is obvious that neither dust nor oil can be allowed to deposit in the cells. Inasmuch as temperature changes would introduce errors, it was imperative to reduce to a minimum the elevation in temperature accompanying the operation of the machine. The rotor warmed up more than 10° above room temperature in a few minutes in air at atmospheric pressure. Svedberg solved this difficulty by evacuating the rotor chamber and feeding in hydrogen to maintain a hydrogen pressure of 15 to 25 mm. of mercury for high-speed operation.

The centrifugal field may be employed in two ways for the determination of particle size: by measurement of the sedimentation velocity or by the attainment of an equilibrium between the rate of diffusion and the rate of sedimentation. The latter method requires only a moderate centrifugal force of about three hundred to nine thousand times that of gravity but a relatively long time, from two to three weeks. The sedimentation-velocity method giving results in about 1 to 5 hr. requires centrifugal forces of about one hundred thousand times that of gravity.

The theory of the sedimentation-equilibrium method as developed by Svedberg and Fahraeus[87] is as follows:

When a solution is centrifuged in a closed cell, a state of equilibrium is finally reached when sedimentation and diffusion balance each other, *i.e.*, when in the time dt the quantity ds of the solute that is driven by centrifugal force through unit surface in the direction of the periphery is the same as that which is diffusing in the direction towards the center of rotation.

For the sedimentation,

$$ds = c\omega^2 x M (1 - V\rho)\frac{1}{f}dt \qquad (17)$$

and for the diffusion

$$ds = -RT\frac{dc}{dx}\frac{1}{f}dt \qquad (18)$$

where R = the gas constant.

   T = absolute temperature.

   M = molecular weight of solute.

   f = the frictional force exerted upon a mole of solute.

   V = the partial specific volume* of solute.

   ρ = the density of solvent.

   c = the concentration.

   ω = the angular velocity of centrifuge.

   x = the distance from the center of rotation (positive in the direction toward center of rotation).

Equating and eliminating,

$$\frac{dc}{c} = -\frac{M(1 - V\rho)\omega^2 x dx}{RT}$$

Upon integrating this expression between the points x_2 and x_1 we have for the molecular weight

$$M = \frac{2RT \ln \frac{c_2}{c_1}}{\omega^2(1 - V\rho)(x_2^2 - x_1^2)} \tag{19}$$

A thermodynamic derivation of Eq. (19) is the following:[88]

In a solution subjected to a centrifugal field of force, the free energy F per mole of solute is a function of x, the distance from the axis of rotation, p the hydrostatic pressure, and c the concentration of the dissolved substance. The change in free energy from point to point in the solution is then

$$dF = \left(\frac{\partial F}{\partial x}\right)dx + \left(\frac{\partial F}{\partial p}\right)dp + \left(\frac{\partial F}{\partial c}\right)dc$$

If the centrifuging is continued long enough to enable the solute to reach equilibrium between centrifugal sedimentation and diffusion, then $dF = 0$. For a dilute solution, $\partial F/\partial x = -M\omega^2 x$; $\partial F/\partial p = MV$; $\partial F/\partial c = RT/c$; $dp = \rho\omega^2 x dx$.

* The partial specific volume of the protein is determined pycnometrically and calculated from the formula

$$V = \frac{w - (l - h)}{\rho h} \tag{20}$$

where w = weight of solvent in the pycnometer, l = weight of the solution, h = weight of the protein, and ρ = density of the solvent.

Substituting $0 = -M\omega^2xdx + MV\rho\omega^2xdx + (RT/c)dx$, or $dc/x = [M(1 - V\rho)\omega^2xdx]/RT$ and upon integration:

$$M = \frac{2RT \ln \frac{c_2}{c_1}}{\omega^2(1 - V\rho)(x_2^2 - x_1^2)} \tag{19}$$

The theory of the sedimentation velocity method follows.[89]

After a short initial period of centrifuging, the centrifugal force per mole

$$M(1 - V\rho)\omega^2x$$

becomes equal to the opposing molar frictional force $f(dx/dt)$. If it is assumed that $f = RT/D$ (where $f =$ molar frictional coefficient, $D =$ diffusion constant of the solute),

$$M = \frac{RT}{D(1 - V\rho)} \cdot \frac{1}{\omega^2x} \frac{dx}{dt} = \frac{RTs}{D(1 - V\rho)} \tag{21}*$$

for small values of x. For large values of x, the following equation [the integral of Eq. (21)] is applied:

$$M = \frac{RT \ln \frac{x_2}{x_1}}{D(1 - V\rho)\omega^2(t_2 - t_1)} \tag{22}$$

Formulas (19), (21), and (22) are valid for the determination of the molecular weight provided the osmotic laws for dilute solutions hold. It is to be noted that the equations contain well-defined, measurable quantities and no hypothetical values. Since Stokes's law is not involved in either equation, the validity is independent of the shape of the particles. Furthermore the validity rests on the absence of electrical forces which would disturb the sedimentation or diffusion.† Consequently an ionizing substance must be measured in an electrolyte-free medium at the isoelectric point or in the presence of a high concentration of a non-sedimenting electrolyte, such as potassium chloride.

* $s = (1/\omega^2x)(dx/dt)$ has been named the *sedimentation-velocity constant* by Svedberg. This is a characteristic constant for a given molecular species in a given solvent at a given temperature.

† The sedimentation of the heavy part of the molecule of an electrically dissociating substance is retarded because of the electrostatic attraction from the lighter ions.

In the derivation of Eq. (21) it was assumed that the molar coefficient of friction (f_s) which appears during sedimentation is identical with the molar coefficient of friction (f_d) of diffusion. This is not always true. A repression of diffusion by interparticle forces, weak gel formation, etc., will by means of the determination of diffusion give a value for f_d which is much larger than the true value f_s of this coefficient found in sedimentation. In diffusion the particles must be free to change their mutual positions without interference in order that a true calculation of the coefficient of friction can be made, while in sedimentation this free movement is not required. In the latter instance, by sedimentation one actually measures only the displacement of a flock of particles as a unit in the centrifugal field. There are cases then where the sedimentation velocity technique gives only the sedimentation velocity and not the molecular weight. Such anomalies in diffusion often disappear at high dilutions. Svedberg has encountered cases where they persist, however, in concentrations of a few hundredths of a per cent.

The discovery of these facts by Svedberg shows that the diffusion of highly dispersed organic colloids such as proteins and carbohydrates depends to a large extent upon the concentration and the experimental conditions. Consequently, the evaluation of molecular weight from diffusion measurements may lead to grossly erroneous values. As an example he cites[90] the normal behavior of cellulose at dilutions of about 0.05 per cent, while at 1.5 per cent the diffusion constant is twenty times smaller. Consequently, previous calculations of the molecular weight of cellulose from measurements in concentrated solutions are wrong.

On the other hand, this difficulty is avoided by use of the sedimentation-equilibrium method. While this method is often sounder for molecular-weight determinations than the sedimentation-velocity method, still the latter is indispensable for the study of the homogeneity and of the degree of symmetry of the particles, as well as for the determination of the range of pH and temperature in which a protein is stable.

The advantages of the sedimentation-velocity method are the following: By means of it the sedimentation constant (s) can be determined in a few hours, while by the sedimentation-equilibrium method several days are required. Consequently, in the shorter time there is less chance for decomposition of the solute. In the case of the presence of a mixture of different particle sizes, the sedimentation-velocity method provides a sharper analysis of the dispersity than the sedimentation-equilibrium method.

In Eq. (21), $M = \dfrac{RTs}{D(1 - V\rho)}$ and taking f (molar coefficient of friction) $= RT$, we get

$$f = \frac{M(1 - V\rho)}{s} \tag{23}$$

which can be solved by the determination of s by the velocity method and of M by the equilibrium method.

Since the coefficient of friction for a spherical particle (f_0) can be calculated by means of Stokes's law,

$$f_0 = 6\pi\eta N\left(\frac{3MV}{4\pi N}\right)^{\frac{1}{3}} \tag{24}$$

it is possible to determine whether or not the protein particles are spherical. For spherical particles the ratio $f/f_0 = 1$. Any deviation of this ratio from 1 is then a measure of the deviation of the particle from spherical symmetry. When the ratio shows that the particles are spherical, the particle diameter can be calculated by means of the equation

$$r = \sqrt[3]{\frac{3MV}{4\pi N}} \tag{25}$$

Svedberg's centrifugal methods have also rendered the important service of determining whether the particles in a given dispersion are uniform or not. For this purpose the sedimentation velocity is the most sensitive. In cases where the diffusion is marked during the centrifuging, there is noticed for a mixture a change in the diffusion constant with time. The border line becomes obliterated owing to the separation of the different particle sizes. In cases where the sedimentation takes place very quickly so that there is no diffusion during the centrifuging, for a simple solution a sharp border line is obtained, while for a mixture a border line obliterating itself with time is obtained. The discovery of the polydispersed nature (*per se* or through

TABLE 63.—MICELLAR WEIGHTS OF PROTEINS IN SOLUTION
(Determined by means of the ultracentrifuge)

Protein	Source	Micellar weight*	Sedimentation constant (s) at 20° (× 10¹³)	Molecular coefficient of friction (f) at 20° (× 10⁻¹⁶)	f/f₀	Radius of molecule, millimicrons	Reference
Group A. *Class 1:*							
Bence-Jones	Pathological urine	35,000	3.55	2.48	1.00	2.18	92
Egg albumin	Hens' eggs	34,500	3.32	2.63	1.06	2.17	88, 94, 100
Insulin	Beef pancreas	35,100	3.47	2.54	1.00	2.18	96
Class 2:							
Hemoglobin	Horse blood	68,000	4.37	3.89	1.25	†	87, 89
Serum albumin	Horse blood	67,500	4.21	4.01	1.29	†	101
Class 3:							
Serum globulin	Horse blood	103,800	5.66	4.57	1.28	†	101
Class 4:							
Amandin	Almonds	208,000	11.41	4.63	1.03	3.94	91
Cocosin	Coconut	208,000				3.95	102
Edestin	Hempseed	212,000	12.8	4.16	0.93	3.94	90, 93
Excelsin	Brazil nut	212,000	11.78	4.63	1.02	3.96	91
Legumin	Vetch	208,000	11.48	4.60	1.02	3.96	97
"C"-phycocyan	Algae	208,000	11.2	4.74	1.05	3.94	98, 103
"R"-phycocyan	Algae	206,000	11.1	4.51	1.00	3.95	103, 104
"R"-phycoerythrin	Algae	209,000	11.5	4.61	1.02	3.95	103, 104
Group B:							
"H"-hemocyanin	Blood of *Helix pomatia*	5,000,000	98.	13.5	1.05	12.0	95, 105
"L"-hemocyanin	Blood of *Limulus polyphemus*	2,000,000	35.7	14.9	1.56	†	106
"O"-hemocyanin	Blood of *Octopus vulgaris*	2,000,000	44.7	11.9	1.24	†	107
Erythrocruorin	*Arenicola marina*	2,850,000	57.4	12.3	1.14	†	116
Erythrocruorin	*Lumbricus terrestris*	2,730,000	60.9	11.1	1.05	9.3	116

* ± 3 per cent.
† Molecules not spherical.

decomposition) of certain protein solutions shows why calculations of their molecular weight by osmotic measurements have given low values in certain instances. For example, Sorensen found the value 45,000 for the molecular weight of serum albumin (by osmotic pressure), while the Svedberg technique shows 67,500 to be the correct figure. Serum albumin easily breaks down to smaller molecules.

The proteins found to be monodispersed (particles uniform in mass) in solution are listed in Table 63. Svedberg found the following to be polydispersed and in general very unstable in solution: euglobulin, fibrinogen, gelatin, gliadin, globin, glutenin,

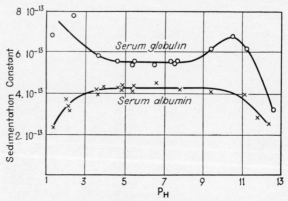

Fig. 104.—Stability as a function of pH.

histone, lactalbumin, legumelin, leucosin, muscle globulin, egg globulin, and pseudo globulin. Svedberg believes that these should be regarded as originally monodispersed particles which have been broken down partially. This view is supported by the circumstance that the monodispersed proteins become polydispersed if their isolation is not carefully done. The polydispersed globin, euglobulin and pseudo globulin arise from monodispersed proteins owing to chemical effects. Probably in the future, methods of preparation will be developed suitable for the monodispersed preparation of proteins now found as polydispersed. Svedberg's technique, making it possible to detect polydispersion, has obviously likewise provided information for testing the stability of protein molecules in solution. In Fig. 104[90] are given two of his sedimentation-constant curves.

It is seen that serum albumin breaks into smaller particles beyond the limits of the stability range, while serum globulin tends to aggregate before it degenerates, at least on the alkaline side. Table 64 lists the pH stability ranges for several proteins as reported from Svedberg's laboratory.

TABLE 64.—pH STABILITY RANGE OF SOME PROTEINS

Protein	Source	Stable in the pH range of	Reference
Amandin	Almonds	4.3 to 10.0	91
Bence-Jones	Pathological urine	3.5 to 7.5	92
Edestin	Hempseed	5.5 to 9.7	93
Egg albumin	Hens' eggs	4.0 to 9.0	94
Erythrocruorin	Blood of *Arenicola marina*	2.6 to 8.0	116
Erythrocruorin	Blood of *Lumbricus terrestris*	2.6 to 10.0	116
Excelsin	Brazil nuts	5.5 to 10.0	91
Hemocyanin	Blood of *Helix pomatia*	4.5 to 7.4	95
CO-hemoglobin	Horse blood hemoglobin plus CO	6.0 to 9.05	89
Insulin	Beef pancreas	4.5 to 7.0	96
Legumin	Vetch	5.0 to 9.0	97
Phycocyan	*Ceramium rubrum*	1.5 to 8.0	98
Serum albumin	Horse blood	4.0 to 9.0	94
Serum globulin	Horse blood	4.0 to 8.0	99

Examination of Table 63 reveals that the molecular weights of the monodispersed proteins fall in two groups: group A, molecular weights between about 35,000 and 210,000, and group B molecular weights in the millions. In the A group, four classes are outstanding:

    1. Molecular weight = 34,500.
    2. Molecular weight = about twice 34,500.
    3. Molecular weight = about thrice 34,500.
    4. Molecular weight = about six times 34,500.

Beyond the pH stability range of the proteins of higher molecular weight in group A, Svedberg noticed that the proteins generally decomposed into particles of molecular weights of one, two, or three times 34,500. Furthermore, he found in such degenerations that the electrochemical and optical properties of the substance suffered but very slight influence. Upon degradation below a molecular weight of 34,500, however, these properties altered considerably. All of these facts impress Svedberg to the view that all proteins are probably similar in structure, consisting of aggregates of primary 34,500 molecular-weight particles.

The ultracentrifuge has shown that casein isolated from cows' milk and purified by Hammarsten's method (or by any method wherein the casein is subjected to temperatures over 40°) has a molecular weight of 375,000 in a solution at pH 6.8. A casein preparation obtained by the van Slyke and Baker method (not heated) was polydispersed, the molecular weight being 75,000 to 100,000.[108] An ultracentrifugal study of gelatin[109] in aqueous solution has revealed that there is very marked aggregation within the region of pH 4.6 to 6.0—the more so the nearer to the isoelectric point—whereas at pH 4.0 and 7.5 there is no aggregation. Sedimentation-equilibrium tests on gelatin solutions at pH 4 showed a drift in the values of the molecular weight from 70,000 to about 10,000. At pH 2.5 there was no appreciable sedimentation in gelatin solutions even at a centrifugal force corresponding to 100,000 times that of gravity, thus indicating that at this pH value the gelatin micelles had been largely decomposed.

Svedberg has made the most extensive survey of the molecular weights of proteins in solution. Results obtained by other investigators who used different methods are given in Table 65.

TABLE 65.—MOLECULAR WEIGHTS OF SOME PROTEINS

Protein	Source	Method	Molecular weight	Reference
Egg albumin.....	Hens' eggs	Osmotic pressure	34,000	110
Egg albumin.....	Hens' eggs	Diffusion	34,000	117
Hemoglobin......	Blood of man, horse, sheep	Osmotic pressure	66,800	111
CO-hemoglobin...	Blood of beef + CO	Diffusion	68,600	112
Serum albumin...	....	Osmotic pressure	62,000	113
Serum albumin...	Horse blood	Osmotic pressure	72,000	114
Serum albumin...	Horse blood	Osmotic pressure	74,600	115

References

1. KLARMANN: *Chem. Rev.*, **4**, 51 (1927).
2. WALKER: *Z. physik. Chem.*, **36**, 546 (1901).
3. ADAMS: *J. Am. Chem. Soc.*, **38**, 1503 (1916).
4. BJERRUM: *Z. physik. Chem.*, **104**, 147 (1923).
5. HARRIS: *Proc. Roy. Soc. (London)*, **97B**, 364 (1925); **104B**, 412 (1929).
6. HARRIS: *Biochem. J.*, **24**, 1080 (1930); BIRCH and HARRIS: *ibid.*, 1086.
7. BORSOOK and MACFADYEN: *J. Gen. Physiol.*, **13**, 509 (1930).
8. EBERT: *Z. physik. Chem.*, **121**, 385 (1926).
9. EDSALL and BLANCHARD: *J. Am. Chem. Soc.*, **55**, 2337 (1933).
10. MICHAELIS and MOSTYNSKI: *Biochem. Z.*, **24**, 79 (1910); MICHAELIS and DAVIDSOHN: *Biochem. Z.*, **30**, 143 (1911); MICHAELIS: *Biochem. Z.*, **33**, 182 (1911).
11. MICHAELIS: "Hydrogen Ion Concentration," translation by Perlzweig, p. 65, Williams & Wilkins Co., Baltimore, 1926.
12. MICHAELIS: *Biochem. Z.*, **47**, 250 (1912).
13. MICHAELIS and DAVIDSOHN: *Biochem. Z.*, **30**, 143 (1911).
14. LEVENE and SIMMS: *J. Biol. Chem.*, **55**, 801 (1923).
15. BUGARSKY and LIEBERMAN: *Arch. ges. Physiol.*, **72**, 51 (1898).
16. OSBORNE: *J. Am. Chem. Soc.*, **21**, 486 (1899); **24**, 39 (1902).
17. HARDY: *Proc. Roy. Soc. (London)*, **66**, 110 (1900); *J. Physiol.*, **24**, 158, 288 (1899).
18. HARDY: *J. Physiol.*, **33**, 351 (1905–1906).
19. D'AGOSTINO and QUAGLIARIELLO: Nernst Festschrift, 27 (1912); through COHN: *Physiol. Rev.*, **5**, 349 (1925).
20. COHN: *Physiol. Rev.*, **5**, 349 (1925), in connection with the criticism of the view of Hoffman-Gortner; see also STEARN: *J. Gen. Physiol.*, **11**, 377 (1928); PERTZOFF and CARPENTER: *ibid.*, **16**, 257 (1932).
21. LOEB: "Proteins and the Theory of Colloidal Behavior," McGraw-Hill Book Company, Inc., New York, 1925.
22. HOFFMAN and GORTNER: Second Colloid Symposium Monograph, p. 209, Chemical Catalog Company, New York, 1925; GORTNER and HOFFMAN: *Science*, **62**, 464 (1925).
23. JORDAN LLOYD: *Proc. Roy. Soc. (London)*, **93B**, 69 (1922).
24. DAVIS, OAKES and SALISBURY: *Ind. Eng. Chem.*, **15**, 182 (1923).
25. COHN and BERGGREN: *J. Gen. Physiol.*, **7**, 45 (1924).
26. HITCHCOCK: *J. Gen. Physiol.*, **16**, 357 (1932).
27. HITCHCOCK: *J. Gen. Physiol.*, **14**, 99 (1930).
28. HITCHCOCK: *J. Gen. Physiol.*, **15**, 125 (1931).
29. HITCHCOCK: *J. Gen. Physiol.*, **12**, 495 (1929).
30. BACON: *J. Phys. Chem.*, **33**, 1843 (1929).
31. FERGUSON and SCHLUCHTER: *J. Gen. Physiol.*, **15**, 463 (1932).
32. COHN, BERGGREN, and HENDRY: *J. Gen. Physiol.*, **7**, 81 (1924).
33. HITCHCOCK: *J. Gen. Physiol.*, **6**, 95 (1923).
34. SIMMS: *J. Gen. Physiol.*, **11**, 629 (1928).
35. LOEBEL: *J. Phys. Chem.*, **32**, 763 (1928).

36. PAULI: *Beitr. chem. Physiol. Path.*, **7**, 531 (1906).

37. PAULI and HANDOVSKY: *ibid.*, **11**, 415 (1908).

38. MICHAELIS: *Biochem. Z.*, **19**, 181 (1909).

39. LOEB: *J. Gen. Physiol.*, **1**, 363 (1918–1919).

40. SORENSEN and HOYRUP: *Compt.-rend. trav. lab. Carlsberg*, **12**, 213 (1915–1917).

41. FERRY: *J. Biol. Chem.*, **57**, 819 (1923).

42. HEIDELBERGER: *J. Biol. Chem.*, **53**, 31 (1922).

43. RONA and MICHAELIS: *Biochem. Z.*, **28**, 193 (1910).

44. MICHAELIS and MENDELSSOHN: *Biochem. Z.*, **65**, 1 (1914).

45. MICHAELIS and PECHSTEIN: *Biochem. Z.*, **47**, 260 (1914).

46. GERNGROSS and BACH: *Biochem. Z.*, **143**, 542 (1923).

47. REINER and MARTON: *Kolloid-Z.*, **32**, 276 (1923).

48. LOEB and KUNITZ: *J. Gen. Physiol.*, **5**, 665 (1923).

49. LOEB and KUNITZ: *J. Gen. Physiol.*, **5**, 693 (1923).

50. BOUSSINGAULT: *Ann. Chemie*, **39**, 310 (1841).

51. HORSFORD: *Ann. Chemie*, **60**, 1 (1846).

52. PFEIFFER and MODELSKI: *Z. physiol. Chem.*, **81**, 329 (1912); **85**, 1 (1913); also see KING and RUTTERFORD: *J. Chem. Soc.*, **1931**, 3131.

53. PFEIFFER: *Z. angew. Chem.*, **36**, 137 (1923).

54. LEUTHARDT: *Helvetica Chim. Acta*, **15**, 540 (1932).

55. LOEB: *J. Gen. Physiol.*, **4**, 741 (1922).

56. ITO: *Biochem. Z.*, **233**, 444 (1931).

57. NORTHROP and KUNITZ: *J. Gen. Physiol.*, **11**, 481 (1928); also see THIMANN: *J. Gen. Physiol.*, **14**, 215 (1930); ORYNG and PAULI: *Biochem. Z.*, **70**, 368 (1915).

58. PRZYLECKI: *Compt. rend. soc. biol.*, **104**, 1079 (1930).

59. THOMAS and NORRIS: *J. Am. Chem. Soc.*, **47**, 501 (1925).

60. PAULI and SCHOEN: *Biochem. Z.*, **153**, 253 (1924).

61. BECHHOLD: *Biochem. Z.*, **199**, 451 (1928); SCHORN: *ibid.*, 459; HEYMANN and OPPENHEIMER: *ibid.*, 468.

62. CARROLL and HUBBARD: *Bur. Standards J. Research*, **7**, 811 (1931).

63. KRUYT and BOLEMAN: *Kolloidchem. Beihefte*, **35**, 165 (1932).

64. UMETSU: *Biochem. Z.*, **137**, 258 (1923).

65. RAWLINS and SCHMIDT: *J. Biol. Chem.*, **82**, 709 (1929); **88**, 271 (1930).

66. STEARN: *J. Phys. Chem.*, **34**, 973 (1930); *J. Biol. Chem.*, **91**, 325 (1931).

67. CHAPMAN, GREENBERG, and SCHMIDT: *J. Biol. Chem.*, **72**, 707 (1927).

68. HEWITT: *Biochem. J.*, **21**, 1305 (1927).

69. HEIDELBERGER and KENDALL: *Proc. Soc. Exptl. Biol. Med.*, **26**, 482 (1929).

70. HOFMEISTER: *Arch. exptl. Path. Pharmakol.*, **24**, 247 (1888).

71. PAULI: *ibid.*, **3**, 223 (1903); **5**, 27 (1904); see also POSTERNACK: *Ann. inst. Pasteur*, **15**, 85, 169, 451, 570 (1901).

72. TRAUBE: *Arch. ges. Physiol.*, **132**, 511 (1910); *J. Phys. Chem.*, **14**, 452 (1910).

73. GORTNER, HOFFMAN, and SINCLAIR: Fifth Colloid Symposium Monograph, Chemical Catalog Company, New York, p. 179, 1928.

74. GUSTAVSON: *J. Am. Leather Chem. Assoc.*, **21**, 366 (1926).
75. PFEIFFER and WURGLER: *Z. physiol. Chem.*, **97**, 128 (1916); see also ANDO: *Biochem. Z.*, **173**, 426 (1926).
76. CHICK and MARTIN: *J. Physiol.*, **40**, 404 (1910); **43**, 1 (1911–1912); **45**, 61, 261 (1912–1913); for a short review see ANSON and MIRSKY: *J. Phys. Chem.*, **35**, 185 (1931); LEWIS: *Chem. Rev.*, **8**, 81 (1931).
77. SORENSEN and SORENSEN: *Compt. rend. trav. lab. Carlsberg*, (9) **15**, 1 (1925).
78. BOOTH: *Biochem. J.*, **24**, 158 (1930).
79. LEWIS: *Biochem. J.*, **21**, 46 (1927).
80. ARNOLD: *Z. physiol. Chem.*, **70**, 300 (1910).
81. WELS and THIELE: *Arch. ges. Physiol.*, **209**, 49 (1925).
82. FERNAU and PAULI: *Biochem. Z.*, **70**, 426 (1915); *Kolloid-Z.*, **30**, 6 (1922).
83. CLARK: *Am. J. Physiol.*, **73**, 647 (1925).
    SPIEGEL-ADOLF: *Biochem. Z.*, **213**, 475 (1929).
84. ANSON and MIRSKY: *J. Gen. Physiol.*, **9**, 169 (1925), and a series of papers in the same journal, **13, 14, 15**; *Physiol. Rev.*, **10**, 506 (1930); *J. Phys. Chem.*, **35**, 185 (1931).
85. SPIEGEL-ADOLF: *Biochem. Z.*, **170**, 126 (1926); **204**, 1 (1929).
86. For descriptions of Svedberg's ultracentrifuge and the theoretical development of the method see SVEDBERG and NICHOLS: *J. Am. Chem. Soc.*, **49**, 2920 (1927); SVEDBERG and SJOGREN: *J. Am. Chem. Soc.*, **51**, 3594 (1929); NICHOLS: *Physics*, **1**, 254 (1931); SVEDBERG: "Colloid Chemistry," A.C.S. Monograph, Chemical Catalog Company, New York, 1928; SVEDBERG: *Kolloid-Z.*, **51**, 10 (1930).
87. SVEDBERG and FAHRAEUS: *J. Am. Chem. Soc.*, **48**, 430 (1926).
88. SVEDBERG and NICHOLS: *J. Am. Chem. Soc.*, **48**, 3081 (1926).
89. SVEDBERG and NICHOLS: Ref. 86.
90. SVEDBERG: *Kolloid-Z.*, **51**, 10 (1930).
91. SVEDBERG and SJOGREN: *J. Am. Chem. Soc.*, **52**, 279 (1930).
92. SVEDBERG and SJOGREN: *ibid.*, **51**, 3594 (1929).
93. SVEDBERG and STAMM: *J. Am. Chem. Soc.*, **51**, 2170 (1929).
94. SJOGREN and SVEDBERG: *ibid.*, **52**, 5187 (1930).
95. SVEDBERG and HEYROTH: *ibid.*, **51**, 550 (1929).
96. SJOGREN and SVEDBERG: *ibid.*, **53**, 2657 (1931).
97. SJOGREN and SVEDBERG: *ibid.*, **52**, 3279 (1930).
98. SVEDBERG and ERIKSSON: *ibid.*, **54**, 3998 (1932).
99. SVEDBERG and SJOGREN: *ibid.*, **52**, 2855 (1930).
100. NICHOLS: *ibid.*, **52**, 5176 (1930).
101. SVEDBERG and SJOGREN: *ibid.*, **50**, 3318 (1928).
102. SJOGREN and SPYCHALSKI: *ibid.*, **52**, 4400 (1930).
103. SVEDBERG and KATSURAI: *ibid.*, **51**, 3573 (1929).
104. SVEDBERG and LEWIS: *ibid.*, **50**, 525 (1928).
105. SVEDBERG and CHIRNOAGA: *ibid.*, **50**, 1399 (1928).
106. SVEDBERG and HEYROTH: *ibid.*, **51**, 539 (1929).

107. Svedberg and Eriksson: *ibid.*, **54**, 4730 (1932).
108. Svedberg, Carpenter, and Carpenter: *ibid.*, **52**, 241, 701 (1930); Carpenter: *ibid.*, **53**, 1812 (1931).
109. Krishnamurti and Svedberg: *ibid.*, **52**, 2897 (1930).
110. Sorensen: *Z. physiol. Chem.*, **106**, 1 (1919).
111. Adair: *Proc. Roy. Soc. (London)*, **109**A, 292 (1925).
112. Northrop and Anson: *J. Gen. Physiol.*, **12**, 543 (1929).
113. Adair: *Skand. Arch. Physiol.*, **49**, 76 (1926); through Ref. 115.
114. Adair and Robinson: *Biochem. J.*, **24**, 1864 (1930).
115. Burk: *J. Biol. Chem.*, **98**, 353 (1932).
116. Svedberg and Eriksson: *J. Am. Chem. Soc.*, **55**, 2834 (1933).
117. McBain, Dawson, and Barker: *J. Am. Chem. Soc.*, **56**, 1021 (1934).

CHAPTER XIII

CARBOHYDRATE COLLOIDS

Cellulose.—Ultimate analysis of cellulose shows that its empirical formula is $C_6H_{10}O_5$. Hydrolysis catalyzed by acid yields glucose as the principal product.

The micelle of cellulose consists of elongated bundles of 40 to 60 long chains held by molecular-cohesive forces in close parallel orientation, the chains being 50 to 80 hexosan units in length, the hexose anhydrides being bound together through strong primary-valence unions. Molecular-cohesive forces have also been suggested as the reason for the connection between

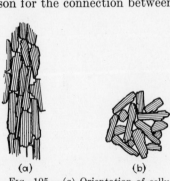

(a)   (b)

FIG. 105.—(a) Orientation of cellulose micelles in ramie; (b) orientation of cellulose micelles in Cellophane.

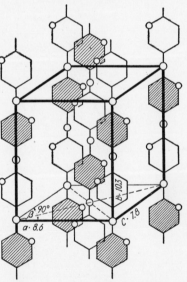

FIG. 106.—Schematic representation of the unit cell for cellulose, showing positions of long primary valence chains. The hexosan units are alternately light and shaded to denote spiral orientation about the b axis.

the chains constituting the fibrils. A picture of cellulose micelles in ramie fiber[1] is shown in Fig. 105a. Here the micelles are oriented longitudinally. On the other hand, the examination

361

of Cellophane reveals a haphazard orientation of the micelles
as illustrated in Fig. 105b.

X-ray diffraction analysis of the cellulose micelle shows[2,3] a
repetition called the *unit cell* consisting of four $C_6H_{10}O_5$ groups.
The dimensions of this unit cell are $a = 8.35$ Å, $b = 10.3$ Å
(along the fiber axis), and $c = 7.9$ Å. A scheme for this cell is
shown in Fig. 106.[2] Each glucosan group is so arranged that a

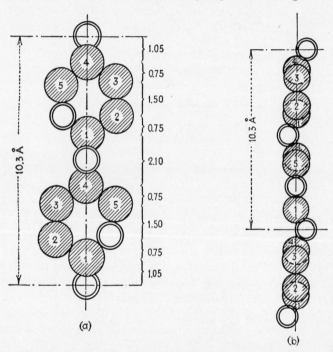

(a)

(b)

Fig. 107.—(a) Two hexosan units united by a 1–4 glucosidic linkage viewed
in the plane of the 1–5 ring. The large dark circles represent carbon atoms;
the smaller double circles are oxygen atoms. The hydrogen atoms are omitted.
(b) The same as in (a) but viewed from the side. In order to render the construction clearer, three hexosan radicals are drawn upon each other.

six-membered ring is formed with five carbons and one oxygen,
the rings being glucosidically bound by 1–4 oxygen linkages, as
in cellobiose. The rings are ordered in the direction of the
fiber in the form of a digonal screw. The structure of these
cellobiose chains may be better visualized by the models[2] shown
in Figs. 107a and 107b.

In chemical reactions of cellulose where it is not decomposed to glucose, as, for example, in the action of alkalies, formation of esters or of ethers, the chains remain intact longitudinally while the reagents accumulate laterally on the chains, causing an opening up and, under certain circumstances, a disruption of the cross section. In solutions of cellulose or of its derivatives the particles present are of such size as to correspond to micelles of the solid substance. Hence the cellulose micelle in either solid or dissolved state may be regarded as a bundle of adhering primary valence chains.

When cellulose fibers are treated with solutions of alkalies in concentrations over 12 per cent, *mercerization* occurs. The X-ray diagram of mercerized cellulose (after washing free from alkali) shows that no change has taken place longitudinally, but that there has been a slight lateral enlargement. A turning of the cellobiose chains about the fiber axis through an angle of approximately 45°, half clockwise and half counterclockwise, supplies an arrangement which agrees with the X-ray data.[1] The lateral enlargement gives mercerized cellulose, an inner micellar surface about double that of untreated cellulose.[4] This accounts for its superiority for dyeing, viscose formation, etc.

Various kinds of cellulose both dry and also swollen with up to 23 per cent water showed the identical X-ray diagrams,[5] thus indicating that the imbibed water was not bound in the unit cells. Cellulose which has been dissolved in an aqueous solution of $[Cu(NH_3)_4](OH)_2$ (Schweitzer's reagent) shows on regeneration, by precipitation with hydrochloric acid, little alteration in its X-ray diffraction. As the cellulose dissolves in Schweitzer's reagent, the partial pressure of the ammonia increases. More copper hydroxide can then be dissolved in the mixture, which results in quite a high concentration of copper and cellulose in combination.

It has been shown[6] that the corresponding ethylenediamine compound, copper diethylenediamine hydroxide is an equally good solvent for cellulose. It has also been demonstrated[6] that $[Cu\ en_2](OH)_2$ reacts with polyhydroxyl compounds such as glycerol, mannitol, and sucrose, forming alcoholates and that these alcoholate solutions are capable of dissolving large quantities of copper hydroxide. These reactions may be expressed by the equations

$$2CH_2OH.CHOH.CH_2OH + [Cu\ en_2](OH)_2 \rightleftharpoons$$
$$[Cu\ en_2](OCH_2 \cdot C_2H_5O_2)_2 + 2H_2O$$

$$[Cu\ en_2](OCH_2.C_2H_5O_2)_2 + Cu(OH)_2 =$$
$$[Cu\ en_2](OCH_2CHOH.CH_2O)_2Cu + 2H_2O$$

or

$$2CH_2OH.CHOH.CH_2OH + 2[Cu\ en_2](OH)_2 =$$
$$[Cu\ en_2][(OCH_2.CHOH.CH_2O)_2Cu] + 4H_2O + 2(en)$$

The parallelism between these two solution processes leads one to suspect that cellulose forms a similar type of compound with copper and ammonia.[7]

Stamm[8] has, by means of Svedberg's ultracentrifuge technique, found cellulose of pure cotton linters in cuprammonium solvent to be monodispersed and to have a molecular weight of 40,000 ± 5,000.

The cuprammonium solution of cellulose is optically active,[9] varying with the relation of dissolved copper to dissolved cellulose, reaching a specific rotation of about −1000° for 1 g. cellulose and 1 g. $Cu(OH)_2$ in 100 cc. of 24 per cent aqueous NH_3.[7]

Cold zinc chloride solutions mercerize cotton in a manner similar to alkali.[10] Hot concentrated solutions as well as those of the chlorides of antimony, mercury, bismuth, tin, and titanium disperse cellulose, accompanied by some decomposition of it.

Many experiments upon the dispersion of cellulose in solutions of neutral salts have been made by von Veimarn,[11] who found the dispersion order

$$Ca > Sr > Ba > Li > Na > K$$
$$CNS > I > Br > Cl$$

The dispersion in neutral salt solutions is carried out by heating in an autoclave, although a high temperature is not required when calcium thiocyanate is used. A solution of this salt so concentrated as to boil at 135 to 140° dissolves bleached cotton to form 10 to 12 per cent solutions at 80 to 100°.[12] On cooling a clear stiff jelly forms. Precipitation of such cellulose solutions by dilution with water yields a product whose X-ray pattern is that of mercerized cellulose.[13]

Hydrogen chloride is bound by cellulose in the ratio of 1 mole hydrogen chloride to each 24 carbon atoms.[14] It is suggested that it combines probably as an oxonium salt[14] because it cannot be removed by gassing with carbon dioxide.

Perchloric acid in not too concentrated aqueous solutions at $0°$ causes cellulose to swell and combines with it in the ratio of 1 mole $HClO_4$ to one cellobiose anhydride.[15] X-ray examination showed the characteristic diagram, the unit cell having the dimensions, $a = 16.5$, $b = 10.3$, and $c = 10.7$ Å.

Numerous studies upon the action of alkalies on cellulose have been made on account of its importance in mercerization and swelling of cellulose, the latter being necessary for the action of carbon bisulfide in the viscose process. Some hold to the view that alkalies are physically adsorbed by cellulose, while others claim chemical combination.[16]

Some investigators contend that reported sorptive properties of cellulose are due to impurities contained therein. Michaelis and Rona[17] found that a surface-active nonelectrolyte such as *n*-octyl alcohol is sorbed only in merest traces, while the apparent sorptions of dyes such as methylene blue hydrochloride and of the ammonium salt of eosin were mere "exchange adsorptions" with ash constituents of the cellulose. The same opinion was shared by Kolthoff[18] concerning the sorption of alkaloids and heavy-metal ions by filter paper. The sorption of alumina from aluminum salt solutions by ash-free cellulose has been found to be distinct although small and is enhanced by presence of ash in the paper.[19]

Chemical combination between carbon bisulfide and alkali cellulose is believed to exist, forming cellulose xanthogenates. These dissolve in alkaline water but are not stable. When these aqueous solutions are ejected through orifices into acid solutions, the cellulose is precipitated forming "Viscose."

Esters and ethers of cellulose are numerous, the most common being the nitrates and acetates. According to the amount of nitro or aceto groups per $C_6H_{10}O_5$ unit, trinitro (or aceto), di-, and mononitro (or aceto) compounds have been postulated. X-ray diagrams, however, reveal the presence of definite crystallites for the trinitro and triaceto esters only.[20] Compounds of lower degree of esterification give the superposed patterns of the triester and unchanged cellulose.

Starches.—Since it has long been known that starches yield glucose upon acid hydrolysis, the empirical formula $(C_6H_{10}O_5)_x$ has been ascribed to them. But starches are not so simple. The intimate binding of phosphorus[21,22,23] in the starch micelle has been known for at least thirty years. Chemically bound fatty acid has also been demonstrated.[24]

Since 1825, starch granules have been known to consist of two portions, one soluble in water and the other insoluble.[25] The water-insoluble fraction, giving a purplish color with iodin, is now called *α-amylose* (formerly *amylopectin*) and the soluble fraction, coloring deep blue with iodin, is now known as *β-amylose* (formerly *amylose*).

Considerable confusion concerning these amyloses and the extent of their occurrence in starches existed until the thorough researches of Taylor and his colleagues[26 to 30] greatly clarified our knowledge concerning their nature, occurrence, and technique of separation. These investigators have shown that the fatty acids and, in some cases, the phosphorus* (the latter as a substituted phosphoric acid) are bound in the α-amylose, the β-amylose being pure carbohydrate. The fatty acids predominate in the cereal starches, while phosphorus is common to the tuber starches. In the case of cornstarch, the presence of palmitic, oleic, and linoleic acids was established. Taylor found that β-amylose does not migrate in an electric field, while α-amylose migrates to the anode, on account of the ionization of its noncarbohydrate constituents. Based on this electrical difference Taylor and his colleagues devised an electrodialytic method for separation of the amyloses.

It is essential that all the granules of raw starch be disrupted before application of electrodialysis. A method applied to cereal starches[30] was as follows:

Two hundred fifty grams of air-dried starch was made into a paste with 170 cc. of alcohol, mixed with 150 cc. of alcoholic hydrogen chloride (0.08 g.

---

* In wheat starch the phosphorus is found primarily in the α-amylose. Potato starch, on the other hand, appears to consist of a series of β-amylose phosphates.

HCl per cubic centimeter of alcoholic HCl reagent) and stirred for 1 hr. at 50°. The magma was then suction filtered and washed free from hydrochloric acid by alcohol. The starch thus treated was introduced slowly into a large mortar containing 90 g. of ammonium thiocyanate in 450 cc. of water and 120 cc. of alcohol. After being ground for 1 hr., the solution became fluid and translucent, microscope examination showing that all granules had been disrupted. The gelatinized starch was thereupon precipitated by alcohol and dehydrated by vigorous and prolonged grinding with absolute alcohol. After washing with ether and drying in air 80 g. was mixed with 300 cc. of alcohol, introduced into 4 liters of water at about 55° with vigorous stirring, and the resulting suspension was submitted to electrodialysis.[28] As an upper clear layer of β-amylose solution formed, it was siphoned off, distilled water added, and the procedure repeated until the upper layer no longer gave a test with iodin. The β-amylose was precipitated by alcohol. The α-amylose was collected on a suction filter and dehydrated by a current of air at 100°.

By means of this type method Taylor and his colleagues arrived at the amylose compositions of some common starches as shown in Table 66.

TABLE 66.—COMPOSITION OF SOME STARCHES

Starch	α-Amylose, per cent	β-Amylose, per cent
Corn	15	85
Rice	18	82
Potato	3(?)	97
Wheat	23.5	76.5
Cassava (tapioca)	16.5	83.5

In 1924, Alsberg[31] showed that prolonged grinding of dry starch disrupts the granules so that leaching with cold water dissolves the β-amylose. Taylor and Beckmann[29] found on application of this mechanical method the same percentage distribution of the amyloses, showing that their own chemical method of disruption had not altered the starches.

X-ray studies of starches, particularly by Katz, have revealed crystalline structure,[32] but the diagrams are not sufficiently clear to deduce exactly structural characteristics. Naray-Szabo[33] has, after X-ray examination of 17 native starches, classified them in two groups: those similar to potato starch and those like rice starch. The spectra of the former are characterized by a strongly marked inner ring which is absent in the latter. This ring permits the calculation of the distance between the planes in the lattice as 16.0 Å. This investigator calculated the volume of the unit cell to be 2.524×10^{-21} cm., which embraces 16 $C_6H_{10}O_5$ groups. He points out that the variation in the X-ray pictures between the two groups was not ascribable to variations in the α-amylose content or to contamination or deformation.

Meyer, Hopff, and Mark[34] contend that X-ray spectra so far do not afford any basis for the establishment of any picture of starch constitution other than that certain parts of the starch are arranged in lattice formation which is connected with the presence of hydrate water. They say that completely dried starch displays only very indistinct interference rings and they have been unable by spinnng of threads, tension, or pressure so to orient the starch micelle that it showed a fiber diagram. From these facts they postulate that the primary-valence chains in starch are shorter than those in cellulose and are not oriented in long parallel bundles but are in some other as yet unknown arrangement.

Starch grains swell in water under the influence of heat and the presence of acid, alkali, and salts. The swelling is affected by salts in the Hofmeister-series order,[35] thiocyanate being the most potent. The nonelectrolytes urea and chloral have a very marked swelling influence upon starch granules in aqueous suspension.

The mechanism of the formation of starch pastes, a subject of industrial importance, has recently been studied in a new manner by Caesar.[36] He measured the power in watts required to stir a heated mixture of starch granules and water. The results of such a study made upon five specimens of starch at 20 per cent concentration are plotted in Fig. 108. The ordinates represent watts, while the abscissas have different significances. In the "heating zone," the abscissas represent temperature of the water jacket, in the "boiling zone" hours, and in the "cooling zone" minutes. Thus the wattage is recorded for the heating-up period, for the period of 2 hr. when the water in the jacket surrounding the container of starch paste was boiling, and for the cooling period while water at 55°F. (12.5°C.) was circulating through the jacket.

The curve for each variety of starch then represents what may be termed its "consistency history" from a suspension of the granules to a cold paste. In the first range, that of swelling of the granules, potato and tapioca starches are much alike. Corn and sago also act alike in reaching the maximum consistency but requiring a higher temperature than potato starch. After the maximum consistency is reached, however, corn and sago differ markedly in behavior. It is seen that the swelling of wheat starch is very slow; when it reached its peak (at 200°F.), the consistencies of the others showed marked losses.

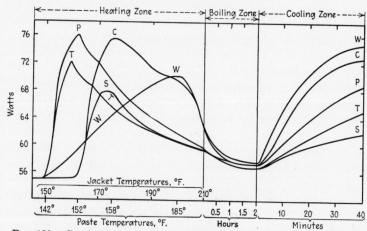

Fig. 108.—Consistency changes in commercial starches mixed with water to a 20 per cent concentration. In the "Heating Zone" the total time to reach the boiling point in the jacket was 95 min. After 2 hr. at the boiling point ("Boiling Zone") in the jacket water, the pastes were cooled by running water at 55°F., through the jacket ("Cooling Zone"). *C*, corn starch; *P*, potato starch; *S*, sago flour; *T*, tapioca flour; and *W*, wheat starch.

Examination of the pastes under a microscope showed the reason for this part of the curves. At 185°F., the wheat-starch grains were practically intact, very little rupture or distortion having taken place. Above 185°, a marked degree of cell rupture was noticed. The grains of tapioca, potato, and sago starches were found relatively fragile. It was also noted that in any given starch the larger granules were the first to swell, the smallest granules being the most resistant to swelling. In the cooling zone, pronounced variations again occurred, potato, tapioca, and sago starches forming rather viscous pastes, while wheat and cornstarches set to plastic jellies (the curves for the latter being misleading on this account).

Investigations of this sort yield information of great value to the industrial chemist. Since for an adhesive the best result theoretically is obtained when the granules have been swollen to the maximum extent and just before their rupture, potato starch is the best for the purpose because it so readily reaches its maximum consistency.

So-called *soluble starches* have been prepared for diverse purposes. The word "soluble" merely means that they form solutions of low viscosity and disperse more readily in warm water than raw starch does. The "solubilizing" treatments include prolonged action of cold dilute acid on aqueous suspensions of starch grains, the action of oxidizing agents, heating in glycerol, and dry grinding.

The cooling of an aqueous solution of a glycerol "solubilized" starch to the jelly state has been examined by means of the X-ray.[37] A solution of 50 per cent of this starch and 50 per cent water, which was clear at 90°, showed an amorphous spectrum; but as it cooled and jellied, a typical crystalline spectrum developed. This disappeared on reheating and reappeared when again cooled.

Just as esters of cellulose have been prepared, so also have starch esters been made. At present they are not important commercially, with the possible exception of "nitrostarch."*

Pectin.—Pectin, or rather its precursor protopectin, is widely distributed in fruits, vegetables, and other parts of plants. The first preparation of a pectic substance was made by Payen,[38] in 1824, and, in 1825, Braconnot[39] first described pectin as the gelatinous principle of fruits. The distinction between pectin and its insoluble precursor protopectin was first made by Fremy.[40] It was later described as a pectin-cellulose[41] complex, this view being held today.[42] Protopectin predominates in immature fruit, being converted to pectin upon ripening.

Hydrolytic agents convert pectin through a series of acidic bodies to an ultimate pectic acid. As a result of the multiplicity

---

* The literature on the starches has been thoroughly reviewed by Walton in his book "A Comprehensive Survey of Starch Chemistry," Chemical Catalog Company, New York, 1928.

of complex colloids arising from the original protopectin, the nomenclature in the literature is confusing. Here we shall adhere to the following terminology:

Protopectin[43] (*pectose,*[44] *pectinogen*). The water-insoluble pectic substances present in the cell walls of plant tissues, apparently in association with cellulose.
Pectin. The water-soluble, completely methoxylated pectic substance as it occurs in plant tissues or as obtained by treatment of protopectin.
Pectinic acids.[44] The primary hydrolysis products of pectin, with varying methoxy content.
Pectic acid. Completely demethoxylated pectin.

The history of the revelations of the constituents of pectin substances, while an interesting example of the difficulties

$$C_5 H_8 O_4 - C_6 H_{10} O_5 - [C_5 H_7 O_4 (COOCH_3)]_4$$

Pectin

$$C_5 H_8 O_4 - C_6 H_{10} O_5 - [C_5 H_7 O_4]_4 (COOH)_{4-n} (COOCH_3)_n$$

Pectinic Acid

$$C_5 H_8 O_4 - C_6 H_{10} O_5 - [C_5 H_7 O_4 COOH]_4$$

Pectic Acid
FIG. 109.

involved in the attempts to elucidate the structure of complex, easily decomposable, and noncrystalline bodies, is too voluminous to undertake here. Contenting ourselves with the final developments as now accepted, we shall presume the structure of pectin and of pectic acid, regardless of the source, to be well known. Based partially on the work of others (Fellenberg, Sucharipa, Carré,[45] Schryver, and Haynes[46]), Nanji, Paton, and Ling[47] concluded that the pectic acid molecule is built up of four units of galacturonic acid with one of arabinose and one of galactose, as shown in Fig. 109.[44] They further stated that pectin is the tetramethoxy ester of pectic acid. Pectic acid, $C_{35}H_{50}O_{33}$, according to the formula in Fig. 109, should yield 69.7 per cent galacturonic anhydride, 14.25 per cent anhydroarabinose, 16.55 per cent anhydrogalactose, and approximately 19.5 per cent of furfural from the arabinose and uronic acid groupings. These calculated values are in good agreement with the experimental values obtained.[47]

The formula for pectin as given in the figure requires a methoxy content of 11.76 per cent, and the pectinic acids: trimethoxy pectinic 8.98 per cent, dimethoxy pectinic 6.04, and monomethoxy pectinic 3.06 per cent, respectively. As high as 11.6 per cent methyl alcohol has been recovered by hydrolysis of pectin[45] and 11.3 per cent has been found often.[42] Lower methyl alcohol yields as frequently reported in the literature indicate that the observers had under examination mixtures of pectinic acids or mixtures of pectin and pectic acid instead of pure pectin.

Pectin, pectinic and pectic acids are soluble in water from which they may be precipitated by the addition of alcohol. Pectic acid forms insoluble combinations with the alkaline earths. An insoluble barium pectate containing 22.3 per cent Ba was described by Fellenberg,[42] while Carré[45] found the insoluble calcium pectate contained 7.6 per cent Ca. The theoretical percentages of Ba and Ca for formation of pectates according to Fig. 109 are 21.65 and 7.46, respectively. Carré has devised a quantitative method for the determination of pectin by means of weighing calcium pectate. This salt is precipitated from an acetic acid solution of pectic acid upon the addition of calcium chloride. Upon being heated and washed with water, the calcium pectate is freed from adhering calcium chloride without dissolution or decomposition.[48]

The alkali salts of pectic acid are very soluble in water. Concerning heavy-metal salts, Fellenberg[42] states that pectin can be precipitated by copper sulfate, lead nitrate, and neutral and basic lead acetate, while it cannot be precipitated by silver, cobalt, nickel, ferrous, zinc, manganese, alkaline-earth, or alkali salts.

The formation of jellies when pectin, sugar, and acid are mixed together in certain proportions is well known to the jam and jelly cook, but the proposed conditions for best results are not in agreement. Since investigators upon this subject have worked with either commercial or laboratory pectins whose methoxy contents were not defined, one cannot expect the prescriptions to agree. The matter is further complicated by the lack of an exact experimental definition of what a satisfactory jelly is.

It is unanimously agreed that pectin and sugar alone will not form a jelly, an acid being required in addition.

Tarr,[49] using apple pectin, found that firm jellies (1.5 per cent pectin per 100 cc.) contained about 67 per cent sucrose, which is that of a saturated aqueous solution of sucrose at 20°. He noted that the nature of the acid did not matter, but that jelly formation was evident first at pH = 3.46, becoming optimum at pH 3.2 to 3.1. Higher acidities produced a syneresis, or a seeping out of the aqueous phase. He found it impossible to form jellies with concentrations of sugar below 64.1 per cent. The experience of Ohn,[50] who used 0.4 per cent solutions of citrus pectin, is different from that of Tarr. She found pH 2.60 and 62.5 per cent sucrose as optima. At pH 3.4 to 3.6, a jelly was obtainable with 54.5 per cent sucrose.

The majority of investigators agree that from 0.2 to 1 per cent pectin is the optimum range for jelly formation.

In jelly making, a certain art must be acquired owing partly to the differing pectin contents of fruits. Too much sugar relative to the pectin at a given pH produces "soft" jellies or syrups, whereas too little sugar produces a "tough" or stringy consistency. According to Dore,[51] at pH 3.37, if the proportion of sugar to pectin is greater than 65:1, the resulting jelly is not firm enough to stand alone. If the pH be increased to 3.1, it is possible to increase the ratio of sugar to pectin to 85 or 90:1.

Nanji and Norman[52] hold that the tetramethoxy and trimethoxy esters of pectic acid have the maximum and equal jellifying powers, while the dimethoxy ester has none. It is generally agreed that pectic acid is useless for jelly making. Consequently, prolonged boiling of a fruit juice to concentrate it to the jellying point may, owing to its acidity, if the original pectin content is too low, fail to produce a jelly because of the hydrolysis of the methoxy groups.

Sugars other than sucrose form jellies with acid solutions of pectin and, in fact, other organic compounds serve instead of sugars. Using a 0.8 per cent pectin solution, the pectin having been isolated from lemon albedo, Glückmann[53] has measured the jellifying action of various organic compounds (Table 67). The pectin when dissolved in water at 0.5 to 1 per cent concentration produced a pH of about 3.0.

Table 67 shows that jellification is favored least by the organic acids, more by polyatomic alcohols, still more by monatomic

TABLE 67.—JELLIFYING ACTION UPON 0.8 PER CENT SOLUTIONS OF PECTIN

Substance added	Gram-moles of added substance in 100 cc. of solution	
	At first sign of jellying	At complete jellification
Methyl acetate............	....	0.40
Sucrose..................	....	0.18
Methyl ethyl ketone........	0.29	0.32
Acetone..................	0.32	0.41
Propyl alcohol.............	0.31	0.35
Ethyl alcohol..............	0.34	0.36
Methyl alcohol............	0.48	0.56
Glycerol..................	0.50	0.54
Ethylene glycol............	....	0.65
Propionic acid.............	0.58	0.68
Acetic acid................	....	1.00

alcohols and ketones, and most by sucrose. In each homologous series, increase in size of the radicals increases the jellifying power. In the case of the alcohols, the increase in the number of hydroxy groups lowers the influence of the alcohol in the jellification.

The order of the compounds in Table 67 is their internal-pressure order as pointed out by Kurbatow.[54]

Glückmann views the setting to jelly as a process in which the pectin particles deposit out of solution. In studies of the influence of added organic substances (4 per cent concentration) on the viscosity of a 0.33 per cent aqueous solution of pectin, he found the following relationship to hold:

$$\eta_{p-\text{org}} = \eta_p \cdot \eta_{\text{org}}$$

where $\eta_{p-\text{org}}$ = relative viscosity of a solution of pectin in water plus the organic compound.

η_p = relative viscosity of the aqueous pectin solution.

η_{org} = relative viscosity of the aqueous solution of the organic compound.

He found the same relationship to hold for pectin solutions containing up to 35 per cent glycerol. Hence since the addition of the organic substance raised the viscosity of water to exactly the same extent as it raised the viscosity of the pectin solution, he concludes that the organic substances did not alter the pectin chemically. The equation also shows that the total volume of the pectin particles in the water and in a given solution remains the same.

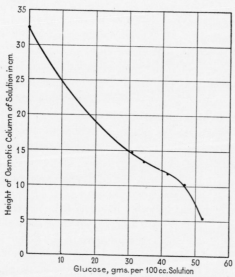

Fig. 110.—Influence of glucose upon the osmotic pressure of a pectin solution.

The theory of Glückmann that jellification of pectin solutions is the conversion of a dispersion of particles to a continuous structure was anticipated by an experiment made by Lucia Edson.[55] She filled a series of 25-cc. size nitrocellulose bags with solutions each containing 1 g. pectin but with concentrations of glucose varying from 25 to 50 g. per 100 cc. of solution. The bags were attached to the manometer tubes and then immersed in solutions (200 cc. volume) containing exactly the same concentrations of glucose as were in the respective nitrocellulose bags. After standing for 48 hr., the solutions showed the osmotic rises plotted in Fig. 110. The glucose concentrations were those of the outer solutions, which also had been found to have remained the same in concentration as the original solutions used. This experiment demonstrated that, as the sugar induced jellification, the number of pectin particles diminished; *i.e.*, aggregation of pectin particles took place; and since the glucose concentration of the outer solution remained unaltered, it might be inferred that the glucose did not combine with the pectin during its setting to the jelly state.

(The fact that pectin is unaltered by setting to a jelly under the influence of sugar has been indicated by an experiment performed by Sucharipa.[56] He extracted the sugar and acid from a jelly with alcohol. The pectin residue was found to redissolve in water and reform a jelly upon addition of sugar and acid.)

Gums.—The gums, occurring as exudates on plants are saltlike compounds (usually potassium, calcium, and magnesium salts) of colloidal carbohydrate acidic bodies. Their acid nature accounts for their anodic electrophoresis. They are apparently not normal products of plant metabolism but are probably pathological products produced by plants when injured mechanically or by bacteria. It has been known[57] since 1861 that bacteria can synthesize gumlike bodies and recently Heidelberger[58] has shown that the immunological specificity of certain types of the pneumococcus resides in the nature of the polysaccharide capsules, and, in fact, a product capable of reacting with pneumonia antisera has been prepared by the partial hydrolysis of gum arabic.[59]

When dry, the gums are rather hard, translucent bodies. Some dissolve in water, while others merely swell in water to form gelatinous lumps or pastes. They are all precipitated from water solution by alcohol or by basic lead acetate.

The reader should note that the word *gum* is properly used only for the hydrophilic carbohydrate bodies discussed here; the varnish maker's "gums" being an improper application of the term to *resins*.

Gum Arabic.—Commercial gum arabic (or acacia) is often a mixture of gums from several species of trees and is therefore a variable product. The best[59] gum arabic is that obtained from *Acacia Senegal*, known as "Hashhab gum," which comes from Khordofan and the Blue Nile district.

Gum arabic is usually completely soluble in water. The earliest exudate does not form a limpid solution, yielding on the contrary a mucus-like fluid. After two or three months' storage,

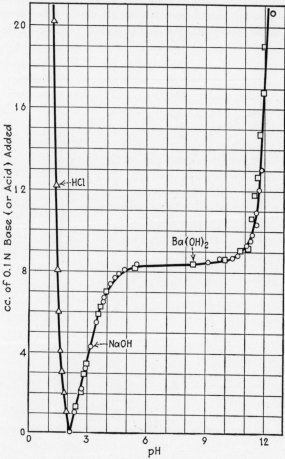

Fig. 111.—Titration of arabic acid with acid and alkali.

however, a change takes place, probably due to enzymes,[60] so that it dissolves entirely.

The gum may be freed from its mineral matter in any one of three ways. Since it is insoluble in an aqueous solution containing more than 60 per cent alcohol, its aqueous solution acidified with hydrochloric acid is treated with alcohol. The precipitate is redissolved in water and reprecipitated several times until ash free. This method is not so good as the following because the demineralized gum becomes changed to a water-insoluble product upon prolonged contact with alcohol. A better method[61] consists in the electrodialysis of the product obtained after two or three alcohol precipitations of the acidified solution.

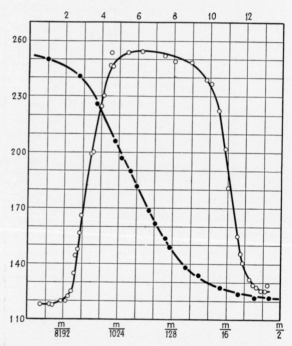

Fig. 112.—Viscosity of arabate solutions as a function of pH (o—o) and of the concentration of NaCl (•—•) at pH 7.85. Top abscissas = pH. Bottom abscissas = salt concentration. Ordinates = relative viscosity; water being taken = 100.

Thomas and Murray[61] found that a product of "gum acid" so obtained gave a strong acid titration curve as plotted in Fig. 111. Inasmuch as they found that it had a combining capacity of about 0.001 mole NaOH per gram, giving an equivalent weight of about 1,000, its strong acid nature was unexpected. The pH value of a 1 per cent solution of the pure "gum acid" was 2.70, which is the same as that of a .002 N solution of hydrochloric acid. The strongly acid nature of the gum acid was also pointed out by Amy[62] and by Taft and Malm.[63]

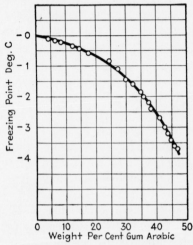

FIG. 113.—Freezing points of gum arabic solutions.[63]

The viscosity of the gum acid changes markedly with pH (Fig. 112[61]), the maximum viscosity lying in the range pH = 5 to 7. The viscosity is diminished by the addition of salts.[61,63,64]

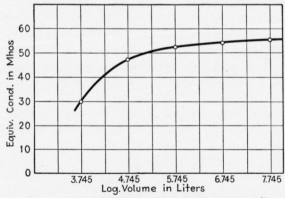

FIG. 114.—Conductivities of gum arabic solutions.[63]

From the results gained from a study of the viscosity as a function of concentration and temperature, the freezing point (Fig. 113) and the conductivity (Fig. 114), made upon the gum,

Taft and Malm[63] concluded that gum arabic is a strong electrolyte, the Ca and Mg salt of a complex organic acid.

Recent investigations of the constitution of gum arabic have been made by Norman[65] and by Butler and Cretcher.[66] The former from experience with more than one specimen concludes that the gum acid is not a substance of a definite empirical formula. He postulates that in its general composition there is a nucleus acid composed of galactose and a uronic acid to which arabinose is bound by glucosidic linkages.

Butler and Cretcher's[66] analysis of a botanically authentic sample of Khordofan gum arabic from *Acacia Senegal* (L.) Willd showed the gum acid to be composed of 1 molecule of galactose-glucuronic acid, 2 of galactose, 3 of arabinose, and 1 of methyl pentose. The figures are only approximate. They found an equivalent weight of 1,030 for the gum acid upon titration with sodium hydroxide. The aldobionic acid was isomeric with that isolated by Heidelberger and Goebel[67] from the polysaccharides produced by certain pneumococcus types.

Other Gums.—Cholla gum, from the white cholla cactus *Opuntia fulgida*, when mixed with ten times its weight of water swells up to a gelatinous mass. About 50 per cent of its weight dissolves in boiling water.[68] Upon hydrolysis it has yielded[69] galacturonic acid, arabinose, galactose, and rhamnose.

Mesquite gum, which is found on the mesquite tree *Prosopis juliflora*, is completely soluble in cold water,[68] its aqueous solutions being less viscous than those of gum arabic. It is believed to be a salt of an organic compound consisting of 4 molecules of arabinose, 3 molecules of galactose, and 1 molecule of methoxyglucuronic acid.[70]

Cherry gum collected from wild-cherry trees at Montezuma, Indiana, has yielded arabinose, xylose, galactose, mannose, and glucuronic acid upon hydrolysis.[71] The acidic nucleus of this gum appears to be different from that of other gums studied, in that it contains two units of uronic acid combined with one sugar group instead of one acid with one sugar residue as is found in the aldobionic acids. The proportions of sugars found indicate the molecular proportions to be arabinose 8, xylose 6, galactose 6, mannose 3, and glucuronic acid 2. Upon hydrolysis in cold 18 per cent hydrochloric acid, a complex acid containing the molecular proportions galactose 6, mannose 3, and uronic acid 2 was obtained. The theoretical molecular weight, if 10 molecules of water are assumed to be split from the sugar residues, is 1,828, which agrees well with the value 1,791, found by titration with alkali.[71]

Gum tragacanth, the product of various species of *Astralagus*, consists of about two-thirds of a water-insoluble part called *bassorin* and about one-third of a water-soluble part, recently named *tragacanthin*.[72] Norman believes the soluble constituent to consist of a ring containing 3 molecules of glucuronic acid and 1 molecule of arabinose, with a side chain of 2 molecules of arabinose.

Flax-seed mucilage yields on hydrolysis *d*-glucose, *d*-galactose, *l*-xylose, and *l*-arabinose, together with an acid by-product.[73] The aldobionic acid formed during the partial hydrolysis of flax-seed mucilage has been identified[74] as consisting of 1 molecule of *d*-galacturonic acid and joined by glucosidic linkage through its aldehyde group and the alcohol group of 1 molecule of *l*-rhamnose.

Gum karaya, or Indian gum, or Bombay gum, which swells in water and only part of which dissolves, has the interesting property of slowly splitting off acetic acid. Bombay gum, the product of a species of *Sterculia*, and the gum of *Cochlospermum gossypium*, both found in India, are very similar in composition. They are regarded as acetyl derivatives, 14 per cent of acetic acid having been found upon distillation.[75]

Carob-seed gum from the seeds contained in the locust bean, or the fruit of the carob tree (*Ceratonia siliqua*), yields upon hydrolysis galactose, mannose, and pentoses.[76] This gum appears on the market blessed with the following names, according to Hart[77]: "locust-kernel, carob-bean gum, gum Hevo, gum Gatto, gum Tragon, Janda gum, Lakoe gum, Lupo-gum, Luposol, Rubigum, Tragarab, Tragasol, etc.!"* When dispersed in hot water, carob-seed gum forms viscous liquids at 0.5 per cent concentration and viscous pastes at 5 per cent. Solutions of this gum have the remarkable property of turning to gels when borax is added to their solutions.[76,77] The gels are so compact

---

* A friend of the author's has informed him of the additional names "St. John's bread," "honey bread," and "algarroba."

that they can be lifted from the container and let stand unsupported.

Seaweed Extracts.—Agar-agar is the name applied to the colloidal carbohydrate substance extracted by boiling certain species of red seaweed, the *Gelidium*, with water.[78] These species are native to California and to the shores bathed by the Japan current. While agar-agar dissolves readily in hot water, its solutions set to rigid jellies upon cooling below about 35° to 40°C. With a good product, as little as 1 part agar to 500 parts of water will form a jelly.

Agar formerly came exclusively from Japan, where it was prepared in more or less primitive ways. A modern factory at San Diego, California, now supplies a more uniform and high-grade product.[78]

Commercial specimens of agar may be contaminated with diatoms, silica spicules, and other detritus. A method of purification is as follows:[79]

One hundred grams of fine-cut agar is added to 3000 cc. of cold 0.5 per cent acetic acid solution and allowed to stand 30 min. The supernatant liquid is poured off and a fresh quantity of the acid solution added. After 30 min. this is poured off and then the swollen agar is soaked in six changes of distilled water during 12 hr. In order to obtain the free agar acid, the agar is then heated in 3,000 cc. of water and electrodialyzed hot.[79,80] The upper clear layer is siphoned off and centrifuged while hot in a continuous-flow type of centrifuge. The effluent may upon cooling to a jelly be sliced and dried.

A striking fact about agar is that it is the calcium salt of the sulfonic ester of a colloidal carbohydrate complex.[80,81,82] A 1 per cent solution of the free agar acid has a pH value of 2.48 and is about 56 per cent ionized.[80] The formula for this acid may be written $R \cdot O \cdot SO_2 \cdot OH$, where R represents the colloidal carbohydrate part. While a 5 per cent solution does not jellify upon cooling, it sets immediately upon neutralization with any base, including aniline or alkaloids.[80,83] The nature of the carbohydrate is not yet known. It has generally been called a *galactan* but this is seriously questioned by Lüdtke,[84] who states that galactose does not constitute more than one-third of the total carbohydrate matter.

The swelling of agar in water is a slow process and is greatly influenced by its previous history. A typical curve[82] is shown in

Fig. 115. If in the purification the agar sol is kept hot for prolonged periods, the final dried product swells less. Likewise, prolonged storage of dry agar results in diminished swelling capacity. Dried agar which swelled to 3,000 per cent in distilled water has been found after standing in the dried state for three years to swell to only 1,000 per cent in distilled water.[85]

Clarke[85] has shown a very curious effect of the degree of desiccation of agar jelly upon the subsequent swelling in distilled water. He prepared a 2.5 per cent solution of agar in boiling water and then allowed the solution to set. Two disks were taken by means of a cork borer. One disk was analyzed

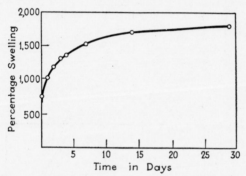

Fig. 115.—Rate of swelling of agar in water at 20°C.

for its water content and the other was placed in 35 cc. of water at 15°C. until swelling equilibrium was reached (usually in about ten days). The remaining mother batch of jelly was meanwhile progressively dried in a current of air, then in the oven at 70°C., and finally in a desiccator over phosphorus pentoxide. Meanwhile disks were removed and treated as above. Thus a series of disks of varying water content were studied. The results are plotted in Fig. 116.

Clarke remarks that his agar gels were opaque when freshly cast and, upon drying down to thin plates, he noticed that at a certain point in the drying process the opacity changed rather sharply to perfect transparency. This point of optical transition coincided with the point indicated by the arrow in Fig. 116.

The swelling of a specimen of agar as a function of pH is given in Fig. 117.[82] The conditions used were 20° for three days.

The term "relative swelling" means the amount of solution relative to that taken up in distilled water, the latter amount

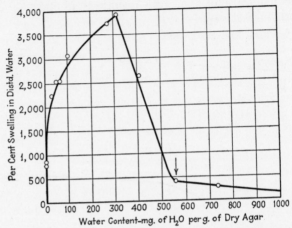

Fig. 116.—Influence of degree of drying of agar jelly upon subsequent swelling in water at 15°C.

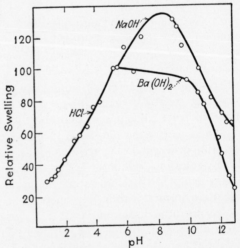

Fig. 117.—Swelling of agar at 20°C. as a function of pH.

being taken as 100. The swelling in hydrochloric, sulfuric, phosphoric, acetic, and oxalic acids were the same when plotted as a function of pH. The swellings in ammonium hydroxide were greater than in sodium hydroxide with a maximum at the same pH value as for sodium hydroxide. Fairbrother and Mastin[82] believe that the effect of added acid is to produce a reversible equilibrium of the type

$$(R \cdot O \cdot SO_2 \cdot O)_2 Ca + 2HCl \rightleftarrows 2R \cdot O \cdot SO_2 \cdot OH + CaCl_2$$

the free acid swelling less in water than the calcium salt, its ionization and swelling being further diminished by the presence of acid.

The viscosity of agar solutions is decreased by salts; the higher the valence of the cation of added salt, the greater is the effect.[86]

The mucilaginous substance extracted by hot water from carrageen, or Irish moss (*Chondrus crispus*), has been shown by Haas[87] to be the calcium salt of a sulfuric ester of a colloidal carbohydrate complex. Haas ascribes to it the formula

$$R \underset{O \cdot SO_2 \cdot O}{\overset{O \cdot SO_2 \cdot O}{\diagup\diagdown}} Ca$$

He found that the calcium could be replaced by an equivalent amount of sodium. He reported a difference between the nature of the material extracted from this seaweed by cold and by hot water. After extracting the dried seaweed with cold water, he subjected the residue to the action of boiling water. Both dried to similar-looking, transparent friable scales, which became soft and pliable upon attainment of equilibrium with the humidity of the air. When placed in cold water, both extracts swelled considerably, the cold-water extract dissolving completely to form a "gummy solution," while the hot-water extract dissolved only to a slight extent. Upon warming, the latter dissolved, a 2 per cent solution formed a thin jelly upon cooling, while 3 to 5 per cent solutions formed stiff jellies.

The extracts differed in another way. When "5 drops of a 20 per cent solution" of Rochelle salt were added to 5 cc. of a 0.75 per cent hot-water extract, the gum was thrown out in the form of a clear gelatinous precipitate which remained suspended in the aqueous medium, but on being boiled, and then allowed to cool, the whole liquid set to a clear stiff jelly.

Harwood[88] has measured the conductivities of carrageen extract at 1.5 per cent concentration, finding at infinite dilution about the same value as for calcium sulfate, thus showing that the colloidal ion possesses a mobility very similar to that of the sulfate ion. He found from his measurements that possibly $Ca(O \cdot SO_2 \cdot - O \cdot R)_2$ is more correct than the formulation made by Haas.

The alginic acid from *Macrocystis pyrifera* has recently been shown to be a polymer of the anhydride of an aldehyde sugar acid (probably mannuronic) in which all aldehyde groups are conjugated and all carboxyl groups free.[89] This acid is very slightly soluble in water but absorbs remarkable amounts of water—two hundred to three hundred times its own weight.

A fibrous material, proving to be the sodium salt of a galactan sulfuric acid ester, has been isolated[90] from the marine alga *Irideae laminarioides*. None of the sulfur is lost upon dialysis. Upon acidification and removal of the sodium ion by dialysis, the acid derivative is obtained. A 1 per cent aqueous solution of this sulfuric acid ester has a pH value of 3.6.

References

1. MEYER: *Biochem. Z.*, **208**, 1 (1929).
2. MEYER and MARK: *Ber.*, **61B**, 593 (1928).
3. MEYER and MARK: *Z. physik. Chem.*, **B2**, 115 (1929).
4. CLARK: *Ind. Eng. Chem.*, **22**, 474 (1930).
5. KATZ: *Physik. Z.*, **25**, 321 (1921).
6. TRAUBE: *Ber.*, **44**, 3319 (1911); **56**, 268 (1923); **54**, 3220 (1921).
7. HESS: *Z. angew Chem.*, **37**, 993 (1924).
   HESS and MESSMER: *Kolloid-Z.*, **36**, 260 (1925).
8. STAMM: *J. Am. Chem. Soc.*, **52**, 3047 (1930).
9. LEVALLOIS: *Compt. rend.*, **99**, 1027, 1122 (1884); **100**, 279, 368 (1885).
10. KATZ: *Physik. Z.*, **25**, 321 (1924).
11. VON VEIMARN: *Kolloid-Z.*, **11**, 41 (1921); **29**, 197 (1921).
12. WILLIAMS: *J. Soc. Chem. Ind.*, **40**, 221 (1921).
13. HERZOG: *Z. physik. Chem.*, **127**, 108 (1927).
14. ODDO: *Gazz. chim. ital.*, **49**, II, 127 (1919).
15. ANDRESS and REINHARDT: *Z. physik. Chem.*, **151A**, 425 (1930).
16. HEUSER: *Z. angew. Chem.*, **37**, 1010 (1924).
    KARRER and NISHIDA: *Cellulosechemie*, **5**, 69 (1924).
    PAVLOV: *Kolloid-Z.*, **44**, 44 (1928).
    PERCIVAL, CUTHBERTSON, and HIBBERT: *J. Am. Chem. Soc.*, **52**, 3257 (1930).
    RUMBOLD: *J. Am. Chem. Soc.*, **52**, 1013 (1930).
17. RONA and MICHAELIS: *Biochem. Z.*, **103**, 19 (1920).

18. KOLTHOFF: *Pharm. Weekblad,* **57,** 1571 (1920); **58,** 233 (1922).

19. PERCIVAL, CUTHBERTSON, and HIBBERT: *J. Am. Chem. Soc.,* **52,** 3448 (1930).

20. NARAY-SZABO and SUSICH: *Z. physik. Chem.,* **130,** 616 (1927); **134,** 264 (1928).

21. FORD: *J. Soc. Chem. Ind.,* **23,** 414 (1904).

22. THOMAS: *Biochem. Bull.,* **3,** 403 (1914).

23. NELSON and NORTHROP: *J. Am. Chem. Soc.,* **38,** 472 (1916).

24. TAYLOR and NELSON: *J. Am. Chem. Soc.,* **42,** 1726 (1920).

25. RASPAIL: *Ann. sciences naturelles,* **6,** 224, 384 (1825).

26. TAYLOR and LEHRMAN: *J. Am. Chem. Soc.,* **48,** 1739 (1926).

27. TAYLOR and WERNTZ: *ibid.,* **49,** 1584 (1927).

28. TAYLOR and IDDLES: *Ind. Eng. Chem.,* **18,** 713 (1926).

29. TAYLOR and BECKMANN: *J. Am. Chem. Soc.,* **51,** 294 (1929).

30. TAYLOR and WALTON: *ibid.,* **51,** 3431 (1929); TAYLOR and SCHOCH: *ibid.,* **55,** 4248 (1933).

31. ALSBERG and PERRY: *Proc. Soc. Exptl. Biol. Med.,* **22,** 60 (1924); ALSBERG: *Ind. Eng. Chem.,* **18,** 190 (1926); ALSBERG, GRIFFING, and FIELD: *J. Am. Chem. Soc.,* **48,** 1299 (1926).

32. HERZOG and JANCKE: *Ber.,* **53,** 2162 (1920); SPONSLER: *J. Gen. Physiol.,* **5,** 757 (1922); OTT: *Physik. Z.,* **27,** 174 (1926); KATZ and MARK: *Physik. Z.,* **25,** 431, 659 (1924); KATZ: *Z. physik. Chem.,* **A150,** 37, 67, 90 (1930); **A155,** 199 (1931).

33. NARAY-SZABO: *Ann.,* **465,** 299 (1928).

34. MEYER, HOPFF, and MARK: *Ber.,* **62B,** 1103 (1929).

35. SAMEC: *Kolloidchem. Beihefte,* **3,** 122 (1911).

36. CAESAR: *Ind. Eng. Chem.,* **24,** 1432 (1932).

37. DERKSEN and KATZ: *Rec. trav. chim.,* **51,** 523 (1932).

38. PAYEN: *Ann. chim. phys.,* **26,** 329 (1924).

39. BRACCANOT: *Ann. chim. phys.,* (2) **28,** 173; **30,** 96 (1825).

40. FREMY: *J. de Pharm.,* (2) **26,** 368 (1840); *J. prakt. Chem.,* **3,** 1 (1840); *J. de Pharm.,* (3) **12,** 13 (1847); *Liebigs Ann. Chem.,* **64,** 383 (1847); *Compt. rend.,* **24,** 1046 (1847); *Ann. chim. phys.,* **24,** 5 (1848); *Liebigs Ann. Chem.,* **67,** 257 (1848).

41. WIESNER: *Sitz. Akad. Wiss. Wien,* **48,** 199 (1863); **50,** 442 (1864).

42. FELLENBERG: *Mitt. Lebensm. Hyg.,* **5,** 225 (1914); **7,** 42 (1916); **8,** 1 (1917); *Biochem. Z.,* **85,** 118 (1918); SUCHARIPA: *J. Am. Chem. Soc.,* **46,** 145 (1924).

43. DORE, BRINTON, WICHMANN, WILLAMAN, and WILSON: *J. Am. Chem. Soc.,* **49,** Proc. 37 (1927).

44. BRANFORT (CARRÉ): Food Investigation Special Report No. 33, His Majesty's Stationery Office, London, 1929.

45. CARRÉ and HAYNES: *Biochem. J.,* **16,** 60 (1922).
    CARRÉ: *Biochem. J.,* **16,** 704 (1922); **19,** 257 (1925).

46. HAYNES: *Biochem. J.,* **8,** 553 (1914).
    SCHRYVER and HAYNES: *Biochem. J.,* **10,** 539 (1916).

47. NANJI, PATON, and LING: *J. Soc. Chem. Ind.,* **44,** 253T (1925).

48. EMMETT and CARRÉ: *Biochem. J.*, **20**, 6 (1926).
49. TARR: Univ. Del. Agr. Exp. Sta. *Bull.*, **133** (1924); **136** (1924); **142** (1926); also MEYERS and BAKER: *Bull.*, **141** (1925); **144**, (1926); **149** (1929); **160** (1929); **167** (1930); *Tech. Bull.*, **12** (1931).
50. OHN: *Ind. Eng. Chem.*, **18**, 1295 (1926); **22**, 635 (1930).
51. DORE: *J. Chem. Education*, **3**, 505 (1926).
52. NANJI and NORMAN: *J. Soc. Chem. Ind.*, **45**, 337T (1926); *Biochem. J.*, **22**, 596 (1928).
53. GLÜCKMANN: *Kolloid-Z.*, **55**, 64 (1931); **57**, 330 (1931).
54. KURBATOW: *Kolloid-Z.*, **55**, 70 (1931).
55. EDSON: Dissertation, Columbia University, 1928.
56. SUCHARIPA: *J. Assoc. Official Agr. Chem.*, **7**, 57 (1923).
57. PASTEUR: *Bull. soc. chim.*, 30 (1861); subject reviewed by BUCHANAN: *Centr. Bakt.*, (II) **22**, 371 (1909).
58. HEIDELBERGER, AVERY, and GOEBEL: *J. Exptl. Med.*, **49**, 847 (1929). HEIDELBERGER and KENDALL: *J. Exptl. Med.*, **53**, 625 (1931). HEIDELBERGER: *Chem. Rev.*, **3**, 403 (1927).
59. STOCKS: First Report on Colloid Chemistry, p. 53, *Brit. Assoc. Advancement Sci.*, London, 1917.
60. REINITZER: *Z. physiol. Chem.*, **61**, 352 (1909).
61. THOMAS and MURRAY: *J. Phys. Chem.*, **32**, 676 (1928).
62. AMY: *Bull. soc. chim. biol.*, **10**, 1079 (1928).
63. TAFT and MALM: *J. Phys. Chem.*, **35**, 874 (1931).
64. KRUYT and TENDELOO: *Kolloidchem. Beihefte*, **29**, 396 (1929).
65. NORMAN: *Biochem. J.*, **23**, 524 (1929).
66. BUTLER and CRETCHER: *J. Am. Chem. Soc.*, **51**, 1519 (1929).
67. HEIDELBERGER and GOEBEL: *J. Biol. Chem.*, **74**, 613, 619 (1927).
68. ANDERSON, SANDS, and STURGIS: *Am. J. Pharm.*, **97**, 589 (1925).
69. SANDS and KLAAS: *J. Am. Chem. Soc.*, **51**, 3441 (1929).
70. ANDERSON and OTIS: *J. Am. Chem. Soc.*, **52**, 4461 (1930).
71. BUTLER and CRETCHER: *J. Am. Chem. Soc.*, **53**, 4160 (1931).
72. NORMAN: *Biochem. J.*, **25**, 200 (1931).
73. HILGER: *Ber.*, **36**, 3197 (1903). NEVILLE: *J. Agr. Sci.*, **5**, 113 (1913); through Ref. 74.
74. ANDERSON and CROWDER: *J. Am. Chem. Soc.*, **52**, 3711 (1930).
75. ROBINSON: *J. Chem. Soc.*, **89**, 1496 (1906).
76. WILLIAMS: *Analyst*, **53**, 411 (1928).
77 HART: *Ind. Eng. Chem.*, Anal. ed., **2**, 329 (1930).
78. ANONYMOUS: *Chem. Met. Eng.*, **34**, 294 (1927).
79. HARVEY: *Am. J. Pharm.*, **97**, 66 (1925).
80. HOFFMAN and GORTNER: *J. Biol. Chem.*, **65**, 371 (1925).
81. SAMEC and ISAJEVIC: *Compt. rend.*, **173**, 1474 (1921); *Kolloidchem. Beihefte*, **16**, 285 (1922).
82. FAIRBROTHER and MASTIN: *J. Chem. Soc.*, **123**, 1412 (1923).
83. DE WAELE: *Ann. physiol. physiochim. biol.*, **5**, 877 (1929); through *Chem. Abs.*, **24**, 3152 (1930).
84. LÜDTKE: *Biochem. Z.*, **212**, 419 (1929).

85. Clarke: *J. Am. Chem. Soc.*, **47**, 1954 (1925).
86. Kruyt and de Jong: *Kolloidchem. Beihefte*, **28**, 1 (1928).
87. Haas: *Biochem. J.*, **15**, 467 (1921).
88. Harwood: *J. Chem. Soc.*, **123**, 2254 (1923).
89. Nelson and Cretcher: *J. Am. Chem. Soc.*, **51**, 1914 (1929).
90. Hassid: *J. Am. Chem. Soc.*, **55**, 4163 (1933).

CHAPTER XIV

SOAP SOLUTIONS

The word *soap* is used as a general term for all metallic salts of the fatty acids, but only those of the alkali metals will be considered here. In Chap. I reference was made to the work of Krafft[1] which showed that colloidality of aqueous soap solutions increases with the molecular weights of the fatty acids and with the concentration. It also increases with temperature decrease. In alcohol, however, even sodium and potassium oleate are dissolved in an unassociated state.[2]

An extensive series of studies on the nature of soap solutions has been reported by McBain[3] and associates since 1910. Finding that the boiling-point elevation method is unreliable and that the freezing-point depression measurement is generally inapplicable, a dew-point method was devised in order to investigate the osmotic activity of soap solutions. In Fig. 118,[4] the dew-point lowering of a series of potassium soaps shows anomalous behavior beginning with the laurate. The sodium soaps which are not included in the figure gave similar results, being in each case a little less colloidal than the corresponding potassium soaps. The curves verify Krafft's statement concerning the increase in colloidality with increase in molecular weight and concentration.

It is to be noted that the measurements given in Fig. 118 were made at 90°C. With drop in temperature, the solutions of the higher molecular-weight soaps become more colloidal and, at 0°C., they are entirely colloidal at concentrations more than 0.4 N. Potassium caprylate (C_8) in solution at 0° is a typical crystalloidal electrolyte in dilute solutions, whereas at high concentrations it is typically colloidal.

Measurements of the hydroxyl ion concentration of soap solutions[5,6] have shown that it is very slight varying from 0.0033 N to 0.00033 N. The soaps of higher molecular weight are the most alkaline and the alkalinity is less at lower temperatures until the system becomes heterogeneous, when the alkalinity increases several fold. In very concentrated soap solutions the hydrolysis diminishes very markedly. McBain disagrees with the idea that hydrolysis produces fatty acid and metallic hydroxide, but

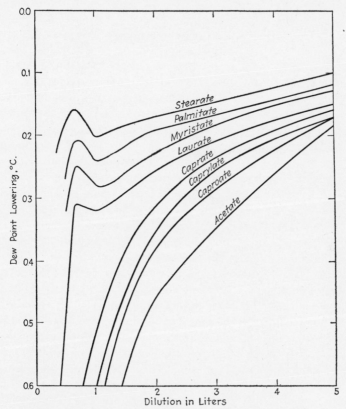

Fig. 118.—Dew-point lowering by potassium salts at 90°C.

in view of the evidence for the existence of acid soaps he postulates reactions of the type

$$2\text{NaP} + \text{H}_2\text{O} \rightleftarrows \text{NaHP}_2 + \text{NaOH}$$

where P signifies the palmitate or other soap radical.

Soap solutions, particularly when quite concentrated, all exhibit a high conductivity. This conductivity must be a property of the soap since there is so little free alkali present.

TABLE 68.—EQUIVALENT CONDUCTIVITIES OF AQUEOUS SOLUTIONS OF
POTASSIUM PALMITATE AT 90°C.

Concentration	KOH	KP	KP/KAc
1.0 N	0.46	123.7	0.70
0.75 N	1.87	126.0	0.69
0.5 N	3.8	123.2	0.63
0.2 N	3.8	107.2	0.49
0.1 N	7.5	99.5	0.42
0.05 N	12.1	98.7	0.40
0.02 N	33.5	99.7	0.38
0.01 N	40.6	131.0	0.44

This is presented well by the data in Table 68[5] which gives the
equivalent conductivity of potassium palmitate solutions divided

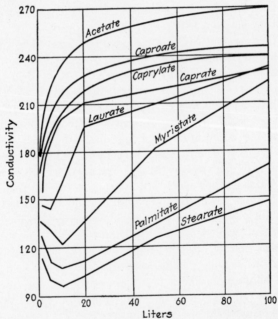

FIG. 119.—Equivalent conductivities of aqueous solutions of potassium salts at 90°C.

into their two components: that due to free hydroxide and the
remainder which has to be ascribed to the soap itself. The ratios

of the conductivity of the soap to that of potassium acetate are given for comparison (under the heading KP/KAc).

The conductivities of a series of potassium soaps are shown in Fig. 119.[7] The form of the conductivity curves for the laurate and higher soaps is peculiar. The conductivity falls with concentration to a minimum value at about 0.1 N and thereafter, instead of decreasing steadily with increasing concentration, the conductivity rises to a pronounced maximum at 0.75 N (see Table 68 especially). McBain points out that this establishes the fact that, when such soap solutions increase in concentration, the palmitate ion is being replaced by some other much better conductor of electricity. Some of the solutions were extremely viscous, while others were quite liquid, and this enormous alteration in viscosity exerted no appreciable effect on the conductivity. In fact McBain found no change in conductivity and vapor pressure (at a given temperature and concentration) when a soap solution set to a jelly.

The experiences of McBain have led him to believe that, as a soap solution concentrates, hydrated aggregates of neutral soap and fatty-acid ions such as $(NaP)_x.(P^-)_n.(H_2O)_m$ arise,* with $(NaP)_x$ very small[8] in comparison with $(P^-)_n$. In very dilute solutions, then, the conductivity is due principally to the Na^+ and P^- ions. Upon concentration the P^- ions aggregate and hence the resistance to the motion of the ionic aggregates (Stokes's law) will increase,[4] but this is more than counterbalanced by the increase in charge of the growing particle. Such a highly charged particle, however, will attract water molecules and become heavily hydrated. This hydration would offset the extra mobility expected and the result would be a colloidal ionic micelle of somewhat less mobility than a rather slow ion. The hydration accounts for the high viscosity observed in soap solutions.

As the solution becomes more concentrated, the equivalent conductivity drops until, at the minimum, the hydration decreases, producing a rise in conductivity to a maximum (0.75 N for potassium palmitate) above which the conductivity falls

---

* This is the same as $(NaP)_x.(HP)_n.(OH^-)_n.(H_2O)_{m-n}$, or $(NaP)_{x-m}.(NaHP_2)_n.(OH^-)_n.(H_2O)_{m-n}$. McBain gave to such charged aggregates the name "ionic micelle."

again, owing to the increase in ratio of x to n producing neutral soap aggregates.

Aqueous soap solutions have surprising densities. Solutions of the oleates, stearates, and palmitates of sodium and potassium are less dense than either component.

Detergent Action of Soap Solutions.—Chevreul (1823) ascribed the detergent value of soap solutions to their emulsifying action upon fats. Fifty-six years later, G. Quincke[9] stated that the emulsified droplets of oil are surrounded by thin layers of soap which prevent coalescence and thereby stabilize the emul-

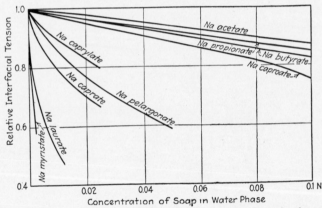

Fig. 120.—Relative lowering of mineral-oil water interfacial tension by sodium salts at 17°C.

sion. In 1903, Hillyer[10] showed that it was a function of the lowering of the oil-water interfacial tension.

In Fig. 120[11] are plotted the relative interfacial tensions for mineral-oil aqueous-soap-solution interfaces. The lowering of this interfacial tension is not very marked up to and including sodium caproate. Actually, pronounced emulsifying action in this case was not observed with the soaps below sodium laurate.[11] It is very striking to observe how little of a higher soap is required greatly to reduce the interfacial tension. This is shown in Fig. 121[12] for benzene-water and air-water interfaces. In order to accomplish emulsifying action it has been learned that, while a small amount of soap serves well, a larger quantity may be useless. This is illustrated by one of Donnan's[11] experiments given in

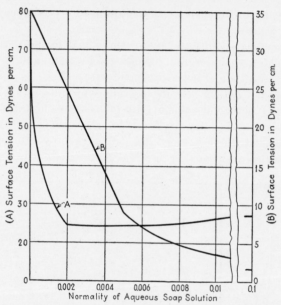

FIG. 121.—*A*, surface tensions of aqueous sodium oleate solutions at 20°C. *B*, effect of sodium oleate upon benzene-water interfacial tensions at 20°C.

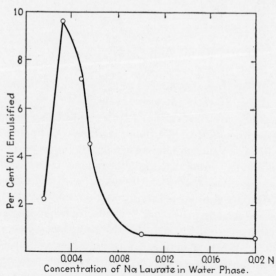

FIG. 122.—Emulsification of a hydrocarbon oil in water.

Fig. 122, demonstrating a sharp optimum for emulsification as a function of concentration of sodium laurate.

The same sort of relationship was found by Spring[13] in the suspending action of mixed soaps for soot, iron oxide, and other insoluble powders. Optimum suspending power in water was manifested best at about 0.5 to 1 per cent concentration of the mixed soap which he used. In one experiment he was surprised to learn that, while water containing 1 per cent soap kept soot suspended for two months, the soot settled out of a 2 per cent soap solution about as fast as from pure water. He noted also

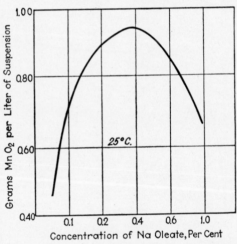

Fig. 123.—Suspension of manganese dioxide particles by aqueous sodium oleate solutions.

that a suspension of soot in 1 per cent or less aqueous soap solutions passed through a filter paper without blackening it, while more soap caused the soot to collect on and clog the paper.

Evidence was found in the foregoing experiments to the effect that some soap is sorbed by the suspended particles. No sorption by particles or stabilizing action was observed in alcoholic soap solutions. Further, when alcoholic soap solutions containing soot were filtered, all the soot was retained by the filter paper. When alcohol is added to aqueous soap solutions, it is observed that at 45 per cent concentration and higher of alcohol the air-liquid interfacial tension is no longer lowered.[14]

A quantitative experiment on the influence of a soap in suspending* solid particles is plotted in Fig. 123[15] where colloid-milled manganese dioxide was used. Added alkali increases the suspending power, as demonstrated by Fig. 124,[16] in which a variety of carbon was employed as solid matter.

The optimum concentration of soap for the cleansing of fabrics is generally given in the range of 0.2 to 0.4 per cent.[15,17,18,19] Of course, this optimum will depend upon the conditions, such

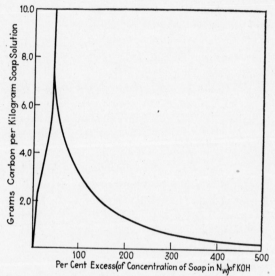

Fig. 124.—Influence of added alkali upon the suspending power of 0.0125 N_w (or 3.22 per cent) solutions of potassium myristate at 15°C.

as nature of soap and dirt, the temperature, and the mode of quantitative estimation of detergent action. Several methods[15,16,17,19] have been proposed for measuring cleansing power of soaps, but as yet no one seems to be satisfied that the problem has been solved. Optimum cleansing action where a series of washings is carried out is obtained by lower concentrations than above stated. For example, in a case where 0.25 per cent soap was optimal for one washing, about the same amount of dirt was removed by solutions containing 0.05 and 0.1 per cent soap in five washings.[18] The detergent action of soap solutions increases with lowering of temperature. Certainly all the facts

* Industrial chemists refer to such action as "deflocculation."

point to cleansing action as a property of *colloidal* soap solutions.

Figure 124 showed that added alkali improves the deflocculating action of soap solutions. The optimum alkalinity for cleansing action of soap solutions has been given as pH = 10.5 or a little higher.[20]

The cleansing action of soap solutions is not fully understood. While lowering of interfacial tension, in the case of liquids, and sorption producing "deflocculation" of aggregates of solid particles or loosening them from surfaces are very prominent factors, there are others in which specific chemical affinities play a rôle. Pickering[21] stated his belief that the solution of oils in soap itself is a factor. He showed, for example, that, when the hands are smeared with paraffin oil and then 3 g. of soap are applied, the soap at first slips about in the hands but suddenly becomes stiff and adherent. A subsequent rinsing in 1 liter of water then suffices to remove the oil from the hands, whereas washing the greased hands in 1 liter of water containing 3 g. of soap dissolved in it is ineffectual.

Interesting experiments on the germicidal action of soaps have been performed by Walker.[22] Sodium and potassium soaps of the same fatty acid do not differ greatly in their effect. Only the higher soaps (*i.e.*, colloidal soaps) are germicidal. The pneumococcus shows marked susceptibility to the action of laurates, oleates, linoleates, and linolenates, being killed in 15 min. by a solution of 1 part of sodium laurate in 50,000 parts of water. A 1 per cent solution of phenol is required to kill it under the same conditions. The streptococcus requires higher concentrations of soap, while *Staphylococcus aureus* is exceedingly difficult to kill. *Bacillus typhosus* is killed in 15 min. in about 1 per cent solutions of the laurate to stearate, inclusive, although it is markedly resistant to the soaps of the unsaturated acids.* The colon, dysentery, and paratyphoid bacilli show the same specificity toward the saturated and unsaturated soaps as *B. typhosus* does. In general, Walker advises that lathering the hands for 3 min. with a coconut-oil soap solution will kill bacteria such as gonococci, pneumococci, meningicocci, streptococci, and diphtheria, colon, typhoid, and paratyphoid bacilli.

* It has been shown that soaps of the highly unsaturated acids are poor detergents.[23]

Detergents Other Than Soaps.—The sodium salts of sulfonated fatty alcohols* (particularly of the alcohols produced by the hydrogenation method of reduction of coconut- and palm-kernel-oil fatty acids) have recently appeared in commerce.[24] They possess excellent lathering and detergent properties and unlike soaps are unaffected by dilute acid solutions and alkaline-earth cations. Reychler[25] demonstrated that cetyl sulfonic acid forms colloidal solutions which possess excellent lathering and detergent properties.

A vast number of "wetting agents" have been patented and promoted as detergents and emulsifiers.[26] They are too numerous even to be mentioned here.

Frequently the alkalies, alkali carbonates, and alkali secondary and tertiary phosphates are referred to as "detergents." They are not detergents *per se;* but when they come in contact with fatty acids, soaps are formed. Sodium carbonate and sodium phosphate solutions are used in hotel dish washing and in the removal of grease from metals,[27] etc. Solutions of the sodium silicates are likewise used in cleansing and their action is similar. Inasmuch as added OH⁻ ion increases the detergent action of soaps, it is obvious that any of these compounds are good "addition agents" to soap solutions. Phosphate is an efficacious addition agent to soap solutions in the removal of grease containing calcium compounds, probably because it precipitates the latter.[28]

References

1. KRAFFT and STERN: *Ber.*, **27**, 1747, 1755 (1894); KRAFFT and WIGLOW: *Ber.*, **28**, 2566, 2573 (1895); KRAFFT and STRUTZ: *Ber.*, **29**, 1328 (1896).
2. LAING: *J. Chem. Soc.*, **113**, 435 (1918); PATRICK, HYDEN, and MILAN: *J. Phys. Chem.*, **29**, 1004 (1925); KRAFFT: *Ber.*, **32**, 1584 (1899).
3. The majority of McBain's articles will be found in the *J. Chem. Soc* and in the *J. Soc. Chem. Ind.* Since 1920, a number of them have appeared in the *J. Am. Chem. Soc.*
4. McBAIN and SALMON: *J. Am. Chem. Soc.*, **42**, 426 (1920).
5. McBAIN and MARTIN: *J. Chem. Soc.*, **105**, 957 (1914); McBAIN and JENKINS: *ibid.*, **121**, 2325 (1922).
6. McBAIN and BOLAM: *ibid.*, **113**, 825 (1918).
7. McBAIN and TAYLOR: *Z. physik. Chem.*, **76**, 179 (1911); BUNBURY and MARTIN: *J. Chem. Soc.*, **105**, 417 (1914); McBAIN: *J. Soc. Chem. Ind.*, **37T**, 249 (1918).

* Known commercially as "Gardinols" and "Avirols."

8. McBAIN and BOWDEN: *J. Chem. Soc.*, **123**, 2417 (1923).

9. QUINCKE: *Arch. ges. Physiol.*, **19**, 129 (1879).

10. HILLYER: *J. Am. Chem. Soc.*, **25**, 511, 525, 1256 (1903).

11. DONNAN and POTTS: *Kolloid-Z.*, **7**, 208 (1910).

12. HARKINS, DAVIES, and CLARK: *J. Am. Chem. Soc.*, **39**, 541 (1917).

13. SPRING: *Kolloid-Z.*, **4**, 161 (1909); **6**, 11, 109, 164 (1910).

14. BIRCUMSHAW: *J. Chem. Soc.*, **123**, 91 (1923).

15. FALL: *J. Phys. Chem.*, **31**, 801 (1927).

16. McBAIN, HARBORNE, and KIND: *J. Soc. Chem. Ind.*, **42**, 373T (1923).

17. ZHUKOV and SCHESTAKOV: *Chem. Ztg.*, **35**, 1027 (1911); LOTTERMOSER and TESCH: *Kolloidchem. Beihefte*, **34**, 339 (1931).

18. RHODES and BRAINARD: *Ind. Eng. Chem.*, **21**, 60 (1929).

19. CHAPIN: *Ind. Eng. Chem.*, **17**, 461, 1187 (1925); **18**, 1313 (1926); *Oil and Fat Ind.*, **5**, 95 (1928); HOYT: *Oil and Fat. Ind.*, **4**, 191, 204 (1927).

20. RHODES and BASCOM: *Ind. Eng. Chem.*, **23**, 778 (1931); BAKER: *ibid.*, 1025; MUNCH: *Seifensieder-Ztg.*, **59**, 733 (1932); SNELL: *Ind. Eng. Chem.*, **24**, 76, 1051 (1932).

21. PICKERING: *J. Chem. Soc.*, **111**, 86 (1917).

22. WALKER: *J. Infectious Diseases*, **35**, 557; **37**, 181 (1925); **38**, 127 (1926); see also TILLEY and SCHAFFER: *ibid.*, **37**, 358 (1925).

23. HIROSE et al.: *J. Soc. Chem. Ind. Japan* **33**, suppl. binding 338 (1930); through *Chem. Abs.*, **25**, 428 (1931).

24. BRISCOE: *Chem. Trade J.*, **90**, 76 (1932); LEHNER: *Am. Dyestuff Rep.*, **22**, 13 (1933); DUNCAN: *Ind. Eng. Chem.*, **26**, 24 (1934).

25. REYCHLER: *Bull. soc. chim. Belg.*, **27**, 110 (1913); *Kolloid-Z.*, **12**, 277; **13**, 252 (1913).

26. Look up "wetting agents" in the indices of *Chem. Abs.*

27. BAKER and SCHNEIDEWIND: *Trans. Am. Electrochem. Soc.*, **45**, 327 (1924).

28. VINCENT: *J. Phys. Chem.*, **31**, 1281 (1927).

CHAPTER XV

FOAMS

Foams are dispersed systems of globular liquid films enclosing vapors or gases. They are of great practical importance in ore flotation and in soap lathering as well as a source of annoyance in the evaporation of liquids. As stated by Foulk,[1] "Even man's social nature is influenced by foams; to such an extent, indeed, that it sometimes demands a stable foam as in beer and soda water and sometimes an instable one as in champagne and ginger ale."

Obviously, owing to effort of the surface energy to approach its minimum level and to the vapor pressure of the liquid, foams cannot be everlasting. Chemically homogeneous liquids do not foam at all. It is agreed that foams will arise only in liquid systems where a difference in concentration may arise between the film and the bulk of the liquid.[1,2,3]

Foams produced in noncolloidal liquid systems last only a few seconds, while colloidal forms may exist for many minutes.*

Foam Production in Noncolloidal Solutions.—Experiments upon the stability of foams produced by shaking air in aqueous solutions of alcohols, fatty acids, and certain ring-structure organic compounds show that the solutions producing the most stable foams are those where the concentration of the surface-tension lowering substance is somewhat less than (or not exceeding) the concentration which produces the greatest lowering of the surface tension.[3,4,5] Table 69 gives the optimal concentrations of some surface-tension lowering substances for foam formation by shaking aqueous solutions and air in closed containers[4] at 18°C.

As regards foam stability, surface-tension lowering substances are divided into two classes. Insoluble substances show a very

* By careful regulation of conditions, Dewar[6] preserved a soap foam for several months.

401

TABLE 69.—OPTIMAL CONCENTRATIONS FOR FOAM FORMATION

Aqueous solution of	Optimum concentration, moles per liter	Maximum life of foam, seconds
Ethyl alcohol	0.28	5
Propyl alcohol	0.34	11
i-Butyl alcohol	0.09	12
i-Amyl alcohol	0.036	17
Tertiary amyl alcohol	0.034	10
Heptyl alcohol	0.0007	8
Octyl alcohol	0.0003	5
Formic acid	0.45	4
Acetic acid	0.20	8
Propionic acid	0.25	11
Butyric acid	1.00	18
Valeric acid	0.015	9
Caproic acid	0.0075	13
Heptylic acid	0.0015	16
Caprylic acid	0.00025	12
Nonylic acid	0.00007	5
Ethylamine. :	0.40	12
Aniline	0.10	11
p-Toluidine	0.04	6
Phenol	0.10	12
Benzyl alcohol	0.10	10
m-Cresol	0.025	9
Nitrobenzene	0.005	6
Acetaldoxime	0.37	10
Paraldehyde	0.03	9
Acetone	0.50	2.5
Methyl propyl ketone	0.05	3
Ethyl propionate	0.01	2.5

sharp optimal concentration as typified by ethyl oleate in Fig. 125, while the stability range for soluble substances is much broader as illustrated by the curve for aniline in Fig. 126. Surface-tension raising solutes, such as inorganic electrolytes, give a stability-concentration curve in which stability rises to a plateau with increase in concentration. Figure 127 is illustrative and shows also that the foam stability is raised if the evaporation of the solvent from the bubble wall is not impeded.

Recently Talmud[3] has suggested the following mechanism for bubble stability:

An air bubble initially formed in the bulk of the solution is not surrounded by an adsorbed film. Such a bubble as it rises is surrounded by an aqueous shell of the same concentration as the bulk of the solution. The gaseous pressure (p) in such a bubble is greater than the atmospheric pressure by

$$p = \frac{2\gamma}{r}$$

where γ = air-water interfacial tension.

r = radius of the bubble.

This excess pressure of the enclosed air is balanced by the capillary pressure arising from the surface tension of the water. When the rising bubble touches the surface film of surface-active substance, at the point of contact the surface tension decreases and the following pressure difference arises

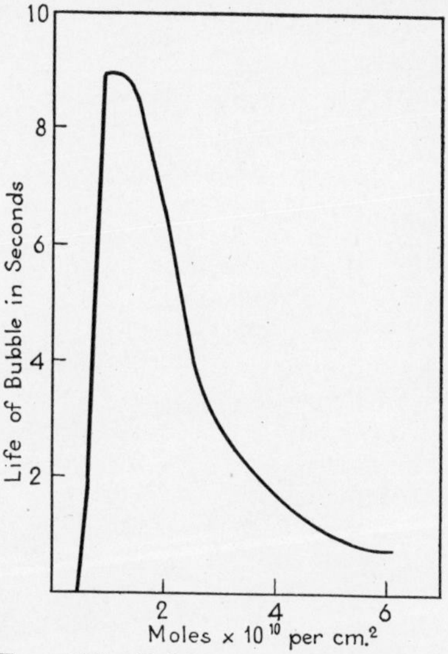

Fig. 125.—Influence of amount of ethyl oleate upon bubble stability.

$$p = \frac{2\Delta\gamma}{r}$$

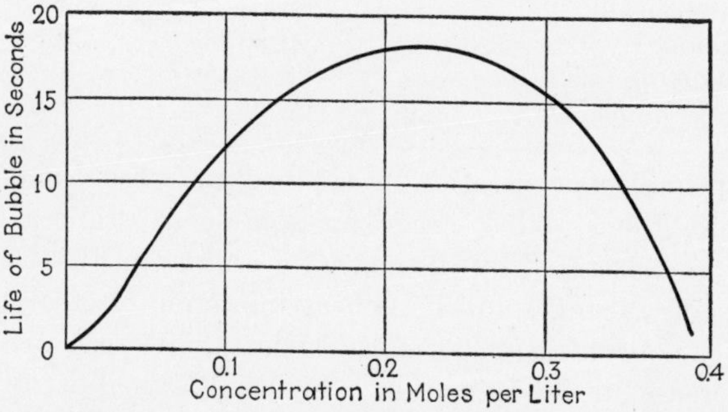

Fig. 126.—Influence of concentration of aniline upon bubble stability.

where $\Delta\gamma$ = the decrease in surface tension. Owing to this pressure difference the bubble bursts.

A stabilization of the bubble under such a pressure difference can arise only where the tensile strength of the bubble film is greater than the pressure differential.

The strength or tenacity of the film is believed to be a function of the degree of hydration of its polar groups.[3] When its molecules are not closely oriented, *i.e.*, lying scattered over the surface (slight changes in concentration do not alter the surface tension), the hydration of the polar groups is slight because the nonpolar chains lying on the surface inhibit the hydration of the polar groups. In a saturated adsorption envelope where the sur-

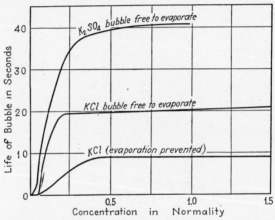

Fig. 127.—Influence of concentration of salts upon bubble stability.

face tension is at a minimum and the adsorbed molecules are in the state of closest packing, the degree of hydration of the molecules of the surface-active substance again approaches a minimum.

Thus the maximum hydration of the polar groups of the molecules or micelles of the surface-active substance lies between two minima of hydration. In the range of maximal hydration of the polar groups, the molecules of the surface-active substance are partly oriented; *i.e.*, they are inclined at various angles to the surface and form a mutually interlacing structure, reminding one of a gel structure. At the state of minimal hydration, the layer consists of pure surface-active substance whose surface strength or tenacity (in the case of a liquid) must be, like pure water, equal to zero. Based on this conception, Talmud assumed that the tenacity of the surface film is proportional to the degree of hydration of the molecules or micelles in the interface. Upon approach to complete orientation of the molecules, the strength of the film diminishes. Thus the bubble again inclines to burst when its strength can no longer exceed the effect of the pressure difference at its point of contact with the surface film.

If this theory is carried to solutions of inorganic electrolytes which raise the surface tension, it is evident that, as the rising bubble arrives at the surface, it comes in contact with a surface layer of water molecules. Thus at the point of contact $\Delta\gamma = 0$ and hence $\Delta p = 0$. Hence increase in concentration of the negatively adsorbed substance should increase the stability of the bubble to a constant level.

There is another factor in foam stability: the mobility of water layers with respect to the adsorbed film of the bubble wall. This is the greater, the longer the chain of the polar molecule in the adsorbed film and also the lower the solubility of the surface-active substance. The reason for this is that the polar molecules in the unsaturated film, *i.e.*, in the state of incomplete orientation, have not only their polar groups but also the entire chain in contact with water. It follows that highly soluble molecules, or polar molecules with short chains, are more hydrated and consequently in closer combination with the deeper layers of water in the bubble wall. Difficultly soluble polar molecules (long chains) are less hydrated and consequently offer less resistance to the motion of the deeper layers of water. The adsorbed layer of long, insoluble polar molecules may be considered as a definite phase which is separated from the contiguous water layer by an interface. In the case of very soluble polar molecules, on the other hand, the adsorbed layer may be regarded as a concentrated solution which is not separated from the lower layers of less concentrated surface-active solution by an interface.

These postulates of the ease of motion of the water layers in the bubble wall explain the interesting fact that surface-active substances with long chains which are difficultly soluble form bubbles with a relatively strong adsorption film but of short life, while readily soluble short-chain surface-active substances form longer lived bubbles with relatively delicate adsorption films.

Although the strength of the maximally hydrated adsorption film of the bubble effected by the aid of a relatively insoluble surface-active substance is great, the maximal hydration is disturbed by the mobility of the underlying layers of water (formation of a black spot) and the strength of the film diminishes (for an insoluble surface-active liquid it drops to zero) to a value below the pressure differential at the point of contact of the bubble with the surface layer of the liquid. In the case where the adsorbed film of the bubble consists of soluble surface-active molecules, the maximal hydration is disturbed very slowly owing to the slight mobility of the underlying water layers. The stability of the bubble is, as a consequence, rather great, although the strength or tenacity of the bubble's liquid adsorbed layer of a dissolved surface-active substance is small in comparison with the strength of films of insoluble adsorbed substances. In this case the black spot forms very slowly.

What has been said is illustrated by the stability curves of bubbles formed by soluble and insoluble surface-active substances. The curves for the latter show an exceedingly narrow zone of stability since the rapid draining away of the water layers under the adsorption film quickly disturbs the maximal hydration. The stability curves of bubbles formed by soluble surface-active substances are flatter. This points to a slow destruction of maximal hydration of the adsorbed layer, *i.e.*, for slow draining off of the underlying layers of water.

The argument above applies only to cases where evaporation of the bubble is prevented. Evaporation influences the stability. According to whether the solvent or the solute evaporates the faster, the stability rises or falls.

Foam Production in Colloidal Solutions.—Hydrophilic colloidal solutions readily form foams. Aqueous soap solutions are excellent for the production of copious and long-lived foams. Johlin[7] states that a 0.019 N sodium oleate solution, which is the concentration for greatest lowering of the surface tension of sodium oleate solutions, gives the longest lived foam, while below 0.00006 N no foam at all is obtained. The soap in the bubble films has been shown to be predominantly acid soap[8] and the permanence of the bubbles is generally ascribed to the semi-solid nature of the concentrated colloidal matter.[8,9] The last-stated theory has been disputed, however,[10] and apparently surface adsorption and its attendant increase in the film viscosity are not the only factors involved.[11]

The volume of lather produced by aqueous solutions of the alkali salts of the C_{18} fatty acids increases with increase in the number of double bonds but the stability of the lather shows a reverse tendency.[12]

Aqueous saponin solutions produce quite stable froths owing to the rigidity of the bubble walls. When saponin bubbles are blown by a pipe, unlike the elastic soap bubbles, they collapse like empty sacks upon suction, unfolding and opening out to a smooth bubble upon reinflation. The addition of glycerol to saponin solutions causes the blown bubbles to become more elastic, approaching soap bubbles in elasticity.

Saponins are used in the carbon dioxide generating type of fire extinguisher. This is the type which, upon inverting, delivers the fire-suffocating gas resulting from the mixing of a solution of sodium bicarbonate with an acid solution containing aluminum ion. The saponin bubbles stabilize the carbon dioxide foam and the aluminum compounds add to the foam stability.

Much attention has been paid to the thickness of soap-bubble films and, from the interference colors, the thickness can now be calculated. These colors arise from the interference of the light reflected from the upper laminae of the bubble film. The original colorless bubble film gradually changes through greenish blue, red, and yellow as its thickness diminishes. Finally a black spot appears on the bubble. This is believed to be due to absence of solution between the outer and inner laminae, the spot consisting of the micelles of acid soap. This hypothesis is supported by the fact that the electrical conductivity is greater through the black area and that the passage of an electric current through the film causing water to electroosmose through the black area results in the disappearance of the latter. The black area is 5 to 15 $m\mu$ thick and the transition from it to the surrounding film is very abrupt, the film bordering it being at least 100 $m\mu$ thick.

Protein solutions produce rather stiff and permanent foams as is well-known in the preparation of "marshmallow" whips from solutions of gelatin and sugar and of meringues from egg white. The foaming power is greatly influenced by the pH of the solution as shown by an experiment upon gelatin plotted in Fig. 128.[13] The greatest amount of foam is obtained in this instance at the isoelectric point where the gelatin is least soluble and thin films of it would be expected to be the most heterogeneous. According to drop-weight and capillary-rise measurements,* the surface tension of protein solutions is at a minimum at or near the isoelectric point.[14] The meringues produced by the whipping of egg white certainly are excellent examples of durability being a

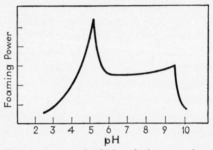

FIG. 128.—Foaming power of gelatin solutions as a function of pH.

function of the solidity of the bubble walls because egg albumin denatures when concentrated in films, thus producing water-insoluble films.

Very finely divided particles which are but poorly wetted by the liquid phase serve as foam stabilizers. Such foams consist of small bubbles coated with the finely divided insoluble matter and are inelastic. The shaking of soot in a dilute aqueous solution results in a rather persistent foam. Hydrophilic or protective colloids prevent the foam-stabilizing action of such powdery matter. A pinch of clay added to a sodium oleate solution, which is too dilute in itself to lather, results in the formation of a persistent lather upon shaking.[16] Aqueous solutions of the acetates of metals froth readily.[17] Here, apparently, the froth stability is promoted by the colloidal metallic oxyacetate present.

Breaking of Foams.—From Gibbs's surface-concentration law, it follows that substance A, which lowers the surface tension

* When measured by the Sugden maximum bubble-pressure method, the surface tension of protein solutions shows decidedly different results.[15]

more than substance B does, will displace B from the interface. The nature of a foam stabilized by B may be altered by the addition of A. For example, the addition of a little soap solution to a saponin solution results in the production of bubbles which are elastic, characteristic of soap bubbles as contrasted with inelastic saponin bubbles. Soaps lower the surface tension much more than saponins do.

If substance B produces rigid films while A produces low viscosity and delicate films, then the addition of A should shorten the life of the foam. Quincke[18] discovered that traces of ethyl ether quickly destroy foams. In fact, it is stated that the opening of a bottle of ether near a glass of beer is sufficient to cause the foam to fall. Ether is used as a foam destroyer in sugar analysis. The protein and gummy substances in raw sugar produce persistent foams when the solution of sugar is shaken. A drop of ether causes the foam to collapse and permits adjustment of the solution in the flask to quantitative volume.

The higher alcohols, especially caprylic, heptylic, and nonylic alcohols, are employed as foam annihilators in laboratory work. A tiny drop effectively breaks and prevents foaming of protein and of tannin solutions in the bubbling-type hydrogen-ion cell. Isoamyl valerate[19] and mixtures of it with isoamyl alcohol are excellent foam inhibitors. Cheaper foam breakers may be prepared by dissolving rosin (20 per cent) in turpentine[20] or by mixing equal volumes of kerosene and caprylic alcohol.[21]

The foaming of boiling liquids is subdued by blowing a current of air or inert gas over the surface. The action is attributed to sudden condensation of the vapor filling the bubbles.[22] This method has been applied to the suppression of foams in yeast-fermentation vats.[23] Foaming in evaporators has also been suppressed by spraying a small amount of nonvolatile oil over the surface.[24] This recalls a previous statement that bubble life in certain cases is shortened by prevention of evaporation (Fig. 127).

Inorganic salts promote the foaming of solutions containing traces of surface-tension lowering solutes. It appears that the foaming troubles experienced at times in the evaporation of brines is due to the presence of traces of surface-active organic matter which is rendered more active upon concentration of the salt solution. Troublesome foaming in the evaporation of potash brines at Deep Springs Valley, California, was overcome by tacking strips of lead to the steel shell of the evaporator so that they hung in the brine. The effect was attributed to the oxidation of organic matter by hypochlorous acid produced by the electrolytic action between the lead and iron.[25] A patent[26] on the prevention of foaming of brines specifies the electrolytic generation of chlorin in the liquid.

Foaming ("priming") in steam boilers is not due to the presence of surface-tension lowering substances according to Millard and Mattson.[27] Foaming in locomotive boilers has been traced to the presence of suspended matter and sludge. Filtration of the water and frequent blowing off of the calcium carbonate sludge have been found remedial.[28] This is an example of undesirable foam stabilization by finely divided solid matter.

References

1. FOULK: *Ind. Eng. Chem.*, **21**, 815 (1929).
2. BANCROFT: "Applied Colloid Chemistry," p. 269, McGraw-Hill Book Company, Inc., New York, 1921.
3. TALMUD and SUKHOVOLSSKAYA: *Z. physik. Chem.*, (A) **154**, 277 (1931).
4. BARTSCH: *Kolloidchem. Beihefte*, **20**, 1 (1925); *Kolloid-Z.*, **38**, 177 (1926).
5. HARDY: *J. Chem. Soc.*, **127**, 1 (1925); REHBINDER and WENSTRÖM: *Kolloid-Z.*, **53**, 145 (1930).
6. DEWAR: *Proc. Roy. Inst. Gt. Brit.*, **22**, 179 (1917).
7. JOHLIN: *J. Biol. Chem.*, **84**, 543 (1929).
8. LAING: *Proc. Roy. Soc. (London)*, **109A**, 28 (1925).
9. GREEN: *Nature*, **126**, 276 (1930).
10. LAWRENCE: *J. Phys. Chem.*, **34**, 263 (1930).
11. PRESTON and RICHARDSON: *J. Phys. Chem.*, **33**, 1142 (1929).
12. HIROSE and KITAJIMA: *J. Soc. Chem. Ind. Japan*, **33**, suppl. binding 340 (1930); through *Chem. Abs.*, **25**, 428 (1931).
13. BOGUE: *J. Am. Chem. Soc.*, **44**, 1343 (1922).
14. DAVIS, SALISBURY, and HARVEY: *Ind. Eng. Chem.*, **16**, 161 (1924); YERMOLENKO: *Kolloid-Z.*, **48**, 141 (1929); FU and WU: *Proc. Soc. Exptl. Biol. Med.*, **27**, 878 (1930); DE CARO and LAPORTA: *Rend. accad. sci. (Napoli)*, (4) **35**, 171 (1929); *Arch. sci. biol. (Italy)*, **14**, 264 (1930); through *Chem. Abs.*, **24**, 1127, 2767 (1930); ARTOM: *Arch. sci. biol. (Italy)*, **14**, 327 (1930); through *Chem. Abs.*, **24**, 3152 (1930).
15. ST. JOHNSTON: *Biochem. J.*, **21**, 1314 (1927); JOHLIN: *J. Biol. Chem.*, **87**, 319 (1930).
16. WESTON: *Chem. Age (London)*, **4**, 604 (1921).

17. GLADSTONE: *Phil. Mag.*, (4) **14**, 314 (1857).
18. QUINCKE: *Wied. Ann.*, **35**, 593 (1888).
19. FISKE: *J. Biol. Chem.*, **35**, 411 (1918).
20. KENDALL: *J. Biol. Chem.*, **38**, 529 (1919).
21. BERNHARD: *J. Am. Med. Assoc.*, **66**, 891 (1916).
22. FANTO: *Z. angew. Chem.*, **20**, 1233 (1907).
23. STICH: *Chem. App.*, **6**, 169 (1919); through *Chem. Abs.*, **14**, 1730 (1920).
24. BRUKNER: *Deut. Zuckerind.*, **57**, 1091 (1932); through *Chem. Abs.*, **27**, 4712 (1931).
25. PALMER: *Chem. Met. Eng.*, **26**, 1034 (1922).
26. DOLBEAR: U. S. Patent No. 1,440,973 (1923).
27. MILLARD and MATTSON: *Ind. Eng. Chem.*, **17**, 685 (1925).
28. KOYL: *Ry. Age*, **71**, 1241 (1921); GREEN: *Ry. Age*, **72**, 313 (1922); CARRICK: *J. Am. Water Works Assoc.*, **9**, 906 (1922); through *Chem. Abs.*, **16**, 2747 (1922); **17**, 604 (1923).

CHAPTER XVI

EMULSIONS

An emulsion is a heterogeneous system consisting of drops of one liquid dispersed in the bulk of a second liquid. In general, such a dispersion may be formed either by mechanical disintegration of bulk material into the droplets forming the dispersed phase or by condensation of molecules of the dispersed phase to larger particles. As fast as a dispersion forms, however, the dispersed particles will coalesce when they touch each other, thus reducing the surface energy of the dispersed system, unless the process of coalescence is inhibited or stopped. To accomplish the latter, a third substance called an "emulsifying agent" must be present. This may be a substance which is much more soluble in one liquid than in the other, or it may be insoluble in both liquids; in this case the more finely pulverized it is, the better it functions.

Hence three components are essential for the formation of an emulsion: two liquids which are immiscible, or nearly so, and an emulsifying agent. The common types of emulsion are those wherein one of the liquids is water. The water may be dispersed in an organic liquid (WO)* and thus be the discontinuous phase, or it may be the continuous phase owing to the dispersion of the organic liquid in it (OW).* The factors governing the OW or WO distribution will be discussed throughout this chapter.

Theory of Emulsions.—Until the beginning of this century, there was no organized fundamental knowledge which might be said to constitute a general theory of emulsions. In the first twenty years of this century there appeared certain generalizations which were attractive, but the experimental data accumulated in recent years demonstrate that emulsions are very complicated systems and it seems that no one simple theory will apply to all emulsions.

* OW will be used to signify emulsions of organic liquid in water, and WO to signify emulsions of water in organic liquid.

One of the theories states that emulsions are formed if the emulsifying agent lowers the interfacial tension between the two liquids[1,2] and thus is concentrated at the interface. The liquid having the lower surface tension constitutes the dispersion medium,[3] or the liquid wetting best the emulsifying agent becomes the dispersion medium.[3] This is called the "surface-tension theory."

Another holds that the emulsifying agent deposits in the interface in a monomolecular layer in such a manner that the group which has an affinity for water is buried therein, while the organophile group is submerged in the organic liquid.[4,5,6] This is known as the "oriented-wedge theory."

Yet another ascribes emulsification to the envelopment of the dispersed droplets by viscous or more or less plastic films of the emulsifying agent, surface tension not being significant.[7]

Quincke[1] prepared emulsions of various fatty oils in aqueous solutions of sodium hydroxide or of gum arabic and showed that the interfacial tensions between the oils and these solutions were lower than those between the oils and pure water. Previous to Quincke's work it had been found that rancid or acidic fatty oils yielded better emulsions in dilute alkaline aqueous solutions than pure oils did.

Donnan's investigation showed that the emulsifying powers of alkali were really due to the soap formed by interaction with the small amount of free fatty acid that is generally present in fatty oils. He proved this by means of the drop-number method and stated that those fatty-acid salts which greatly lower the surface tension are good emulsifiers, and that since they lower the surface tension they must concentrate in the surface layers about the droplets of oil, and since the soap layer is still more concentrated at the points of contact, where bubbles might happen to come together, capillary forces tend to separate them.

In a later work, Donnan and Potts[2] measured the drop numbers of aqueous solutions of the sodium salts of the saturated fatty acids from acetic to lauric in which it was found that all lowered surface tension—the lowering effect increasing with the higher molecular weights—but that it is strongly evident first with sodium caprylate (Fig. 120).

While pronounced lowering of oil-water interfacial tension is evidenced first by sodium caprylate, suitable emulsifying power is not afforded, however, until sodium laurate is reached. This points to an additional factor. Sodium salts of the lower fatty acids form true solutions, while, starting with sodium caprylate, evidence of colloidal solution is first noted which becomes more pronounced with sodium laurate.[8] Donnan and Potts concluded therefore that, while lowering of interfacial tension accounts for the concentrated films of the salts at the interface, very viscous

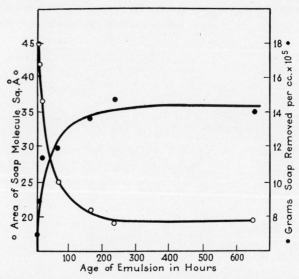

Fig. 129.—Decrease in the molecular area of sodium oleate in emulsion.

or possibly gelatinous films which offer resistance to the coalescence of the globules are essential for stability of emulsions.

According to the surface-tension theory, the amount of soap taken from the aqueous phase and deposited at the oil-water interface should increase with the degree of dispersion of the oil in water. This has been experimentally verified (benzene-in-water emulsions).[9]

It is to be expected that, when the emulsifying agent lowers the interfacial tension, the mechanical disintegration of the liquids will be materially aided. Harkins[10] showed this for the benzene-water interface where the interfacial tension (35.0 dynes per

centimeter at 20°) is reduced to $\frac{1}{219}$ of this value by the presence
of sodium hydroxide in the water and oleic acid in the benzene
to the extent of 0.1 N. He observed that when the interfacial
tension was below 10 dynes the benzene emulsified easily in the
water, while when below 1 dyne it emulsified spontaneously.

It has been mentioned previously that some investigators
believe that a monomolecular layer of the emulsifying agent
deposits in the interface. Experimental work here has been
confined to the soaps as emulsifying agents. Recently Harkins[11]
has made careful measurements of the amount of soap concentrated in the interfacial film surrounding paraffin-oil globules

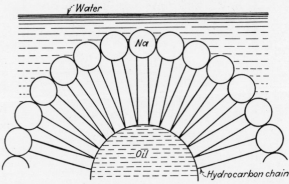

Fig. 130.—A drop of oil emulsified in water by an alkali soap according to the
oriented-wedge theory.

emulsified in 0.02 M aqueous sodium oleate solution. The
initial molecular area of soap in the film was 44.5 $\mathring{A}^2$ and this
decreased gradually until the area fell to about 20 $\mathring{A}^2$, at which
value it remained constant, corresponding to a "condensed"
or closest packed film. The time effect is shown in Fig. 129 and
it is stated that increasing the concentration of soap in the aqueous phase produces the closest packed film more rapidly.[11]
An illustration of this idea is given in Fig. 130.

If this picture represents the true state of affairs, then if the
group soluble in the water occupies more space than is necessary
for the closest packing of the hydrocarbon chain, the latter can
be packed more closely if the film is convex on the water side,
as illustrated in the figure, and hence the name "oriented
wedge."

The size of the drops and the stability of the emulsions should vary with the dimensions of the polar head of the soap molecules. This was once thought to be true[5,6] but the original experimental evidence has been disproved.[12,13] Since the radii of the droplets in such emulsions are at least 250 times greater than the lengths of the soap molecules, it is improbable that the latter can affect the size of the emulsified drops. In solutions as complicated as those of soaps, it is doubtful also whether simple molecular orientation is general.

Inasmuch as soaps of the di- and trivalent metals show a tendency to make *WO* emulsions, the "oriented-wedge" theory was extended in the following manner.[6] The direction as well

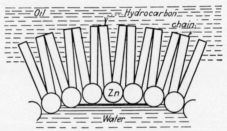

Fig. 131.—A drop of water held in oil by a heavy-metal soap according to the oriented-wedge theory.

as the degree of curvature should vary, first, with the atomic volume of the metal, being more convex the larger this volume, and, second, with the number of hydrocarbon chains attached to a single metallic atom, according to its valence. Zinc soap, for example, would correspond to Fig. 131, making the interface convex toward the oil side, while an aluminum soap should give still more curvature and more stable emulsions of water in oil. Where the cross section of the hydrocarbon chain and that of the metallic end are of the same magnitude, there would be no tendency to curvature, and no very stable emulsion, in spite of the high adsorption of soap at the interface which is still possible.

According to this theory, then, the relative emulsifying powers of a series of soaps should be predictable, if the atomic volumes of the metallic ends are known. From the work of Hull,[14] Bragg,[15] and Richards[16] the data in Table 70 were made available.

TABLE 70.—RELATIVE SIZES OF ATOMS

| Element | Atomic diameters | | | Atomic volumes |
| | In metal (Hull) | In halides | | |
		Bragg	Richards	
Cs	....	4.75	3.8	70.6
K	....	4.15	3.46 (in KCl)	45.3
Na	3.72	3.55	2.85 (in NaCl)	22.9
Ag	2.87	3.55	....	10.3
Ca	3.93	3.40	....	12.6
Mg	3.22	2.85	....	7.0
Zn	2.67	2.65	....	4.6
Al	2.86	2.70	....	3.4
Fe	2.48	2.80	....	2.3

According to Hildebrand,[6]

. . . these figures would indicate that the ability of soaps of caesium, potassium, sodium, and silver to emulsify oil in water would *decrease* in the order given; or, viewed from the other angle, their ability to emulsify water in oil should increase in this order; that the soaps of the divalent metals calcium, magnesium, and zinc should have much *less* ability to emulsify oil in water or much *greater* ability to emulsify water in oil, and further, that they should vary in these respects in the order given. . . . The soaps of the trivalent metals aluminum and iron should exhibit the greatest tendency to emulsify water in oil.

Criticism of this theory has been made[13] on the basis of the improbability of the existence of simple molecules of soaps of the polyvalent metals. The same critics also doubt the formation of simple and regular monomolecular films.

Tartar and associates,[17, 18] working with various organic liquids and water, using several soaps as emulsifying agents, have shown how complicated these systems may be. Shaking 12 cc. of benzene with 4 cc. of 1 per cent aqueous solution of sodium oleate or of sodium stearate, they obtained *OW* emulsions as expected; but when a certain amount of sodium chloride was present, *WO* emulsions were formed. Addition of sodium hydroxide also favored *WO* emulsions. With sodium laurate the emulsions were never *WO* in the presence of sodium chloride, or in the presence of potassium chloride when potassium laurate, stearate, or oleate was used as emulsifying agent. On reversing the volume ratios of benzene to water, they obtained similar results, although increase of the ratio of benzene to water favored the *WO* type. The latter type was likewise favored by increasing the concentration of soap. Further, it was found that elevation of temperature favored the *OW* type. A *WO* emulsion (sodium stearate as emulsifier), on being warmed and shaken, inverted to the *OW* type and reversed again on cooling.

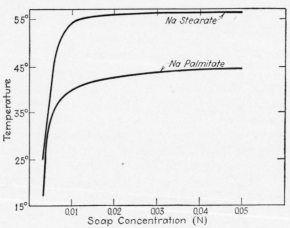

Fig. 132.—Effect of temperature and of concentration of soap upon inversion of benzene-water emulsions.

Investigation revealed the fact that these unexpected formations of *WO* emulsions took place when soap was extracted from the aqueous phase by the benzene. One would not have expected this in the case of sodium soaps, but it was demonstrated that under the conditions which produced *WO* emulsions the soap had moved into the benzene, forming a transparent benzenogel. Sodium laurate and the potassium soaps which never formed *WO* emulsions did not transfer from the water to the benzene.

Owing to an accidental discovery of the influence of temperature, the investigators studied the effect of temperature and of soap concentration upon this phenomenon, producing the information plotted in Fig. 132. Five cubic centimeters of benzene were added to 5 cc. of the hot aqueous soap solution. The container was stoppered and allowed to cool to 5° and shaken vigorously for 5 min. After being tested for type, the emulsion was kept at 2.5° higher temperature for 20 min., again shaken, examined for type, and so on.

To the left and above each curve, the soap was unable to stabilize *WO* emulsions, whereas the area under the curve represents the conditions for *WO* emulsions. The greater water solubility of the palmitate over that of the stearate is reflected in the lower limiting temperature of inversion, *i.e.*, where the curves flatten out.

Near the temperature of inversion dual systems were obtained, consisting of large water drops in which organic globules were suspended.

Weichherz[19] obtained analogous results using tetralin, paraffin oil, and xylene. Dry sodium oleate was dispersed in the hot organic liquid which gelled upon cooling. Then shaking with water produced *WO* emulsions which upon addition of water inverted to *OW* at a critical concentration (irrespective of the phase-volume ratio).

When Tartar used nitrobenzene instead of benzene, the emulsions were always *OW* with all of the soaps mentioned, although toluene, xylene, carbon tetrachloride, and chloroform acted qualitatively like benzene. In comparing the results obtained with the soaps with respect to ease of emulsifiability, the addition of $-CH_3$ groups to the benzene ring was beneficial; $-NH_2$ seemed to exert an inhibitory influence, while the further addition of $2CH_3$ groups seemed to overcome this as revealed by experiments with dimethylaniline. A nitro group, as in nitrobenzene, favored emulsification.

The influence of the chemical nature of one of the liquids upon phase distribution is shown in experiments upon lecithin and water. When oleic acid was the other liquid, the emulsions were always *WO*, but always *OW* when aniline and other basic organic liquids were used.[20]

Ordinarily bivalent metallic soaps are considered to serve as *WO* emulsifiers, but Tartar and his associates found that dilute aqueous solutions of magnesium heptylate, caprylate, and caproate and calcium valerate formed *OW* emulsions when shaken with benzene. These emulsions were stable for only 2 to 4 hr., however. The *WO* emulsions formed when the aqueous soap solutions were sufficiently concentrated as to contain "colloidal soap" or suspended solid particles. When benzene solutions of calcium and of magnesium oleates were shaken with water, the influence of the phase-volume ratio became marked, the phase of greater volume usually becoming the continuous one.

When equal volumes of the systems just mentioned were shaken gently, WO emulsions were produced, while violent shaking produced the OW type.* The latter were the more stable, persisting for several hours, while the WO usually broke in 10 to 15 min.; temperature and concentration of the soap in the benzene did not seem to have any influence.

Holmes claims that an optimum viscosity of the interfacial film is more important than lowered surface tension, as a result of studies of kerosene-oil-water emulsions, using gelatin[21] and pyroxylin[22] as emulsifying agents.

A substance which lowers the interfacial tension will deposit at the interface and thus give rise to an emulsion, but in the words of Ramsden[23] the "persistence of many emulsions is determined largely, among other factors, by the presence of solid or highly viscous matter at the interfaces of the two liquids."

The optimum amount of gelatin for emulsification was found to be one that gives the aqueous solution a viscosity slightly greater than that of water. This can be accomplished by using a small amount of gelatin in pure water (0.1 to 0.3 per cent) or, better, by using an excessive amount in the presence of a salt which liquefies gelatin, such as sodium iodide. For example, a 2.4 per cent aqueous solution of gelatin did not yield a stable emulsion of kerosene in water, but upon the addition of sodium iodide it gave a very stable emulsion. Salts which solidify gelatin, such as sulfates, produced the opposite effect.

The influence of density and viscosity of one of the liquids upon the distribution of phases shows up in some of Seifriz's[24] experiments upon mineral oil-casein-water emulsification (Table 71).

The casein was dissolved in dilute potassium hydroxide solution and brought to "the neutral point" with acetic acid, yielding a fine colloidal suspension of casein which was dialyzed to remove

---

* The same phenomenon has been reported for the case of toluene-lecithin-water.[20]

Table 71.—Influence of Density of Oil on Emulsion Type

Specific gravity of oil	Type of emulsion	Texture	Stability
0.664[a]	*OW*	Fine[g]	Stable[h]
0.726[b]	*OW*	Fine	Stable
0.803	*OW*	Fine	Stable
0.818	*OW*	Fine	Stable
0.820[c]	*OW*	Medium	Moderately stable
0.828	*OW*	Coarse	Unstable
0.839	......	....	Separates immediately
0.849	......	....	Separates immediately
0.856	......	....	Separates immediately
	1 *OW*	Coarse	Unstable
0.857	or *WO*[f]	Fine	Stable
	2 *WO*	Medium	Moderately stable
0.869[d]	*WO*	Medium	Stable
0.874	*WO*	Fine	Stable
0.884	*WO*	Fine	Stable
0.895[e]	*WO*	Fine	Stable

[a] Isohexane (boiling point = 77°C.).

[b] Isooctane (boiling point = 118°C.).

[c] Boiling range = 130 to 150°C. at 67 mm. Hg pressure.

[d] Boiling range = 210 to 230°C. at 67 mm. Hg pressure.

[e] Boiling range = over 270°C. at 67 mm. Hg pressure.

[f] Both types coexist in the same emulsion.

[g] A fine texture is one in which the oil or water droplets average 0.02 mm. or less: in an emulsion of medium texture the globules vary from 0.02 to 0.5 mm.: and a coarse emulsion is one in which the dispersed oil or water drops are over 0.5 mm. in diameter.

[h] Stability is purely a relative term here. Since most emulsions were treated with electrolytes, they were not allowed to stand, except in a few instances, for more than 15 min. An emulsion which showed little or no sign of separating during that time was recorded as "stable." A "moderately stable" emulsion was stable for several minutes only. An "unstable" emulsion separated in less than a minute.

the electrolytes. The concentration of casein was 0.2 per cent of the aqueous phase. Equal volumes of oil and water were shaken together by the Briggs's intermittent method.

From Seifriz's data it seems that when petroleum distillates are emulsified with water and "neutral" casein and are (1) of less than 0.820 specific gravity, they form fine, stable *OW* emulsions; (2) of 0.820 to 0.828 specific gravity, they form coarse and poorly stable *OW* emulsions; (3) of 0.828 to 0.857 specific gravity, which constitutes a zone of instability, no emulsion at all is formed; (4) of 0.857 to 0.869 specific gravity, the oils form coarse to medium, poorly to moderately stable *WO* emulsions; and (5) of 0.869 to 0.895 specific gravity and above, fine and stable *WO* emulsions are produced.

When sodium or barium hydroxide was added to these emulsions, the *OW* emulsions became more stable, while the *WO* ones were reversed. Thorium nitrate and aluminum sulfate exhibited the same effect although much less readily.

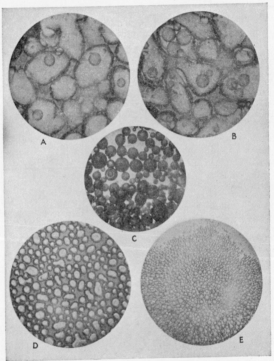

Fig. 133.—Some of Seifriz's emulsions.

The behavior of a similar casein emulsion of olive oil in water was different.[25] Neutral casein emulsified water in olive oil. The addition of sodium hydroxide reversed it to *OW*, while the subsequent addition of barium chloride or barium hydroxide reversed it back again to *WO*. Olive oil-in-water emulsions emulsified by gliadin or cholesterol behaved similarly.

It is difficult indeed to crystallize any general rule of behavior from such confusion. Part of the conflict in behavior may be cleared up by a more exact definition of an emulsion. The writer is inclined to think this from an examination of one of Seifriz's experiments on "double reversal of emulsions" which he describes as follows:

A mixture of 25 cc. of a petroleum distillate of 0.834 specific gravity and 25 cc. of an aqueous casein dispersion cannot be emulsified by repeated shaking. The two phases separate immediately. The addition of 0.03 cc. of 0.2 M barium hydroxide causes, after shaking, the production of a coarse but moderately stable water-in-oil emulsion, in the large water globules of which are a few scattered oil droplets. These latter are the forerunners of the future oil-in-water emulsions (A).* One drop more of 0.2 M Ba(OH)$_2$ (0.66 cc. of hydroxide in 50 cc. of emulsion) leaves the coarse water-in-oil emulsion unchanged but increases the amount of dispersed oil in the water globules (B). One cc. of 0.2 M Ba(OH)$_2$ reverses the entire emulsion into a stable oil-in-water system (C). . . .

While the above description is the usual effect of barium hydroxide and of sodium hydroxide on the petroleum distillates which lie in the zone of instability (specific gravity 0.828 to 0.857), some surprising variations of this behavior often occur. Two samples of an unstable mixture of a hydrocarbon oil of 0.828 specific gravity behaved quite differently as follows. One sample practically duplicated in behavior the emulsion described above. It gradually became a fine stable water-in-oil system on the addition of 0.2 cc. of 0.2 M NaOH. Further addition of alkali coarsened the water-in-oil emulsion until at a concentration of 5 cc. of 0.2 M NaOH the two phases separated. One more cc. of hydroxide produced a fine stable oil-in-water emulsion. A second sample of this same originally unstable mixture became immediately a fine and stable oil-in-water emulsion on the addition of barium hydroxide, thus omitting altogether the preliminary water-in-oil stage through which its sister sample went. . . .

Still another unstable emulsion of a petroleum distillate of 0.852 specific gravity passed through the preliminary stages of establishing a water-in-oil emulsion but instead of this emulsion subsequently reversing into an oil-in-water one at a moderate concentration of hydroxide, it became so thoroughly established that at 25 cc. of 0.2 M Ba(OH)$_2$ the system was still a fine water-in-oil one with no indication of reversal into the opposite type (D). Ten more cc. (total 35 cc.) of hydroxide reversed the system into a fine stable oil-in-water emulsion (E). The

* The author is indebted to Dr. William Seifriz for the photographs A, B, C, D, and E in Fig. 133.

firm establishing of this water-in-oil emulsion is possibly in part accounted for by the fact that the oil (specific gravity 0.852), though within the unemulsifiable zone of instability, is very near the upper limit of the zone (specific gravity 0.857) at which point petroleum oils form stable water-in-oil emulsions without the addition of any electrolyte. The first oil discussed (specific gravity 0.834) which became at the outset a water-in-oil emulsion and later reversed with a low (1 cc.) concentration of hydroxide, is near the other end of the unstable zone below which point (specific gravity 0.828) the petroleum distillations form stable oil-in-water emulsions without the addition of an electrolyte. . . .

These double reversals of petroleum oil emulsions with the same electrolyte take place only on the addition of a hydroxide, and more frequently with barium than sodium hydroxide; and only with petroleum distillates which lie in the zone of instability.

The emulsion of large drops of water in oil, as depicted in A of Fig. 133 with the small oil drops emulsified in each large globule of water, should be called a "pseudo-emulsion"; *i.e.*, the shaking up of equal volumes of oil and water with casein (which is on the edge of precipitation) results in breaking up the water phase as well as the oil phase, the former being held broken up by the viscous films of deposited casein and the viscosity of the magma generally. The whole changes to a real OW emulsion when the casein has been dissolved to a clear solution of barium or sodium caseinate.

Emulsifying Agents.—There are three groups of emulsifying agents: crystalloid, colloid, and insoluble solids. It will be convenient to apply to the first two the term *hydrotropic* agents which was suggested by Neuberg[26] to designate wetting, detergent, and emulsifying agents.

The crystalloidal hydrotropic agents[27] are generally salts either of carboxyl groups (-COOM), of sulfonic (-SO₃M), of sulfinic (-SO₂M), of ethereal sulfuric radicals (-O · SO₃M) or of phenolic groups (-OM). The compounds may be straight chains or rings. So long as the salt-forming group is not altered, there may be many substituents (halogen, amino, nitro, or hydroxyl groups) without spoiling the hydrotropic properties. The number of groups and their position play a leading rôle. There are hydrotropes which are active in a dilution of as high as one in a thousand.

Neuberg has shown that they peptize water-insoluble proteins and prevent the precipitation of proteins by alcohols and heat. They also inhibit the precipitation of water-insoluble inorganic compounds.

As detergents they are valuable owing to their stability in presence of acids and lime salts. Here high molecular sulfoacids, joined to insoluble alcohols (such as cyclohexanol and benzyl-alcohol) or to simple and chlorinated hydrocarbons, or hydrogenated naphthalenes are used either alone or mixed with soaps.

Of a large number of compounds studied by Neuberg, the following were found to be hydrotropic: benzoic acid, benzenesulfonic acid, their homologues and substitution products, naphthoic acids and derivatives, naphthalene sulfonic acids, thiophene carboxylic acid, pyromucic acid, phenylacetic acid and homologues, aliphatic-aromatic acids, further the benzene- and toluene-sulfinic acids, nitrobenzoic acid, the amino, halogen, oxy, and methoxy derivatives of benzoic, mandelic and cinnamic acids, as well as a large number of acids of the naphthalene series. Hydrotropic properties are especially marked with acids and their derivatives in the hydroaromatic series.

Neuberg's method of investigation was to add the hydrotropic agent to water and then add a substance to be stabilized such as amyl alcohol, cyclohexanol or benzyl alcohol, noting how much water could be present without rendering the homogeneous-looking, clear solution turbid. He found the following to be very good hydrotropes: anthranilic acid, hippuric acid, sodium phenolate, and salicylic acid.

On the other hand m-oxybenzoic acid was only weakly hydrotropic and p-oxybenzoic acid was practically inert.

Other very good hydrotropes were the alkali salts of cresotinic, anisic, phenylacetic, hydrocinnamic, α-phenylpropionic, pyromucic, and oxynaphthoic acid.

Good hydrotropic action was shown by the alkali salts of abietic acid and cyclohexane carboxylic acids, benzenesulfonic, toluenesulfonic, naphthalene sulfonic, and of amyl sulfonic acids.

The hydrotropic properties of phenylacetic acid are eclipsed by phenylglycine and by phenylglycine-o-carboxylic acid. A further increase in hydrotropic nature is obtained by introduction of a benzyl group on a nitrogen atom as in n-benzyl phenyl glycine. A corresponding substitution product of phenyl glycine-*o*-carboxylic acid with greater activity is *n*-benzylphenylglycine-*o*-carboxylic acid, $C_6H_4(COOH).N(CH_2.C_6H_5).CH_2.COOH$.

In a similar manner more active derivatives of anthranilic acid are prepared, *e.g.*, monobenzyl anthranilic acid and dibenzyl anthranilic acid, the latter being more active than the former.

A powerful nitrogenous hydrotrope is the sodium salt of 2-phenylquinoline-4-carboxylic acid.

The simple compounds methyl and ethyl alcohols, phenol, and resorcinol have been shown to emulsify benzene in water.[28]

The colloidally dissolving emulsifying agents which are commonly used are soaps, resinates, proteins (such as casein, gelatin, albumin, hemoglobin, gliadin), protein hydrolysis products (such as peptones, gelatoses), water-soluble gums and mucilages (such as arabic, tragacanth, Irish moss), colloidal carbohydrates (such as starches, dextrins), egg yolk, lanolin, cholesterol, lecithin, saponin, sulfonated oils, gum·resins (such as dammar, elemi), amylene, triethanolamine soaps, and trihydroxy ethylamine stearate. They produce more stable emulsions undoubtedly owing to the semisolid interfacial films formed by them.[29]

This statement is supported by the fact that gelatin yields the most stable emulsions of benzene in water when the pH value of the aqueous phase is at the isoelectric point of gelatin.[30] The pH value of the solution is undoubtedly significant for other colloidal emulsifiers; *OW* emulsions of fatty oils are the most stable at pH = 4.1 to 4.3 with gum arabic and at pH = 2.5 with gum tragacanth.[31]

The distribution of the phases (*i.e., OW* or *WO*) has been believed to be unerringly predictable on the criterion of wetting or solubility, the liquid best wetting or dissolving the emulsifying agent being the dispersing liquid. In the light of recent work, however, this rule has been found to fail in certain cases, since the distribution of the phases is influenced by the volume ratios of the two liquids, the manner of mixing and agitating, and their chemical nature, as well as by the nature of the emulsifying agents. Only as a first approximation can the rule of wetting or solubility be used. For example, we have seen that *WO* emulsions can be formed with alkali soaps or *OW* with higher valence metallic soaps, although they may not, however, be so stable as the form predictable by the idea of preferential wetting or solubility. While proteins invariably give *OW* emulsions, yet we have seen that Seifriz obtained *WO* emulsions in certain cases, using casein. In his case, the highly viscous liquid entrapped the low-viscosity water. Had he used a larger ratio of water to oil, he might have obtained *OW* emulsions. The superior volume of one phase may make it the continuous phase,[32,33] regardless of the wetting of the emulsifier, although if the continuous liquid is not viscous the emulsion may not be very stable. That this may happen is obvious from a purely mechanical aspect of the disintegration of the liquid particles.

This is in fact illustrated by one of Seifriz's experiments, wherein the volumes of water and of heavy petroleum were varied, and "neutral" casein was used as emulsifying agent. With 25 volumes of oil and 10 volumes of water, a *WO* system resulted, while 25 volumes of oil and 35 volumes of water gave an *OW* emulsion. Further, *WO* systems of equal volumes of heavy mineral oil and water, when allowed to stand 20 min., yielded *OW* emulsions upon reshaking.

Further evidence of the influence of volume relationships on distribution of phases has been given in the emulsification of water-oleic acid mixtures in a colloid mill.[13] For volume compositions from 5 to 40 per cent oleic acid, the oleic acid was the dispersed phase; while with mixtures containing greater volumes of oleic acid, water was the dispersed phase. No emulsifying agent was used. An experiment where "Stanolax" (a heavy mineral oil) was used gave a similar effect.[13] With 50 per cent by volume of oil, water was the dispersed phase, but with 40 per cent of oil, the oil was the dispersed phase.

A similar behavior has been observed in the emulsification of water-cresylic acid mixtures, using gelatin as stabilizing agent, and the "shake" method of disintegration.[34] Other factors, such as the mode of shaking and the age of the gelatin solution, also affected the phase distribution, a fresh aqueous gelatin solution giving the *WO* type, an old one the *OW* type; gentle shaking favored the *OW* type, while vigorous shaking favored the reverse type.

An excellent example of the effect of the mode of emulsifying is referred to by Clayton, *viz.*, in margarin manufacture, where about 80 volumes of oil are emulsified with 20 volumes of water and milk, which should promote the oil-in-water type of emulsion. If the oils are slowly run in the milk at about 30°C. with constant agitation, a thick and quite stable emulsion of oil-in-milk results. If, however, both phases are placed in bulk in a churn and then agitated, an emulsion of milk in oil is obtained, but of poor stability. The latter result is obtained if the milk is slowly added to the total volume of oils in the churn with constant agitation.[35]

The use of an insoluble solid as emulsifying agent seems to have been reported first by Tfol[36] who found that an argillaceous earth readily emulsified oils in water. His interest was aroused by the knowledge that Arabs in Northern Africa used this earth as a substitute for soap in washing linen.

Pickering[37] was probably the first to study the efficacy of certain solids as emulsification agents, finding that basic copper sulfate made by adding 1 part of CaO to 7 parts $CuSO_4.5H_2O$ in solution in water is an excellent emulsifier. At least 1 part of $CuSO_4.5H_2O$ converted to the basic salt is needed to emulsify 120 parts of paraffin oil. Immediate and stable emulsification results by a few strokes of a syringe and the product is said to be efficient as a germicidal spray in agriculture.

Kaolin, fuller's earth, and colloidal clay have been found to act as satisfactory emulsifiers of mineral oil in water for insecticidal sprays and have been found less likely to "burn" the foliage than when soap is used.[38]

Pickering's experiments with other solid substances showed the following emulsifying action of solids: Basic ferrous sulfate, basic copper sulfate, and basic nickel sulfate are the best. Ferrous and ferric hydroxides are good. Basic zinc and basic aluminum sulfates give good emulsions temporarily. The precipitate formed by adding sodium carbonate to copper sulfate is good. Calcium carbonate and arsenate are good when freshly precipitated but they soon become crystalline and deemulsification follows. Lead arsenate and some unheated fine clays are good. Iron sulfide is good for small amounts of oil and zinc oxychloride is fair.

Silver dichromate has been used to emulsify chloroform in water.[39]

Pickering pointed out that, for an insoluble solid to form an emulsion of oil in water, its particles must be exceedingly fine, it must be readily wetted by water and preferably amorphous. It would follow from Pickering's work that a finely divided solid which is wetted better by an oil than by water should emulsify water in oil. It has been found that soot will emulsify water in kerosene, turpentine, benzene, or toluene.[40] With 60 cc. kerosene, 240 cc. water, and 1.5 g. soot an almost solid water-in-oil emulsion is obtained. Aqueous ammonium chloride solutions can be emulsified in kerosene by the aid of lamp black.[41] Highly calcined lamp black and petroleum coke are not satisfactory emulsifying agents.

If the angles of contact between liquids and insoluble solids were known, it would be possible to predict which liquid of the

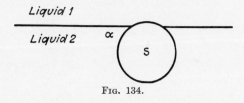

FIG. 134.

two would be the internal phase in an emulsion with a given insoluble powder.

If S in Fig. 134 is a small solid sphere, the condition for equilibrium is

$$\gamma_{1,s} = \gamma_{2,s} + \gamma_{1,s} \cos \alpha$$

where γ = interfacial tension. When $\gamma_{1,s} > \gamma_{2,s}$, then $\cos \alpha$ is plus and α is less than 90°. The solid will tend to be drawn into liquid 2. When $\gamma_{1,s} < \gamma_{2,s}$, $\cos \alpha$ is minus and $\alpha > 90°$ and the solid will be drawn into liquid 1. In order that a powder may serve as an efficient emulsifying agent, it must be wetted to a certain extent by both liquids.

If there are enough particles to fill the interface, the tendency of the interface to contract will cause it to bend, as shown in Fig. 135, in the direction of the more poorly wetting liquid, which makes it easy for the latter to become the dispersed phase.[16] The solid, in order to behave in this way, must be easily dispersed in the outer liquid, its particles not tending to agglomerate therein or to stick together when serving as a protective coating for the emulsified drops.   If a solid is wetted equally well by both liquids, emulsification obviously cannot be obtained.

Emulsions with solid emulsifiers may arise when a hydrosol is shaken with an oil, provided some precipitating factor is present, as illustrated by the experiments made by Briggs.[42]   Ferric oxide hydrosol was shaken in a bottle with benzene (or kerosene), but no emulsion was produced, the benzene and water separating into two continuous layers shortly after shaking ceased.   When, however, some sodium chloride was added to the ferric oxide hydrosol and the latter was shaken anew with benzene, a coarse

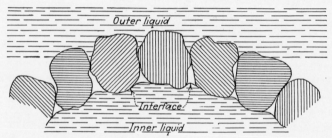

FIG. 135.—Particles of a finely divided solid acting as emulsifying agent.

unstable *OW* emulsion was produced.   As the concentration of salt was increased, the stability and the degree of dispersion of the emulsified benzene were greatly enhanced, fairly permanent emulsions being ultimately obtained.   In time the emulsified benzene in water floated to the top of the water layer in the form of a brownish-yellow cream and carried with it a large proportion of the iron oxide originally suspended in the aqueous phase.

These experiments indicate that sodium chloride, a weak flocculating agent, drives ferric oxide out of colloidal solution and forces it into the interface.   By doing so, it causes the finely precipitated oxide to act as an emulsifying agent.   Barium chloride, also a weak precipitating agent toward ferric oxide sol, behaved like sodium chloride in bringing about emulsification. But when sodium sulfate was added, no emulsions were produced because the ferric oxide was precipitated in flocculi which were too coarse.

Arsenious sulfide sol acted like ferric oxide sol when treated with sodium chloride but was precipitated in too large flocculi by barium chloride.

The emulsifying efficiency of an insoluble powder is affected by the presence of a suitable solute in one of the liquids. For example, while pure benzene is not emulsified in pure water by clay powder, an emulsion will result upon addition of a drop of pyridine, nitrobenzene, amyl alcohol, alcohol, acetic acid, sodium hydroxide, barium chloride, or sodium nitrate.[43] These adjuncts must effect a change in the wetting powers of the two liquids toward the powder.

Determination of Phase Distribution.—An emulsion can be diluted with its dispersion medium, as might be expected. Consequently, an *OW* emulsion will be freely miscible with water, while a portion of a *WO* emulsion will float on water like a piece of grease, whereas an *OW* emulsion will not disperse in some of its organic liquid phase. It is perhaps better to make the tests upon drops on a microscope slide and a warning has been published against making the tests on emulsions too soon after their preparation.[44]

Addition of a dye soluble in the oil phase has been proposed[45] as a test. Sudan III is soluble in oil but not in water. If, after such a dye is dusted over the surface of an emulsion, a series of discontinuous dots is seen, the emulsion is *OW*. A water-soluble colored substance such as potassium permanganate has been used to show the same discontinuities with *WO* emulsions. Iodin has been employed to determine phase distribution in benzene-water emulsions.[46] The dye method is said to be less trustworthy than the dilution test.[47]

In following the distribution of phases in a given series of experiments, electrical conductivity has been suggested as a tool[48] and successfully utilized.[49,50] The conductivity drops abruptly when an *OW* emulsion inverts to the *WO* type.

Preparation of Emulsions.—If one shakes together benzene and an aqueous solution of sodium oleate, carrying out the process steadily and without interruption, the time required for *complete* emulsification of the benzene in the water increases very rapidly as the ratio of benzene to water becomes larger.[51] Table **72** illustrates this fact.[52]

TABLE 72.—TIME REQUIRED FOR EMULSIFICATION WITH CONTINUOUS AGITATION*

Benzene and 1 per cent aqueous sodium oleate

Volume benzene in 100 volumes	Time, minutes	Volume benzene in 100 volumes	Time, minutes
30	< 1	80	15
40	1	90	22
50	3	95	40
60	7	96	125
70	10	99	480

* Performed in a machine providing 400 oscillations per minute, so that the time in minutes multiplied by 400 = number of shakes.

When benzene is slowly added to the aqueous solution with agitation, an emulsion of 96 to 99 volumes of it is effected more easily.

If benzene is shaken *intermittently* with an aqueous sodium oleate solution, complete emulsification is effected with much less agitation. An example is given in Table 73, where the

TABLE 73.—EMULSIFICATION BY INTERMITTENT SHAKING

Benzene in 1 per cent aqueous sodium oleate solution

Volume benzene in 100 volumes	Time required to emulsify, minutes	Number of shakes
80	3.5	7
84	6.5	13
86	7.	14
88	9.	18
90	12.5	25
92	15.5	31
94	22.5	45
96	40.	80

shaking was done by hand and between each shake the mixture was allowed to stand quietly for 30 sec.; in this rest interval the unemulsified benzene floated to the surface of the incomplete emulsion.

When emulsions are prepared by the method of slowly running the liquid to be dispersed into the dispersing liquid, such as benzene into a soap solution, the volume of the soap solution plus emulsified benzene is large in comparison with the unemulsified layer of benzene. Under these conditions, for a given mode of shaking, the ease of emulsification increases with the volume of the soap solution and the emulsified benzene. Briggs's experience with intermittent shaking reveals, however, that there is an additional factor involved. The formation of a complete emulsion is facilitated by allowing the emulsion mixture and the benzene phase to form two distinct layers before each shake. This probably means that emulsions are formed most readily when relatively little benzene is agitated briefly while in contact with a large and continuous volume of the dispersing liquid.

Continuous shaking disintegrates the aqueous phase as well as the benzene. Any process tending to break up the continuous phase must retard emulsification just as any process which breaks up the phase to be dispersed aids emulsification. It should be more difficult to break up the soap solution into droplets than the benzene when the volume of the former is large and hence in such a case the formation of an emulsion of benzene in water should be easy. When benzene drops are formed in a soap solution, the soap films prevent the coalescence of the drops. There is nothing, however, to prevent the rapid coalescence of water drops in benzene. Consequently, the best method is to break up the benzene particles without keeping the water phase broken up, which explains why intermittent shaking produces the result more efficiently. A method by which benzene may be disintegrated under conditions unfavorable to the simultaneous disintegration of the soap solution consists in rolling the mixture in a bottle. Briggs effected complete emulsification of 90 volumes of benzene in 100 volumes of mixture in 2 min. continuous rolling.

It seems to be a general idea in emulsification practice that the oil and aqueous phases should be agitated as violently as possible in order that small globules be formed. Excessive agitation may, however, increase the size of the emulsifying globules.[53] In a study of the resistance of lubricating oils to emulsification in water, Herschel[54] found for a given time that increasing the speed of paddling produced an increase in emulsification up to 1,500 r.p.m.; above this speed the efficiency of emulsification decreased with certain oils (Fig. 136).

Agitation at a given intensity for too long a time may be inadvisable as shown by Moore's[41] results with water-in-kerosene oil emulsions using lamp black as emulsifier (Fig. 137).

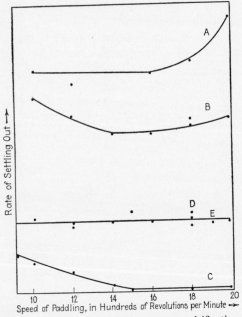

Fig. 136.—Influence of speed of paddling upon emulsification. *A, B, C, D,* and *E* represent five different lubricating oils studied. Although the efficiency of emulsification of oils *D* and *E* is constant within the limits of the speeds tried, and although nothing is gained in agitating oil *C* faster than 1,500 r.p.m., a loss of efficiency is noted above this speed in the cases *A* and *B*.

Sheppard[55] found that nitrobenzene is emulsified in sulfuric acid by gentle and rapid shaking. Slow shaking or in some cases a single vibration, however, resulted in deemulsification.

Sometimes the vibration involved in shipment of emulsions by truck or railroad will incite breakdown of emulsions. This is well known in commercial mayonnaise practice where trucks equipped with special springs to reduce shock are frequently used for transportation. Ayres[56] mentions a case of an oil-field emulsion, so stable as to resist separation in a centrifuge, but which separated into water and oil after transit in an express train. Nugent[57] found that a very stable emulsion of benzene in aqueous gelatin solution broke when a tube containing the emulsion was attached to the spoke of a wheel which rotated in a vertical plane at a rate of 3 r.p.m. This happened only when an air space was present, probably owing to the deposition of the emulsifying agent at the air-water interface.

The process of homogenization, wherein the mixture of two liquids is forced under high pressure through small tubes against a solid surface, is used in large-scale operations, particularly for

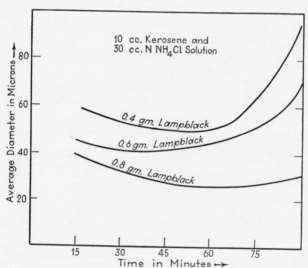

Fig. 137.—Influence of time at constant speed of paddling upon efficiency of emulsification.

breaking up the globules of emulsions already formed into finer drops, as, for example, in cream. Homogenized milk and cream are, as might be expected, much more stable emulsions than the raw product. With the increase in oil-water interfacial area, there is a greater protein interfacial deposition, resulting in an increased viscosity. The fat globules of milk (ordinarily 2 to 10 μ in diameter) and of cream (3 to 5 μ) are reduced one-tenth[58,59] to one-hundredth of their original size. Homogenized cream cannot be "whipped." Ice cream made from it is a much smoother product and it is said that a 15 per cent cream, after homogenization, is a good substitute for a 25 per cent cream in culinary operations.[60] Battleships carry skim-milk powder and sweet butter instead of milk. When milk or cream is desired, the butter fat is emulsified by means of an homogenizer in a solution of milk powder. The product is quite palatable, differing from milk by its "cooked-milk" taste.

A simple laboratory homogenizer has been devised by Briggs.[61] It consists of three flasks. The mixture of liquids is drawn from the first flask into the second flask, which has been evacuated. The liquid mixture enters the second flask through a tube bent at right angles so that it impinges forcibly against the wall of the flask. The mixture is returned to the first flask and the operation is repeated until emulsification is complete. The third flask serves as a suction trap. Stopcocks are inserted between the flasks.

When a mixture of liquids has been agitated sufficiently with a colloidal emulsifying agent to form an emulsion, it should be allowed to stand quietly for about an hour before moving or subjecting it to shocks. It has been found that benzene-in-water emulsions, emulsified by gelatin,[57] require from 5 to 75 min. standing to attain maximum stability. This is well known in commercial mayonnaise practice. Evidently the time is required for the complete diffusion of the emulsifying agent to the interface to complete the viscous film essential to stability.

In small-scale pharmaceutical practice, emulsions of oil in water are prepared by triturating oil and a gum in a mortar followed by addition of water.[62,63] The best proportions are oil 4 parts, gum arabic 2 parts, and water 3 parts. The gum is ground to a pasty mass with the oil in a large mortar. The water is then added all at once while being triturated, whereupon a creamy emulsion nucleus arises almost immediately which can then be diluted as desired with water. This is known as the "Continental" method. For success, the gum must be dry and well ground in the oil, and the water must be added all at once. If the water is added gradually, the gum particles coalesce to sticky masses which adhere to the mortar. Sometimes gum tragacanth is used instead of acacia in preparing these emulsions.

Briggs's study[64] of the Continental method has yielded a plausible explanation which follows. He found that a finely ground powder such as silica or glass served as well as gum arabic for the nucleus emulsification, and hence the presence of the same or of gum assists the formation of the emulsion by increasing the interface between oil and water. Since the gum particles (which are ground in the oil) are more readily wetted by water than by oil, the subsequently added water displaces the oil from the gum particles so that each particle becomes coated with an aqueous film. The interface between water and oil thus becomes very great. The gum soon dissolves, leaving drops of aqueous gum solution scattered momentarily throughout the oil. The triturating action flattens out these drops, and in the process, oil is disintegrated and emulsified in the solution. The drops of gum solution, as they are stirred around in the mixture, exert an interfacial tearing effect upon the oil and help its dispersion, and the large drops of gum solution with their emulsified oil particles coalesce to form the emulsion nucleus. Sodium oleate may be used to form emulsions in a similar manner.

It has been suggested[64] that, if a colloidal suspension of a hydrophilic colloid were prepared in a dispersion medium such as benzene, an emulsion would form practically spontaneously upon addition of water.

A *WO* emulsion can be prepared by the Continental method if a substance more readily wetted by oil is ground in water and the oil subsequently added.

Heavy mineral oils give rise to dilute *OW* emulsions when dissolved in alcohol and poured into water where precipitation of fine droplets ensues, or upon boiling with water under a reflux condenser.[65] These are similar to the unwelcome emulsions obtained in engine-room practice. The precipitating effect of electrolytes upon these emulsions is identical with the behavior of electrolytes upon anodic colloids.[66] The emulsifying agent must be some polar compound originally in the oil which pushes its polar end into the water.* These emulsions are rendered more stable by sodium hydroxide which leads one to suspect that the polar group is a phenolic —OH, or a —COOH group.

If the solubility of one liquid in another is increased by temperature, an emulsion can be formed by allowing a warm saturated solution to cool, as, for example, aniline in water. Such

* The experiments by Holmes and Williams[28] offer evidence for this.

emulsions are encountered in steam distillation of organic substances.

Attention to the cleanliness of the apparatus employed in making emulsions is required. For example, it has been found that in the making of an OW emulsion, the process is inhibited if the walls and agitators are covered by a film of oil, and *vice versa*.[67] The reason is, in the first case, that the oil particles arising through the disruptive forces fuse with the oil film on the apparatus as they touch it before they are completely enveloped by the emulsifer film.

Inversion of Phases.—When calcium chloride (or other di- or trivalent metallic salt) is added to an emulsion of a fatty oil in water, emulsified by alkali soap, the emulsion will break when the ratio of calcium chloride to alkali soap is 1 mole: 4 moles, or where the calcium and sodium soaps are present in equivalent proportions. When calcium chloride is added in excess of this ratio, the emulsion inverts to one of water in oil. This behavior was first quantitatively exposed by Clowes.[68]

The metathetic inversion of olive oil-water emulsions has been found to hold for medium-body mineral oils and water.[69,70] Sodium oleate mineral oil-in-water emulsions were reversed by salts of Al^{+++}, Cr^{+++}, Fe^{+++}, Fe^{++}, Ni^{++}, Pb^{++}, Ba^{++}, Sr^{++}, and Mg^{++}. Just as Clowes found, the inversion with the divalent salts was effected when the equivalent concentration exceeded that of sodium oleate. The inversion by magnesium chloride yielded the most stable inverted emulsion.

When mineral oil containing dissolved magnesium oleate is agitated with water containing sodium oleate, the effect has been reported to be entirely different.[69] A large number of emulsions of equal volumes of oil and water have been studied, in which the ratio of equivalent concentrations of magnesium oleate to sodium oleate was varied from 25 to 0.5. In all cases the resulting emulsions settled out in three layers, oil on top, water on the bottom, and varying amounts of emulsion between. In many cases both types of emulsion were found in this middle layer, WO in the upper portion and OW in the lower portion, between which, after standing for several days, a distinct line of demarcation was shown.

This phenomenon was noticed in six emulsions in a series where the ratio of magnesium oleate to sodium oleate varied from 1.0 to 10. It appeared that an equilibrium was set up between the two types of emulsions and that, on standing, the less stable *WO* emulsion, which was much coarser grained than the *OW*, apparently underwent gradual breaking, with the separation of oil. In these experiments the systems were prepared in several different ways. In some cases an *OW* emulsion was made and then treated with magnesium oleate; in others the *WO* was prepared and treated with sodium oleate; in others a solution of sodium oleate in water and of magnesium oleate in oil were mixed simultaneously, all of the foregoing series being put through the homogenizer. The presence of both types of emulsion was independent of the method of preparation.

Similar results have been obtained with antagonistic solid emulsifiers.[71] Since among solid emulsifiers carbon black is known to emulsify water in oil, while finely divided silica emulsifies oil in water, one should expect to find a similar antagonistic action between these two solids when they are used together. This was shown to be true in the following manner by Briggs:

To 15 cc. of kerosene was added 0.8 g. of carbon black, which formed a black and fairly stable suspension in the oil. To this suspension in a bottle 25 cc. of water were introduced slowly and with shaking. In this way an emulsion of water in oil was formed. Finely pulverized silica (350 mesh) was added to a second bottle containing the above-mentioned quantities of kerosene and carbon black, and water was introduced as before. It was found that the silica exerted a marked antagonistic effect on the carbon black and rendered it much more difficult to emulsify the water. When the amount of silica exceeded 0.1 g., it was found impossible to emulsify any water at all, the mixture in the bottle separating after shaking into two sharply defined layers, an upper one of kerosene and carbon black and a lower one of water containing some silica in suspension. Likewise no emulsion was formed when equal parts of silica and carbon black were mixed.

On adding 15 cc. of kerosene to 25 cc. of water containing only pulverized silica, the oil was completely emulsified on shaking. Water was now the outside phase, for the emulsion mixed freely with water but not with oil. A small amount of carbon black added to the silica, however, sufficed to keep the oil from being emulsified. In a similar experiment with kerosene, water, silica, and powdered mercuric iodide (the last, like carbon black, being readily wetted by oil), it was found that approximately 1 part of mercuric iodide in 20 parts of silica was enough to prevent the silica from emulsifying 25 cc. of kerosene in 25 cc. of water.

Reversal of kerosene oil-water emulsions with solid emulsifying agent can be effected by certain electrolytes.[72] Carbon, freshly precipitated zinc hydroxide, and lead oxide produce WO emulsions which are reversed by hydroxyl ion. Freshly precipitated aluminum hydroxide produces an unstable pseudo-emulsion of WO which is reversed to a stable emulsion by alkali. The alkaline zinc hydroxide oil-in-water emulsion is reversed by Al^{+++}, Th^{++++}, and H^{+}.

Breaking of Emulsions.—In general, deemulsification can be accomplished by:

1. Addition of excess of dispersed phase followed by agitation.
2. Addition of a liquid in which the two liquid phases are soluble.
3. Destruction of the emulsifying agent.
4. Addition of a substance which will reverse the emulsion or of an emulsifying agent which emulsifies in the reverse direction.
5. Filtration.
6. Heating or plunging a hot blade into the emulsion.
7. Freezing.
8. Electrolyzing.
9. Centrifuging.
10. Mechanical action such as churning.

Methods 1 and 2 require no further discussion. The method of destroying the emulsifying agent depends upon the chemical nature of the same and is obvious when the nature of it is known. In the addition of substances which tend to reverse the emulsion, care must be observed not to add too much since an overdose will result in a stable emulsion of the reverse type.

Filtration of engine-room emulsions is advocated by Hatschek.[73] He found that filter beds of amorphous calcium or magnesium carbonate (causticizing mud) completely broke such emulsions, as well as oil-in-water soap and saponin emulsions. On a 4.5 sq. ft. filtering surface covered 0.125 in. thick with amorphous calcium carbonate he was able to filter 30 cu. ft. per hour under 10 lb. per square inch pressure. The adhering oil broke loose from the filtering surface and floated to the surface. The permeability of the filter was but slightly diminished after 6 hr. filtration. He advises using the calcium carbonate in a filter press at not higher than 50 lb. pressure because higher pressures squeeze the emulsified oil drops between the interstices in the filter bed.

Heat treatment, either direct or by steam, has been found efficacious in the breaking of certain petroleum-oil emulsions.[74]

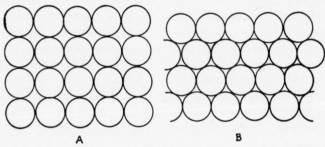

A   B

Fig. 138.

When emulsions are frozen, the "break" is generally perfect.

Electrolysis has been found useful for breaking engine-room or petroleum emulsions.[75]

Centrifuging is not always efficacious. It works best where the phases differ considerably in density and on pseudo- or viscous emulsions.

A well-known example of method 10 is the churning of milk to make butter.

Creaming and "Closest Packing Ratio."—If the globules of an emulsion are uniform in size, then according as the spheres are packed together as in Fig. 138A or in Fig. 138B the ratio of volumes of internal to external phase will be 52:48 or 74:26.

Since emulsions seldom contain uniform particles, the closest packing ratio of 74:26 is rarely encountered. It was once thought that the closest packing ratio defined the volumes in a stable emulsion. Obviously, however, smaller particles can fill the interstices between the larger ones and, further, the globules hardly remain spherical but become polyhedral owing to the squeezing together. The emulsifying agent also takes up space not allowed for in the calculation of the closest packing ratio.

Emulsions of 99 volumes of paraffin oil[37] or of benzene[76] in 1 volume of aqueous soap solution have been prepared, the latter emulsion being stable for six weeks when protected against evaporation of the water. Both these emulsions were, as might be expected, exceedingly stiff.

Upon long standing, dilute emulsions will frequently "cream"; *i.e.*, a concentrated emulsion will rise to the surface, leaving water behind, and the volume ratio of dispersed phase to dispersion medium will approximate the closest packing ratio. For example, a series of volumes of paraffin oil emulsified in water by various amounts of soap (by Pickering) creamed out on 12 weeks standing; the oil volumes in the creams were 72 to 82 per cent.

If the oil particles were all of the same size and if the soap films occupied but slight volume, such creams would be expected to approach closely the 74-oil to 26-water volume ratio. Careful manipulation with a very weakly alkaline aqueous solution, yielding emulsions of olive oil in water of uniform particle size, has given creams containing 74 volumes of oil to 26 volumes of water.[77]

Petroleum-field Emulsions.—Oil-field emulsions belong to the water-in-oil type and as such must be formed by an oil-soluble colloid or a solid material more easily wetted by oil acting as emulsifier. The character of this emulsifier may most easily be shown by the actions of the emulsions under certain conditions of test.

Certain water-soluble colloids, such as sodium oleate and the sodium salts of certain sulfonic acids, render these emulsions unstable and precipitate the water if added in proper proportion.

The action of certain organic solvents upon these emulsions probably throws more light on the nature of the emulsifying agent present than any of the other reactions. A standard method for determining the percentage of water in an emulsion consists in adding light gasoline to the emulsion and centrifuging the mixture when the amount of water in the sample can be read off from the graduated centrifuge tube. It has been found that ether serves even better than gasoline for this test.

The effect of these organic solvents in breaking the emulsions was thought to be due to the fact that the solvent mixing with the oil phase increased the difference in density of the two phases to such an extent that the emulsifier was no longer powerful enough to hold the emulsion. It was found, however, that a mixture of ether and carbon bisulfide of the same density as the emulsion served to break the emulsion more easily even than the light liquid ether.

The substances, other than water and oil, present in these emulsions are the following:

Electrolytes in solution in the water phase.

Hydrated earthy material.

Heavy hydrocarbons, such as asphalt and asphaltenes, probably present in colloidal solution in the oil.

It seems entirely probable, then, that the hydrated earthy material, sorbing the heavy asphalt-like bodies of the crude oil becomes an oil-soluble colloid and as such forms tough elastic membranes about the drops of water. Richardson[78] has found such an oil-soluble colloid in Trinidad asphalt and has even reproduced such a colloid by mixing a water solution of colloidal clay with asphalts and asphalt oils and driving off most of the water with heat. It is probable that some such process took place during the formation of the crude petroleums, leaving them charged with such an oil-soluble colloid which later served as an emulsifier when the oils came in contact with water under conditions favorable for emulsion formation. Since the earthy material is an oil-soluble colloid by virtue of the fact that it carries sorbed asphalt, when such asphalt is removed by organic solvents, the earthy matter is no longer oil soluble and cannot therefore protect a *WO* emulsion.[79]

Methods used in treating oil-field emulsions in addition to those mentioned above are steaming, centrifuging, and "topping" or direct heating at 350 to 500°F.[80]

Similar emulsions are formed sometimes in the oil tanks of oil-burning steamships. As the oil is used up, sea water is run into the tanks and, as a result of the rolling and splashing, thick *WO* emulsions arise.

Transparent and Chromatic Emulsions.—Emulsions exhibiting a wide range of structural colors were first prepared by Bodroux,[81] who, however, neglected to use an emulsifying agent. Consequently, his emulsions quickly separated into two layers.

Holmes and Cameron,[82] in an attempt to prepare transparent emulsions, found by a selection of liquids with cellulose nitrate as emulsifying agent that remarkably beautiful emulsions, stable for several weeks, can be made. The results of their experiments follow:

Ordinarily, when two transparent liquids are emulsified, a milky-white mixture results. For example, kerosene shaken with water gives such an emulsion. If both phases have the same refractive index, there will be neither reflection nor refraction and the system will appear homogeneous and entirely transparent.

Glycerol and olive oil are mutually insoluble and emulsify on shaking, forming a rather transparent emulsion. A more transparent mixture is obtained by dispersing glycerol in carbon tetrachloride, with calcium oleate (previously dissolved in the carbon tetrachloride) as the emulsifying agent.

Glycerol and amyl acetate are mutually insoluble and yield an excellent creamy emulsion on shaking. The same is true of water and amyl acetate. Yet when a mixture of water and glycerol having the same index of refraction as amyl acetate was shaken with the latter liquid, a transparent emulsion was obtained. Cellulose nitrate dissolved in the amyl acetate served as emulsifying agent.

The refractive indices of these liquids were as follows:

	N_D^{20}		N_D^{20}
Olive oil	1.4690	Water	1.3330
Glycerol	1.4660	Glycerol-water	1.4028
Carbon tetrachloride	1.4600	Amyl acetate containing 6 per cent of cellulose nitrate	1.4045

With the pyroxylin dissolved in amyl acetate the glycerol-water becomes the dispersed phase but with sodium oleate as the emulsifying agent dissolved in the water the phases are reversed—without loss of transparency.

"Nujol" containing 2 per cent of *crêpe* rubber, when shaken with an equal volume of glycerol, yields a very good transparent emulsion. Here the rubber is the emulsifying agent and the glycerol the dispersed phase.

In attempting to disperse glycerol in an acetone solution of cellulose nitrate Holmes and Cameron[82] failed to get transparency. Since the index of refraction of the acetone (1.35886) was lower than that of the glycerol (1.4660), they added benzene (1.50144) cautiously to the milky emulsion in order to equalize the indices of the two liquid phases, benzene diluting the acetone, thus becoming a part of the continuous phase. With cautious additions, and shaking, increased transparency was secured but accomplished by a startling development of colors. At first the emulsion became yellow, as viewed from the side, and a soft blue when held between the eye and the source of light. With further addition of benzene the yellow changed to a beautiful pink, while the blue became green. More benzene changed the pink to lavender and later to a peacock blue. Finally, the emulsion lost color and became milky. The colors were restored, in reverse order, by cautious additions of acetone.

The explanation of this phenomenon as given by Christiansen* and Bodroux† was verified by an examination of the Landolt-Börnstein tables of optical dispersive power of liquids. Benzene has more than twice the dispersive power of acetone. Optical dispersion is measured as the difference in the indices of refraction for light of two different wave lengths. In other words, a prism filled with benzene spreads light into a broader spectrum than does a prism filled with acetone. Consequently, drops of one liquid in another of very different optical dispersive power must give the effect of a great number of lenses or prisms with inevitable prismatic color effects. Transparency is essential in chromatic emulsions, for light of some color must pass directly through the emulsion. Yet transparency alone is not sufficient as shown by such emulsions as glycerol in carbon tetrachloride. The selection of liquids for chromatic or structural color emulsions involves two factors: equality of mean indices of refraction

* Christiansen, *Wied. Ann.*, **23**, 289 (1884), shook fragments of glass with a mixture of benzene and carbon disulfide.

† Bodroux shook a saturated aqueous solution of sodium chloride with ethyl acetate and at a definite temperature found this transient emulsion transparent for light of a definite color. Holmes and Cameron secure their color change by carefully changing the proportions of the two miscible liquids in the continuous phase. Furthermore, their use of an emulsifying agent stabilizes the emulsions.

and the greatest possible difference in optical dispersive power. From such values as those in Table 74 they were able to substitute other liquids for those first used.[82]

TABLE 74.—REFRACTION OF LIQUIDS

	Index of refraction		Optical dispersive power	
	n_D	°C.	$(n_F - n_C)$	°C.
Dispersed phase:				
Glycerol....................	1.466	20	0.007	20
Continuous phase:				
Acetone.....................	1.35886	19.4	0.00684	19.4
Amyl acetate................	1.40170	17.9	0.007	17.9
Carbon disulfide.............	1.61847	20	0.03210	20
Benzene.....................	1.50144	20	0.01664	20
Toluene.....................	1.4992	18.7	0.0160	14.7
Brombenzene................	1.55977	20	0.01923	20
Ethyl bromide...............	1.53806	20	0.01422	20
Benzyl acetate..............	1.50682	17.3	0.01660	17.3

Water may be substituted for glycerol, but the high viscosity of the latter adds to the stability of the emulsions and also to their beauty.

It is necessary to have two mutually soluble liquids for the continuous phase, one of them of high refractive index and high optical dispersive power. On careful addition of this liquid to a milky emulsion already prepared, it is possible to change gradually both the refractive index and the optical dispersive power. This insures the chromatic range of colors. Carbon disulfide is an excellent liquid to use because it stands high in both the essential physical properties. The colors change somewhat with change in temperature since there is an unequal temperature effect on the optical dispersive power of the two phases. As Bodroux used only two liquids in each emulsion, he was forced to secure his color effects by temperature change.

Cellulose nitrate is an excellent emulsifying agent since it dissolves readily in acetone, amyl acetate, and some other liquids, thus forcing the glycerol to become the dispersed phase, as desired. Raw *crêpe* rubber may be substituted for the cellulose ester. For example, a 2 per cent solution of rubber in toluene may be shaken with water which has been saturated with cane sugar to give it high optical dispersive power and high refractive index. Emulsions with a beautiful play of colors are secured. A trace of gasoline lowers the refractive index of toluene to a suitable point.

Potassium iodide gives water high optical dispersive power and a high index of refraction. "Nujol" may be dispersed in such a saturated solution by using sodium oleate in water as the emulsifying agent. Prismatic colors are secured.

As a specific experiment, Holmes and Cameron suggest the following:

Shake together 4 volumes of glycerol and 4 volumes of a 2 to 4 per cent solution of cellulose nitrate in amyl acetate. To this 5 to 10 volumes of benzene are added, then more glycerol until rather viscous, and finally more benzene in small additions, with shaking, until colors appear.

The final emulsion may contain over 30 per cent of glycerol. To view it best a 4-oz. oil-specimen bottle is used as container and held some distance from the source of light. A single source is best. On standing, these emulsions "cream" downward but vigorous shaking restores much of their beauty.

References

1. QUINCKE: *Wied. Ann.* **35**, 571 (1888).
2. DONNAN: *Z. physik. Chem.*, **31**, 42 (1899); DONNAN and POTTS: *Kolloid-Z.*, **7**, 208 (1910).
3. BANCROFT: *J. Phys. Chem.*, **17**, 501 (1913); BANCROFT and TUCKER: *J. Phys. Chem.*, **31**, 1681 (1927).
4. LANGMUIR: *J. Am. Chem. Soc.*, **39**, 1848 (1917).
5. HARKINS, DAVIES, and CLARK: *J. Am. Chem. Soc.*, **39**, 541 (1917).
6. FINKLE, DRAPER, and HILDEBRAND: *J. Am. Chem. Soc.*, **45**, 2780 (1923).
7. HOLMES and CAMERON: *J. Am. Chem. Soc.*, **42**, 2049 (1920); **44**, 66 (1922).
8. MAYER, SCHAEFFER, and TERROINE: *Compt. rend.*, **146**, 484 (1908).
9. BRIGGS: *J. Phys. Chem.*, **19**, 210 (1915).
10. HARKINS and ZOLLMAN: *J. Am. Chem. Soc.*, **48**, 69 (1926).
11. FISCHER and HARKINS: *J. Phys. Chem.*, **36**, 98 (1932); see also in this connection HARKINS and BEEMAN: *J. Am. Chem. Soc.*, **51**, 1674 (1929); GRIFFIN: *J. Am. Chem. Soc.*, **45**, 1648 (1923); VAN DER MEULEN and RIEMAN: *J. Am. Chem. Soc.*, **46**, 876 (1924).
12. HARKINS and BEEMAN: *Proc. Nat. Acad. Sci.*, **11**, 631 (1925).
13. STAMM and KRAEMER: *J. Phys. Chem.*, **30**, 992 (1926).

14. HULL: *Proc. Am. Inst. Elec. Eng.*, **38**, 1171 (1919); *Science*, **52**, 227 (1920).

15. BRAGG: *Phil. Mag.*, (6) **40**, 169 (1920).

16. RICHARDS: *J. Am. Chem. Soc.*, **45**, 422 (1923).

17. TARTAR, DUNCAN, SHEA, and FERRIER: *J. Phys. Chem.*, **33**, 435 (1929); TARTAR, LOTHROP, and PETTENGILL: *J. Phys. Chem.*, **34**, 373 (1930).

18. WELLMAN and TARTAR: *J. Phys. Chem.*, **59**, 1061 (1927).

19. WEICHHERZ: *Kolloid-Z.*, **47**, 133 (1929).

20. WOODMAN: *J. Soc. Chem. Ind.*, **51**, 95T (1932).

21. HOLMES and CHILD: *J. Am. Chem. Soc.*, **42**, 2049 (1920).

22. HOLMES and CAMERON: *J. Am. Chem. Soc.*, **44**, 66 (1921).

23. RAMSDEN: *Proc. Roy. Soc. (London)* **72A**, 156 (1903).

24. SEIFRIZ: *J. Phys. Chem.*, **29**, 587, 738, 834 (1925).

25. SEIFRIZ: *Am. J. Physiol.*, **66**, 124 (1923).

26. NEUBERG: *Biochem. Z.*, **76**, 107 (1916).

27. WILHELMI: *Chem. Umschau*, **36**, 198, 213 (1929).

28. HOLMES and WILLIAMS: Second Colloid Symposium Monograph, p. 138, Chemical Catalog Company, New York, 1925.

29. SERRALLACH, JONES, and OWEN: *Ind. Eng. Chem.*, **25**, 816 (1933).

30. ZHUKOV and BUSHMAKIN: *J. Russ. Phys.-Chem. Soc.*, **59**, 1061 (1927); through *Chem. Abs.*, **22**, 3303 (1928).

31. KRANTZ and GORDON: Colloid Symposium Monograph, Vol. 6, p. 173, Chemical Catalog Co., New York, 1928; *J. Am. Pharm. Assoc.*, **18**, 463 (1929).

32. CLAYTON: *J. Soc. Chem. Ind.*, **45**, 288T (1926).

33. SANYAL and JOSHI: *J. Phys. Chem.*, **26**, 481 (1922).

34. WOODMAN: *J. Phys. Chem.*, **30**, 658 (1926).

35. CLAYTON: *Trans. Faraday Soc.*, **16**, Appendix 23 (1921).

36. TFOL: *Pharm. J.*, (4) **6**, 1228 (1898).

37. PICKERING: *J. Chem. Soc.*, **91**, 2001 (1907).

38. YOTHERS and WINSTON: *J. Agr. Research*, **31**, 59 (1925).

39. HOFMANN: *Z. Biol.*, **63**, 395 (1914).

40. SCHLAEPFER: *J. Chem. Soc.*, **113**, 522 (1918).

41. MOORE: *J. Am. Chem. Soc.*, **41**, 940 (1919).

42. BRIGGS: *J. Ind. Eng. Chem.*, **13**, 1008 (1921).

43. BECHHOLD, DEDE, and REINER: *Kolloid-Z.*, **28**, 6 (1921).

44. WOODMAN: *Chem. News*, **144**, 225 (1932); see also Ref. 20.

45. ROBERTSON: *Kolloid-Z.*, **7**, 7 (1910).

46. NEWMAN: *J. Phys. Chem.*, **18**, 34 (1914).

47. HALL: *J. Phys. Chem.*, **21**, 616 (1917).

48. CLAYTON: *Brit. Assoc. Advancement Sci., Second Report on Colloid Chemistry*, 114 (1918).

49. SHERRICK: *J. Ind. Eng. Chem.*, **12**, 135 (1920).

50. BHATNAGAR: *J. Chem. Soc.*, **117**, 542 (1920).

51. BRIGGS and SCHMIDT: *J. Phys. Chem.*, **19**, 478 (1915).

52. BRIGGS: *J. Phys. Chem.*, **24**, 120 (1920).

53. AYRES: *Chem. Met. Eng.*, **22**, 1059 (1920).

54. HERSCHEL: *U. S. Bur. Standards Tech. Paper* 86 (1917).
55. SHEPPARD: *J. Phys. Chem.*, **23**, 634 (1919).
56. AYRES: *J. Soc. Chem. Ind.*, **35**, 678 (1916).
57. NUGENT: *Trans. Faraday Soc.*, **17**, 703 (1922).
58. WIEGENER: *Kolloid-Z.*, **15**, 105 (1914).
59. BALDWIN: *Am. J. Public Health*, **6**, 862 (1916).
60. CLAYTON: "Theory of Emulsions and Emulsification," p. 121, P. Blakiston's Son & Co., Philadelphia, 1923.
61. BRIGGS: *J. Phys. Chem.*, **19**, 210 (1915).
62. ROON and OFSPER: *J. Ind. Eng. Chem.*, **9**, 156 (1917).
63. CROCKETT and OESPER: *J. Ind. Eng. Chem.*, **9**, 966 (1917).
64. BRIGGS, DuCASSÉ, and CLARK: *J. Phys. Chem.*, **24**, 147 (1920).
65. LEWIS: *Kolloid-Z.*, **4**, 211 (1909).
66. POWIS: *Z. physik. Chem.*, **89**, 91 (1914).
67. WALTHER OSTWALD: *Kolloid-Z.*, **6**, 103 (1910).
68. CLOWES: *J. Phys. Chem.*, **20**, 407 (1916).
69. PARSONS and WILSON: *J. Ind. Eng. Chem.*, **13**, 1116 (1921).
70. BHATNAGAR: *J. Chem. Soc.*, **119**, 1760 (1921).
71. BRIGGS: *J. Ind. Eng. Chem.*, **13**, 1008 (1921).
72. BHATNAGAR: *J. Chem. Soc.*, **119**, 1760 (1921).
73. HATSCHEK: *J. Soc. Chem. Ind.*, **29**, 125 (1910).
74. PILAT and PIOTROWSKI: *Petroleum Z.*, **13**, 1045 (1918); KOETSCHAU: *Z. angew. Chem.*, **32**, 45 (1919); BORN: *J. Ind. Eng. Chem.*, **13**, 1013 (1921).
75. DIJXHOOM: *Papier*, **22**, 53 (1919); HARRIS: U. S. Patent No. 1,281,952 (1919).
76. NEWMAN: *J. Phys. Chem.*, **18**, 34 (1912).
77. BHATNAGAR: *J. Chem. Soc.*, **117**, 542 (1920).
78. RICHARDSON: *J. Phys. Chem.*, **19**, 241 (1915).
79. SHERRICK: *J. Ind. Eng. Chem.*, **1**, 133 (1920); **13**, 1010 (1921).
80. BORN: Ref. 74.
81. BODROUX: *Compt. rend.*, **156**, 772 (1913).
82. HOLMES and CAMERON: *J. Am. Chem. Soc.*, **44**, 71 (1922); see also BHALLA, BHATNAGAR, and YAJNIK: *Kolloid-Z.*, **43**, 366 (1927).

CHAPTER XVII

MUTUAL REACTIONS

When colloidal solutions are mixed, decrease in stability leading to precipitation may result. If one of the components of the mixture is a very stable colloid (hydrophilic) and is added in excess,* while the other is rather unstable (hydrophobic), no visible change may take place and the dispersion will be found to show the stability and properties of the hydrophilic colloid.

The latter phenomenon is called *protective action*. The former case—mutual precipitation of colloids—will be considered first.

Mutual Precipitation.—The phenomenon of mutual precipitation of certain colloids was noted by Thomas Graham.[1] Linder and Picton[2] showed that mutually precipitating sols migrated oppositely in an electrical field. A sequence of confirmations[3] of this fact led to the generalization that oppositely charged micelles precipitate each other. Biltz[4] sought a stoichiometrical equivalence but failed, owing to the complexity of the sols as we now know them and to his consideration of them only, *e.g.*, as Fe_2O_3, Sb_2S_3, etc. Billitzer[5] suggested that the equivalence is electrical, since at maximum precipitation there is no migration in an electrical field, and on either side of this equivalence the migration is in the direction of the sol in excess. He thought the equivalence would not be exact because of variations in the size and numbers of particles and in the concentration of the sols.

The data in Table 75 are typical of his results. Billitzer noted also that, when two colloids of like charge are mixed, the less stable one becomes more stable, acquiring the properties of the more stable sol.

---

* An excess of the hydrophilic colloid is required for stabilization if the charge of its micelles is of opposite sign to that of the hydrophobic micelles. When like charged, a very small amount of the hydrophilic micelles produces a marked increase in stability.

It is noted that, in the presence of a very large excess of one sol, no change in appearance of the system takes place. The lack of precipitation in such cases is ascribed to the fact that, while a neutralization of charges takes place, flocculation of the particles does not ensue, owing to the fact that they are sorbed or protected by the colloid in excess. That mixture which results in complete precipitation is frequently called the *isoelectric* mixture.

TABLE 75.—ARSENIOUS SULFIDE SOL MIXED WITH FERRIC OXIDE SOL

The As_2S_3 sol contained 2.07 mg. As_2S_3 per cubic centimeter, and the Fe_2O_3 sol, 3.036 mg. Fe_2O_3 per cubic centimeter

Cubic centimeters in 10 cc. of mixture		Appearance	Migration in electrical field of unprecipitated portion
Fe_2O_3 sol	As_2S_3 sol		
9.0	1.0	No change, clear	To cathode
8.0	2.0	Slight turbidity	To cathode
7.0	3.0	Immediate turbidity, then precipitation	To cathode
5.0	5.0	Immediate precipitation	To cathode
3.0	7.0	Nearly complete precipitation	
2.0	8.0	Immediate precipitation	To anode
1.0	9.0	Immediate precipitation	To anode
0.2	9.8	Turbidity	To anode
10 cc. of 20 times diluted solution	10	No change, clear	To anode

The theory of mutual precipitation which arose from the foregoing experiments is that when oppositely charged colloidal particles are brought together an electrical neutralization ensues, resulting in agglomeration of the particles; there being no electrical repulsive forces left, the particles must settle out of solution.

In 1910, Lottermoser[6] suggested that the equivalence may be that of the small amounts of stabilizing electrolyte in the sol, and that the precipitation may be due to a chemical reaction between the crystalloid ions. To test this, he mixed positive silver iodide sols stabilized by silver nitrate and negative silver iodide sols stabilized by potassium iodide. The results summarized in Table 76 indicate that the explanation holds for this precipitation at least. The quantities given are millimoles at maximum precipitation and obviously they point to a simple chemical reaction between the stabilizing electrolytes of the colloidal complexes in the precipitation.

TABLE 76.—MUTUAL PRECIPITATION OF xAgI·AgNO₃ AND xAgI·IK HYDROSOLS*

Experiment number	Positive sol		Negative sol	
	AgI	AgNO₃	KI	AgI
1	0.210	0.052	0.055	0.220
2	0.220	0.055	0.050	0.200
3	0.225	0.009	0.010	0.245
4	0.245	0.010	0.017	0.180
5	0.270	0.009	0.010	0.040
6	0.240	0.010	0.007	0.033
7	0.038	0.007	0.010	0.240
8	0.040	0.010	0.008	0.196
9	0.115	0.010	0.010	0.240
10	0.115	0.010	0.007	0.170
11	0.225	0.009	0.010	0.115
12	0.240	0.010	0.008	0.088

* Lottermoser.

Freundlich and Nathansohn[7] have shown that the mixing of pairs of certain like-charged colloids may result in mutual precipitation. For example, they found that arsenic trisulfide hydrosol precipitates Odén's sulfur hydrosol, the micelles of both of which migrate to the anode in an electrical field. The electrical-charge neutralization theory fails in this instance. Since Odén's sulfur sol contains polythionic acids, these would be expected to react with the hydrogen sulfide of the arsenious sulfide sol in the following manner, using pentathionic acid as typical:

$$5H_2S + H_2S_5O_6 \rightarrow 10S + 6H_2O$$

The soluble parts of both sols having been destroyed, the inert parts precipitate.

It was shown further by these investigators that the following combinations of negatively charged hydrosols result in coagulation: Odén's sulfur and Carey Lea's silver; von Veimarn's sulfur (made by pouring an alcoholic solution of sulfur into water) and Carey Lea's silver; Odén's sulfur and Kruyt's selenium. When Carey Lea's silver sol is mixed with arsenious sulfide hydrosol, a series of color changes is noted, different in the dark from those exposed to light. One of the products of the reaction seems to be silver thioarsenite.[8] The reaction does not take place if gelatin is added to the sols before they are brought together.[8]

Vanadium pentoxide and uranyl oxide hydrosols, both containing negatively charged micelles, react when mixed together to form the soluble complex $UO_3.2V_2O_5$.[9] The reaction has been shown to take place between the portions which are in crystalloid solution, until, owing to the decomposition of the colloid portion of each sol to restore the equilibrium, all is used up.

Experiments by Thomas and Johnson[10] on the mutual precipitation of certain oppositely charged micelles show that consideration of the chemical reactions between the associated ions is more illuminating than the older idea of simple charge neutralization. Truly, there is a charge neutralization in so far as the micelles are concerned, but, since the charges are carried by ions or by ionic micelles, the simple charge-neutralization theory is rather superficial.

In one series of experiments they studied the mutual effects of ferricoxychloride and silica-sodium-silicate hydrosols. These were selected for convenience and feasibility of complete quantitative analysis. The optimal precipitation mixtures of a series of both sols were found to be such that the total possible hydrochloric acid from hydrolysis of the ferricoxychloride sol was chemically equivalent to the maximal possible sodium hydroxide of the "silicate" sol. The supernatant solution for this optimum was neutral, while in the cases of incomplete precipitation it was acid or alkaline, depending upon whether the ferricoxychloride or silicate sol was slightly in excess. Such a direct stoichiometric relationship was not found in all of their experiments. Where one (or both) of the sols was either of "low purity" or rather concentrated it failed. This might be expected owing to occlusion of unreacted material in the coagulum.

From their studies of the mutual precipitation of ferric-oxychloride and arsenious sulfide sols, the same investigators[10] assumed it a result of the reaction

$$2Fe^{+++} + S^= \rightarrow S^0 + 2Fe^{++}$$

for the reason that sulfur was found in the coagulum.

Wintgen[11] has submitted evidence in favor of the view that mutual precipitation takes place through reactions between the crystalloid-ion parts of the micelles, although he doubts that it involves so much of the crystalloid ions as stated above for ferric-oxychloride and silicate sols.*

Hydrophilic colloids, such as the proteins, precipitate each other under certain conditions. It has long been known that the protamines and histones precipitate other proteins.[13] Mutual precipitations between clupein, thymushistone, casein, and hemoglobin have been reported by Beth af Ugglas.[14] The protamine precipitates hemoglobin, the coagulum being peptized by excess of hemoglobin and by acid. The coagula obtained always had the composition of 95 per cent hemoglobin and 5 per cent protamine. Histone acts like the protamine on hemoglobin, the coagulum consisting of 1 part histone to 2 parts of hemoglobin. In both cases the dissolution of the coagulum by acid was reversed upon addition of ammonia.

The precipitation of casein by protamine as shown by Hunter[13] was also studied by af Ugglas, who found that a "neutral" protamine precipitated a "neutral" caseinate. The coagulum is insoluble in cold water, but soluble in warm water and in saturated sodium chloride solution. It is also peptized by excess of casein. The composition of the coagulum was about 94 per cent casein and 6 per cent protamine. Histone was found to act upon casein just like the protamine, the precipitate dissolving in dilute alkali and in excess of casein. When dissolved in alkali and reprecipitated by acid, the coagulum showed no alteration in composition from the ratio of 71 per cent casein and 29 per cent histone.

Hemoglobin and casein were found not to react in slightly alkaline solution but precipitated each other in "neutral" solu-

* The chemical interaction point of view, despite the evidence offered by reactions between like-charged micelles, still has its opponents.[12]

tion, the coagulum dissolving in dilute alkaline solution and reprecipitating upon acidification. Af Ugglas found the coagulum to be composed of 2 parts of hemoglobin to 1 of casein. In the experiments reported by af Ugglas the significance of the hydrogen ion activities of the solutions in the precipitations is evident, although unfortunately not measured by the investigator.

The significance of the hydrogen ion concentration of the solution in the mutual precipitation of proteins was demonstrated by Michaelis and Davidsohn.[15] They stated that, when two amphoteric colloids, such as proteins, are brought together in solution, a complex compound may precipitate, the condition for most complete precipitation being a hydrogen ion concentration between those of the isoelectric points of the reacting ampholytes. Thus, when one protein is present as a cation and the other as an anion, a union is to be expected; whereas when both proteins are on the same side of their isoelectric points, interreaction would not be expected. The combination between pairs of proteins has resulted in insoluble complexes in practically all cases tried, but, since a great deal of work has yet to be done on this subject, it is not safe at present to state that proteins always precipitate one another if mixed together at a pH value between their isoelectric points. Michaelis and Davidsohn found also that the optimum pH for the mutual precipitation of proteins varies with the relative amounts of the proteins reacting; when a large excess of one component is present, the pH optimum for precipitation will shift toward the isoelectric point of this component.

The precipitation optimum for a mixture of aqueous dispersions of nucleic acid and serum albumin was found to be at pH 4.05 to 4.22, which is between the isoelectric points of the components, while a mixture of nucleic acid and heat-denatured serum albumin precipitated best at pH 3.8. When the ratio of nucleic acid to the albumin was increased, the optimum reaction for precipitation shifted toward the acid side, *i.e.*, toward the isoelectric point of nucleic acid.

Casein and nucleic acid precipitated each other in a pH range of 4.05 to 2.52, depending upon whether casein or nucleic acid was present in excess. Mixtures of casein with both genuine and denatured serum albumin were found to result in precipitation. Variation in the mass relationships made no difference, owing to the fact that the isoelectric points of these proteins are so close together.

De Jong,[16] in a recent study of gluten, finds that gliadin and glutenin mutually combine when brought together at a pH value between 5 and 7. Thus, gluten may owe its peculiar properties to the fact that gliadin and glutenin chemically combine.

Michaelis and Davidsohn[17] investigated the influence of pH in specific precipitations. Using as precipitin the serum of a rabbit that had been previously sensitized with sheep serum, flocculation of this precipitin and sheep serum was obtained equally as well at pH 9 as at pH 5, thus showing no dependence upon the hydrogen ion concentration. This sort of reaction is then different from protein mutual precipitation. De Kruif and Northrop[18] have shown the same to be true for the agglutination of *Bacillus typhosus* by immune serum. They found that the amount of immune body combined with the organisms is constant from pH 9 to pH 3.7, and that the combination is not caused by a difference in sign of the charge carried by the immune body and the organism.

The flocculation of bacteria by proteins, however, has been found to be similar to protein mutual precipitations. Eggerth and Bellows[19] found that a suspension of *Bacterium coli* is agglutinated by gelatin, crystallized egg albumin, proteoses, edestin, and oxyhemoglobin at pH values between the isoelectric point of the protein and the acid flocculation zone of the bacterial suspensions, the latter having been found to lie between pH 1.6 and 3.0. Table 77 is typical of a series reported by these investigators. A second strain of the organism was agglutinated at pH 4.7 by an albumin concentration of 1:150. It is seen that, as the ratio of albumin to bacteria increases, the optimum flocculation point shifts toward the isoelectric point of the albumin.

The proteins of blood serum are precipitated by lecithin suspensions at pH values between the isoelectric points of the reacting substances. The isoelectric points of lecithins have been found to vary from pH 2 to 4, depending upon the source.[20] As the proportion of blood serum to lecithin is increased, the optimum precipitation tends to shift toward the reaction of the isoelectric point of the blood-serum proteins.

An interesting example of the mutual precipitation of hydrophilic or "protective" colloids is that of gelatin with gum arabic. One would expect a precipitation of gelatin by gum arabic in solutions on the acid side of pH 4.7 (the isoelectric point of gelatin), if gelatin "arabate" is an insoluble complex. Thomas Graham (1861) showed that gelatin is precipitated by "gummic acid," the coagulum settling out to form a jelly-like mass. This reaction

TABLE 77.—FLOCCULATION OF B. COLI SUSPENSION WITH EGG
ALBUMIN
1.0 cc. buffer mixture + 0.5 cc. albumin solution + 0.5 cc. *B. coli* suspension

Concentration of albumin								
0	−	−	−	−	−	+	−	−
1:400,000	−	−	−	−	−	+	−	−
1:40,000	−	−	−	+	+	+	+	−
1:4,000	−	X	X	X	X	X	+	−
1:400	−	X	X	−	−	−	−	−
pH =	4.7	4.4	4.1	3.8	3.5	3.3	3.0	2.7

Temperature = 40°C.   X = agglutination within 1 hr.   + = agglutination within 4 hr.

has been rediscovered by Tiebackx,[21] whose attention to it was aroused by the fact that oil-in-water emulsions "broke" upon mixing if one was emulsified with gum arabic and if gelatin was the emulsifying agent in the other. He found that gelatin and gum arabic mutually precipitate in a solution sufficiently acid to insure the presence of gelatin cations, the coagulum setting to a jelly when warmed. In the presence of an excess of gelatin this precipitation does not occur. This is an example of the "protective" effect of an excess of one component as seen in the mutual precipitation of inorganic colloids discussed earlier in this chapter and will be referred to again later. Tiebackx noted also that gum tragacanth precipitates gelatin.

Other organic colloidal mutual precipitations reported in the literature are: albumin combines with α-amylose[22] at pH values lower than 4.7; albumin precipitates cholesterol hydrosol;[23] gelatin and hemoglobin precipitate gum benzoin hydrosol[24] if the pH value is less than that of the protein's isoelectric point; tannin precipitates gelatin[25] at pH values less than 4.7 and tannin precipitates starch and gum tragacanth[26] in acid solutions.

In all cases where one attempts to effect a mutual precipitation between two hydrophiles or between a hydrophile and a less stable dispersion, rigorous adherence to the minutiae of detail is essential. A slight excess of one hydrophile may fail to produce precipitation for the reason that, although chemical reaction producing insoluble particles has taken place, yet before these can coalesce to form large flocks, they become coated by the hydrophile in excess and are thus held in suspension, or "protected." In many instances (always with proteins) the pH value of the mixture is important.

An illustration may be useful here. When 1 volume of an ordinary gum benzoin hydrosol[24] is mixed with 1 volume of a gelatin solution containing 2×10^{-6} g. of gelatin, and the resulting pH is less than 4.7, a mutual coagulation ensues. If three times this much gelatin at pH less than 4.7 is added, there is no precipitation, the gelatinated benzoin particles being cathodic in electromigration. If the pH value of the mixture is greater than 4.7, there is no precipitation at any concentration of gelatin because the resin is acidic in nature.

The foregoing facts explain why mutual precipitations involving hydrophiles have been so generally overlooked.

Protective Action.—When a solution of a hydrophilic colloid is added to a less stable colloidal dispersion, or suspension, generally there is no change in appearance of the system and the less stable dispersion is found to have become more stable; *i.e.*, it is no longer so sensitive toward either the addition of electrolytes or evaporation to dryness. The less stable dispersion is said to have been *protected* by the hydrophilic colloid; hence the term *protective colloid* which is commonly applied to the hydrophilic colloids, such as gelatin, gum arabic, soap.

The discovery of protective action may be attributed to Michael Faraday, who noted that the addition of gelatin to his colloidal gold dispersions rendered them so stable that it was possible to evaporate them to dryness without change in color.[27]

Since there appears to be a general tendency to regard "protective" colloids as a class that always confers increased stability upon hydrophobic colloids, it would be well to stop for a moment in order to show that protective colloids do not differ so radically from others in their behavior in mutual reactions. It is more a difference in degree than in kind. For example, hydrophilic colloids may precipitate other dispersions.

The precipitation of alumina hydrosol by gelatin was observed by Thomas Graham, who also described the mutual precipitation of colloidal silica by gelatin,[28] finding that "in the humid state the gelatin of this compound does not putrefy."

This appears to have been overlooked, since in modern colloid literature one frequently notes reports of the discovery that sometimes protective colloids do not protect. One such report is that of Brossa and Freundlich.[29] These authors found that the addition of a small amount of well-dialyzed albumin solution to "ferric oxide" hydrosol rendered the latter more sensitive toward the precipitating influence of electrolytes, rather than more stable. The explanation for this is simple and will be returned to later.

Protective colloids may protect less stable dispersions or may render them still less stable, even resulting in mutual precipitation, depending upon the signs of the charges of the protector and hydrophobe and upon the relative proportions of the two sols brought together. The significance of the signs of the charges carried by the two colloids interacting was shown by Billitzer.[5] He pointed out that, when a negative charge is conferred upon the gelatin by addition of a very small amount of ammonium hydroxide, it will then mutually precipitate with ferric oxide sol. If, however, a slightly positive gelatin is mixed with the ferric oxide sol, protection takes place. The latter complex is not precipitated by the addition of a slight amount of ammonium hydroxide, but the sign of the charge of the complex is changed from positive to negative.

In view of the modern chemistry of protein solutions, and the envelope theory of protection enunciated by Bechhold,[30] an explanation is available. The solution of gelatin in dilute ammonium hydroxide contains not only ammonium and gelatinate ions but also hydroxide ion. When this mixture is added to the acidic dispersion of ferricoxychloride micelles, the effect of the former on the latter is obvious. These micelles are converted to insoluble hydrous ferric oxide as well as, perhaps, to insoluble basic ferric gelatinates. Likewise, the H^+ ion of the ferric-oxychloride solution tends to bring the gelatin to its isoelectric point where it is least stable. Now, when slightly acid gelatin is added to the ferricoxychloride sol and later rendered slightly alkaline, no precipitate is obtained because the gelatin micelles envelop the inorganic colloid particles. Further, when an excess of alkaline gelatin solution is added to the ferricoxychloride hydrosol, no precipitation ensues because the insoluble inorganic particles become enveloped by gelatin micelles (are thus protected) before they can coalesce. Billitzer, likewise, found that judicious additions of acidified gelatin solutions to an arsenious sulfide hydrosol produced a mutual precipitation.

The sensitizing action of well-dialyzed albumin[29] upon ferric oxide hydrosol can be explained as above, since in pure aqueous solution this protein is on the alkaline side of its isoelectric point and will therefore promote hydrolysis of the ferricoxychloride complexes.

Several instances of flocculations of diverse inorganic micelles by proteins have been published.[31]

Gold Number.—Various hydrophilic colloids show different protective effects. Zsigmondy[32] devised the *gold-number* method as a means of defining the protective power of a given protective colloid. The gold number of a protective colloid is defined by Zsigmondy as the number of milligrams of the protective colloid which just fails to prevent the change of color of 10 cc. of red-gold hydrosol to blue upon the addition of 1 cc. of a 10 per cent sodium chloride solution. Zsigmondy prescribes the use of a gold hydrosol that shows a weak brownish opalescence to reflected light and a clear bright-red color to transmitted light. It must not show even a trace of violet or blue. Such a sol was prepared by his formaldehyde-reduction method.

Zsigmondy's technique is as follows:

Into three beakers, 0.01, 0.1, and 1 cc. of the protective colloid solution are pipetted and 10 cc. of gold hydrosol are added to each, followed by vigorous agitation for 3 min. Then 1 cc. of 10 per cent sodium chloride solution is run into each beaker while it is stirred. If it is assumed that change of color takes place in the first beaker and not in the others, the gold number is between the values represented by the amounts of protective colloid in 0.01 and 0.1 cc. For a more exact determination, the procedure is repeated on amounts between these limits.

The very different protective powers of the hydrophiles are seen in Table 78. In addition to Zsigmondy's values,[33] recent determinations by Gortner[34] are given.

TABLE 78.—GOLD NUMBERS

Colloid	Gold number	
	Zsigmondy	Gortner
Gelatin..........................	0.005 to 0.01	0.005 to 0.0125
Isinglass........................	0.01 to 0.02	
Casein..........................	0.01	
Egg albumin.....................	....	0.08 to 0.10
"Protalbinic acid"*.............	0.03 to 0.08 (Na salt)	0.15 to 0.20
"Lysalbinic acid"*..............	0.02 to 0.60 (Na salt)	0.10 to 0.125
Gum arabic......................	0.15 to 0.5	0.10 to 0.125
Gum tragacanth.................	About 2	
Dextrins........................	6 to 20	
Dextrin (British gum)...........	....	125 to 150
Soluble starch..................	....	10 to 15
Potato starch...................	About 25	
Sodium oleate..................	0.4 to 1	2 to 4

* These are protein degradation products so named by Paal [*Ber.*, **35**, 2195 (1902)], prepared by heating egg albumin in alkaline solution and precipitating by acetic acid. He uses these products in the preparation of protected metallic dispersions.

These numbers are useful as rough indices of relative protective powers only. Probably the concentration and degree of dispersion of the gold sol influence the result. The pH of the solution used certainly affects the values.[35] If the protective colloid solution is slightly acid, it will show a poorer protective action than one which is neutral or slightly alkaline. One sample of gelatin tested by the author precipitated the gold sol.*

The protective effect is not instantaneous. Some time must elapse after mixing for the optimum effect; 3 min. is usually sufficient. Dilution is also a factor. In a certain case, Zsigmondy found that 0.015 mg. of gelatin in 23 cc. of water did not protect 10 cc. of a gold hydrosol, but, when added in 3 cc.

* Data such as these are given by Ogiu and Pauli.[31] Zsigmondy,[36] noting that acid gold sols are precipitated by proteins, invented the method of measuring the *Umschlag Zahl* or literally the "upset number" of the substance. It is of little, if any, value.

volume and then diluted with 20 cc. of water, it did protect the sol. Apparently, when protection has taken place, dilution does not affect it.

The degree of dispersion of the protecting colloid also affects its gold number, as shown for gelatin[37] by Elliott and Sheppard.[38] This is demonstrated clearly by experiments in which solutions of gelatin were prepared as follows:

1. By making up the solutions directly without subsequent dilution, as 1 g. gelatin to 100 cc. solution for a 1 per cent solution, to be heated for 4 hr. at 50°C. to establish equilibrium and cooled in a water bath at 20°, at which temperature all gold numbers were determined.

2. By making an original solution of 1 per cent, heating at 50° for 4 hr., cooling, and diluting to 0.01 and 0.001 per cent at 20°.

3. By making the original solution of 1 per cent at 50°, heating for 4 hr., and making further dilutions of 0.01 and 0.001 per cent at 50°, with a further 2-hr. heating to equilibrium and cooling at 20°.

The results shown in Table 79 under "original" clearly indicate that the gold number decreases with decreasing concentration.

TABLE 79.—SOME FACTORS INFLUENCING THE GOLD NUMBER OF GELATIN

Strength of Solution, per cent	Gold Number
Original	
1.0	0.15
0.01	0.02
0.001	about 0.015
Diluted at 50°	
0.01	0.0075
0.001	0.02
Diluted at 20°	
0.01	0.0075
0.001	0.02

The protective action itself is not increased by a decrease in the quantity of gelatin, but, as the concentration is lowered, the state of dispersion of the gelatin present is altered. At high concentrations there is a majority of large particles with some smaller particles also; at low concentrations, a majority of very fine particles and very few of the larger particles. The larger jelly particles exert very little, if any, protective action. It is evident that gelatin must be completely in solution to show its maximum protective effect.

Elliott and Sheppard[38] also found that the gold number of gelatin solutions increases upon standing, which is concomitant with decrease in degree of dispersion of the gelatin.* After determining the gold numbers of 17 different gelatins of all grades and methods of manufacture, they concluded that this method is of little or no value in the grading of gelatins. The gold numbers differed but little and the classification thus made possible was too rough, bearing no simple relation to those properties which are of chief interest to users of gelatins.

Heubner and Jacobs[39] have tried to determine the gold numbers of purified blood proteins but found that the gold number of a given protein varied with the method of preparation. Some of their samples caused the gold sol to turn violet in color. Reitstötter[40] claims that the gold numbers of the various fractions of sera from a number of animals, both normal and diseased, are characteristic in most cases, the pathological condition of the animal influencing the same. It is interesting to note that he finds that the relative protective action, expressed as gold number, is altered by the acidity of the medium.

The gold numbers of a series of protein degradation products, such as proteoses and peptones, have been determined.[41] Attempts have been made to apply the gold-number method to analysis of urines. The presence of protective substances in urines has been found,[42] but it is doubtful whether the method can have any diagnostic value, for reasons already shown in other instances. Furthermore, Ottenstein[43] has been unable to find characteristic gold numbers in urines from certain pathological cases. He finds that the gold numbers of the well-dialyzed solids of normal urines range from 3.5 to 7.0, while, in disease, fluctuating values are found both above and below the normal values and are not at all characteristic for any one pathological condition.

Protective colloids inhibit the decomposition of hydrogen peroxide by platinum hydrosol. Determinations[44] of the effect of gelatin, gum arabic, and dextrin are shown in Table 80. The time for 50 per cent decomposition of a given amount of hydrogen peroxide by a fixed quantity of platinum hydrosol was deter-

* This is illustrated in Table 79 by the values for 0.001 per cent gelatin diluted at 20° and at 50°. These solutions had stood 2 days after having been made and doubtless had time to agglomerate.

mined in both the absence and presence of varying amounts of protective colloid by means of permanganate titrations of samples of the mixture withdrawn at given intervals.

TABLE 80.—INHIBITION OF DECOMPOSITION OF HYDROGEN PEROXIDE BY COLLOIDAL PLATINUM

Protective colloid	Time for 50 per cent decomposition, minutes	Protective colloid	Time for 50 per cent decomposition, minutes
None	20		
0.1% { Gelatin	265	0.001% { Gelatin	103
Gum arabic	86	Gum arabic	21
Dextrin	66	Dextrin	23
0.01% { Gelatin	150		
Gum arabic	39	0.0001% gelatin	71
Dextrin	28		

The order of effectiveness in inhibition of the catalysis is seen to be the same as that of protective powers shown by the Zsigmondy gold numbers. Confirmation of these results is found in a paper by Iredale[45] where the *inhibition number, i.e.,* that percentage of protective colloid which is just insufficient to inhibit the catalytic action of colloidal platinum upon hydrogen peroxide, is found to run parallel to the gold number (Table 81).

TABLE 81.—COMPARISON OF INHIBITION AND GOLD NUMBERS

Colloid	Gold number	Inhibition number	Gold-number ratios	Inhibition-number ratios
Gelatin	0.02	2×10^{-6}	100.	100.
Egg albumin	0.1	1×10^{-5}	20.	20.
Dextrin	3.	2×10^{-4}	0.66	1.
Starch	5.	6×10^{-4}	0.40	0.33

Iredale explains the inhibitory effects of the protective colloids "on the ground of selective adsorption resulting in a decreased concentration of hydrogen peroxide at the platinum surface. . . . "

The envelope theory of protective action has been supported by Loeb.[46] He prepared nitrocellulose suspensions by dissolving dried nitrocellulose in pure acetone, adding water to appearance of turbidity, and distilling off the acetone under reduced pressure, whereupon a creamy suspension of nitrocellulose particles was obtained.[47] The preparation of protein-coated collodion particles was suggested by his previous experience with collodion membranes,[48] where he found:

When collodion membranes are filled with a 1 per cent solution of a protein, such as gelatin, crystalline egg albumin, casein, or oxyhemoglobin, there is formed overnight inside the membrane a durable film of solid protein which cannot be washed away, even if the interior is rinsed out as often as ten or twenty times with warm water. This film betrays itself by its color in the case of oxyhemoglobin. The forces which make the film adhere to the collodion must be very strong, but they do not depend upon the ionization of the protein, since the films are formed no matter whether the protein is at the isoelectric point, or whether it is on the alkaline or on the acid side of the isoelectric point. The forces which cause the film formation must be those forces of secondary valency responsible for phenomena of adhesion and cohesion in general.*

Loeb allowed a small quantity of collodion suspension to remain overnight in an aqueous solution of a protein. The next morning the particles were centrifuged from the protein solution and made up to a creamy suspension in water at a desired pH. This suspension of protein-coated particles was added to various salt solutions to note the behavior. The effects of various salts were followed by electrophoresis measurements and observation of the concentrations of a given electrolyte which caused precipitation. It was found that the behavior of the protein-coated particles is identical with that of a solution of the protein. The concentrations of different salts required to precipitate suspensions of gelatin-coated collodion particles in water are practically identical with the concentrations of the same salts required to

* This conduct is like that of gold foil in gelatin solutions observed by Zsigmondy as early as 1900 (Zsigmondy-Spear, p. 112). Gold foil covered itself with a film of gelatin that could not be removed by boiling water. This layer prevented the amalgamation of the gold with mercury.

"salt out" gelatin from aqueous solutions. Furthermore, Loeb found that, just as the stability of gelatin at its isoelectric point (pH 4.7) is increased by the addition of certain kinds and amounts of salts, so are gelatin-coated collodion particles rendered more stable when protected by isoelectric gelatin.

Loeb noted a peculiar behavior in the case of egg albumin. He found that it is not a good protective colloid for collodion suspensions. Investigation of the properties of albumin-coated collodion particles showed them to be practically identical in stability with that of suspensions of denatured albumin particles. He believed that, when egg albumin forms a film of its solution around collodion particles, the albumin molecule undergoes a rearrangement or orientation to render its water-soluble groups ineffective. He recalled the observation of Ramsden on the films of certain proteins which form in aqueous solutions, owing to the lowering of the surface tension of water. Ramsden said that some of these films undergo coagulation. It is likewise well to recall that mechanical grinding of a dry powder of soluble blood albumin renders the albumin insoluble.[49]

Loeb also found casein and edestin to be poor protectors for collodion particles.

Beans and Beaver[50] have performed an experiment which shows that the protection of colloidal gold by gelatin is due to sorption of the gelatin by the gold particles. They found that the gold particles of a red-gold hydrosol (Bredig) were completely precipitated by centrifuging for 3 min. at a force equivalent to 32,000 times gravity. The precipitate was black and irreversible. Centrifuging a mixture of 5 cc. of a 0.1 per cent gelatin solution and 50 cc. of the gold sol resulted in deposition of the gold particles in 16 min., but the precipitate was red in this instance and could be redispersed to a red sol upon shaking with water. On heating some of this precipitate, it evidenced a slight charring, indicating the presence of gelatin. The same concentration of pure gelatin showed no precipitation of gelatin even after 30 min. centrifuging at 32,000 times gravity.

The majority of the investigations on protective colloids have been made upon aqueous dispersions, as is to be expected, but it is well to bear in mind that their usefulness is not restricted to water solutions. Bancroft[51] points out that aniline dyes which are insoluble in benzene can be dispersed therein by the aid of a benzenophilic colloid, such as zinc or magnesium resinate, and thus be used in lacquers.

A practical use of protective colloids is shown by Wegelin,[52] who found that the adhesion of metallic particles in grinding could be overcome by the presence of an aqueous gelatin solution.

Protective colloids have been found useful in the manufacture of ice cream, their presence preventing the formation of large ice crystals and thus insuring smoothness. Gelatin, egg albumin, and karaya gum are the most popular colloids for this purpose. A discussion of the effect of gelatin in ice cream is given by Alexander.[53] The latter has also observed that the presence of protective colloids in milk prevents the formation of lumpy curd when the milk is acidified.[54]

The presence of protective colloids is avoided in analytical chemistry, since it has been known, long before they were recognized as such, that their presence prevented the precipitation of insoluble compounds.

Protective action is not restricted to the hydrophiles. Inorganic dispersions frequently act as stabilizing agents. The fact that no precipitation is observed when an excess of one inorganic dispersion is added to another is evidence of the stabilizing action of the excess upon the precipitated particles. The protective power of hydrophobes is practically nil, of course, while that of the intermediates is quite noticeable.

Lange Test of Cerebrospinal Fluid.—In 1912, Lange[55] made some observations upon the reaction of Zsigmondy formol gold hydrosol with diluted cerebrospinal fluid which has proved of great value in the diagnosis of certain diseases. When the cerebrospinal fluid of a healthy person is diluted with 0.4 per cent aqueous sodium chloride solution, the diluted specimens do not alter the color of a red-gold hydrosol. Pathological fluids at certain dilutions produce coagulative effects, evidenced by the change in color of the gold sol; *i.e.*, in these cases the protective action of the hydrophiles of the normal fluid is lacking at certain dilutions of pathological fluids.

The Lange test is carried out as follows:[56]

Cerebrospinal fluid, free from blood, is diluted with 0.4 per cent sterile sodium chloride solution in the ratio of 1:10. Then in the first of a series of 12 tubes, there is placed 1 cc. of this diluted solution, in the second, 1 cc. diluted 1:20, and so on, to the twelfth tube in which 1 cc. of a 1:25,000 dilution is placed. Then 5 cc. of the gold hydrosol is quickly added to each and shaken. The colors are noted and graphed empirically as shown in Fig. 139.[57]

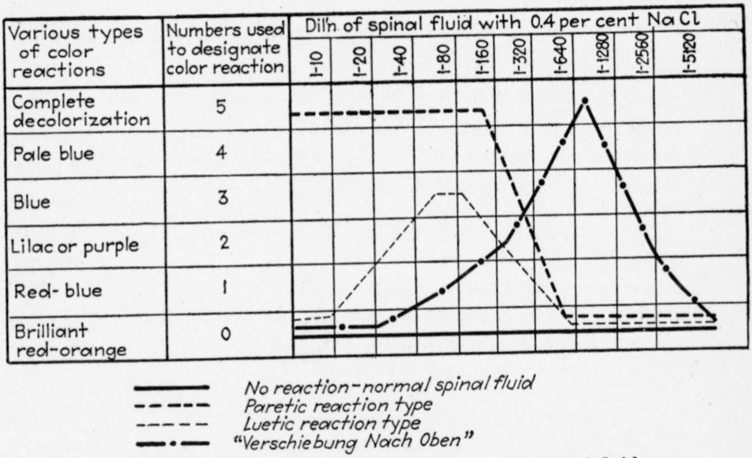

Various types of color reactions	Numbers used to designate color reaction	Diln of spinal fluid with 0.4 per cent NaCl									
		1-10	1-20	1-40	1-80	1-160	1-320	1-640	1-1280	1-2560	1-5120
Complete decolorization	5										
Pale blue	4										
Blue	3										
Lilac or purple	2										
Red-blue	1										
Brilliant red-orange	0										

——— No reaction-normal spinal fluid
− − − − Paretic reaction type
— — — Luetic reaction type
—·— "Verschiebung Nach Oben"

FIG. 139.—Graphs of the Lange test of cerebrospinal fluids.

The graphs are characteristic for certain diseases.

Large quantities of formol gold hydrosol are made in hospitals, for use in the Lange test. The Gettler and Jackson method for its preparation has been described in Chap. VI. Bredig gold sol[58] and phosphorus-reduced gold sol[59] are said to serve as well as the formol-reduced gold. Apparently the gold sol should be neutral or slightly alkaline.[60]

Pathologic cerebrospinal fluid reacts characteristically with hydrophobic dispersions of certain gum resins; mastic,[61] benzoin,[62] and myrrh[63] having been employed. The systems are too complicated to theorize about.

References

1. GRAHAM: *J. Chem. Soc.*, **15**, 246 (1862).
2. LINDER and PICTON: *J. Chem. Soc.*, **71**, 586 (1897).
3. LOTTERMOSER: "Anorganische Kolloide," Stuttgart, 1901; BECHHOLD: *Z. physik. Chem.*, **48**, 385 (1904); NEISSER and FRIEDMANN: *Münch. med. Wochschr.*, **51**, 465, 827 (1904); HENRI: *Compt. rend. soc. biol.*, **55**, 1666 (1903); TEAGUE and BUXTON: *Z. physik. Chem.*, **60**, 489 (1907).

4. BILTZ: *Ber.*, **37**, 1095 (1904).

5. BILLITZER: *Z. physik. Chem.*, **51**, 120 (1905).

6. LOTTERMOSER: *Kolloid-Z.*, **6**, 78 (1910).

7. FREUNDLICH and NATHANSOHN: *Kolloid-Z.*, **28**, 258 (1920); **29**, 16 (1921).

8. FREUNDLICH and MOOR: *Kolloid-Z.*, **36**, 17 (1925).

9. KARGIN: *Z. anorg. allgem. Chem.*, **198**, 79 (1931).

10. THOMAS and JOHNSON: *J. Am. Chem. Soc.*, **45**, 2532 (1923); First Colloid Symposium Monograph, p. 187, University of Wisconsin, Madison, Wis., 1923; see also BAHL: *Kolloid-Z.*, **59**, 60 (1932).

11. WINTGEN and LOWENTHAL: *Z. physik. Chem.*, **109**, 391 (1924); see also LOTTERMOSER and MAY: *Kolloid-Z.*, **58**, 61 (1932).

12. WEISER and CHAPMAN: *J. Phys. Chem.*, **35**, 543 (1931); **36**, 713 (1932); HAZEL and McQUEEN: *ibid.*, **37**, 571 (1933).

13. KUTSCHER: *Z. Physiol. Chem.*, **23**, 117 (1897); BANG: *ibid.*, **27**, 483 (1899); MALENGREAU: *Cellule*, **21**, 121 (1903); HUNTER *Z. Physiol. Chem.*, **53**, 526 (1907).

14. BETH AF UGGLAS: *Biochem. Z.*, **61**, 469 (1914).

15. MICHAELIS and DAVIDSOHN: *Biochem. Z.*, **39**, 496 (1912).

16. DE JONG: *Trans. Faraday Soc.*, **28**, 798 (1932).

17. MICHAELIS and DAVIDSOHN: *Biochem. Z.*, **47**, 59 (1912).

18. DE KRUIF and NORTHROP: *J. Gen. Physiol.*, **5**, 127 (1922).

19. EGGERTH and BELLOWS: *J. Gen. Physiol.*, **4**, 669 (1922).

20. FEINSCHMIDT: *Biochem. Z.*, **38**, 244 (1912); JARISCH: *Klin. Wochschr.*, **1**, 71 (1922); through *Chem. Abs.*, **16**, 2871 (1922).

21. TIEBACKX: *Kolloid-Z.*, **8**, 198, 238 (1911); **31**, 102 (1922); see also LUPPO-CRAMER: *Phot. Korr.*, **51**, 111 (1913).

22. VON PRZYLECKI and MAJMIN: *Biochem. Z.*, **240**, 98 (1931); VON PRXY-LECKI and DOBROWOLSKA: *ibid.*, **245**, 388 (1932).

23. STERN: *Biochem. Z.*, **187**, 315 (1927).

24. WRIGHT and KERMACK: *Biochem. J.*, **17**, 635 (1923).

25. SEGUIN: *Ann. chim.*, **20**, 15 (1796); DAVEY: *Phil. Trans. Roy. Soc., London*, **93**, 233 (1803); THOMAS and FRIEDEN: *Ind. Eng. Chem.*, **15**, 839 (1923).

26. STOCKS and GREENWOOD: *J. Intern. Soc. Leather Trades Chem.*, **9**, 315 (1925); **10**, 404 (1926).

27. FARADAY: *Phil. Trans. Roy. Soc. London*, **147**, 184 (1857).

28. GRAHAM: *J. Chem. Soc.*, **15**, 246 (1862); see also LESLEY: *Trans. Faraday Soc.*, **25**, 570 (1929); **26**, 69 (1930).

29. BROSSA and FREUNDLICH: *Z. physik. Chem.*, **89**, 306 (1915).

30. BECHHOLD: *Z. physik. Chem.*, **48**, 385 (1904).

31. FRIEDMANN: *Arch. Hygiene*, **55**, 361 (1906); PAULI and FLECKER: *Biochem. Z.*, **41**, 461 (1912); OGIU and PAULI: *ibid.*, **250**, 535 (1932).

32. ZSIGMONDY: *Z. anal. Chem.*, **40**, 697 (1901).

33. ZSIGMONDY: Ref. 32; ZSIGMONDY-SPEAR: "Chemistry of Colloids," pp. 107, 212, John Wiley & Sons, Inc., New York, 1917.

34. GORTNER: *J. Am. Chem. Soc.*, **42**, 595 (1920).

35. TARTAR and LORAH: *J. Phys. Chem.*, **29**, 792 (1925).

36. ZSIGMONDY: *Nachr. kgl. Ges. Wiss. Göttingen Math. Phys. Klasse*, 177 (1916); through JOEL: Ref. 56; see also GANN: *Kolloidchem. Beihefte*, **8**, 251 (1917).

37. MENZ: *Z. physik. Chem.*, **66**, 129 (1909).

38. ELLIOTT and SHEPPARD: *J. Ind. Eng. Chem.*, **13**, 699 (1921).

39. HEUBNER and JACOBS: *Biochem. Z.*, **58**, 352 (1914).

40. REITSTÖTTER: *Oesterr. Chem.-Ztg.*, **25**, 29 (1922).

41. ZUNZ: *Arch. intern. physiol.*, **1**, 427 (1904); **5**, 111, 245 (1907); *Bull. soc. roy. sci. med. et nat.*, **64**, 187 (1906); ZSIGMONDY-SPEAR, Ref. 33, pp. 108–109.

42. LICHTWITZ and ROSENBACH: *Z. physiol. Chem.*, **61**, 112 (1909); LICHTWITZ: *ibid.*, **64**, 144 (1910).

43. OTTENSTEIN: *Biochem. Z.*, **128**, 382 (1922).

44. GROH: *Z. physik. Chem.*, **88**, 414 (1914).

45. IREDALE: *J. Chem. Soc.*, **119**, 109 (1921); **121**, 1536 (1922).

46. LOEB: *J. Gen. Physiol.*, **5**, 479 (1922–1923).

47. LOEB: *J. Gen. Physiol.*, **5**, 109 (1922–1923).

48. LOEB: *J. Gen. Physiol.*, **2**, 577 (1919–1920).

49. HERZFELD and KLINGER: *Biochem. Z.*, **78**, 349 (1917); WIECHOWSKI: *ibid.*, **81**, 278 (1917).

50. BEAVER: Dissertation, Columbia University, 1921.

51. BANCROFT: *J. Phys. Chem.*, **24**, 21 (1920).

52. WEGELIN: *Kolloid-Z.*, **14**, 65 (1914).

53. ALEXANDER: *Kolloid-Z.*, **5**, 101 (1909).

54. ALEXANDER: *Kolloid-Z.*, **6**, 197 (1910); ALEXANDER and BULLOWA: *J. Am. Med. Assoc.*, **55**, 1196 (1910); *Arch. Pediatrics*, 17 (1910).

55. LANGE: *Z. Chemotherapie*, **1**, 44 (1912); through *Chem. Abs.*, **6**, 2458 (1912).

56. JOEL: "Das Kolloide Gold in Biologie und Medezin," Akademische Verlagsgesellschaft m.b.H., Leipzig, 1925.

57. MILLER, BRUSH, HAMMERS, and FELTON: *Bull. Johns Hopkins Hosp.*, **26**, 391 (1915).

58. MANHEIMS and BERNHARD: *J. Lab. Clin. Med.*, **11**, 235 (1925).

59. ETTISCH and EINSTEIN: *Naturwissenschaften*, **19**, 506 (1931).

60. NOVICK: *Arch. Neurol. Psychiatry*, **15**, 471 (1926); NICOL: *J. Soc. Chem. Ind.*, **48**, 100T (1929).

61. URECHIA and JORGULESCU: *Compt. rend. soc. biol.*, **79**, 893 (1916); STANTON: *Arch. Neurol. Psychiatry*, **3**, 301 (1920); CAMP: *Am. J. Syphilis*, **4**, 301 (1920).

62. GUILLAIN, LAROCHE, and LECHELLE: *Bull. mém. soc. méd. hôp. Paris*, **36**, 1299 (1920); **37**, 355 (1921); DUHOT and CRAMPON: *ibid.*, 307 (1920); WRIGHT and OGILVY: *Edinburgh Med. J.*, **30**, 252 (1923); KERMACK and VOGE: *ibid.*, **36**, 94 (1929); WRIGHT and KERMACK: *Biochem. J.*, **17**, 658 (1923).

63. QUARTI: *Boll. soc. ital. biol. sper.*, **3**, 1145 (1928).

CHAPTER XVIII

GELS AND JELLIES

The term *gel* which has been so widely used and so little understood is gradually becoming restricted in use to denote transparent or translucent bodies containing a considerable proportion of liquid, but maintaining shape and exhibiting rigidity.* The word *jelly* is applied to those gels which are heat reversible, as, for example, aqueous gelatin or agar-agar, or cellulose acetate benzyl alcohol systems.

If a classification of gels is wanted, perhaps Hatschek's system[1] will serve: First, one is reminded of the heat-reversible type, of which gelatin is a well-known example. Dry gelatin when placed in water swells to several times its original volume. On warming to over 30° it forms a sol and sets to a gel upon cooling. The "melting" and "setting" temperatures are not sharp, but when measured by some conventional method the "setting point" is always found to be a few degrees (generally 5 to 10) lower than the "melting point"; *i.e.*, there is a hysteresis range in which the system may exist either as a sol or as a gel. For agar-agar this range is much larger, its hydrogel is transformed to a sol on heating to about 95°, and it sets upon cooling to below 35°.

A second type of gel is formed by the irreversible transformation of a sol at ordinary temperatures. The best known gel of this type is silicic acid. It is conveniently formed by pouring "water glass" of about 1.15 specific gravity into an equal volume of 6 M hydrochloric acid. The resulting clear sol of silicic acid assumes a bluish opalescence and sets to a gel in about an hour at room temperature.[2]

A third type, which is unstable, is formed on cooling solutions of suitable concentration of substances which occur in definite

---

* In this book, the term *gel* is not applied to dry amorphous bodies. If a name is desired for these, then Freundlich's suggestion of "xerogel" is recommended.

crystals, or on producing such substances by a suitable reaction. As examples of the former there are "azomethine"[3] (5-dimethyl-amino-anilino-3-4-diphenyl cyclopentene-1-2-dione), dibenzoyl-*l*-cystine,[4] and camphoryl phenyl thiosemicarbazide.[5] These dissolve in certain hot solvents and form clear gels on cooling, which after a few minutes to several months, depending upon the solvent and the concentration, become opaque, segregating solvent and crystals. Manganous arsenate,[6] formed by the reaction between potassium dihydrogen arsenate and manganous chloride, is an instance of the second kind. The reaction mixture sets to a clear gel which after standing deposits spherical aggregates of crystals.*

A fourth type of gel is that formed by the gradual replacement of a solvent liquid by a nonsolvent liquid, as, for example, in the preparation of nitrocellulose membranes. This gel which is remarkable for its tenacity dries irreversibly; *i.e.*, it will not reimbibe the nonsolvent liquid after it has been dried.

Some Physical Properties.—The third and fourth types have not been studied as gels to any appreciable extent.

The most extensively studied example of the first type is gelatin gel. (Agar has received but a small amount of attention.) While upon cooling a gelatin sol there is a continuous increase in viscosity finally to the extent where viscosity measurements fail, it has been established that certain physical properties, such as refractive index,[7] do not change more than can be accounted for by the change in temperature or volume. Some writers hold that the principal difference between the sol and gel is the elastic properties of the latter.[8]

Investigations of the elastic constants of gelatin gels were started about fifty years ago by physicists interested in a transparent isotropic material permitting considerable deformation.[9] The results of these investigations have produced the following information: Gelatin gels are perfectly elastic for small stresses applied for short times. The volume remains unchanged even

---

* The formation of such gels has been extensively discussed by von Veimarn (see Ref. 6, Chap. I), who has attempted to formulate general laws governing their formation. For a criticism of von Veimarn's generalizations see Weiser, "The Colloidal Salts," Chap. I, McGraw-Hill Book Company, Inc., New York, 1928.

for considerable deformation.[10] The stress required to maintain a given deformation decreases with the duration of application but does not become zero; i.e., the gel shows relaxation which does not become complete.[11] The optical anisotropy produced by the stress does not decrease with it but remains at the value corresponding to the first application of the stress.[12]

Gels of silicic acid possess marked rigidity when of suitable concentration. They vibrate audibly when the tubes containing them are tapped[13] and have for that reason been called "musical" gels. The frequency of vibration of cylinders of the gel set in glass test tubes is, beyond a certain minimum, independent of the length but decreases with increasing diameter. The frequency rises with the silica content and varies in the presence of different acids at a constant silica content. The fresh gel which adheres tenaciously to the glass walls is under tension. If a gel is cast in a vaseline-coated tube to which it does not adhere, it shortens and when tapped vibrates at a lower frequency than one of the same diameter adhering to the clean glass walls. The difference in frequency of vibration shows that the one formed in the greased tube is under less tension. Hatschek[1] has searched for double refraction in silicic acid gels and found none.

Structure of Gels.—The majority of workers assume that gels are two-phase systems. Wilhelm Ostwald's idea of two liquid phases has been shown to be untenable,[14] and the honeycomb structure postulated by Bütschli and so often referred to in general scientific literature has been discarded. A part of the evidence arrayed against the conception of a network in gels was the lenticular shape of gas bubbles generated in gels. These bubbles place themselves at a right angle to pressure and parallel to tension applied to the gel.[15]

At present, the accepted structure, at least for gels formed by hydrophilic colloids, is a mass of long intertwined fibrils, enmeshing solvent or dilute solution,* as well as binding liquid of solvation, the filaments being composed of adhering particles.[8,16] Thus one has a two-phase, solid-liquid structure where both phases are continuous. X-ray examination of gelatin and of

---

* When gels are protected against evaporation, the process of contraction results in the exudation of some of this liquid phase. Graham (1864) named this process *syneresis*.

agar gels has revealed crystal interference rings, from which Katz[17] concludes that gelation is a crystallization phenomenon. This confirms Bradford's[16] belief and is a return to the earliest of theories of gel structure.[18]

Thixotropy.—Gels exist which upon mechanical manipulation such as gentle shaking or stirring reverse to sols and, when then allowed to stand quietly, jellify again. These are known as *thixotropic* gels and were so named by Peterfi,[19] who found that the stiff consistency of a living cell broke down to limpid fluidity when the cell was probed and stirred by a micromanipulator, the cell contents becoming stiff again upon subsequent quiet standing. Thixotropic behavior of "iron oxide" sols which had gelled upon the addition of a salt insufficient to precipitate the sol was reported in 1923.[20] Since then numerous reports have been made upon this behavior for a variety of systems.[21] One can imagine the fibrils orienting in an entangled meshwork which upon agitation are disentangled. Ultrasonic vibrations convert thixotropic iron oxide and alumina gels to sol consistency.[22]

Drying of Gels.—The classical studies made by van Bemmelen upon the vapor pressures of inorganic gels, especially his detailed measurements upon aqueous silicic acid gel[23] and their interpretation by Zsigmondy,[24] contribute to the present-day theory of gel structure, showing that capillary forces play a prominent part in the process. First, there is a rapid fall in vapor pressure with shrinkage of the gel as it loses water to a point beyond which the loss of water takes place at almost constant vapor pressure, to a second point from which the vapor pressure drops fairly abruptly. If the capillary spaces are assumed to be spherical, a shape which is rather doubtful,[25] calculations of their diameters have been made[26] yielding values less than 6 mμ. Except for "dried" gels of rather low water content, reimbibition to a given water content can be effected only at higher vapor pressures; the partially dried capillary spaces are not so readily rewetted and apparently do not expand to their original volume.

The drying of the heat-reversible gels is different. The vapor pressure of these jellies is about the same as that of pure water.[27] As they dry, they shrink to compact hard masses. Cubes of gelatin jelly become remarkably distorted upon drying, shrinking in at the face centers, producing sharp knifelike edges.[28]

As a film of gelatin jelly dries on a clean glass surface, its shrinkage causes layers of glass to be torn away, owing to its strong adhesion to the glass.

While the silicic acid type of gel will, after loss of water, reimbibe any solvent, the first type of gel (the heat reversible) will not reimbibe a solvent in which it does not dissolve. This is due to the cementing together of the intermicellar spaces brought about by the deposition of solute in the drying process. Once a gelatin gel has been "hardened" or tanned,[29] it will act like a silicic acid gel on drying and then will also reimbibe any liquid much as silicic acid gel does.

Imbibition and Swelling.—When certain xerogels* are placed in liquids for which they have an affinity, or in the vapors of such liquids, they swell. The sticking of wooden doors and drawers in damp weather is a well-known example of this increase in volume with imbibition of vapor or liquid. The swelling occurs even against high pressure.† The historical experiment by Reinke,[30] who measured the degree of imbibition of water by pieces of seaweed called *Laminaria* is tabulated in Table 82.

If the converse of the facts cited in Table 82 is considered, it is obvious that squeezing is not a promising method for the removal of water from certain gels.

Although the gel expands, the volume of gel plus liquid decreases during swelling.[31] The contraction is greatest for the first small amount of liquid imbibed by the dry solid. Consequently, heat should be liberated during swelling, and this has been found to be the case.[32] Hence, in preparing a solution

---

* High molecular-weight substances such as polysaccharides, proteins, or polymerized substances (rubber, polystyrols, etc.).

† In the *New York Evening Post* of July 29, 1926, there appeared the following item:

"HUMBLE BEAN DESTROYS SHIP

"*Hankow, July* 28, (*AP*).—The power of the humble bean has been forcibly illustrated on the Yangtse River. The Hamburg Amerika motorship *Rhineland*, filled with beans, collided with the Japanese steamship *Mitsuki Maru* about forty miles below Hankow.

"The Rhineland sprang a leak, the beans began to swell, decks to bulge, and seams to open. Salvage craft came to the rescue, but the beans had all the best of it. The Rhineland was an almost total loss."

of a hydrophile, it should be permitted to swell in the cold solvent
before heat is applied.

TABLE 82.—IMBIBITION OF WATER BY LAMINARIA[30]

Applied Pressure, Atmospheres	Percentage Increase in Volume
41.2	16
31.2	23
21.2	35
11.2	89
7.2	97
3.2	205
1.2	318
1.0	330

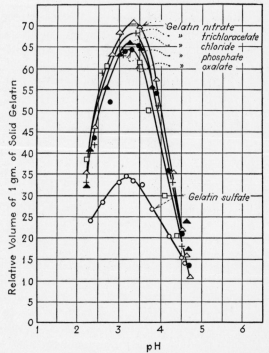

FIG. 140.—The influence of acids upon the swelling of gelatin.

The swelling of gelatin in water is markedly influenced by
electrolytes and nonelectrolytes. The influence of pH upon
swelling of gelatin is illustrated by Figs. 140 and 141.[33] A

quantitative explanation for these volume changes as a function of pH was provided by Procter and Wilson.[34] The investigations culminating in the Procter-Wilson theory were begun by Procter (in 1897) who, while attempting to arrive at a rational explanation of the molecular mechanism of tanning, was continually confronted by the necessity of first explaining the mechanism of swelling. Quantitative development of his theory of swelling, however, had to await the appearance of Donnan's theory of membrane equilibria.

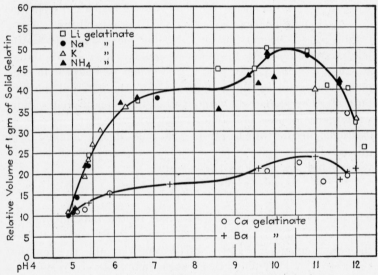

FIG. 141.—The influence of bases upon the swelling of gelatin.

The Procter-Wilson theory states that H^+ of the interdiffusing acid combines with the protein, thus converting the latter to a cationic micelle, its charge being balanced by the free anion of the acid. The intermicellar liquid contains H^+ and anions, just as the liquid outside the jelly does, and at equilibrium the following Donnan product holds for a monobasic acid:

$$[H^+]_s \cdot [A^-]_s = [H^+]_i \cdot [A^-]_i \qquad (1)$$

where the subscripts s and j refer to outer solution and jelly phase, respectively. Expressing Eq. (1) in the familiar values of Chap. V,

$$x^2 = y(y + z) \qquad (2)$$

where $x = [H^+] = [A^-]$ in the outer solution.

$\quad y = [H^+]$ free in the intermicellar liquid.

$\quad z = [A^-]$ balanced by the positive charges on the protein.

Hence $y + z =$ total $[A^-]$ in the intermicellar liquid.

Thus since

$$2y + z > 2x \qquad (3)$$
$$2y + z = 2x + e \qquad (4)$$

where $e =$ excess concentration of the diffusible ions in the jelly phase over that of the external solution.

Since the concentration of diffusible ions is greater in the jelly, water will osmose into the jelly capillary spaces and produce swelling. Or, as Wilson puts it, the anions of the protein compound will tend to diffuse outward into the external solution, but this they cannot do without dragging their protein cations with them. These protein cations, however, form part of an elastic structure which resists the pull of the anions. The quantitative measure of this outward pull is represented by the value e and, according to Hooke's law,

$$e = CV \qquad (5)$$

where C is a constant corresponding to the bulk modulus of the gelatin and V is the increase in volume. By combination of the equations given, Procter and Wilson were able to show that the results predicted by them were quantitatively verified by laboratory measurements. This was the first application of the Donnan equilibrium to a protein system. Some scientists have expressed doubt over the validity of the application of the Donnan equilibrium to the swelling of protein jellies, but as yet no better mechanism has been offered.

The Donnan equilibrium does not account for the swelling of isoelectric gelatin in pure water and the influence of neutral substances thereon, or, for that matter, for the swelling of organophiles in organic liquids. Northrop and Kunitz[35] offer an explanation for the former. Having found that gelatin consists of at least two substances, one of which is insoluble in cold water and another more soluble component, they attribute the swelling of isoelectric gelatin in water to the osmotic pressure of the soluble part of the gelatin in the fibrillar network. Water therefore enters the network and thereby puts it under elastic strain, the process continuing until the elastic force is equal to the osmotic pressure. Their papers describe a simple apparatus for measuring the swelling pressure. Further, they find that electrolytes (such as thiocyanates) which promote the swelling of the isoelectric gelatin also raise the osmotic pressure of gelatin solutions.

Many organic substances, such as thiourea, chloralhydrate, resorcinol, benzene sulfonates, enhance the swelling of polysaccharides and proteins just as thiocyanates and iodides do. Organic compounds containing halogens give pronounced swelling; in one series the order is trichlor- > dichlor- > monochloracetate. The reason is not clear, although Katz[31] suggests that the nonpolar groups are attached to the micellar structure leaving the hydrophile groups free to bind water. Strangely enough, small amounts of propyl and of butyl alcohol promote the swelling of gelatin and of casein in water, although in larger proportions they dehydrate these gels.

Diffusion in Gels.—Inasmuch as Graham found that sodium chloride diffused as readily through gelatin jellies as through water—which was subsequently confirmed for a few other salts and through agar jellies as well[36]—it has been generally stated that the diffusion of crystalloids is not impeded by the gel structure. More recent measurements prove this statement to be incorrect.[37,38] The diffusion of electrolytes and of nonelectrolytes is impeded by gelatin and by agar jellies in proportion to the concentration of the solid matter in the jelly. Gelatin jellies which were set at low temperatures have been found more permeable than those that were jellified at higher temperature[38] although of identical concentration. Calculation of the "pore radii" based on the diffusion of nonelectrolytes shows them to vary from less than 1 mμ to about 6 mμ for agar and for gelatin, the pores in agar gels being smaller than those in gelatin gels of the same concentration.[38] These magnitudes reveal why gels prevent the diffusion of colloidal particles.

The mobility (in electric field) of particles of zinc dust and of quartz particles through a 1 per cent gelatin jelly has been reported to be the same as that through the sol before it had set to the jelly state.[39]

Liesegang Rings.—Liesegang, in 1896, called attention to a curious rhythmically banded structure of silver chromate which formed when a crystal of silver nitrate was placed on a sheet of gelatin impregnated with a small amount of potassium dichromate. A typical repetition of Liesegang's original structure is shown in Fig. 142. Since then a voluminous literature has accumulated and such banded structures resulting from reactions in gels

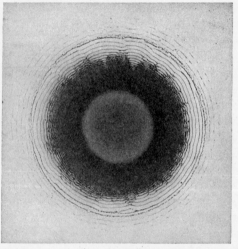

Fig. 142.—Liesegang rings of silver chromate on a flat surface of gelatin jelly.

are called *Liesegang rings*. Hepburn[40] states, however, that Ord prepared stratified precipitates of calcium oxalate in 1869.

A recipe for the formation of silver chromate rings is as follows: To 50 cc. of a hot aqueous 10 per cent solution of gelatin add about 25 mg. of potassium dichromate and pour on to a glass plate. When it has set to a jelly, place a crystal of silver nitrate (or a drop of a saturated solution) upon the center of the sheet of jelly. Cover with an inverted beaker to retard evaporation and, after letting it stand overnight, note the effect.

If the hot gelatin solution is allowed to set in a test tube and silver nitrate solution is placed on top of the jelly, an effect as seen in Fig. 143 is obtained.

Any gel and any combination of reactants producing a precipitate may be used for the production of these banded precipitates, some of the effects obtained being rather beautiful,[41] even deposition of glistening metallic crystals having been produced.[42]

The bands become spaced farther apart as they form farther away from the source of the concentrated spot of the one diffusing reactant. Sometimes the bands form spirals.[43] The reader who anticipates an explanation will be disappointed, inasmuch as the four outstanding theories[44] have been found untenable.[45] This "colloid" phenomenon has been found to occur in the absence of colloids.

Rhythmic rings of ammonium chloride form when ammonia and hydrogen chloride gases interdiffuse.[46] Banded deposits of sodium chloride crystals form when 0.5 mm. capillaries containing a solution of sodium chloride are immersed in concentrated hydrochloric acid.[47] A drop of oil placed on a smoked glass causes rearrangement of the previously continuous soot film into alternate opaque and clear concentric rings under the spreading drop.[48] Some other analogous cases are cited by Veil.[49]

Natural periodic banded structures are frequently encountered in geology and biology.[50] While such structures in geological specimens[51] may be accounted for by interdiffusion of reactants, it is well to be cautious in applying the effect to biological phenomena. Misguided worship of the mysteries of

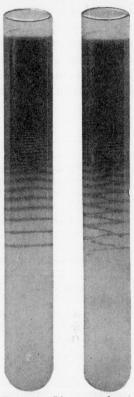

Fig. 143.—Liesegang phenomena in tubes of gelatin jelly.

The bands of silver chromate are discontinuous in the tube on the left (the usual Liesegang ring effect) while a continuous spiral structure, a most uncommon phenomenon, is seen in the tube on the right. These tubes were prepared by the author who poured the identical warm mixed solution of gelatin and potassium bichromate, used to make the flat plate shown in Fig. 142, into each of the two tubes. When the jellies had set, an unmeasured small amount of saturated silver nitrate solution was placed on the top of each jelly. The tubes were stoppered and stored in a dark place at room temperature for 10 days when they were photographed.

colloidal phenomena has occasionally gone too far in the application of colloid chemistry to biology. The most recent of strange colloidal reports has been that curious "mitogenetic radiations" from onions influence the formation of Liesegang bands. Onion fragments do affect their formation, but it is due to the vaporization of allyl isothiocyanate[52] from the onion.

References

1. HATSCHEK: *Chem. Ind.*, **48**, 389 (1929).
2. For details of preparation see HOLMES: *J. Phys. Chem.*, **22**, 510 (1918); HOLMES and FALL: *J. Am. Chem. Soc.*, **41**, 763 (1919).
3. HARDY: *Proc. Roy. Soc. (London)*, **87A**, 29 (1912).
4. GORTNER and HOFFMAN: *J. Am. Chem. Soc.*, **43**, 2199 (1921).
5. HATSCHEK: *Kolloid-Z.*, **11**, 158 (1912); **51**, 44 (1930). A study of a variety of gel-forming crystalline organic compounds was made by THOMAS and SIBI: *Rev. gen. colloides*, **8**, 68, 105 (1930).
6. DEISS: *Kolloid-Z.*, **14**, 139 (1914).
7. WALPOLE: *Kolloid-Z.*, **13**, 241 (1913).
8. LAING and McBAIN: *J. Chem. Soc.*, **117**, 1506 (1920); DRAKE, McBAIN, and SALMON: *Proc. Roy. Soc. (London)*, **98A**, 395 (1921).
9. For recent work see SHEPPARD and SWEET: *J. Am. Chem. Soc.*, **43**, 539 (1921); POOLE: *Trans. Faraday Soc.*, **21**, 82 (1926); also HATSCHEK: Ref. 1.
10. BJERKEN: *Ann. Physik.*, **28**, 628 (1891).
11. RANKINE: *Phil. Mag.*, **11**, 447 (1906).
12. HATSCHEK: *Trans. Faraday Soc.*, **15**, 218 (1920).
13. KOHLRAUSCH: *Z. physik. Chem.*, **12**, 773 (1893); HOLMES, KAUFMAN, and NICHOLAS: *J. Am. Chem. Soc.*, **41**, 1329 (1919); PRASAD: *Kolloid-Z.*, **33**, 279 (1924).
14. HATSCHEK: *Trans. Faraday Soc.*, **12**, 17 (1917).
15. HATSCHEK: *Kolloid-Z.*, **15**, 226 (1914).
16. BRADFORD: *Biochem. J.*, **12**, 351 (1918); **17**, 230 (1923); BARRATT: *Biochem. J.*, **14**, 189 (1920); BOGUE: *Chem. Met. Eng.*, **23**, 61 (1920); *J. Am. Chem. Soc.*, **44**, 1343 (1922); POOLE: *Trans. Faraday Soc.*, **21**, Pt. 1, 114 (1925); Pt. 2, 82 (1926).
17. KATZ and DERKSEN: *Rec. trav. chim.*, **51**, 513 (1932); KATZ: *ibid.*, 835 (1932).
18. FRANKENHEIM (1835); through BOGUE: *J. Am. Chem. Soc.*, **44**, 1343 (1922); NÄGELI: "Die Stärkekörner," Zurich (1858); *Sitzb.*, K. *Akad. Wiss. München*, **1**, 290 (1862).
19. PETERFI: *Arch. Entwickl. mech. Organ.*, **112**, 660 (1927); through FREUNDLICH: *Kolloid-Z.*, **46**, 289 (1928).
20. SCHALEK and SZEGVARY: *Kolloid-Z.*, **32**, 318; **33**, 326 (1923).

21. The following citations will serve as a guide to the literature on thixotropy: FREUNDLICH, SCHMIDT, and LINDAU: *Kolloidchem. Beihefte*, **36**, 43 (1932); HAUSER: *J. Rheol.*, **2**, 5 (1931); KARRER: *J. Rheol.*, **3**, 334 (1932); KISTLER: *J. Phys. Chem.*, **36**, 2948 (1932); Ref. 19.

22. FREUNDLICH, ROGOVSKI, and SOLLNER: *Z. physik. Chem.*, **160A**, 469 (1932); *Kolloidchem. Beihefte*, **37**, 223 (1933).

23. VAN BEMMELEN: *Z. anorg. Chem.*, **18**, 98 (1898).

24. ZSIGMONDY: *Z. anorg. Chem.*, **71**, 356 (1911); **75**, 189 (1912); ZSIGMONDY-SPEAR: "The Chemistry of Colloids," pp. 142ff., John Wiley & Sons, Inc., New York, 1917.

25. SCHULTZE: *Kolloid-Z.*, **38**, 232 (1926).

26. ANDERSON: *Z. physik. Chem.*, **88**, 191 (1914).

27. GERIKE: *Kolloid-Z.*, **17**, 78 (1915).

28. SHEPPARD and ELLIOTT: *J. Am. Chem. Soc.*, **44**, 373 (1922); HATSCHEK: Ref. 1.

29. BACHMANN: *Z. anorg. Chem.*, **100**, 1 (1917).

30. REINKE: *Hanstein's Botan. Abh.*, **4**, 1 (1879); see also POSJNAK: *Kolloidchem. Beihefte*, **3**, 417 (1912).

31. LÜDEKING: *Ann. Phys. Chem.*, **35**, 552 (1888); RODEWALD: *Z. physik. Chem.*, **24**, 193 (1897); KATZ: *Trans. Faraday Soc.*, **29**, 279 (1933).

32. WIEDEMANN and LÜDEKING: *Ann. Phys. Chem.*, **25**, 145 (1885); RODEWALD: *Z. physik. Chem.*, **33**, 593 (1900); KATZ: *Kolloidchem. Beihefte*, **9**, 1 (1917).

33. LOEB: *J. Gen. Physiol.*, **3**, 247 (1920); see also LLOYD: *Biochem. J.*, **14**, 147 (1920).

34. PROCTER and WILSON: *J. Chem. Soc.*, **109**, 307 (1916); WILSON: First Colloid Symposium Monograph, p. 210, 1923; WILSON: "The Chemistry of Leather Manufacture," Vol. I, Chemical Catalog Company, New York, 1928.

35. NORTHROP and KUNITZ: *J. Gen. Physiol.*, **8**, 317 (1926); **10**, 161, 893, 905 (1927); KUNITZ: *J. Gen. Physiol.*, **10**, 811 (1927); **13**, 565 (1930); see also LLOYD: *Biochem. J.*, **21**, 1352 (1927); **24**, 1460 (1930).

36. DE VRIES: *Rec. trav. chim.*, **3**, 375 (1884); VOIGTLANDER: *Z. physik. Chem.*, **3**, 316 (1889).

37. STILES and ADAIR: *Biochem. J.*, **15**, 620 (1921); *J. Am. Chem. Soc.*, **53**, 619 (1931).

38. FRIEDMAN and KRAEMER: *J. Am. Chem. Soc.*, **52**, 1295; FRIEDMAN: *ibid.*, **52**, 1305, 1311 (1930).

39. FREUNDLICH and ABRAMSON: *Z. physik. Chem.*, **133**, 51 (1928).

40. HEPBURN: *Nature*, **112**, 439 (1923).

41. DAVIES: *J. Am. Chem. Soc.*, **45**, 2261 (1923); HATSCHEK: *Kolloid-Z.*, **38**, 151 (1926); HOLMES: *J. Am. Chem. Soc.*, **40**, 1187 (1918); LIESEGANG: "Abderhalden's Handbuch der Biologischen Arbeitsmethoden," Abt. III, Teil B, p. 33, 1920.

42. DEDRICK: *J. Phys. Chem.*, **35**, 1777 (1931).

43. LIESEGANG: *Naturwissenschaften*, **18**, 645 (1930); VEIL: *Compt. rend.*, **193**, 1337 (1931).

44. WILHELM OSTWALD: "Lehrbuch der Allgemeinen Chemie," p. 778, Leipzig, 1898; BRADFORD: *Biochem. J.*, **14**, 29, 474 (1920); *Kolloid-Z.*, **30**, 364 (1922); DHAR and CHATTERJI: *Kolloid-Z.*, **31**, 15 (1922); **40**, 97 (1926); WO. OSTWALD: *Kolloid-Z.*, **36**, 380 (1925).
45. HEDGES: *Rev. gen. colloides*, **8**, 193 (1930).
46. KOENIG: *J. Phys. Chem.*, **24**, 466 (1920); KARRER: *J. Am. Chem. Soc.*, **44**, 951 (1922); HEDGES: *J. Chem. Soc.*, **1929**, 1848.
47. HEDGES: *J. Chem. Soc.*, **1929**, 2779; see also DOYLE and RYAN: *Proc. Roy. Irish Acad.*, **38B**, 435 (1929); through *Chem. Abs.*, **24**, 2359 (1930).
48. BLACKTIN: *Nature*, **129**, 401 (1932).
49. VEIL: *Revue gen. sci.*, **43**, 535 (1932).
50. SWEET: *Colloid Symposium Annual*, **7**, 249 (1929).
51. LIESEGANG: *Kolloid-Z.*, **16**, 20 (1915); STORZ: *ibid.*, **45**, 231 (1928).
52. SIEBERT: *Biochem. Z.*, **220**, 487 (1930); KOWARCZYK: *Acta Biol. Expt. Warsaw*, **6**, 29 (1930); through *Chem. Abs.*, **25**, 3902 (1931).

AUTHOR INDEX

A

Abderhalden, 270, 310, 315, 316
Abramson, 215, 216, 230, 232, 234, 235, 483
Adair, 360, 483
Adam, 250, 252, 255, 258, 260, 270, 271
Adams, 137, 317, 357
Alekseevskii, 313
Alexander, 467, 470
Allmand, 286, 312
Alsberg, 135, 367, 387
Amy, 379, 388
Anderson, 33, 388, 483
Anderssen, 234
Andersson, 313
Ando, 359
Andrén, 12, 13, 33
Andress, 386
Andrianov, 234
Anson, 359, 360
Archbutt, 271
Arendt, 313
Armstrong, 205
Arnold, 359
Arrhenius, 97, 146, 284, 312
Artom, 410
Auspitzer, 135
Avery, 388
Ayres, 67, 123, 138, 434, 449

B

Bach, 182, 201, 358
Bache, 48
Bächle, 139
Bachmann, 57, 96, 140, 271, 483
Bacon, 357
Baeyertz, 136

Bahl, 469
Bailey, 137
Baker, 356, 388, 400
Balandine, 313
Baldwin, 449
Balkin, 234
Bancroft, 33, 64, 67, 410, 447, 466, 470
Bandemer, 313
Bang, 469
Barab, 97, 125, 126, 138
Baranetzky, 96
Barger, 8, 308, 309, 315
Barker, 59, 244, 270, 313, 360
Barnard, 57
Barratt, 482
Bartell, 265, 271, 287, 289, 313, 314
Bartsch, 410
Barus, 8
Bary, 234
Bascom, 400
Bassett, 167, 176, 194, 202
Beans, 102, 103, 105, 106, 136, 141, 164, 165, 166, 176, 466
Beaver, 111, 136, 176, 202, 466, 470
Bechhold, 39, 57, 67, 68, 72, 73, 74, 95, 96, 358, 448, 459, 468, 469
Becker, 33
Beckmann, 367, 387
Becquerel, 205
Beekley, 314
Beeman, 447
Bellows, 456, 469
Bennett, 234
Benson, 250, 270
Benton, 286, 312
Berczeller, 314

485

SUBJECT INDEX

A

Absorption, definition of, 272
Acacia gum (*see* Gum arabic)
Adhesion, work of, 257
Adsorption, definition of, 272–273
  at liquid-liquid and at liquid-gas interfaces (*see* Surface concentration)
  (*See also* Sorption)
Aerosols, 9
  ammonium chloride, 19
  condensation, influence of nuclei, 16–17
  electric charge, 20–23
    origin of, 21–22
  electrostatic precipitation, 27
  explosions of, 29–32
  filtration of, 28–29
  flocculation of, 23–29
  formation of, by adiabatic expansion, 11–13
    by chemical interaction, 19–20
    by condensation, 10, 20
    by dispersion, 9
    effect of nuclei, 14–17
  photophoresis of, 20
  settling of, 23–25
  supercooling of, 14
  thermal effects of, 29
  thermal gradient, effect of, 27–28
Agar-agar, 382–385
  acidity of, 382
  chemical nature of, 382
  gel (*see* Gels)
  purification of, 382
  swelling of, 382–385
Albumin (*see* Proteins)
Alcosol, definition of, 63

Alginic bodies (*see* Sea-weed extracts)
Alkali-metal salts, precipitation by, 181–182, 187–188
Alkaline-earth salts, precipitation by, 182, 188
Alumina, gel, use in sorption, 305
  hydrous, relative peptizing effect of acids, 163
  two-dimensional picture, 161
Aluminum acetate, basic, effect of added oxalate, 150
Aluminum oxide sols, negatively charged micelles, 163–164
Aluminum oxysalt sols, effect of heating, 156
  pH, effect of salts on, 150, 152, 153, 155, 156
  preparation of, 126, 130
  titration with silver salts, 158–159
Aluminum salts, hydrolysis, mechanism of, 146
Amicroscopic particles, definition of, 45
Amino acids, acidic dissociation constant, 318–319
  amphoteric properties of, 317–322
  basic dissociation constant, 319
  Bjerrum's K_A, K_B, definition of, 320
  combination with acids and bases, 317–322
  effect of salts on, 345
  isoelectric point of, 322–326
    estimation of, 324–325
  titration curves, effect of formaldehyde, 320–322
Ampholytes, undissociated fraction, 322–323

501